# TREATISE ON ANALYTICAL CHEMISTRY

*A comprehensive account in three parts*

*PART I*

THEORY AND PRACTICE

*PART II*

ANALYTICAL CHEMISTRY OF
INORGANIC AND ORGANIC COMPOUNDS

*PART III*

ANALYTICAL CHEMISTRY IN INDUSTRY

# TREATISE ON ANALYTICAL CHEMISTRY

*PART III*

## ANALYTICAL CHEMISTRY IN INDUSTRY

*VOLUME 2*

Edited by I. M. KOLTHOFF
*Department of Chemistry,*
*University of Minnesota,*
*Minneapolis, Minnesota*

PHILIP J. ELVING
*Department of Chemistry, University of*
*Michigan, Ann Arbor, Michigan*

and FRED H. STROSS
*Shell Development Company*
*Emeryville, California*

**WILEY–INTERSCIENCE**

*A division of John Wiley & Sons, Inc., New York–London–Sydney–Toronto*

Library of Congress Catalog Card Number: 59-12439

ISBN 0-471-50011-9

Printed in the United States of America

10 9 8 7 6 5 4 3 2 1

# TREATISE ON ANALYTICAL CHEMISTRY

*PART III*

ANALYTICAL CHEMISTRY IN INDUSTRY

SECTION B

Industrial Toxicology and Environmental Pollution and Its Control

## AUTHORS OF VOLUME 2

DWIGHT G. BALLINGER

ROBERT L. BUNCH

HERVEY B. ELKINS

ROBERT C. KRONER

JAMES P. LODGE, JR.

K. H. MANCY

LEONARD D. PAGNOTTO

JOHN B. PATE

FLOYD B. TAYLOR

AMOS TURK

W. J. WEBER, JR.

## Preface to Part III

In 1959 when the first volume of Part I of this Treatise appeared, we defined its function as follows: "The aims and objectives of this Treatise are to present a concise, critical, comprehensive and systematic but not exhaustive, treatment of all aspects of classical and modern analytical chemistry. The Treatise is designed to be a valuable source of information to all analytical chemists, to stimulate fundamental research in pure and applied analytical chemistry, and to illustrate the close relationship between academic and industrial analytical chemistry."

Part I deals systematically with the theoretical and practical principles of analytical chemistry and its methods. Part II critically reviews the analytical chemistry, inorganic and organic, of all the elements and functional groups; it is not encyclopedic in nature.

It was our original intention to treat critically in Part III the analytical chemistry of industrial materials. However, on further consideration it became apparent to us that it would not be possible to present this area with the same systematic and critical treatment attempted in Parts I and II. We therefore decided, in the interest of uniformity of style and approach of the whole work, to modify our original program insofar as Part III was concerned. Since we felt that an encyclopedic treatment would do better justice to the requirements of the practicing analytical chemist, especially with respect to procedures, a viewpoint shared by the publishers, the latter initiated a comprehensive reference work on analytical methods and procedures for industrially important compounds and materials: the *Encyclopedia of Industrial Chemical Analysis*, edited by Foster Dee Snell and Clifford Hilton, of which several volumes have already appeared. (This Encyclopedia is a companion to Part III of the Treatise and does not duplicate the material in this part of the Treatise.)

However, we still felt that our Treatise would be complete and would fulfill its major objectives in an industrial laboratory only if certain areas and topics were included which deal with common procedures and activities of the industrial analytical laboratory and which could not be accommodated within the organization of Parts I and II. Consequently, we have organized Part III, whose subject matter deals mainly with (*1*) the function and organization of the industrial analytical laboratory in this country and abroad within the framework of the industrial plant as a whole, (*2*) standard nonchemical materials testing methods (mechanical, electrical, physiological, etc.), (*3*) areas on the borderline of analytical chemistry and other disciplines such as microbiology (air pollution) and pharmacology (toxicology), and (*4*) topics which are so common that even the chemist in the research laboratory is not infrequently called upon to deal with them, e.g., water analysis.

The editors welcome Dr. F. H. Stross as a coeditor for Part III. With his help, we have obtained a balance between the industrial and the more academic viewpoints.

We also want to express our indebtedness to the authors of the chapters in Part III, most of whom have been recruited from industry or laboratories closely related to industrial analytical problems. Their enthusiastic response to our invitation to participate in the preparation of Part III gives us confidence that this part of the Treatise fulfills the limited aims and objectives which the Editors had formulated.

I. M. KOLTHOFF
P. J. ELVING

*July 1970*

# Authors of Volume 2

**Dwight G. Ballinger**

*Physics and Chemistry Section, FWQA, AQC, Cincinnati, Ohio*

**Robert L. Bunch**

*Department of the Interior, Robert A. Taft Water Research Center, Cincinnati, Ohio*

**Hervey B. Elkins**

*Massachusetts Department of Labor and Industries, Division of Occupational Hygiene, Boston, Massachusetts*

**Robert C. Kroner**

*Physics and Chemistry Section, FWQA, AQC, Cincinnati, Ohio*

**James P. Lodge, Jr.**

*National Center for Atmospheric Research, Boulder, Colorado*

**K. H. Mancy**

*The University of Michigan, Ann Arbor, Michigan*

**Leonard D. Pagnotto**

*Massachusetts Depart-
ment of Labor and
Industries, Division of
Occupational Hygiene,
Boston, Massachusetts*

**John B. Pate**

*National Center for
Atmospheric Research,
Boulder, Colorado*

**Floyd B. Taylor**

*Carlisle, Massachusetts*

**Amos Turk**

*Department of Chemis-
try, The City College of
the City University of
New York, New York*

**W. J. Weber, Jr.**

*The University of Michi-
gan, Ann Arbor, Michigan*

# PART III. ANALYTICAL CHEMISTRY IN INDUSTRY

## CONTENTS—VOLUME 2

### SECTION B. INDUSTRIAL TOXICOLOGY AND ENVIRONMENTAL POLLUTION AND ITS CONTROL

# CONTENTS

**Potable and Sanitary Water.** By *Robert C. Kroner* and *Dwight G. Ballinger* .............................................. 343

# SECTION B: Industrial Toxicology and Environmental Pollution and Its Control

Part III
Section B

# INDUSTRIAL HEALTH HAZARDS

By Hervey B. Elkins and Leonard D. Pagnotto,
*Massachusetts Department of Labor and Industries,
Division of Occupational Hygiene, Boston, Massachusetts*

Contents

**Contents** (*continued*)

**Contents** (*continued*)

**Contents** (*continued*)

**Contents** (*continued*)

**Contents** (*continued*)

**Contents** (*continued*)

**Contents** (*continued*)

**Contents** (*continued*)

# I. INTRODUCTION

The majority of the thousands of substances used as raw materials, intermediates, and finished products in the complex of industry present little or no hazard to the health of the worker. A considerable number, however, do require certain precautions if adverse effects on the employee who handle them are to be prevented. Some are poisonous in the conventional sense, some are irritating to the eyes or mucous membranes of the respiratory passages, while others, harmless under some circumstances, can be injurious when present in certain physical or mechanical states.

## A. CLASSIFICATION

Industrial hazards may be classified by their physical state, by the type of harmful effect produced, and, in a few instances, by commercial application.

### 1. Gases

Because of their nature, gases are used in industry chiefly as fuels, as raw materials in chemical processes, or in closed systems such as air conditioning units. Leakage of such gases may produce hazards in confined areas. Some of the most toxic gases are hydrides of heavy elements, such as arsenic, antimony, and selenium, which are usually found as by-products of chemical reactions. The most important gaseous health hazard is carbon monoxide, produced whenever carbon compounds are burned in the absence of an excess of oxygen.

Gases are absorbed primarily through inhalation, although small amounts may penetrate the skin and a number are important eye irritants.

## 2. Liquids and Vapors

Aside from water, which is nontoxic, relatively few inorganic compounds of industrial importance and only one element, mercury, are liquids at room temperature. The liquids most commonly encountered are organic solvents, many of which are highly hazardous. In comparison with gases, the effects of liquids on the skin are frequently of major importance. Many are extremely irritating, and some are readily absorbed through the unbroken skin.

The volatile solvents, those boiling below about 150°C, will frequently give off enough vapor to produce an inhalation hazard if exposed to the air at room temperature, while less volatile liquids may be vaporized if heated, sprayed, or otherwise dispersed into the atmosphere.

## 3. Toxic Fumes and Dusts

A few solids are sufficiently volatile to produce a vapor hazard, but the majority can exist dispersed in the air in significant amounts only in the form of fume or dust. Fumes, resulting usually from heating a substance well above its melting point, are commonly more finely divided than dusts which are produced mechanically, e.g., by grinding. Many solid substances are handled as finely divided powders, which are readily dispersed into the air. In such cases considerable amounts may be ingested, as well as inhaled. As a rule absorption through the skin is not an important avenue of intoxication by solid substances, but there are exceptions. A number of solid materials are irritating to the skin.

## 4. Mineral and Organic Dusts

Several minerals contain toxic elements, such as fluorine, lead, manganese, and beryllium, but these are usually insoluble and relatively inert in comparison with other compounds of the same elements which are frequently encountered. Inhalation of the dusts of many minerals and some other substances which are virtually nontoxic when ingested may cause serious injury to the lungs. The most important are free silica (quartz) and asbestos, each of which has been responsible for many disabling and fatal cases of pulmonary disease. Other mineral dusts cause more or less nonspecific effects, which often lead to impaired respiratory function. Organic dusts frequently carry organisms which produce typical local reactions in the respiratory tract (farmer's lung).

## 5. Pesticides

Pesticides are used because they are poisonous to insects or other animal pests, and many of them are highly toxic to humans as well. Some are gases or volatile liquids. The majority are high-boiling liquids or solids, but are usually applied as a spray or dust, so they may be inhaled during use. Moreover, many of the newer organic insecticides are readily absorbed through the skin. Since they are usually systemic poisons, intoxication can also result from accidental ingestion.

## 6. Plastics and Polymers

The majority of synthetic organic substances are relatively inert and nontoxic in finished form. However, many are made from highly toxic raw materials. Others are reactive in the uncured state and may be irritating to eyes, respiratory passages, or skin. Some partially polymerized substances contain small amounts of volatile compounds which can evaporate in sufficient quantity to cause a vapor hazard, especially when subjected to mild heating. A few plastics give off highly toxic decomposition products when strongly heated.

## 7. Skin Irritants

Skin irritants are divided into two groups: primary irritants and sensitizers. The former include strong acids, alkalies, the salts of many heavy metals, most organic solvents, and many waxes (517). Sensitizing agents do not necessarily cause irritation at the first contact, but effect specific changes so that, after a few days, further contact, frequently with dilute solutions, will cause a dermatitis. Many of the primary irritants are also sensitizers.

Schwartz, Tulipan, and Birmingham list the following groups of substances encountered in industry which are frequently sensitizers (517):

1. Dye intermediates
2. Dyes
3. Photo developers
4. Rubber accelerators and antioxidants
5. Soaps
6. Insecticides
7. Cosmetics
8. Oils
9. Resins
10. Coal tar and derivatives
11. Explosives
12. Plasticizers

## B. TOXIC EFFECTS

Depending on the chemical, physical, and mechanical properties of the material involved, industrial health hazards may produce a wide variety of injurious effects. Some of the most important are discussed below.

### 1. Asphyxiation

Many gases, such as nitrogen, hydrogen, the inert gases, and low molecular weight hydrocarbons, have little harmful effect in themselves, but by diluting or displacing the air may reduce its oxygen content to a point below that needed to support normal activity, or even life. Table I indicates the major effects of reduced oxygen pressure in inhaled air.

It is readily calculated that at sea level a concentration of inert gas of 20% by volume is necessary to reduce the oxygen content of the air to a harmful degree.

Other gases react chemically in such a way as to produce asphyxiation, the best known examples being carbon monoxide and hydrogen cyanide.

### 2. Irritation

Caustic and corrosive substances, such as strong acids, alkalies, and oxidizing agents, usually act primarily by irritating the skin, eyes, or respiratory passages. The most dangerous compounds are those which produce little immediate effect on the eyes, nose, and throat, but injure the lower lungs. Certain gases, such as nitrogen dioxide and phosgene, and metal fumes, such as those of cadmium and beryllium oxide, fall into this category.

TABLE I[a]

Effect of Reduced Oxygen

| Partial pressure of $O_2$, mm Hg | Oxygen in air at sea level, (%) | Response |
|---|---|---|
| 120–160 | 16–21 | No notable effect |
| 90–120 | 12–16 | Increased respiration, slight diminution of coordination |
| 76–90 | 10–12 | Loss of ability to think clearly |
| 45–76 | 6–10 | Loss of consciousness, death |

[a] From Henderson and Haggard (247).

Of the organic compounds, aldehydes are, as a group, strong irritants; many less reactive compounds, such as the higher hydrocarbons, alcohols, and esters, are also quite irritating.

### 3. Pneumoconiosis

Pneumoconiosis is a term for lung disease due to dust. Ordinarily it refers to the chronic effect of a dust not toxic in the conventional sense. The most serious pneumoconioses are those caused by dusts of quartz (and other forms of free silica), asbestos, and beryllium compounds, although some consider berylliosis a systemic disease. Talcosis, siderosis (from iron oxide), anthracosis, silicatosis, and byssinosis (from cotton dust) are terms used to designate other less serious forms of pneumoconiosis (139). Shaver's disease is a pulmonary disability observed in workers exposed to high concentrations of alumina and silica fume (527).

### 4. Narcosis

Nearly all organic solvent vapors have some narcotic or anesthetic action. With the majority of the lower boiling hydrocarbon solvents, many halogenated hydrocarbons, and some esters, ketones, and ethers, the narcotic effect predominates. Even those solvents, such as benzene and carbon tetrachloride, which produce systemic intoxication, may act primarily as narcotics in short exposures.

There is little indication that repeated inhalation of mildly narcotic concentrations of many solvent vapors has any permanent ill effect. On the other hand, the common belief that these effects are completely reversible has not yet been conclusively established.

### 5. Systemic Intoxication

Irreversible injury, or damage from which recovery is slow, to the vital organs, central nervous system, or hematopoietic system is termed systemic intoxication.

#### a. HEMOTOXIC EFFECTS

The substance most commonly associated with industrial blood disease is benzene, which causes aplastic anemia and has been suspected of producing leukemia. Trinitrotoluene has a somewhat similar effect.

Anemia is a common finding in lead poisoning, although other symptoms usually predominate.

A number of substances, especially aromatic amines and nitrocompounds, convert hemoglobin to methemoglobin. The effects of acute poisoning by such compounds are similar to those of asphyxiation.

Several other substances have been shown to produce significant blood changes in animals, but industrial exposures adequate to result in similar findings in humans have rarely been observed.

### b. Hepatic and Renal Effects

Damage to the liver and/or kidneys is frequently observed in animals exposed to chemicals. Substances which are particularly prone to injure the vital organs include many halogenated hydrocarbons; compounds of arsenic, mercury, selenium, and uranium; and many amines and nitrocompounds. Industrially the worst offenders have been carbon tetrachloride, tetrachloroethane, trinitrotoluene, and arsine.

Among the solvents, a tendency to produce liver or kidney injury, especially on prolonged or repeated exposure, is the most common hallmark of the "toxic" as opposed to the "nontoxic" solvent. The effects of the latter are mainly confined to narcosis or irritation of the respiratory passages.

### c. Neurotoxic Effects

Permanent or slowly reversible damage to the central nervous system is a characteristic of a number of industrial poisons. The symptoms range from tremor (mercury) and paralysis (manganese and certain organic phosphates) to primarily mental disturbances (carbon disulfide and methyl bromide). The organic insecticides, of both the chlorinated and organic phosphate type, are for the most part poisons of the central nervous system.

### 6. Cancer

A number of chemicals used in industry are carcinogenic, the best known being 3,4-benzpyrene and other hydrocarbons found in coal tar. These have been responsible for many cases of skin cancer and, in certain instances (chimney sweeps and mule spinners), cancer of the scrotum.

The most potent carcinogens found commercially appear to be the amines beta-naphthylamine and benzidine. An extremely high incidence of bladder tumors occurs among workers in plants using these compounds.

An increased incidence of lung cancer in workers exposed to dusts of certain chromium compounds, to nickel carbonyl and to asbestos has been established.

The influence of oil fume, smoke, and other combustion products of coal, oil, and other fuels on the incidence of lung cancer among workers, as well as the general public, has not yet been determined.

### 7. Dermatitis

Irritation of the skin is the most common occupational disease. While such afflictions are rarely permanently disabling, sensitization to a substance or class of substances may occur which may make a worker incapable of working on processes where such materials are handled. In some cases, on the other hand, immunity develops.

Little quantitative information is available on concentrations, times of contact, etc. which can be tolerated without danger of dermatitis. Rules of thumb and empirical procedures are usually relied upon to prevent skin disease. Dermatological investigations, based on patch tests, are frequently necessary to establish the source of dermatitis when a number of chemicals are handled.

## II. ANALYTICAL PROBLEMS

### A. RAW MATERIALS

With a few exceptions, analysis of raw materials and intermediates for industrial toxicology purposes presents no particular problem. If the presence and approximate percentage of a suspected toxic ingredient, such as lead or mercury, need to be ascertained, conventional qualitative and semiquantitative methods can be employed. There are three problems of material analysis, however, which are to a considerable degree characteristic of industrial hygiene. These are discussed below.

### 1. Minerals

Although some minerals contain toxic elements (lead, fluorine, etc.) in substantial amounts, the occupational health hazards most commonly associated with them are the pneumoconioses, caused usually by inhalation of dusts of substances which are otherwise essentially harmless. Silicosis is the most important of these diseases and results only from the inhalation of *free* crystalline silica. While the dusts of some silicates, such as asbestos and talc, can cause lung diseases, combined silica in itself is not pathogenic.

The determination of free silica (usually quartz) in minerals which also contain silicates requires special techniques. Chemical, petrographic, and X-ray diffraction methods and various combinations of the three may be employed.

In addition to chemical composition, particle size is an important property to measure in dusts for an evaluation of the health hazards. Silicosis is caused chiefly by particles below $5\mu$ in diameter, and in many other industrial lung diseases, particles of this size, or even smaller, are the primary cause of injury.

## 2. Solvents

Since organic solvents of similar physical properties and uses may vary greatly in toxicity, identification of the components of solvent mixtures is a frequent problem in industrial hygiene. Fractional distillation, with determination of such physical properties as refractive index and density, is an adequate procedure for the analysis of many such mixtures. The solubility in water of the lower alcohols, ketones, and glycol derivatives is frequently a useful property for identification and separation from other types of solvents. Esters and the higher alcohols and ketones are miscible with 80% sulfuric acid, while hydrocarbons and their halogenated derivatives are insoluble in this reagent.

More modern methods include vapor chromatography and infrared spectrum measurements. Ultraviolet spectrophotometry is also useful, especially in the identification and determination of aromatic hydrocarbons. Various group chemical reactions, such as the Beilstein test for halogens, the iodoform test for methyl ketones and hydrolysis with alkali of esters, are useful upon occasion in such analyses.

## 3. Skin Irritants

Chemical analysis of substances suspected of causing dermatitis is a less important procedure than might be expected. Among the more important skin irritants are alkalies, strong acids, oxidizing agents, certain metals (e.g., nickel, mercury, arsenic, chromium), many amines, some chlorinated aromatics, and solvents of many kinds. While the determination of pH or the detection of these various components is frequently of some value, dermatological (patch) tests are usually necessary, the chemical analysis being of secondary importance. The most essential function of the analytical chemist in such studies is usually to supplement the work of the dermatologist by ascertaining which elements or compounds may be the offending agents in a material found to give a positive patch test on afflicted workers.

## B. ANALYSIS OF WORKROOM AIR

### 1. Principles

Analysis of air by the industrial hygienist may be for one of several purposes. The most important is to determine the average concentration of contaminant in the air breathed by a given worker or workers. In such cases it may be necessary to take the sample close to the face of the worker and to move the sampling device with him throughout a definite work cycle. Sampling units attached to workers have been used to some extent.

Frequently there are several sources of contamination, not necessarily associated with individual workers. In these instances analysis of the general workroom air is an adequate procedure. Samples can be taken in fixed areas throughout the occupied portion of the room.

Sometimes it is desirable to evaluate the importance of sources of contamination, such as leaks, open tanks, mixers, etc. In such cases samples may be taken in unoccupied places to provide data useful for the design of control measures.

For some purposes immediate knowledge of the result is essential and direct reading detectors or tests which can be carried out in the field are necessary. At other times, especially when chronic effects only are to be expected, subsequent analysis of the sample is satisfactory. Frequently both methods are employed, with direct reading methods providing approximate results, while more accurate determinations are made on samples analyzed in the laboratory.

The length of the sampling period desirable will depend to some extent on the toxic effect of the contaminant. With irritants and other rapidly acting substances, sampling periods of 10 min or less are preferable in order to determine peaks of concentration. With narcotic vapors 30-min samples may be satisfactory, while with chronic poisons samples up to several hours long are frequently useful.

Samples of general air can be taken with relatively fragile and complicated equipment. For estimating the exposure of a mobile worker or evaluating sources of contaminant, simple and readily portable sampling units or detecting devices are needed.

### 2. Direct-Reading Methods

Devices for directly determining gases, vapors, and particulate matter in the air vary from simple colorimetric test units to complicated and sophisticated instruments. For most industrial hygiene purposes, easily portable instruments capable of measuring concentrations of a few parts per million, or even lower, are desirable.

### a. Manometric or Gasometric Methods

The Fyrite analyzer (Bacharach) employs the Orsat method of volumetric measurement before and after absorption of a component of the sample by a chemical reagent. A unique feature of this device is that the absorbing fluid is also used as the indicating liquid, and one vessel functions both as measuring buret and absorption pipette.

Units are available containing alkali absorbent, for carbon dioxide determination, or chromous chloride, for measurement of oxygen.

### b. Thermometric Methods

#### (1) Combustible Gas Indicators

Several portable instruments are available for measuring combustible gases and vapors in the air. They vary in the features available, but are essentially the same in operating principle. An instrument which gives a full scale reading at the lower explosive limit for a vapor such as hexane will detect concentrations of most flammable solvent vapors well below 100 parts per million parts of air. The air is drawn over a heated filament, usually of platinum, which is connected as one arm of a balanced Wheatstone bridge. The combustible gas burns and raises the temperature of the coil, and the change in electrical resistance of the filament unbalances the bridge. This imbalance is measured by an indicating meter whose scale provides the reading in terms of percentage of the lower explosive limit of the gas in air. Calibration curves for conversion to parts per million are available for a number of solvents and gases.

Most instruments are operated manually with squeeze bulbs, but some are equipped with air sampling pumps that provide a continuous flow. They may be modified for specific needs; for example, units for measuring acetylene have flow systems containing no copper or silver to prevent the formation of the corresponding acetylides. The Davis ethane detector is equipped with a gas chromatograph column to permit the separate measurement of ethane and methane.

#### (2) Catalytic Combustion Indicators

A catalyst—hopcalite (a mixture of manganese and copper oxides)—which will promote the oxidation by air of carbon monoxide, is the basis of the MSA carbon monoxide indicator. Air is drawn into this instrument at a constant rate by a hand-operated or electrically driven pump, being first dried by passage through a dehydrating canister. The rise in temperature resulting from the heat of oxidation of CO to $CO_2$ is measured by a sensitive thermocouple. Concentrations of CO as low as 10 ppm can be estimated.

### (3) Thermal Conductivity Analyzers

Changes in thermal conductivity produced by gases and vapors in the range of hygienic interest are generally not great enough to be measured accurately. Thermal conductivity analyzers have found some use in measuring carbon dioxide and also solvent vapors in or near the explosive range.

### c. ELECTROMETRIC METHODS

### (1) Conductivity Analyzers

Portable instruments designed primarily for sulfur dioxide measurement, which depend on measuring the conductivity of water containing a small amount of hydrogen peroxide before and after air is passed through, are available from several manufacturers.

### (2) Coulometric Analyzers

Instruments for measuring ozone are frequently based on the oxidation of potassium iodide at polarized electrodes. In the Mast ozone meter a measured volume of air is brought into a micro-fed stream of 2% potassium iodide and 5% potassium bromide buffered solution. Free iodine resulting from the interaction of ozone with the sensing solution removes hydrogen from the cathode and produces a repolarization current. The Beckman ozone monitor is based on a similar principle. A chromium trioxide scrubber eliminates interference by sulfur dioxide, and the design of the sensing cell is said to minimize the response from nitrogen dioxide.

Other strongly oxidizing gases can be determined by these instruments. A coulometric titration instrument for determination of hydrazine and its derivatives is made by American Systems Incorporated.

### (3) Flame Ionization

Flame ionization meters are among the most sensitive instruments for the determination of gases and vapors of carbon compounds in air. The sample is drawn directly into a flame ionization cell fed by hydrogen. Any carbon compounds in the flame produce carbon ions which bring about an ion current flow between the flame jet and a collector electrode placed above it. An indicating meter registers the measurement signal from a highly sensitive electrometer tube circuit. On high sensitivity full scale reading may indicate as little as 5 ppm of some compounds.

The Davis meter is portable and the Beckman meter is semiportable and primarily a bench instrument.

### (4) Paramagnetic Instruments

The fact that oxygen is strongly paramagnetic, in contrast to other common gases, forms the basis of an instrument for oxygen determination. Beckman instruments employ a small glass dumbbell suspended on a taut quartz fiber in a nonuniform magnetic field. In the absence of oxygen the magnetic force balances the tongue of the fiber. When oxygen is introduced the magnetic force is altered and the dumbbell rotates.

### (5) Polarographic Methods

Instruments for measurement of oxygen based on electrolysis are available from several manufacturers (MSA, Cole-Palmer, Beckman). Air samples are drawn into oxygen-sensing cells which contain two electrodes covered by a thin membrane of Teflon. Oxygen diffuses through the membrane to the cathode and is consumed. This upsets the potential across the electrodes and current flows in proportion to the pressure of oxygen present.

### d. PHOTOMETRIC METHODS

#### (1) Ultraviolet Photometers

Field instruments for measuring mercury vapor in air are portable ultraviolet photometers of high sensitivity. The light source is a mercury vapor lamp and the intense line at 253.7 m$\mu$ is strongly absorbed by mercury vapor. The absorption upsets a photoelectric balance in the instrument and the resulting change is sensed, amplified, and indicated on a meter. Other vapors that absorb uv light will interfere to some extent, but only at relatively high concentrations.

In the Modern and Classical Instruments detectors the ultraviolet light is split into two beams of equal intensity, one of which passes through a sealed chamber. The other beam passes through a chamber into which the sampled air is drawn at a constant rate. Models are available for battery or line operation.

The Sunshine Scientific Instrument instantaneous vapor detector has two phototubes in the exposure chamber. The reference, enclosed in a hollow cylinder of pyrex glass which serves as a low-pass filter, receives cell radiation from the ultraviolet lamp except that at 253.7 m$\mu$. The second tube which receives the full range of radiation is sensitive to any changes in the intensity of uv light reaching it. A constant volume of air is drawn through the chamber.

The Beckman meter must be placed in the air to be tested since no sampling pump is provided. The lamp is located in the lower portion of the case at one end of the unit and the reference phototube at the other end.

## (2) Infrared Analyzers

Nondispersive infrared analyzers, such as those available from MSA or Beckman, are semiportable. The detectors in these units are altered to specifically monitor any one of a number of heteratomic gases in a mixture of several components.

Two sources of infrared provide radiation energy for the sample and reference cells. The detector is a sealed two-compartment container filled with the gas being monitored. As radiation enters each compartment the gas in the detector absorbs its own characteristic wavelength (4.6 $\mu$ for carbon monoxide). If any of this radiation is absorbed in the sample chamber, an unbalance occurs in the detector cell. A diaphragm separating the two compartments expands toward the sample side. Interruption of the radiation by a beam chopper causes the pressure in the two compartments to equalize and the diaphragm returns to normal. The diaphragm movement with each revolution of the chopper causes a change in electrical capacitance in the instrument that generates a measurable electric signal.

For industrial hygiene purposes infrared analyzers are used chiefly for carbon monoxide and less frequently for carbon dioxide.

## (3) Particle Counters

The Sinclair-Phoenix aerosol photometer (Phoenix Precision Instrument Co.) measures the mass concentration of particulates in the air. The optical system measures the forward scattering of light from particles of smoke, dust, and fume drawn continuously through a dark field illumination chamber. Fraser found that it was necessary to calibrate the instrument for the type of dust being measured (190). Where this was possible the device was found useful in monitoring concentrations of silica dust between 2 and 50 millions of particles per cubic foot of air in animal chamber tests.

The Monitron (Engineering Specialties Co.) is a right angle scattering photometer. It has the feature of a split light beam, one half of which is used as a reference, and measures dust concentration. However, the device was found to have little sizing capability (90,422).

The Royco Instruments particle counter is designed to count particles larger than 0.32 $\mu$. Fifteen discriminating channels are provided, the last of which measures all particles greater than 8 $\mu$. The instrument has been shown to give particle counting and sizing data relative to findings by microscopic analysis (90).

Although these instruments have been used in certain industrial hygiene applications, they are basically laboratory units and are best suited for fixed installations.

The aerosol photometer developed by the Southern Research Institute is a light-weight battery-operated unit that indicates results in millions of particles per cubic foot of air. A discriminator circuit can be adjusted manually in 0.1-$\mu$ increments to count only particles larger than a preselected size, within a range of 0.3–2 $\mu$. It will count particles larger than 2 $\mu$, but without discrimination. In operation the sampled aerosol passes through a beam of light, and scattering from individual particles is sensed by a phototube and indicated as particle concentration on the panel meter. A dilution valve permits a range of full scale readings from 5 to 100 million particles per cubic foot.

Laboratory tests by Hosey et al. on six types of dust indicated that this photometer with proper adjustment can be used with the same degree of accuracy as the impinger technique (271). Particle size distribution curves obtained with the unit were in reasonably good agreement with membrane filter results. Channell and Hanna operated this instrument under rugged field conditions and found its counts compared favorably with midget impinger results, but not consistently with membrane filter samples (90). They concluded that good results can be obtained with this instrument, but calibration is very important for accurate and size distribution data.

### (4) Halide Meter

The Davis halide meter is designed to measure the majority of chlorinated hydrocarbon vapors in concentrations from 0 to 500 ppm. The sample to be tested is drawn into the instrument at a constant rate and passed into an arc chamber where the halide vapor reacts with a hot electrode to form a copper halide which is vaporized. The copper halide produces an intense blue color in the arc which is continuously measured with a photometer using a blue-sensitive phototube fitted with a blue filter. Meter readings from 0 to 50 $\mu$A are converted to parts per million by means of calibration curves. A 10-$\mu$A reading corresponds to 15–100 ppm, depending in part on the number of chlorine atoms in the molecule. Organic bromides and chlorides can be determined.

### (5) Colorimetric Reaction Instruments

Instruments are available that will continuously monitor gases which form colors with suitable reagents. The PSD atmospheric monitor (Precision Scientific Development Co.) uses the West-Gaeke reagent for determination of $SO_2$ and a modification of the Griess-Saltzman reagent for measurement of $NO_2$. The gas being determined is continuously reacted with reagent and the color of the reacted solution measured photometrically and automatically discarded.

### (6) Interferometer

Measurement of the refractive index of air by means of an interferometer, using a long cell, has been used for the determination of solvent vapors. Because it is expensive, somewhat fragile, nonspecific, and not very sensitive, this method has not been widely employed for hygienic air analysis.

### e. RADIOACTIVE CLATHRATE MONITOR

The Tracer Lab toxic gas monitor is designed to detect and measure strongly oxidizing gases in the air in the parts per million range. Concentrations as low as 0.1 ppm of gases such as ozone, fluorine, chlorine, chlorine trifluoride, and chlorine dioxide can be detected.

The core of the unit is a clathrate cell formed by passing krypton 85 gas under pressure into liquefied hydroquinone. Upon solidification the hydroquinone crystals entrap krypton atoms. Ozone and similar gases destroy the crystalline cages thus formed and release the radioactive krypton, which is drawn into a cell where it is counted by standard nuclear techniques. Both battery- and line-operated units are available.

By first passing the air through suitable chemicals, other types of gases can be determined. For example, acid gases such as $SO_2$ will release $ClO_2$ from solid sodium chlorite.

### f. TEST SOLUTIONS

### (1) Air Titration

Gases or vapors which are acids, bases, or strong reducing agents can be absorbed in measured volumes of dilute standard solutions, to which a suitable indicator has been added. Air is passed through the solution at a measured rate until the reagent is used up and the indicator changes. These methods are not especially sensitive and are most satisfactory for gases quite soluble in water; for those not soluble in water the gas will not be absorbed completely when the reagent nears exhaustion. For this reason this method is not recommended for carbon dioxide, but works reasonably well for ammonia and sulfur dioxide (where a dilute iodine solution is used).

### (2) Colorimetric Reactions

Absorption directly in reagents with which they develop colors is a convenient procedure for a few gases and vapors for which suitable reactions are available. Bromine and chlorine can be absorbed in o-tolidine reagent, nitrogen dioxide in Saltzman reagent, etc. The colors can be compared in the field with reference standards.

### g. INDICATOR TUBES

A number of field-type indicator test tubes are available commercially. These units are provided in kit form where a single aspirating device is used for all tubes or in individual sets where a pump is supplied with each specific gas.

Various devices are available as sources of suction for these tubes. They vary in efficiency of operation and, as shown in a study made by Kusnetz (336), their air-flow characteristics should be checked carefully. A bellows-type unit relies primarily on the packing of the tube to regulate air flow. There are also in use cylinder-type pumps fitted with a piston and a critical orifice, spring loaded diaphragm positive displacement pumps, and squeeze bulbs with and without check valves.

Most tubes consist of granular silica gel impregnated with an indicating chemical sealed in a glass tube. When ready for use, the tips of the tube are broken off and one end is connected to a source of suction. Other tubes require mixing of two components and packing a sampling tube just before use.

Two types of response are obtained: (1) a change in color tint of the indicating reagent and (2) development of a stain whose length is proportional to the gas concentration sampled. In the first type of tube the test gas is only slightly absorbed by the indicator gel. Its concentration in the exit stream is almost the same as in the entering mixture. If temperature, flow rate, and sample volume are controlled, the concentration of the test gas is determined by a comparison of the change in color with prepared standards. In the second type the gas in the length of stain detectors is completely absorbed and a portion of the indicator tube is discolored. Frequently the stain will vary in color, but its length will increase in approximately a linear relationship with the contaminant sampled.

Mathematical expressions have been developed for these tubes to permit calibrations based on theoretical relationships (33,497). Important variables considered are sample volume, flow rate, gel size, and activities of different gels. According to Saltzman, the most serious errors in indicator readings, however, result from variations in indicator gel from batch to batch, short shelf life of the reagent in the tubes, and errors in calibration. Other errors may be caused by interfering gases, variations in ambient temperature, pressure, and humidity.

A number of these indicator tubes from various suppliers were studied by the Occupational Health Program of the United States Public Health Service. Their ratings on specific gases tested varied from good to completely unsatisfactory. They concluded that gas detecting tubes in general were semiquantitative devices quite useful in screening or preliminary survey work. It was suggested that where facilities and trained personnel were available, quality control measures should be carried out. Several papers are available on the preparation and analysis of low concentrations of toxic gases for this purpose (496,507,524).

In a report of his practical experience with these tubes, Ketchman emphasized the existing and potential problems connected with their use (316). He stated that the tubes were valuable tools in the hands of experienced personnel. Silverman and Gardner (536) in their study of a potassium pallado sulfite carbon monoxide detector tube, estimated its accuracy to be ±25% of the reading, but stated that it could be 35–40% depending on the type of sample pump used. They felt this variation was typical of other indicator tube methods also, but in view of the biological variations encountered in establishing MAC's, such methods were nevertheless reliable enough.

The value and need of rapid and direct reading devices are well recognized by industrial hygienists and others interested in this field. Their importance is such that a continuing study of these tubes is being made by the Committee on Direct Reading, Gas Indicating Tube Systems sponsored jointly by the American Industrial Hygiene Association and American Conference of Governmental Industrial Hygienists. It is also becoming evident that manufacturers are making a sincere effort to improve their products in many instances. New developments in this field could easily outdate any existing reports.

## h. TEST PAPERS

Papers impregnated with reagents which react to give color changes with gases or particulates can be used for qualitative tests. If the rate of air flow through (or sometimes past) the paper is known, semiquantitative results can be obtained. Some of the substances which can be determined in this manner, together with the suggested reagents, are shown in Table II (534).

Procedures involving direct treatment of samples collected on paper have been suggested for a number of contaminants. Commercial kits are available for chromic acid (MSA), soluble fluorides (Precision Instrument), lead (MSA, UNICO), and a few additional toxic gases or fumes. The results are rarely as reliable as those obtained by conventional wet methods.

## 3. Sampling

Methods of sampling workroom air vary to some extent, depending on the physical state of the contaminant.

### a. GASES

In sampling air for gases, either instantaneous (grab) samples or continuous, integrated samples may be taken.

## TABLE II
### Test Paper Methods

| Contaminant | Reagent | Limit of sensitivity |
|---|---|---|
| Ammonia | Phenolphthalein | 10 ppm |
| Arsine | Mercuric bromide | 4 ppm |
| Carbon dioxide | Strontium hydroxide and indicator | 1% |
| Carbon monoxide | Palladium chloride | 25 ppm |
| Chlorine | Starch iodide | 0.25 ppm |
| Hydrogen cyanide | Benzidine and copper acetate | 10 ppm |
| Hydrogen sulfide | Lead acetate | 7 ppm |
| Mercury vapor | Selenium sulfide | 0.1 mg/m$^3$ |
| Methyl bromide | Fluorescein–NaOH | — |
| Phosgene | Diphenylamine and $p$-dimethylamine benzaldehyde | 1 ppm |
| Phosphine | Silver nitrate | 1 ppm |
| Stibine | Silver nitrate | 1 ppm |
| Sulfur dioxide | Starch–iodide–iodate | 4 ppm |
| Welding fumes (iron) | White paper | 5 mg/m$^3$ |
| Zinc oxide | Black paper | 10 mg/m$^3$ |

## (1) Grab Samples

Grab samples of air, such as are taken for conventional gas analysis, are used to some extent in the determination of harmful gases. Since the concentrations of contaminant are usually low, relatively large samples may be required. Acid bottles of $2\frac{1}{2}$-liter capacity have been employed for such determinations as carbon dioxide and oxides of nitrogen, but smaller samples are frequently sufficient. For some purposes air samples have been taken in plastic bags (112).

## (2) Bubblers

The most common method of sampling air for toxic gases is to draw it through a bubbler containing a solution which will react rapidly with the gas in question. Gases which are somewhat soluble in water can usually be absorbed quite rapidly in simple bubblers of the petri type.

Saltzman found the midget impinger, containing 10 ml of reagent and with air flows of 0.5 or 1 liter/min, was satisfactory for the collection of bromine, chlorine, ammonia, and nitrogen dioxide, but that a fritted disk bubbler was needed for carbon dioxide (496). The theory of gas absorption by bubblers has been discussed by Calvert and Workman (74).

### b. VAPORS

In contrast to gases, the majority of which are inorganic, the vapors of interest to the industrial hygienist are mainly organic compounds.

## (1) Reagents

Many organic reactions are relatively slow in comparison with ionic reactions and are ordinarily unsuitable for use in sampling devices for the determination of vapor in air. Alcohol vapors, as well as those of some other organic compounds, can be collected in solutions of oxidizing agents, such as dichromate or permanganate. Carbon disulfide is absorbed in diethylamine copper acetate reagent. Many of the aromatic hydrocarbons are sometimes sampled by passing the air through nitrating acid, usually with the formation of the dinitro derivative.

## (2) Solvents

For practical purposes a number of organic solvent vapors can be collected with satisfactory efficiency by passing the air through a liquid which is miscible with the solvent in question. Thus the lower alcohols can be collected in water, esters in ethyl alcohol, etc.

A fact not generally appreciated is that the variable determining effi-

TABLE III
Collection of Vapors in Liquids with 95% Efficiency

| Vapor | Solvent | Volume of air per 10 ml solvent per bubbler, liters | |
| | | One bubbler | Two bubblers (in series) |
|---|---|---|---|
| Acetone | Water | 0.8 | 5.4 |
| Methanol | Water | 9 | 62 |
| n-Butanol | Water | 10 | 68 |
| Carbon tetrachloride | Isopropanol | 0.5 | 3.4 |
| Carbon tetrachloride | Amyl acetate | 1.2 | 8.1 |

ciency of collection in a given system is the ratio of volume of air to the volume of collecting liquid. The concentration of vapor in the air has, for practical purposes, no effect on the collection efficiency. As a rule the more volatile vapors are less completely retained than those of high-boiling liquids.

Elkins has determined the volume of air which can be passed through 10 ml of liquid with a theoretical collection efficiency of 95% for a number of vapors and sampling liquids. If two bubblers in series (each with 10 ml of liquid) are used, the efficiency of collection is increased nearly sevenfold (159) (see Table III).

Cooling the sampling liquid will also markedly increase the volume of air which can be sampled efficiently.

(3) Adsorbents

In the majority of cases, collection of solvent vapors from air is most conveniently achieved by passage through a column filled with adsorbent material in granular form. Silica gel is most frequently employed, although activated charcoal has a greater capacity for nonpolar solvents. Analysis of the sample is simpler when silica gel is used.

As with collection in solvents, the volume of air which can be sampled efficiently with silica gel is limited, but much greater than that collected by a corresponding weight of solvent. Under typical conditions of temperature and humidity, 10 g of silica gel will remove carbon tetrachloride vapor from 50 liters of air, in comparison with about 1 liter by 10 g of amyl acetate (in a single bubbler).

Factors affecting efficiency of collection include the volatility of the vapor, rate of air flow (at increased air flows the apparent volume of adsorbent is reduced), temperature, shape of adsorbent bed, mesh size of gel, and humidity. Since water vapor is strongly adsorbed on silica gel, it tends to displace nonpolar solvent vapors, and air samples collected in humid air may need to be restricted in volume, in comparison with those taken in dry air (160). Alternatively, collection efficiency can be increased by introducing a drying agent into the train (643).

Samples collected on silica gel may be treated with a liquid, such as water and alcohol, which will displace the adsorbed vapor. Or the gel may be heated and the vapor driven off into a suitable reagent or instrument. In a few cases reagent is added directly to the gel.

As a rule, nonpolar liquids are unsuitable for displacing vapors from silica gel. Aliphatic hydrocarbons, for example, will not displace benzene (160). In such instances it is necessary to first wet the gel with water and then extract with the desired solvent.

### c. Particulates

Dusts, mists, fumes, and sprays are particulate forms of air contaminant, and sampling methods are generally different than for gases and vapors.

#### (1) Filters

A convenient method of collecting particulates is to pass the air through filter paper. This technique has the advantage that high rates of air flow are readily attained. For most purposes Whatman 40 or its equivalent, or even coarser papers, are satisfactory. For fumes of very small particle size, paper of very fine porosity (millipore, etc.) may be desirable. Filters of asbestos or glass fibers are advantageous for certain purposes.

The use of filter papers for collecting fumes and dust has been discussed in several papers (89,179,228).

#### (2) Impingers

Dust particles in a gas tend to collect on the surface of any obstacle around which the gas flows. According to Drinker and Hatch, the strength of the precipitating force will vary with the kinetic energy of the particle (mass and velocity), the air resistance imposed on the particle, and the sharpness with which the air flows around the obstruction (139). For sampling air containing dust, mist, or fume, this principle is employed in various impingement devices.

The most generally applicable are the so-called impingers, in which a jet of air is forced against a flat plate immersed in water or other suitable liquid. Two sizes are commonly used, the standard and midget impingers, which ordinarily sample at 1 ft³ and 0.1 ft³/min, respectively. Most dusts are collected with fair efficiency by impingers, but complete collection of finely divided particulates (e.g., lead fume) cannot be achieved with the impinger. Some increase in efficiency can be obtained by increasing the sampling rate, however (159).

Other impingement devices collecting small samples (Konimeter, Owens dust counter, Bausch and Lomb dust counter) on dry plates are used almost exclusively for dust counting purposes.

The cascade impactor is an impingement device with several stages, in which particles of increasingly smaller size are collected on plates. The velocity of impingement is relatively low for the first stage and as high as practicable for the last. These devices are useful primarily for particle size analysis (391).

(3) Precipitators

The basic principle of the Cottrell electric precipitator for dust and smoke removal has been applied to air analysis by the development of portable instruments. Both ac (140) and dc (26) devices have been described, and the latter is available commercially. This unit features preionization of dust particles and their collection in an aluminum tube, with a sampling rate of 3 ft³/min.

In the thermal precipitator air is passed through a narrow slot in the center of which a hot (electrically heated) wire is placed. As a result of the thermal gradient between the wire and the walls of the slot, dust is collected on the latter. Because only low rates of air flow are feasible, this instrument is used primarily for dust counting purposes (219).

### d. Sources of Suction

The majority of air sampling procedures require a relatively constant source of suction. A vacuum line, if available, is usually satisfactory. Otherwise the most useful device is a small electric-powered blower or pump. If electricity is not available or if flammable vapors present a fire hazard, a hand-driven pump (midget impinger), an ejector utilizing compressed air, or a portable unit containing cans of compressed gas (Unijet Sampler), a water aspirator, or battery-powered device can be employed.

### e. Measurement of Air Flow

While the air volume sampled is sometimes measured directly by means of an aspirator bottle or dry or wet gas meter, the common procedure is to sample for a measured time at a constant known rate of air flow. A simple procedure is to introduce a capillary tube or other resistance into the line behind the sampling unit and determine the resulting pressure drop. The air flow at various pressure differentials is determined by calibration. Direct measurement of air flow by means of a rotameter measuring device may be employed, especially if the resistance of the sampling unit is prone to vary, as is the situation with filter paper samplers.

## C. BIOLOGICAL SAMPLES

The use of expired air, urine, blood, and other biological samples for evaluation of exposures to toxic substances has increased in recent years with the availability of new analytical techniques. The interest in this type of analysis is obvious in view of the wealth of information that can be obtained from it. In instances where correlations with exposure are known, analysis of the biological sample permits ideally an integrated measure of the individual's actual exposure in widely varying environments. These tests can also reveal careless working habits or accidental incidents that can frequently go unnoticed if air sampling is the only means employed to monitor harmful substances in the air.

### 1. Breath Samples

Analysis of expired air is performed for volatile and unreactive substances that are eliminated in measurable quantities via the lung. Notable in this field of investigation are the recent studies of a group of Dow Chemical workers on the measurement of chlorinated hydrocarbons in expired air as an index of exposure to these substances. More familiar, perhaps, is its use in detection of recent exposures to carbon monoxide and in spot tests employed by law-enforcing agencies to check an individual's state of sobriety. These analyses are successful also in the measurement of radium stored in the body. Radon gas given off by radium deposits in bones finds its way into the blood and lungs and is exhaled.

### 2. Urinalyses

Urine specimens are much easier to obtain from personnel than other biological samples and so urinalyses have had wide application for routine monitoring of exposure. They are useful for determining absorption of lead, mercury, arsenic, cadmium, fluorides, selenium, tellurium, uranium, trichloroethylene, methanol, benzene, toluene, trinitrotoluene, and many radioisotopes and pesticides.

### a. ELEMENTS

The metals in general are excreted slowly over a relatively long period of time. Samples can be collected for analysis with little reference to time in cases where chronic exposures are involved. Statistical correlations of urinary lead and mercury have been reported with exposure, but the relationship does not always hold up on an individual basis. For other metals the element in the urine may indicate only that exposure has taken place, either recently or some time in the past.

### b. METABOLITES

Many organic substances are excreted unchanged, but usually in very small amounts. It is usually preferable to measure the metabolites of these substances which are present in greater quantities. In many cases excretion of the metabolite is rapid and spot samples at the end of the work day need to be taken. Correlations have been found for urine sulfate ratio or phenol, dichlorophenol, and hippuric acid excretion with exposure to benzene, dichlorobenzene, and toluene, respectively. For other substances, such as methanol and trichloroethylene or its metabolites, the excretion is slow, and a few, such as DDT, are stored in the body for considerable periods of time.

### c. PATHOLOGY

Certain pathological tests are performed to detect early stages of poisoning which depend on measuring damage already done to the body. A routine medical laboratory procedure may be involved, such as a test for proteinuria on workers exposed to cadmium, or a more specialized technique of measuring coproporphyrin in urine of lead workers. A rise in coproporphyrin content ordinarily precedes other signs of lead poisoning.

### d. EXPRESSION OF RESULTS

The collection of samples and the expression of urinary results have not yet been standardized, frequently making it difficult to relate findings from different laboratories. The medical profession prefers to express results in terms of 24-hr or other timed intervals of excretion. This can be done easily enough in a hospital situation where proper supervision is available, but is usually impractical in industry. It is often difficult to obtain full cooperation from individuals at work even when there is a sincere willingness on their part.

The spot sample from a single voiding is easier to obtain, requires a minimum of cooperation from the worker, and is usually more applicable to industrial hygiene work. This type of sample is preferable when measuring metabolites of absorbed industrial products that are rapidly excreted and reach peak concentrations within a given period of time. The urinalysis results can be expressed as milligrams per liter or parts per million and provide useful information in many instances. On the other hand, in cases where there is considerable variation in urinary volume, to be consistent and meaningful the results must also be corrected for urine concentration.

A specific gravity adjustment has been proposed by Levine and Fahy (351a) to relate lead results to the total solid content of the urine. The measured concentration of lead in milligrams per liter is multiplied by a factor $24/G$, where $G$ represents the increment over unity of the specific gravity of the sample. This has the virtue of being a simple test, requiring no costly equipment or special skill. Although the procedure was evolved originally for lead, the logic would be equally applicable to many other substances. However, there are certain inherent drawbacks to its use. The measurement is subject to appreciable error, especially in dilute samples. Commercial urinometers are not only calibrated inaccurately, but temperature control is needed. Furthermore, according to physiologists specific gravity is not an ideal measure of urine concentration.

Osmolality is believed to be a better measure of urine concentration than specific gravity. It is a function of osmotic pressure and is determined ordinarily by measuring the freezing point of the urine. Osmolality can be measured more accurately with an osmometer than specific gravity with a urinometer. The presence of high molecular weight glucose in diabetic urine or protein has a lesser effect on osmolality than on specific gravity.

Another means of estimating urine concentration is the determination of the urinary creatinine content. Creatinine is of endogenous origin and is excreted at a relatively constant rate. It may be determined by a simple test involving addition of picric acid and alkali and measurement of the color produced. The total excretion is dependent on the body creatine content and therefore on the weight of muscle.

### 3. Blood Analyses

Blood analyses have been performed for metals, organic solvents and their metabolites, and other substances. Because of its widespread use and toxicological importance, lead has received considerable study in this field. Some authorities prefer blood-lead measurements to any other index of lead exposure, particularly in the case of active plumbism. Analysis of blood for manganese has been of some practical use as an index of exposure to this metal. The majority of heavy metals, however, are not present in blood in sufficient concentration to make analysis of this fluid useful as a measure of industrial exposure.

Unchanged organic solvents have been determined in the blood of exposed individuals, but with few exceptions are present in amounts too small to be of practical importance. Ordinarily it is more useful to avail oneself of techniques for measuring their metabolites.

Blood analyses have been successfully employed for measuring cholinesterase activity in poisoning by organic phosphate insecticides and carboxyhemoglobin formed by the combination of carbon monoxide with hemoglobin in cases of carbon monoxide exposure. Other examples are bromide analyses in cases of methyl bromide poisoning, and methemoglobin formation following exposure to aromatic amines and nitro compounds, such as aniline and nitrobenzene.

### 4. Hair and Fingernails

Arsenic is deposited in the hair and nails and analyses of these materials are useful in determining a past arsenic exposure. Cystine content of fingernails among workers exposed to vanadium is suggested as a basis to detect the early effects of vanadium absorption.

### 5. Tissues

Analyses of tissue obtained at autopsy and biopsy specimens are of considerable value in confirming diagnoses of certain diseases where occupational exposure is in question. Much can be learned also about the distribution and solubility of substances inhaled or absorbed by examination of tissue from the lungs, bone, and various organs.

## THRESHOLD LIMIT VALUES OF AIRBORNE CONTAMINANTS

### ADOPTED BY ACGIH FOR 1969* AND INTENDED CHANGES

Copyright 1969, by American Conference of Governmental Industrial Hygienists.

## Documentation of Threshold Limit Values

A separate companion piece to the TLVs is issued by ACGIH under this title. This publication gives the pertinent scientific information and data with reference to literature sources that were used to base each limit. Each documentation also contains a statement defining the type of response against which the limit is safeguarding the worker. For a better understanding of the TLVs it is essential that the Documentation be consulted when the TLVs are being used.

### Preface

Threshold limit values refer to airborne concentrations of substances and represent conditions under which it is believed that nearly all workers may be repeatedly exposed day after day without adverse effect. Because of wide variation in individual susceptibility, however, a small percentage of workers may experience discomfort from some substances at concentrations at or below the threshold limit, a smaller percentage may be affected more seriously by aggravation of a pre-existing condition or by development of an occupational illness.

Simple tests are now available (J. Occup. Med. 9, 537, 1967; Ann. N.Y. Acad. Sci. 151 Art. 2, p. 968, 1968) that may be used to detect those individuals hypersusceptible to a variety of industrial chemicals (respiratory irritants, hemolytic chemicals, organic isocyanates, carbon disulfide). These tests may be used to screen out by appropriate job placement the hyperreactive worker and thus in effect improve this "coverage" of the TLVs.

Threshold limit values refer to time-weighted concentrations for a 7 or 8-hour workday and 40-hour workweek. They should be used as guides in the control of health hazards and should not be used as fine lines between safe and dangerous concentrations. (Exceptions are the substances listed in Appendices A and E and those substances designated with a "C" or Ceiling value, Appendix C.)

Time-weighted averages permit excursions above the limit provided they are compensated by equivalent excursions below the limit during the workday. In some instances it may be permissible to calculate the average concentration for a workweek rather than for a workday. The degree of permissible excursion is related to the magnitude of the threshold limit value of a particular substance as given in Appendix C. The relationship between threshold limit and permissible excursion is a rule of thumb and in certain cases may not apply. The amount by which threshold limits may be exceeded for short periods without injury to health depends upon a number of factors such as the nature of the contaminant, whether very high concentrations—even for short periods—produce acute poisoning, whether the effects are cumulative, the frequency with which high concentrations occur, and the duration of such periods. All factors must be taken into consideration in arriving at decision as to whether a hazardous condition exists.

Threshold limits are based on the best available information from industrial experience, from experimental human and animal studies, and, when possible, from a combination of the three. The basis on which the values are established may differ from substance to substance; protection against impairment of health may be a guiding factor for some, whereas reasonable freedom from irritation, narcosis, nuisance or other forms of stress may form the basis for others.

The committee holds to the opinion that limits based on physical irritation should be considered no less binding than those based on physical impairment. There is increasing evidence that physical irritation may initiate, promote or accelerate physical impairment through interaction with other chemical or biologic agents.

In spite of the fact that serious injury is not believed likely as a result of exposure to the threshold limit concentrations, the best practice is to maintain concentrations of all atmospheric contaminants as low as is practical.

These limits are intended for use in the practice of industrial hygiene and should be interpreted and applied only by a person trained in this discipline. They are not intended for use, or for modification for use, (1) as a relative index of hazard or toxicity (2) in the evaluation or control of community air pollution or air pollution nuisances, (3) in estimating the toxic potential of continuous uninterrupted exposures, (4) as proof or disproof of an existing disease or physical conditions, or (5) for adoption by countries whose working conditions differ from those in the United States of America and where substances and processes differ.

### Ceiling vs Time-Weighted Average Limits

Although the time-weighted average concentration provides the most satisfactory, practical way of monitoring airborne agents for compliance with the limits, there are certain substances for which it is inappropriate. In the latter group are substances which are predominantly fast acting and whose threshold limit is more appropriately based on this particular response. Substances with this type of response are best controlled by a ceiling "C" limit that should not be exceeded. It is implicit in these definitions that the manner of sampling to determine compliance with the limits for each group must differ; a single brief sample, that is applicable to a "C" limit, is not appropriate to the time-weighted limit: here, a sufficient number of samples are needed to permit a time-weighted average concentration throughout a complete cycle of operations or throughout the work shift.

Whereas the ceiling limit places a definite boundary which concentrations should not be permitted to exceed, the time-weighted average limit requires an explicit limit to the excursions that are permissible above the listed values. The magnitude of these excursions may be pegged to the magnitude of the threshold limit by an appropriate factor shown in Appendix C. It should be noted that the same factors are used by the Committee in making a judgment whether to include or exclude a substance for a "C" listing.

### "Skin" Notation

Listed substances followed by the designation "Skin" refer to the potential contribution to the over-all exposure by the cutaneous route including mucous membranes and eye, either by air-borne, or more particularly, by direct contact with the substance. Vehicles can alter skin absorption. This attention-calling designation is intended to suggest appropriate measures for the prevention of cutaneous absorption so that the threshold limit is not invalidated.

### Mixtures

Special consideration should be given also to the application of the TLVs in assessing the health hazards which may be associated with exposure to mixtures of two or more substances. A brief discussion of basic considerations involved in developing threshold limit values for mixtures, and methods for their development, amplified by specific examples are given in Appendix B.

### "Inert" or Nuisance Particulates

A number of dusts or particulates that occur in the working environment ordinarily produce no specific effects upon prolonged inhalation. Some insoluble substances are classed as inert (e.g., iron and steel dusts, cement, silicon carbide, titanium dioxide, cellulose) ; others may be soluble (starch, soluble oils, calcium carbonate) but are of such a low order of activity that in concentrations ordinarily encountered do not cause physiologic impairment; still others may be rapidly eliminated or destroyed by the body (vegetable oils, glycerine, sucrose). In the case of the insoluble substances, there may be some accumulation in the respiratory passages. In the case of the soluble substances, this accumulation will ordinarily be temporary but may interfere to some extent with respiratory processes. Hence, it is desirable to control the concentrations of such particulates in the air breathed by any individual, in keeping with good industrial hygiene practice.

A threshold limit of 15mg/$M^3$, or 50 mppcf, of total dust $<1\%SiO_2$, whichever is less, is recommended for substances in these categories and for which no specific threshold limits have been assigned. This limit, for a normal workday, does not apply to brief exposures at higher concentrations. Neither does it apply to those substances which may cause physiologic impairment at lower concentrations but for which a threshold limit has not yet been adopted. Some "inert" particulates are given in Appendix D.

### Simple Asphyxiants—"Inert" Gases or Vapors

A number of gases and vapors, when present in high concentrations in air, act primarily as simple asphyxiants without other significant physiologic effects. A TLV may not be recommended for each simple asphyxiant because the limiting factor is the available oxygen. The minimal oxygen content should be 18 percent by volume under normal atmospheric pressure (equivalent to a partial pressure, $pO_2$ of 135 mm Hg). Atmospheres deficient in $O_2$ do not provide adequate warning and most simple asphyxiants are ordorless. Several simple asphyxiants present an explosion hazard. Account should be taken of this factor in limiting the concentration of the asphyxiant. Specific examples are listed in Appendix E.

### Physical Factors

It is recognized that such physical factors as heat, ultraviolet and ionizing radiation, humidity, abnormal pressure (altitude) and the like may place added stress on the body so that the effects from exposure at a threshold limit may be altered. Most of these stresses act adversely to increase the toxic response of a substance. Although most threshold limits have built-in safety factors to guard against adverse effects to moderate deviations from normal environments, the safety factors of most substances are not of such a magnitude as to take care of gross deviations. For example, continuous work at temperatures above 90°F or over-time extending the workweek more than 25%, might be considered gross deviations. In such instances judgment must be exercised in the proper adjustments of the threshold limit values.

## "Notice of Intent"

At the beginning of each year, proposed actions of the Committee for the forthcoming year are issued in the form of a "Notice of Intent." This Notice provides not only an opportunity for comment, but solicits suggestions of substances to be added to the list. The suggestions should be accompanied by substantiating evidence.

## As Legislative Code

Although the Conference does not consider the TLVs appropriate matter for adoption into legislative codes and regulations, it recognizes that the values may be so used. If so used, the intent of the concepts contained in the Preface should be maintained and provisions should be made to keep the list current. These values are reviewed annually by the Committee on Threshold Limits for revision or additions, as further information becomes available.

## Reprint Permission

This publication may be reprinted provided that written permission is obtained from the Secretary-Treasurer of the Conference and that it be published in its entirety.

Adopted Values
(In Alphabetical Order)

| Substance | ppm[a] | mg/M³ [b] |
|---|---|---|
| * Abate............................................. | — | 15 |
| Acetaldehyde...................................... | 200 | 360 |
| Acetic acid........................................ | 10 | 25 |
| Acetic anhydride................................. | 5 | 20 |

a) Parts of vapor or gas per million parts of contaminated air by volume at 25°C and 760 mm. Hg pressure.

b) Approximate milligrams of particulate per cubic meter of air.

A Numbers, See Appendix A

* 1969 addition

** See Notice of Intended Changes

(continued)

Adopted Values (*continued*)

| Substance | ppm[a)] | mg/M³ [b)] |
|---|---|---|
| Acetone............................................. | 1,000 | 2,400 |
| Acetonitrile....................................... | 40 | 70 |
| Acetylene dichloride, see 1, 2 Dicloroethylene......... | | |
| Acetylene tetrabromide............................ | 1 | 14 |
| Acrolein........................................... | 0.1 | 0.25 |
| Acrylamide-Skin ................................. | — | 0.3 |
| Acrylonitrile-Skin................................. | 20 | 45 |
| Aldrin-Skin....................................... | — | 0.25 |
| Allyl alcohol-Skin................................. | 2 | 5 |
| Allyl chloride..................................... | 1 | 3 |
| C Allyl glycidyl ether (AGE)........................ | 10 | 45 |
| Allyl propyl disulfide.............................. | 2 | 12 |
| 2-Aminoethanol, see Ethanolamine................... | | |
| 2-Aminopyridine................................... | 0.5 | 2 |
| ** Ammonia......................................... | 50 | 35 |
| Ammonium sulfamate (Ammate).................... | — | 15 |
| n-Amyl acetate................................... | 100 | 525 |
| sec-Amyl acetate................................. | 125 | 650 |
| Aniline-Skin...................................... | 5 | 19 |
| Anisidine (o,p-isomers)-Skin....................... | — | 0.5 |
| Antimony & compounds (as Sb).................... | — | 0.5 |
| ANTU (alpha naphthyl thiourea)................... | — | 0.3 |
| Arsenic & Compounds (as As)...................... | — | 0.5 |
| Arsine............................................ | 0.05 | 0.2 |
| Azinphos-methyl-Skin ............................ | — | 0.2 |
| Barium (soluble compounds)....................... | — | 0.5 |
| C Benzene (benzol)-Skin............................ | 25 | 80 |
| Benzidine-Skin.................................... | — | A[1] |
| p-Benzoquinone, see Quinone...................... | | |
| Benzoyl peroxide................................. | — | 5 |
| Benzyl chloride................................... | 1 | 5 |
| Beryllium......................................... | — | 0.002 |
| Biphenyl, see Diphenyl............................ | | |
| Boron oxide....................................... | — | 15 |
| * Boron tribromide................................. | 1 | — |
| C Boron trifluoride................................. | 1 | 3 |
| Bromine.......................................... | 0.1 | 0.7 |
| * Bromine pentafluoride............................ | 0.1 | — |
| Bromoform-Skin.................................. | 0.5 | 5 |
| Butadiene (1, 3-butadiene)......................... | 1,000 | 2,200 |
| Butanethiol, see Butyl mercaptan................... | | |
| 2-Butanone....................................... | 200 | 590 |
| 2-Butoxy ethanol (Butyl Cellosolve) Skin............. | 50 | 240 |
| n-Butyl acetate................................... | 150 | 710 |

(*continued*)

Adopted Values (*continued*)

| Substance | ppm[a] | mg/M³ [b] |
|---|---|---|
| sec-Butyl acetate | 200 | 950 |
| tert-Butyl acetate | 200 | 950 |
| Butyl alcohol | 100 | 300 |
| sec-Butyl alcohol | 150 | 450 |
| tert. Butyl alcohol | 100 | 300 |
| C Butylamine-Skin | 5 | 15 |
| C tert. Butyl chromate (as CrO3)-Skin | — | 0.1 |
| n-Butyl glycidyl ether (BGE) | 50 | 270 |
| ** Butyl mercaptan | 10 | 35 |
| p-tert. Butyltoluene | 10 | 60 |
| Cadmium (Metal dust and soluble salts) | — | 0.2 |
| ** Cadmium oxide fume | — | 0.1 |
| Calcium arsenate | — | 1 |
| Calcium oxide | — | 5 |
| * Camphor | 2 | — |
| Carbaryl (Sevin®) | — | 5 |
| Carbon black | — | 3.5 |
| Carbon dioxide | 5,000 | 9,000 |
| Carbon disulfide-Skin | 20 | 60 |
| Carbon monoxide | 50 | 55 |
| Carbon tetrachloride-Skin | 10 | 65 |
| Chlordane-Skin | — | 0.5 |
| Chlorinated camphene-Skin | — | 0.5 |
| Chlorinated diphenyl oxide | — | 0.5 |
| * Chlorine | 1 | — |
| Chlorine dioxide | 0.1 | 0.3 |
| C Chlorine trifluoride | 0.1 | 0.4 |
| C Chloroacetaldehyde | 1 | 3 |
| α-Chloroacetophenone (phenacyl-chloride) | 0.05 | 0.3 |
| Chlorobenzene (monochlorobenzene) | 75 | 350 |
| o-Chlorobenzylidene malononitrile (OCBM) | 0.05 | 0.4 |
| Chlorobromomethane | 200 | 1,050 |
| 2-Chloro-1, 3 butadiene, see Chloroprene | | |
| Chlorodiphenyl (42% Chlorine)-Skin | — | 1 |
| Chlorodiphenyl (54% Chlorine)-Skin | — | 0.5 |
| 1, Chloro, 2, 3 epoxypropane, see Epichlorhydrin | | |
| 2, Chloroethanol, see Ethylene chlorohydrin | | |
| Chloroethylene, see Vinyl chloride | | |
| C Chloroform (trichloromethane) | 50 | 240 |
| 1-Chloro-1-nitropropane | 20 | 100 |
| Chloropicrin | 0.1 | 0.7 |
| Chloroprene (2-chloro-1, 3-butadiene)-Skin | 25 | 90 |
| Chromic acid and chromates (as CrO₃) | — | 0.1 |
| Chromium, sol. chromic, chromous salts as Cr | — | 0.5 |

(*continued*)

Adopted Values (*continued*)

| Substance | ppm[a)] | mg/M³ [b)] |
|---|---|---|
| Metal & insol. salts............................... | — | 1 |
| Coal tar pitch volatiles (benzene soluble fraction) anthracene, BaP, phenanthrene, acridine, chrysene, pyrene). | — | 0.2 |
| Cobalt, metal fume & dust......................... | — | 0.1 |
| Copper fume...................................... | — | 0.1 |
| Dusts and Mists.............................. | — | 1 |
| Cotton dust (raw)............................... | — | 1 |
| Crag® herbicide.................................. | — | 15 |
| Cresol (all isomers)-Skin.......................... | 5 | 22 |
| Crotonaldehyde.................................. | 2 | 6 |
| Cumene-Skin..................................... | 50 | 245 |
| Cyanide (as CN)-Skin............................ | — | 5 |
| * Cyanogen........................................ | 10 | — |
| Cyclohexane..................................... | 300 | 1,050 |
| Cyclohexanol.................................... | 50 | 200 |
| Cyclohexanone................................... | 50 | 200 |
| Cyclohexene..................................... | 300 | 1,015 |
| Cyclopentadiene................................. | 75 | 200 |
| 2, 4-D........................................... | — | 10 |
| DDT-Skin........................................ | — | 1 |
| DDVP-Skin....................................... | — | 1 |
| Decaborane-Skin................................. | 0.05 | 0.3 |
| Demeton®-Skin................................... | — | 0.1 |
| Diacetone alcohol (4-methyl-2-pentanone)............. | 50 | 240 |
| 1, 2 Diaminoethane, see Ethylenediamine Diazomethane | 0.2 | 0.4 |
| Diborane........................................ | 0.1 | 0.1 |
| C 1, 2-Dibromoethane (ethylene dibromide)-Skin........ | 25 | 190 |
| Dibutyl phosphate............................... | 1 | 5 |
| Dibutylphthalate................................. | — | 5 |
| C o-Dichlorobenzene............................... | 50 | 300 |
| p-Dichlorobenzene............................... | 75 | 450 |
| Dichlorodifluoromethane........................... | 1,000 | 4,950 |
| 1, 3-Dichloro-5, dimethyl hydantoin................. | — | 0.2 |
| 1, 1-Dichloroethane............................. | 100 | 400 |
| 1, 2-Dichloroethane............................. | 50 | 200 |
| 1, 2-Dichloroethylene............................ | 200 | 790 |
| C Dichloroethyl ether-Skin......................... | 15 | 90 |
| Dichloromethane, see Methylenechloride.............. | | |
| Dichloromonofluoromethane........................ | 1,000 | 4,200 |
| C 1, 1-Dichloro-1-nitroethane....................... | 10 | 60 |
| 1, 2-Dichloropropane, see Propylenedichloride......... | | |
| Dichlorotetrafluoroethane........................ | 1,000 | 7,000 |
| Dieldrin-Skin.................................... | — | 0.25 |
| Diethylamine.................................... | 25 | 75 |
| Diethylamino ethanol-Skin........................ | 10 | 50 |

(*continued*)

Adopted Values *(contnuedi)*

| Substance | ppm[a] | mg/M³ [b] |
|---|---|---|
| *C Diethylene triamine-Skin | 10 | — |
| Diethylether, see Ethyl ether | | |
| Difluorodibromomethane | 100 | 860 |
| C Diglycidyl ether (DGE) | 0.5 | 2.8 |
| Dihydroxybenzene, see Hydroquinone | | |
| Diisobutyl ketone | 50 | 290 |
| Diisopropylamine-Skin | 5 | 20 |
| * Diphenyl amine | — | 10 |
| Dimethoxymethane, see Methylal | | |
| Dimethyl acetamide-Skin | 10 | 35 |
| Dimethylamine | 10 | 18 |
| Dimethylaminobenzene, see Xylidene | | |
| Dimethylaniline(N-dimethylaniline)-Skin | 5 | 25 |
| Dimethylbenzene, see Xylene | | |
| Dimethyl 1, 2-dibromo-2, 2-dichloroethyl phosphate, (Dibrom) | — | 3 |
| Dimethylformamide-Skin | 10 | 30 |
| 2,6 Dimethylheptanone, see Diisobutyl ketone | | |
| 1, 1-Dimethylhydrazine-Skin | 0.5 | 1 |
| Dimethylphthalate | — | 5 |
| Dimethylsulfate-Skin | 1 | 5 |
| Dinitrobenzene (all isomers)-Skin | — | 1 |
| Dinitro-o-cresol-Skin | — | 0.2 |
| Dinitrotoluene-Skin | — | 1.5 |
| Dioxane (Diethylene dioxide)-Skin | 100 | 360 |
| Diphenyl | 0.2 | 1 |
| * Diphenyl Amine | — | 10 |
| Diphenylmethane diisocyanate (see Methylene bisphenyl isocyanate (MDI) | | |
| Dipropylene glycol methyl ether-Skin | 100 | 600 |
| Di-sec, octyl phthalate (Di-2-ethylhexylphthalate) | — | 5 |
| Endrin-Skin | — | 0.1 |
| Epichlorhydrin-Skin | 5 | 19 |
| EPN-Skin | — | 0.5 |
| 1,2-Epoxypropane, see Propyleneoxide | | |
| 2,3-Epoxy-1-propanol, see Glycidol | | |
| Ethanethiol, see Ethylmercaptan | | |
| Ethanolamine | 3 | 6 |
| 2 Ethoxyethanol-Skin | 200 | 740 |
| 2 Ethoxyethylacetate (Cellosolve acetate)-Skin | 100 | 540 |
| Ethyl acetate | 400 | 1,400 |
| Ethyl acrylate-Skin | 25 | 100 |
| Ethyl alcohol (ethanol) | 1,000 | 1,900 |
| Ethylamine | 10 | 18 |
| Ethyl sec-amyl ketone (5-methyl-3-heptanone) | 25 | 130 |

*(continued)*

Adopted Values (continued)

| Substance | ppm[a] | mg/M³ [b] |
|---|---|---|
| Ethyl benzene | 100 | 435 |
| Ethyl bromide | 200 | 890 |
| Ethyl butyl ketone (3-Heptanone) | 50 | 230 |
| Ethyl chloride | 1,000 | 2,600 |
| Ethyl ether | 400 | 1,200 |
| Ethyl formate | 100 | 300 |
| ** Ethyl mercaptan | 10 | 25 |
| Ethyl silicate | 100 | 850 |
| Ethylene chlorohydrin-Skin | 5 | 16 |
| Ethylenediamine | 10 | 25 |
| Ethylene dibromide, see 1,2-Dibromoethane | | |
| Ethylene dichloride, see 1,2-Dichloroethane | | |
| C Ethylene glycol dinitrate and/or Nitroglycerin-Skin | 0.2[d] | 1 |
| Ethylene glycol monomethyl ether acetate, see Methyl cellosolve acetate | | |
| Ethylene imine-Skin | 0.5 | 1 |
| Ethylene oxide | 50 | 90 |
| Ethylidine chloride, see 1,1-Dichloroethane | | |
| N-Ethylmorpholine-Skin | 20 | 94 |
| Ferbam | — | 15 |
| Ferrovanadium dust | — | 1 |
| Fluoride (as F) | — | 2.5 |
| Fluorine | 0.1 | 0.2 |
| Fluorotrichloromethane | 1,000 | 5,600 |
| C Formaldehyde | 5 | 6 |
| Formic acid | 5 | 9 |
| Furfural-Skin | 5 | 20 |
| Furfuryl alcohol | 50 | 200 |
| Gasoline | — | A³ |
| Glycidol (2,3-Epoxy-1-propanol) | 50 | 150 |
| Glycol monoethyl ether, see 2-Ethoxyethanol | | |
| Guthion,® see Azinphosmethyl | | |
| Hafnium | — | 0.5 |
| Heptachlor-Skin | — | 0.5 |
| ** Heptane (n-heptane) | 500 | 2,000 |
| Hexachloroethane-Skin | 1 | 10 |
| Hexachloronaphthalene-Skin | — | 0.2 |
| Hexane (n-hexane) | 500 | 1,800 |
| 2-Hexanone | 100 | 410 |
| Hexone | 100 | 410 |
| sec-Hexyl acetate | 50 | 300 |
| Hydrazine-Skin | 1 | 1.3 |
| Hydrogen bromide | 3 | 10 |
| C Hydrogen chloride | 5 | 7 |
| Hydrogen cyanide-Skin | 10 | 11 |

(continued)

Adopted Values (*continued*)

| Substance | ppm[a] | mg/M³ [b] |
|---|---|---|
| Hydrogen fluoride | 3 | 2 |
| ** Hydrogen peroxide, 90% | 1 | 1.4 |
| Hydrogen selenide | 0.05 | 0.2 |
| Hydrogen sulfide | 10 | 15 |
| Hydroquinone | — | 2 |
| * Indium and compounds, as In | — | 0.1 |
| C Iodine | 0.1 | 1 |
| Iron oxide fume | — | 10 |
| * Iron salts, soluble, as Fe | — | 1 |
| Isoamyl acetate | 100 | 525 |
| Isoamyl alcohol | 100 | 360 |
| Isobutyl acetate | 150 | 700 |
| Isobutyl alcohol | 100 | 300 |
| Isophorone | 25 | 140 |
| Isopropyl acetate | 250 | 950 |
| Isopropyl alcohol | 400 | 980 |
| Isopropylamine | 5 | 12 |
| Isopropylether | 500 | 2,100 |
| Isopropyl glycidyl ether (IGE) | 50 | 240 |
| Ketene | 0.5 | 0.9 |
| Lead | — | 0.2 |
| Lead arsenate | — | 0.15 |
| Lindane-Skin | — | 0.5 |
| Lithium hydride | — | 0.025 |
| L. P. G. (Liquified petroleum gas) | 1,000 | 1,800 |
| Magnesium oxide fume | — | 15 |
| Malathion-Skin | — | 15 |
| Maleic anhydride | 0.25 | 1 |
| C Manganese | — | 5 |
| ** Mercury-Skin | — | 0.1 |
| ** Mercury (organic compounds)-Skin | —— | 0.01 |
| Mesityl oxide | 25 | 100 |
| Methanethiol, see Methyl mercaptan | | |
| Methoxychlor | —— | 15 |
| 2-Methoxyethanol, see Methyl cellosolve | | |
| Methyl acetate | 200 | 610 |
| Methyl acetylene (propyne) | 1,000 | 1,650 |
| Methyl acetylene-propadiene mixture (MAPP) | 1,000 | 1,800 |
| Methyl acrylate-Skin | 10 | 35 |
| Methylal (dimethoxymethane) | 1,000 | 3,100 |
| Methyl alcohol (methanol) | 200 | 260 |
| Methylamine | 10 | 12 |
| Methyl amyl alcohol, see Methyl isobutyl carbinol | | |
| Methyl (n-amyl) ketone (2-Heptanone) | 100 | 465 |
| C Methyl bromide-Skin | 20 | 80 |

(*continued*)

## Adopted Values (continued)

| Substance | ppm[a)] | mg/M[3 b)] |
|---|---|---|
| Methyl butyl ketone, see 2-Hexanone................ | | |
| Methyl cellosolve-Skin............................. | 25 | 80 |
| Methyl cellosolve acetate-Skin..................... | 25 | 120 |
| C Methyl chloride................................. | 100 | 210 |
| Methyl chloroform................................. | 350 | 1,900 |
| Methylcyclohexane................................. | 500 | 2,000 |
| Methylcyclohexanol................................ | 100 | 470 |
| o-Methylcyclohexanone-Skin........................ | 100 | 460 |
| Methyl ethyl ketone (MEK), see 2-Butanone.......... | | |
| Methyl formate.................................... | 100 | 250 |
| Methyl iodide-Skin................................ | 5 | 28 |
| Methyl isobutyl carbinol-Skin...................... | 25 | 100 |
| Methyl isobutyl ketone, see Hexone................. | | |
| Methyl isocyanate-Skin............................ | 0.02 | 0.05 |
| **C Methyl mercaptan............................... | 10 | 20 |
| Methyl methacrylate............................... | 100 | 410 |
| Methyl propyl ketone, see 2-Pentanone.............. | | |
| *C Methyl silicate................................. | 5 | —— |
| C α Methyl styrene................................ | 100 | 480 |
| C Methylene bisphenyl isocyanate (MDI).............. | 0.02 | 0.2 |
| Methylene chloride (dichloromethane)................ | 500 | 1,740 |
| Molybdenum (soluble compounds).................. | — | 5 |
| (insoluble compounds)................ | — | 15 |
| Monomethyl aniline-Skin........................... | 2 | 9 |
| C Monomethyl hydrazine-Skin....................... | 0.2 | 0.35 |
| Morpholine-Skin................................... | 20 | 70 |
| Naphtha (coal tar)................................. | 100 | 400 |
| Naphthalene....................................... | 10 | 50 |
| β-Naphthylamine................................... | — | A[1] |
| Nickel carbonyl.................................... | 0.001 | 0.007 |
| Nickel, metal and soluble cmpds.................... | — | 1 |
| Nicotine-Skin...................................... | — | 0.5 |
| Nitric acid........................................ | 2 | 5 |
| Nitric oxide....................................... | 25 | 30 |
| p-Nitroaniline-Skin................................ | 1 | 6 |
| Nitrobenzene-Skin................................. | 1 | 5 |
| p-Nitrochloro-benzene-Skin........................ | — | 1 |
| Nitroethane....................................... | 100 | 310 |
| C Nitrogen dioxide................................. | 5 | 9 |
| Nitrogen Trifluoride............................... | 10 | 29 |
| C Nitroglycerin-Skin............................... | 0.2 | 2 |
| Nitromethane..................................... | 100 | 250 |
| 1-Nitropropane.................................... | 25 | 90 |
| 2-Nitropropane.................................... | 25 | 90 |
| N-Nitrosodimethyl-amine (Dimethyl-nitrosoamine)-Skin | — | A[1] |

(continued)

Adopted Values (*continued*)

| Substance | ppm[a)] | mg/M$^{3}$ [b)] |
|---|---|---|
| Nitrotoluene-Skin.................................. | 5 | 30 |
| Nitrotrichloromethane, see Chloropicrin............. | | |
| Octachloronaphthalene-Skin........................ | — | 0.1 |
| ** Octane......................................... | 500 | 2,350 |
| ** Oil mist (mineral)............................... | — | 5 |
| Osmium tetroxide................................. | — | 0.002 |
| Oxalic acid....................................... | — | 1 |
| Oxygen difluoride................................. | 0.05 | 0.1 |
| Ozone............................................ | 0.1 | 0.2 |
| Paraquat-Skin.................................... | — | 0.5 |
| Parathion-Skin................................... | — | 0.1 |
| Pentaborane...................................... | 0.005 | 0.01 |
| Pentachloronaphthalene-Skin....................... | — | 0.5 |
| Pentachlorophenol-Skin............................ | — | 0.5 |
| ** Pentane........................................ | 1,000 | 2,950 |
| 2-Pentanone...................................... | 200 | 700 |
| Perchloroethylene................................. | 100 | 670 |
| Perchloromethyl mercaptan......................... | 0.1 | 0.8 |
| Perchloryl fluoride................................ | 3 | 13.5 |
| ** Petroleum Distillates (naphtha)................... | 500 | 2,000 |
| Phenol-Skin...................................... | 5 | 19 |
| p-Phenylene diamine-Skin.......................... | — | 0.1 |
| Phenyl ether (vapor).............................. | 1 | 7 |
| Phenyl ether-Biphenyl mixture (vapor).............. | 1 | 7 |
| Phenylethylene, see Styrene........................ | | |
| Phenyl glycidyl ether (PGE)....................... | 10 | 60 |
| Phenylhydrazine-Skin............................. | 5 | 22 |
| Phosdrin (Mevinphos)® -Skin...................... | — | 0.1 |
| Phosgene (carbonyl chloride)....................... | 0.1 | 0.4 |
| Phosphine........................................ | 0.3 | 0.4 |
| Phosphoric acid................................... | — | 1 |
| Phosphorus (yellow).............................. | — | 0.1 |
| Phosphorus pentachloride.......................... | — | 1 |
| Phosphorus pentasulfide........................... | — | 1 |
| Phosphorus trichloride............................ | 0.5 | 3 |
| Phthalic anhydride................................ | 2 | 12 |
| Picric acid-Skin................................... | — | 0.1 |
| Pival® (2-Pivalyl-1,3-indandione).................. | — | 0.1 |
| Platinum (Soluble Salts).......................... | — | 0.002 |
| Polytetrafluoroethylene decomposition products........ | — | A$^{2}$ |
| Propane.......................................... | 1,000 | 1,800 |
| β Propiolactone................................... | — | A$^{1}$ |
| * Propargyl alcohol-Skin........................... | 1 | — |
| n-Propyl acetate.................................. | 200 | 840 |
| Propyl alcohol.................................... | 200 | 500 |

(*continued*)

Adopted Values (*continued*)

| Substance | ppm[a)] | mg/M³ [b)] |
|---|---|---|
| n-Propyl nitrate | 25 | 110 |
| Propylene dichloride | 75 | 350 |
| Propylene imine-Skin | 2 | 5 |
| Propylene oxide | 100 | 240 |
| Propyne, see Methylacetylene | | |
| Pyrethrum | — | 5 |
| Pyridine | 5 | 15 |
| Quinone | 0.1 | 0.4 |
| * RDX-Skin | — | 1.5 |
| Rhodium, Metal fume and dusts | — | 0.1 |
| Soluble salts | — | 0.001 |
| Ronnel | — | 15 |
| Rotenone (commercial) | — | 5 |
| Selenium compounds (as Se) | — | 0.2 |
| Selenium hexafluoride | 0.05 | 0.4 |
| Silver, metal and soluble compounds | — | 0.01 |
| Sodium fluroacetate (1080)-Skin | — | 0.05 |
| Sodium hydroxide | — | 2 |
| Stibine | 0.1 | 0.5 |
| ** Stoddard solvent | 500 | 2,900 |
| Strychnine | — | 0.15 |
| **C Styrene monomer (phenylethylene) | 100 | 420 |
| Sulfur dioxide | 5 | 13 |
| Sulfur hexafluoride | 1,000 | 6,000 |
| Sulfuric acid | — | 1 |
| Sulfur monochloride | 1 | 6 |
| Sulfur pentafluoride | 0.025 | 0.25 |
| Sulfuryl fluoride | 5 | 20 |
| Systox,® see Demeton | | |
| 2, 4, 5 T | — | 10 |
| Tantalum | — | 5 |
| TEDP-Skin | — | 0.2 |
| Teflon® decomposition products | — | A⁴ |
| Tellurium | — | 0.1 |
| Tellurium hexafluoride | 0.02 | 0.2 |
| TEPP-Skin | — | 0.05 |
| C Terphenyls | 1 | 9 |
| 1, 1, 1, 2-Tetrachloro-2, 2-difluoroethane | 500 | 4,170 |
| 1, 1, 2, 2-Tetrachloro-1, 2-difluoroethane | 500 | 4,170 |
| 1, 1, 2, 2-Tetrachloroethane-Skin | 5 | 35 |
| Tetrachloroethylene, see Perchloroethylene | | |
| Tetrachloromethane, see Carbon tetrachloride | | |
| Tetrachloronaphthalene-Skin | — | 2 |
| ** Tetraethyl lead (as Pb)-Skin | — | 0.075 |
| Tetrahydrofuran | 200 | 590 |

(*continued*)

Adopted Values (*continued*)

| Substance | ppm[a] | mg/M³ [b] |
|---|---|---|
| ** Tetramethyl lead (TML) (as Pb)-Skin | — | 0.075 |
| Tetramethyl succinonitrile-Skin | 0.5 | 3 |
| Tetranitromethane | 1 | 8 |
| Tetryl (2, 4, 6-trinitrophenylmethylnitramine)-Skin | — | 1.5 |
| Thallium (soluble compounds)-Skin | — | 0.1 |
| Thiram | — | 5 |
| Tin (inorganic cmpds, except $SnH_4$ and $SnO_2$) | — | 2 |
| Tin (organic cmpds) | — | 0.1 |
| Titanium dioxide | — | 15 |
| Toluene (toluol) | 200 | 750 |
| C Toluene-2, 4-diisocyanate | 0.02 | 0.14 |
| o-Toluidine-Skin | 5 | 22 |
| Toxaphene, see Chlorinated camphene | | |
| Tributyl phosphate | — | 5 |
| 1, 1, 1-Trichloroethane, see Methyl chloroform | | |
| 1, 1, 2-Trichloroethane-Skin | 10 | 45 |
| Trichloroethylene | 100 | 535 |
| Trichloromethane, see Chloroform | | |
| Trichloronaphthalene-Skin | — | 5 |
| 1, 2, 3-Trichloropropane | 50 | 300 |
| 1, 1, 2-Trichloro 1, 2, 2-trifluoroethane | 1,000 | 7,600 |
| Triethylamine | 25 | 100 |
| Trifluoromonobromomethane | 1,000 | 6,100 |
| 2, 4, 6-Trinitrophenol see Picric acid | | |
| 2, 4, 6-Trinitrophenylmethylnitramine, see Tetryl | | |
| Trinitrotoluene-Skin | — | 1.5 |
| Triorthocresyl phosphate | — | 0.1 |
| Triphenyl phosphate | — | 3 |
| * Tungsten & Compounds, as W | | |
| Soluble | — | 1 |
| Insoluble | — | 5 |
| Turpentine | 100 | 560 |
| * Uranium (natural) sol. & insol. compounds as U | — | 0.2 |
| C Vanadium ($V_2O_5$ dust) | — | 0.5 |
| ($V_2O_5$ fume) | — | 0.1 |
| C Vinyl chloride | 500 | 1,300 |
| Vinylcyanide, see Acrylonitrile | | |
| Vinyl toluene | 100 | 480 |
| Warfarin | — | 0.1 |
| Xylene (xylol) | 100 | 435 |
| Xylidine-Skin | 5 | 25 |
| Yttrium | — | 1 |
| Zinc chloride fume | — | 1 |
| Zinc oxide fume | — | 5 |
| Zirconium compounds (as Zr) | — | 5 |

(*continued*)

### Adopted Values (continued)

Radioactivity: For permissible concentrations of radioisotopes in air, see U.S. Department of Commerce, National Bureau of Standards, Handbook 69, "Maximum Permissible Body Burdens and Maximum Permissible Concentrations of Radio-nuclides in Air and in Water for Occupational Exposure," June 5, 1959. Also, see U.S. Department of Commerce National Bureau of Standards, Handbook 59, "Permissible Dose from External Sources of Ionizing Radiation," September 24, 1954, and addendum of April 15, 1958.

### Mineral Dusts

| Substance | m.p.p.c.f.[e] |
|---|---|
| SILICA | |
|   Crystalline | |
|   ** Quartz, Threshold Limit calculated from the formula........... | $\dfrac{300^{[f]}}{\%SiO_2 + 10}$ |
|   ** Cristobalite   "        "        " | |
|   Amorphous, including natural diatomaceous earth................ | 20 |
| SILICATES (less than 1% crystalline silica) | |
|   ** Asbestos............................................... | 5 |
|     Mica.................................................. | 20 |
|     Soapstone............................................. | 20 |
|     Talc.................................................. | 20 |
|     Tremolite............................................. | 5 |
|     Portland Cement....................................... | 50 |
| GRAPHITE (natural)....................................... | 15 |
| "Inert" or Nuisance Particulates............ 50 (or 15 mg/M³ whichever is the | |
| see Appendix D                  smaller) of total dust <1% SiO₂ | |
| Conversion factors | |
|   mppcf × 35.3 = million particles per cubic meter | |
|               = particles per c.c. | |

e) Millions of particles per cubic foot of air, based on impinger samples counted by light-field technics.

f) The percentage of crystalline silica in the formula is the amount determined from air-borne samples, except in those instances in which other methods have been shown to be applicable.

** See Notice of Intended Changes

### Notice of Intended Changes

These substances, with their corresponding values, comprise those for which either a limit has been proposed for the first time, or for which a change in the "Adopted" listing has been proposed. In both cases, the proposed limits should be considered trial limits that will remain in the listing for a period of at least two years. During this time, the previously Adopted Limit will remain in effect. If, after two years no evidence comes to light that questions the appropriateness of the values herein, the values will be placed in the "Adopted" list. Documentation is available for each of these substances.

(continued)

Notice of Intended Changes (*continued*)

| Substance | ppm[a] | mg/[3 b] |
|---|---|---|
| +C Ammonia | 50 | 35 |
| ++ 2-Acetylaminofluorene | — | A[1] |
| ++ 4-Aminodiphenyl | — | A[1] |
| ++ Ammonium chloride fume | — | 1 |
| ++ Asphalt (Petroleum) fumes | — | 2 |
| Butyl mercaptan | 0.5 | — |
| C Cadmium oxide fume (as Cd) | — | 0.1 |
| C Dichloroacetylene | 0.1 | — |
| ++ Dichlorobenzidine | — | A[1] |
| ++ 4-Dimethylaminoazobenzene | — | A[1] |
| Endosulfan (Thiodan®)—Skin | — | 0.1 |
| Ethyl mercaptan | 0.5 | — |
| + Fibrous glass | [g] — | Appendix D |
| Heptane | 500 | 2,000 |
| + Hydrogen peroxide | 1 | 1 |
| Indene | 10 | — |
| + Mercury vapor, inorganic and organic cmpds, excluding alkyl Mercury—Skin | — | 0.05 |
| + Methyl 2-cyanoacrylate | 2 | |
| + Methyl demeton—Skin | — | 0.5 |
| Methyl isoamyl ketone | 100 | 475 |
| Methyl mercaptan | 0.5 | — |
| ++ Methyl parathion—Skin | — | 0.2 |
| ++ 4-Dimethylaminoazobenzene | — | A[1] |
| Octane | 400 | 1,900 |
| Oil mist (particulate) | — | 5[h] |
| Oil vapors | [i] A[3] | — |
| Pentaerythritol (tetramethylomethane) | — | 15 |
| Pentane | 500 | 1,500 |
| Petroleum distillates | [i] A[3] | — |
| ++ Phenolthiazine—Skin | — | 5 |
| Stoddard Solvent | 200 | — |
| + Styrene | 100 | — |
| Tetraethyl lead (as Pb)—Skin | — | 0.100[j] |
| Tetramethyl lead (as Pb)—Skin | — | 0.150[j] |
| Trimethyl benzene | 25 | — |
| ++ Vinyl acetate | 10 | — |
| ++ Wood Dust (total dust) | — | 10 |

*a*) Parts of vapor or gas per million parts of contaminated air by volume at 25°C and 760 mm. Hg pressure.

*b*) Approximate milligrams of particulate per cubic meter of air.

+ 1969 Revision

++ 1969 Addition

*g*) <5–7μ Diameter. No TLV for coarse fibrous glass has yet been set.

*h*) As sampled by method that does not collect vapors.

*i*) According to analytically determined composition.

*j*) For control of general room air; biologic monitoring is essential for personnel control.

(*continued*)

Notice of Intended Changes (continued)
Mineral Dust

| Substance | |
| --- | --- |
| Asbestos | 12 fibers/ml $> 5\mu$ in length[k], or 2 mppfc[m] |
| ++ Coal Dust (bituminous) | 3.5 mg/M$^3$ (respirable dust)[n] |
| Cristobalite | Use one-half the value calculated from the count or mass formulae for quartz. |
| Quartz | (1) TLV for respirable dust in mg/M$^3$: $$\frac{10 \text{ mg/M}^{3\,p)}}{\% \text{ Respirable Quartz} + 2}$$ (2) "Total dust" respirable and nonrespirable: $$\frac{30 \text{ mg/M}^3}{\% \text{ Quartz} + 2}$$ |
| ++ Fused Silica | Use quartz formulae. |
| Tridymite | Use one-half the value calculated from formulae for quartz. |

k) As determined by the membrane filter method at 430 × phase contrast magnification.

m) As counted by the standard impinger, light-field count technique.

n) "Respirable" dust as defined by the British Medical Research Council Criteria[1] and as sampled by a device producing equivalent results[2].

(1) Hatch, T. E. and Gross, P., Pulmonary Deposition and Retention of Inhaled Aerosols, p. 149. Academic Press, New York, New York, 1964.

(2) Interim Guide for Respirable Mass Sampling, AIHA Aerosol Technology Committee. In draft form, to be published in late 1969.

p) Both concentration and per cent quartz for the application of this limit are to be determined from the fraction passing a size-selector with the following characteristics:

| Aerodynamic Diameter ($\mu$) (unit density sphere) | % passing selector |
| --- | --- |
| $\lessgtr 2$ | 90 |
| 2.5 | 75 |
| 3.5 | 50 |
| 5.0 | 25 |
| 10 | 0 |

+ 1969 Revision
++ 1969 Addition

# APPENDIX A

A$^1$  Because of the high incidence of cancer, either in man or in animals, no exposure or contact by any route, respiratory, oral or skin should be permitted for the compounds:

| | |
| --- | --- |
| 2-Acetylaminofluorene | beta-Naphthylamine |
| 4-Aminodiphenyl | 4-Nitrodiphenyl |

Benzidine & its salts        N-Nitrodimethylamine

Dichlorobenzidine           beta-Propiolactone

4-Dimethylaminoazobenzene

Because of the extremely high incidence of bladder tumors in workers handling beta-naphthylamine and the potential carcinogenic activity of the other compounds, the State of Pennsylvania prohibits the manufacture, use and other activities that involve human exposure without express approval by the Department of Health.

$A^2$  **Polytetrafluoroethylene\* decomposition products.** Thermal decomposition of the fluorocarbon chain in air leads to the formation of oxidized products containing carbon, fluorine and oxygen. Because these products decompose in part by hydrolysis in alkaline solution, they can be quantitatively determined in air as fluoride to provide an index or exposure. No TLV is recommended pending determination of the toxicity of the products, but air concentrations should be minimal.

$A^3$  **Gasoline and/or Petroleum Distillates.** The composition of these materials varies greatly and thus a single TLV for all types of these materials is no longer applicable. In general, the aromatic hydrocarbon content will determine what TLV applies. Consequently the content of benzene, other aromatics and additives should be determined to arrive at the appropriate TLV (Elkins, et al. A.I.H.A.J. 24, 99, 1963).

## APPENDIX B

### B.1 Threshold Limit Values for Mixtures

When two or more hazardous substances are present, their combined effect, rather than that of either individually, should be given primary consideration. In the absence of information to the contrary, the effects of the different hazards should be considered as additive. That is, if the sum of the following fractions,

$$\frac{C_1}{T_1} + \frac{C_2}{T_2} + \cdots \frac{C_n}{T_n}$$

exceeds unity, then the threshold limit of the mixture should be considered as being exceeded. $C_1$ indicates the observed atmospheric concentration, and $T_1$ the corresponding threshold limit (See Example 1A.a.)

---

\* Trade Names: Algoflon, Fluon, Halon, Teflon, Tetran

Exceptions to the above rule may be made when there is good reason to believe that the chief effects of the different harmful substances are not in fact additive, but independent as when purely local effects on different organs of the body are produced by the various components of the mixture. In such cases the threshold limit ordinarily is exceeded only when at least one member of the series $\left(\dfrac{C_1}{T_1} + \text{or} + \dfrac{C_2}{T_2} \text{etc.}\right)$ itself has a value exceeding unity (See Example 1A.b.)

Antagonistic action or potentiation may occur with some combinations of atmospheric contaminants. Such cases at present must be determined individually. Potentiating or antagonistic agents are not necessarily harmful by themselves. Potentiating effects of exposure to such agents by routes other than that of inhalation is also possible, e.g. imbibed alcohol and inhaled narcotic (thichloroethylene). Potentiation is characteristically exhibited at high concentrations, less probably at low.

When a given operation or process characteristically emits a number of harmful dusts, fumes, vapors or gases, it will frequently be only feasible to attempt to evaluate the hazard by measurement of a single substance. In such cases, the threshold limit used for this substance should be reduced by a suitable factor, the magnitude of which will depend on the number, toxicity and relative quantity of the other contaminants ordinarily present.

Examples of processes which are typically associated with two or more harmful atmospheric contaminants are welding, automobile repair, blasting, painting, lacquering, certain foundry operations, diesel exhausts, etc. (Example 2.)

Threshold Limit Values for Mixtures
Examples

1A.  General case, where air is analyzed for each component.
  a. ADDITIVE EFFECTS

$$\frac{C_1}{T_1} + \frac{C_2}{T_2} + \frac{C_3}{T_3} + \cdots \frac{C_n}{T_n} = 1$$

Air contains 5 ppm of carbon tetrachloride
(TLV, 10), 20 ppm of ethylene dichloride
(TLV, 50) and 10 ppm of ethylene dibromide,
(TLV, 25).

$$\frac{5}{10} + \frac{20}{50} + \frac{10}{25} = \frac{65}{50} = 1.3$$

Threshold limit is exceeded.

### b. INDEPENDENT EFFECTS

Air contains 0.15 mg/M³ of lead (TLV, 0.2)
and 0.7 mg/M₃ of sulfuric acid (TLV, 1).

$$\frac{0.15}{0.20} = 0.75; \qquad \frac{0.7}{1} = 0.7$$

Threshold limit is not exceeded.

1B. Special case when source of contaminant is a mixture and atmospheric composition is assumed similar to that of original material, i.e., vapor pressure of each component is the same at the observed temperature.

### a. ADDITIVE EFFECTS, approximate solution.

1. A mixture of equal parts (1) trichloroethylene (TLV, 100), and (2) methyl chloroform (TLV, 350).

$$\frac{C_1}{100} + \frac{350}{C_2} = \frac{C_m}{C_m}$$   Solution applicable to "spot" solvent mixture usage, where all or nearly all, solvent evaporates.

$$C_1 = C_2 = \tfrac{1}{2}C_m$$

$$\frac{C_1}{100} + \frac{C_1}{350} = \frac{2C_1}{T_m}$$

$$\frac{7C_1}{700} + \frac{2C_1}{700} = \frac{2C_1}{T_m}$$

$$T_m = 700 \times \tfrac{2}{9} = 155 \text{ ppm}$$

1B.b. General Exact Solution for Mixtures of N Components With Additive Effects and Different Vapor Pressures.

(1) $\dfrac{C_1}{T_1} + \dfrac{C_2}{T_2} + \cdots + \dfrac{C_n}{T_n} = 1;$

(2) $C_1 + C_2 + \cdots + C_n = T;$

(2.1) $\dfrac{C_1}{T} + \dfrac{C_2}{T} + \cdots + \dfrac{C_n}{T} = 1.$

By the Law of Partial Pressures,

(3) $C_1 = ap_1,$
and by Raoult's Law,

(4) $p_1 = F_1p_1°.$
Combine (3) and (4) to obtain

(5) $C_1 = aF_1p_1°.$
Combining (1), (2, 1) and (5), we obtain

(6) $\dfrac{F_1p_1^{\circ}}{T} + \dfrac{F_2p_2^{\circ}}{T} + \cdots + \dfrac{F_np_n^{\circ}}{T} =$

$\dfrac{F_1p_1^{\circ}}{T_1} + \dfrac{F_2p_2^{\circ}}{T_2} + \cdots + \dfrac{F_np_n^{\circ}}{T_n}$

and solving for T,

(6.1) $T = \dfrac{F_1p_1^{\circ} + F_2p_2^{\circ} + \cdots + F_np_n^{\circ}}{\dfrac{F_1p_1^{\circ}}{T_1} + \dfrac{F_2p_2^{\circ}}{T_2} + \cdots + \dfrac{F_np_n^{\circ}}{T_n}}$

or

(6.2) $T = \dfrac{\displaystyle\sum_{i=1}^{i=n} F_1p_1^{\circ}}{\displaystyle\sum_{i=1}^{i=n} \dfrac{F_1p_1^{\circ}}{T_1}}$

T = Threshold Limit Value in ppm
C = Vapor concentration in ppm.
p = Vapor pressure of component in solution
$p^{\circ}$ = Vapor pressure of pure component.
F = Mol fraction of component in solution.
a = A constant of proportionality.
Subscripts 1, 2, . . . n relate the above quantities to components 1, 2, . . . n, respectively.
Subscript i refers to an arbitrary component from 1 to n.
Absence of subscript relates the quantity to the mixture.
Solution to be applied when there is a reservoir of the solvent mixture whose composition does not change appreciably by evaporation.

Exact Arithmetic Solution of Specific Mixture

|  | Mol. wt. | Density | T | $p^{\circ}$ at 25°C | Mol fraction in half-and-half solution by volume |
|---|---|---|---|---|---|
| Trichloro-ethylene (1) | 131.4 | 1.46g/ml | 100 | 73mm Hg | 0.527 |
| Methylchloroform (2) | 133.42 | 1.33g/ml | 350 | 125mm Hg | 0.473 |

$$F_1 p_1{}^\circ = (0.527)(73) \; = 38.2$$

$$F_2 p_2{}^\circ = (0.473)(125) = 59.2$$

$$T = \frac{38.2 + 59.2}{\dfrac{38.2}{100} + \dfrac{59.2}{350}} = \frac{(97.4)(350)}{133.8 + 59.2} = \frac{(97.4)(350)}{193.0} = 177$$

$T = 177$ ppm    (Note difference in TLV when account is taken of vapor pressure and mol fraction in comparison with above example where such account is not taken.)

2. A mixture of one part of (1) parathion (TLV, 0.1) and two parts of (2) EPN (TLV, 0.5).

$$\frac{C_1}{0.1} + \frac{C_2}{0.5} = \frac{T_m}{C_m}, \; C_2 = 2C_1$$

$$C_m = 3C_1$$

$$\frac{C_1}{0.1} + \frac{2C_1}{0.5} = \frac{3C_1}{T_m}$$

$$\frac{7C_1}{0.5} = \frac{3C_1}{T_m}$$

$$T_m = \frac{1.5}{7} = 0.21 \; mg/M^3$$

1C. TLV for Mixtures of Mineral Dusts.

For mixtures of biologically active mineral dusts the general formula for mixtures may be used. With the exception of asbestos, pure minerals are assigned TLV of 2, 5, 20 or 50.

For a mixture containing 80% talc and 20% quartz, the TLV for 100% of the mixture "C" is given by:

$$TLV = \frac{1}{\dfrac{0.8}{20} + \dfrac{0.2}{2.5}} = 8.4 \; mppcf$$

Essentially the same result will be obtained if the limit of the more (most) toxic component is used provided the effects are additive. In the above example the limit for 20% quartz is 10 mppcf.

For another mixture of 25% quartz 25% amorphous silica and

50% talc:

$$\text{TLV} = \frac{1}{\dfrac{0.25}{2.5} + \dfrac{0.25}{20} + \dfrac{0.5}{20}} = 7.3 \text{ mppcf}$$

The limit for 25% quartz approximates 8 mppcf.

## APPENDIX C

### Bases for Assigning Limiting "C" Values

By definition in the Preface, a listed value bearing a "C" designation refers to 'ceiling' value that should not be exceeded; all values should fluctuate below the listed value. In general the bases for assigning or not assigning a "C" value rest on whether excursions of concentration above a proposed limit for periods up to 15 minutes may result in a) intolerable irritation, b) chronic, or irreversible tissue change, or c) narcosis of sufficient degree to increase accident proneness, impair self rescue or materially reduce work efficiency.

| T.L.V. RANGE ppm or mg/M³ | Test T.L.V. factor | Examples |
|---|---|---|
| 0 to 1 | 3 | Toluene diisocyanate—T.L.V., 0.02 ppm, if permitted to rise above 0.06 ppm may result in sensitization in a single subsequent exposure. "C" listing recommended on category b. |
| 1 + to 10 | 2 | Manganese—T.L.V., 5 mg/M³, contains little or no safety factor. All values should fluctuate below 5mg/M³. "C" listing recommended on category b. |
| 10 + to 100 | 1.5 | Methyl styrene—T.L.V. 100, if encountered at levels of 150 ppm will prove intensely irritating. "C" listing recommended on category a. |
| 100 + to 1000 | 1.25 | Methyl chloroform—T.L.V. 350 ppm, at 438 ppm for periods not exceeding 15 minutes is not expected to result in untoward effects relating to category c. No "C" listing recommended. |

### Permissible Excursions for Time-Weighted Average (TWA) Limits

The test TLV Factor in the Table serves also as a guide to the magnitude of the permissible excursion above the limit for those substances not given a "C" designation i.e. the TWA limits. Thus for HF, with a TWA limit of 3 ppm, a concentration of 6 ppm is permissible for periods not exceeding 15 minutes, provided an equivalent exposure below the limit is experienced.

## APPENDIX D

### Some "Inert" or Nuisance Particulates [q]

| | |
|---|---|
| Alundum (Al$_2$O$_3$) | Limestone |
| Calcium carbonate | Magnesite |
| Cellulose | Marble |
| Portland Cement | Pentaerythritol |
| Corundum (Al$_2$O$_3$) | Plaster of Paris |
| Emery | Rouge |
| Glycerine Mist | Silicon Carbide |
| Graphite (synthetic) | Starch |
| Gypsum | Sucrose |
| Vegetable oil mists | Tin Oxide |
| (except castor, cashew | Titanium Dioxide |
| nut, or similar irritant | |
| oils) | |

[q] When toxic impurities are not present, e.g. quartz < %.

## APPENDIX E

### Some Simple Asphyxiants—"Inert" Gases and Vapors

| | |
|---|---|
| Acetylene | Hydrogen |
| Argon | Methane |
| Ethane | Neon |
| Ethylene | Nitrogen |
| Helium | Nitrous Oxide |
| | Propane |

### 1969 TLV COMMITTEE MEMBERS

| | |
|---|---|
| Paul Caplan | Wayland J. Hayes, Jr., M.D. |
| Hervey B. Elkins, Ph.D. | Harold N. MacFarland, Ph.D. |
| W. G. Fredrick, Ph.D. | Consultant |
| Bernard Grabois, P.E. | Frederick T. McDermott |
| Paul Gross, M.D. | E. Mastromatteo, M.D. |

Walter W. Melvin, M.D.          Ralph G. Smith, Ph.D.
Ronald T. Richards          Mitchell R. Zavon, M.D.
          Herbert E. Stokinger, Ph.D., Chairman
          William D. Wagner, Recording Sec'y

## III. INORGANIC COMPOUNDS

### A. BORON COMPOUNDS

Although there have been a number of serious intoxications from boric acid, resulting from its use in surgical dressings or from accidental ingestion, it is not an important industrial hazard. Animals exposed to high concentrations of boron oxide suffered no significant ill effects (644), and borates have been widely used without causing injury.

Several of the hydrides of boron, however, are highly toxic. Diborane ($B_2H_6$), a gas, is primarily a respiratory irritant. Repeated daily exposures to 5 ppm were fatal to animals (486). Pentaborane ($B_5H_9$), a liquid boiling at 58°C, and decaborane ($B_{10}H_{14}$), a solid, are primarily central nervous system poisons (367). Animals were affected by repeated exposures to 0.2 ppm of pentaborane (352).

### 1. Determination of Boron Hydrides in Air

A general method for determination of boron hydrides is the passage of the air through a portable electric furnace followed by collection of the boric acid formed and its colorimetric determination with carmine (197).

Pentaborane and decaborane can be determined by the color produced by the reduction of triphenyl-tetrazonium chloride (258,334).

Methods for the determination of decaborane in air include absorption in a solution of dipyridyl ethylene in xylene (450), absorption in aqueous triethanolamine followed by determination of absorption in the uv at 265–270 m$\mu$, and measurement of the color produced in a solution of quinoline in xylene (257).

### 2. Determination of Boron in Biological Materials

The carmine colorimetric method has been employed for analysis of biological materials for boron (259), and normal levels of boron in blood and urine have been reported (288).

## B. CARBON COMPOUNDS

### 1. Carbon Monoxide (CO)

By far the most important gaseous health hazard is carbon monoxide, which is formed whenever carbonaceous material is burned in the absence of an excess of oxygen. The danger from this gas is accentuated by the absence of odor or other warning properties. When soft coal, crude oil, wood, paper, and similar materials are burned, the smoke contains numerous irritants, hence fires involving these substances do not frequently result in carbon monoxide poisoning. On the other hand, the combustion products of coke, hard coal, natural gas, and light fuel oils contain few irritating ingredients and are often sources of carbon monoxide intoxication. One of the commonest sources of this gas is the exhaust from internal combustion engines, especially those burning gasoline.

The toxic action of carbon monoxide is due to its affinity for hemoglobin, from which it displaces oxygen, thereby causing asphyxiation. 100 ppm of carbon monoxide will result in a carboxyhemoglobin concentration of 18–20%, 50 ppm of 8–10% (11).

Levels of carboxyhemoglobin as low as 5% impair the function of the brain (515) and reduce visual acuity (395). Headaches appear when 10–20% of the hemoglobin is converted to carboxyhemoglobin; with increasing degrees of saturation, nausea, dizziness, weakness, mental confusion, loss of consciousness, and death will occur. In some cases of severe poisoning the skin and mucous membranes are a cherry-red color, but more frequently the victim appears pale.

If prolonged unconsciousness occurs, permanent brain damage may result. There is little evidence of chronic poisoning from repeated exposure to low concentrations, however (137).

#### a. DETERMINATION IN AIR

Because of its importance as a health hazard many procedures for the detection and determination of carbon monoxide in air have been developed. The more important methods have been critically reviewed by Beatty (33).

#### (1) Chemical Methods

The majority of chemical procedures are based on the reducing properties of the gas. Palladium salts are readily reduced by CO at room temperature, and a number of procedures are based on this reaction. Palladium chloride-impregnated paper or cloth has been used for detection and semiquantitative estimation. Reaction with $PdCl_2$ solution followed by photometric determination of excess Pd has been described as a quantitative method (469).

Others have used a combination of palladium salt and complex molybdate, with the measurement of the green to blue color resulting from reduction. While wet methods based on this principle have been employed (458), the most widely used procedure utilizes the indicator tubes developed by the National Bureau of Standards. These contain silica gel impregnated with palladium sulfate and ammonium molybdate, prepared as described by Shepherd (529).

The reaction of iodine pentoxide with carbon monoxide at elevated

$$I_2O_5 + 5CO = 5CO_2 + I_2$$

temperature (about 150°C) was long considered the standard analytical method for accurate work (33). The iodine is volatilized, collected in potassium iodide solution, and determined volumetrically. A mixture of iodine pentoxide and sulfuric acid has been employed in indicator tubes.

Procedures based on the reduction of the silver salt of parasulfaminobenzoic acid (350) and mercuric oxide (36) have been described.

One of the few chemical procedures not depending on oxidation of carbon monoxide is the pyrotannic acid method, in which the air sample is shaken with a dilute blood solution, and the color developed when pyrogallic and tannic acids are added is compared with standards (33).

(2) Catalytic Oxidation

The heat developed by the catalytic oxidation of carbon monoxide on hopcalite has been used to measure its concentration in the air by measurement of the rise in temperature of the catalyst. Both stationary recording devices and portable instruments are available.

(3) Physical Methods

Infrared recorders and indicators provide an accurate and specific method for determining carbon monoxide in air (176). However, no readily portable infrared analyzer suitable for field use is available at present.

Samples of air containing carbon monoxide can also be analyzed by gas chromatography.

Except for the hopcalite indicator and the various tubes and papers, most of the above methods are designed primarily for the analysis of grab samples.

### b. Determination in Blood

The pyrotannic acid method (33) can be used directly for the determination of carbon monoxide in blood. Other methods depend on the change in the absorption bands in visible light when oxyhemoglobin is converted to carboxyhemoglobin (604). Various gasometric procedures have been described for determining CO in blood (448,509). Other methods involve release of the CO from the blood followed by determination with palladium salts (389) or by infrared analysis (199,345).

### c. Determination in Expired Air

The methods used for CO in air can be employed for analysis of breath. The relationship between the CO content of blood and expired air has been determined by several investigators (302,469).

## 2. Carbon Dioxide ($CO_2$)

Carbon dioxide is not usually considered a toxic gas, being a normal product of body metabolism. Its concentration in the blood affects the rate of breathing, which is measurably increased when the $CO_2$ content of the inspired air reaches 1%. Headaches are sometimes observed by persons exposed to these or higher concentrations, and levels of 5% or higher rapidly become intolerable.

Most serious accidents involving carbon dioxide have resulted from asphyxiation due to oxygen deficiency, the air having been displaced in low places by the heavier gas. Normal air contains about 300 ppm of $CO_2$, with slightly higher concentrations in occupied buildings.

### a. Determination in Air

Devices which measure pH may be employed to determine $CO_2$ in the field (365). Indicator tubes are available.

Grab samples may be analyzed by absorbing the $CO_2$ in standard alkali, with back-titration of excess, or by infrared or gas chromatographic methods. Higher concentrations can be measured by conventional gas analysis techniques.

## C. NITROGEN COMPOUNDS

### 1. Ammonia ($NH_3$)

Due to its alkaline properties, ammonia is irritating to the mucous membranes of the nose, throat, and eyes, and, in high concentrations, to the skin. Mild irritation of the throat is observed at 50 ppm, but severe effects require several hundred parts per million.

### a. DETERMINATION IN AIR

The air is passed through 10 ml of 0.1 $N$ $H_2SO_4$ in a bubbler or midget impinger at a rate of 1–3 liters/min for 10–30 min. The sample is diluted to 50 ml with water, 1 ml is diluted to mark in a Nessler tube, Nessler reagent is added and the results are compared with standards similarly treated (159).

## 2. Hydrazine ($NH_2NH_2$)

Hydrazine, a liquid boiling at 114°C, is highly irritating and toxic. Inhalation of the vapor can result in injury to lungs, liver, and kidneys. Concentrations below 5 ppm were reportedly not injurious to animals (111). Hydrazine is absorbable through the skin and can produce dermatitis, which has been the most common effect noted in industry.

### a. DETERMINATION

A number of methods of determination of hydrazine depend on its reducing properties, such as the color change produced by its reaction with phosphomolybdic acid (175). A spectrophotometric procedure using $p$-dimethylaminobenzaldehyde is reportedly suitable for analysis of air or biological materials (119).

## 3. Cyanides

Hydrogen cyanide (HCN) is used as a fumigant and chemical intermediate; its salts, especially NaCN, are widely employed in electroplating, extraction of precious metals, and heat treating of steel.

All soluble cyanides are highly toxic, causing asphyxiation by inhibiting enzyme activity. The effects are extremely fast; 270 ppm of HCN are rapidly fatal to animals, and 100–135 ppm are dangerous or fatal in $\frac{1}{2}$ to 1 hr (185,418). Since cyanide is quickly converted in the body to thiocyanate, chronic cyanide poisoning is not usually a serious problem.

### a. DETERMINATION IN AIR

Hydrogen cyanide and mists of alkaline cyanides in air can be collected by means of an impinger containing dilute NaOH. Volumetric determination with 0.01 $N$ AgNO$_3$, using KI as indicator, in weakly alkaline solution can be employed.

A satisfactory colorimetric method, depending on the conversion of cyanide to cyanogen bromide, has been described (5,204). After removal of excess bromine with arsenite, benzidine–pyridine reagent is added and the color measured.

Several colorimetric procedures using phenolphthalin have been described. In one method the air is passed through a solution of 3 parts of 0.005 $m$ Na$_2$HPO$_4$ and one part phenolphtalin reagent (1 ml of 0.5% phenolphthalin in alcohol and 99 ml of 0.01% CuSO$_4 \cdot 5H_2O$). One part of 0.1 $N$ KOH is then added, and the red color measured (477). Test paper methods have utilized similar reactions, e.g., that between cyanide, benzidine, and copper acetate (551).

The reaction of cyanide with methemoglobin and the reduction of the red color of the latter has been suggested as a specific analytical method for cyanide in grab samples of air (349).

## 4. Nitrogen Dioxide (NO$_2$)

Nitrogen dioxide in a pure state is in equilibrium with nitrogen tetroxide, N$_2$O$_4$, bp 22°C. In concentrations of a few parts per million in air, little N$_2$O$_4$ is present.

NO$_2$ is formed by reduction of nitric acid, by decomposition of nitrite, by oxidation of NO, and in the combustion of nitrogenous materials. Nitric oxide is formed from combination of the oxygen and nitrogen of the air at high temperatures, such as may be achieved in electric arcs, oxy-gas flames and internal combustion engines. At high concentrations the conversion of NO to NO$_2$ in the air is virtually instantaneous, but in concentrations of 100 ppm or less the reaction is rather slow, and nitric oxide can persist in air at such levels for prolonged periods (156,629).

NO$_2$ is the most dangerous of the common irritant gases, the literature containing reports of some 90 deaths prior to 1930 (623) and over 60 between 1930 and 1956 (629). A relatively recent clinical entity, "silo-filler's disease," appears to be NO$_2$ poisoning resulting from the presence of the gas in silos containing ensilage with a high nitrogen content (368).

The toxic action of NO$_2$ is primarily irritation of the lower respiratory passages, with pulmonary edema developing in severe cases, usually after a latent period of 5–12 hr. In milder forms of poisoning, symptoms such as nausea, vomiting, and vertigo, with cyanosis and methemoglobinemia, may be observed (623).

Data on the concentrations of $NO_2$ required to cause toxic effects are conflicting. Recent reports indicate the $LC_{50}$ for rats for 60-min exposures to be 115 ppm (83) and the threshold for toxic effect 28 ppm. Wagner et al. found only slight effects in animals exposed repeatedly to 25 ppm, but consider 5 ppm a suitable threshold limit (630).

Reports of human exposure vary from mild effects at 2.5 ppm to no effects at 10–20 ppm (218,444).

### a. DETERMINATION IN AIR

The phenoldisulfonic acid method for nitrate in water can be used for the determination of $NO_2$ and NO in air. A grab sample of 500–2500 cc of air is allowed to stand for several hours with a small volume of dilute sulfuric acid containing a few drops of hydrogen peroxide. After neutralization the solution is evaporated to dryness and nitrate determined in the usual way (14,34).

If the air is passed through silica gel, approximately 70% of the $NO_2$ is collected, the remainder being converted to NO (629). The reaction is apparently with the small amount of residual moisture on the gel (223):

$$3NO_2 + H_2O = 2HNO_3 + NO$$

Gill, however, found great variation in the efficiency of adsorption of $NO_2$ on silica gel (209).

The Griess-Ilosvay reagent has been used for the determination of $NO_2$ in grab samples and in indicator tubes (318,445).

Saltzman has developed a modification of this reagent which can be used in a bubbler for collection of integrated samples (494). Air is passed at 0.4 liter/min through a fritted bubbler containing 10 ml of reagent [5 g of sulfanilic acid, 140 ml of glacial acetic acid, and 20 ml of 0.1% $N$ (1-naphthyl) ethylene diamine dihydrochloride, made up to 1 liter with water]. The color which develops if $NO_2$ is present in the air sampled can be compared with standards or read in a colorimeter at 550 m$\mu$.

Continuous recording devices using similar reagents have also been described (3,500,589). These methods are said to be nearly specific for $NO_2$. Gill has reported that the Griess-Ilosvay reagents are somewhat sensitive to NO, however (209).

### 5. Nitric Oxide (NO)

Although nitric oxide is toxic in high concentrations, it is usually found in combination with the more dangerous $NO_2$.

### a. Determination in Air

Nitric oxide can be determined by first measuring the $NO_2$ and then allowing the NO to oxidize and determining it as $NO_2$. Direct oxidation by passing the air through glass fiber paper impregnated with a solution of chromate and sulfuric acid has been described (476).

## D. PHOSPHORUS COMPOUNDS

Phosphates are essential to body metabolism and are nontoxic. Elemental (yellow) phosphorus, phosphine, and reactive metal phosphides are highly toxic and find extensive use as pesticides.

### 1. Yellow Phosphorus

Chronic phosphorus poisoning, resulting eventually in necrosis of the bone (chiefly the jaw) was fairly common in match manufacturing when yellow phosphorus tips were used. It has since been observed occasionally in the chemical industry (244,282,428).

The agent responsible for occupational phosphorus poisoning is believed to be phosphorus vapor, but other causes, such as suboxides of phosphorus, have been suggested.

### a. Determination of Phosphorus Vapor in Air

Very little work has been done on methods for measuring phosphorus vapor concentrations in air. Rushing has proposed a tentative method, involving absorption in xylene (490). Phosphorus pentoxide is removed by washing with water, and the phosphorus is then extracted by means of silver nitrate solution and converted to phosphoric acid with nitric acid. After removal of the silver, the phosphate is determined colorimetrically with molybdate and ferrous sulfate.

### 2. Phosphine ($PH_3$)

The hydride of phosphorus, a gas with bp $-87.4°C$, is the most toxic simple compound of this element. Although animal experiments have indicated that chronic intoxication can occur, nearly all cases of human poisoning by phosphine have been acute or subacute in nature.

Workers exposed intermittently to phosphine used in the fumigation of wheat, in concentrations of several parts per million parts of air, exhibited a variety of symptoms, the most common being diarrhea, nausea, headache, epigastric pain and tightness of the chest (302).

### a. DETERMINATION IN AIR

Several methods for determination of phosphine depend on the reduction of silver nitrate. The length of the stain produced on silica gel impregnated with $AgNO_3$ (425) and the depth of the stain developed in filter paper similarly treated (281) have been used to estimate phosphine concentration. The silver nitrate remaining in the paper may be removed by washing with hot $KNO_3$ solution and the residual silver dissolved and measured by any of several micro-methods (281).

## E. OXYGEN AND SULFUR COMPOUNDS

### 1. Oxygen

Although abnormally high pressures of oxygen can be harmful on prolonged exposure, a condition more frequently encountered is oxygen deficiency. This can result from consumption of oxygen by reducing agents or by dilution of the air by another gas. Such incidents are nearly always in small confined spaces, such as wells, pits, mines, the holds of ships, silos, and so forth. Significant oxygen deficiency is rarely encountered in conventional occupied rooms. Symptoms attributed to this condition are usually due to poor circulation of air or the presence of other gases, such as carbon monoxide, if combustion processes are involved.

### a. DETERMINATION

Conventional gas analysis procedures can be used for determining oxygen, since trace amounts are not involved. Direct reading instruments are available for testing the oxygen content of the air in manholes, etc.

### 2. Ozone ($O_3$)

Ozone is a highly irritating and toxic gas. It is formed from the oxygen of the air under the influence of short ultraviolet radiation (e.g., shielded arc welding, mercury arc lamps) or high-voltage electric discharges. It is employed to some extent as a disinfecting agent and in odor control, where its effectiveness is primarily due to its masking action.

The $LC_{50}$ for mice and rats for 3-hr exposures has been reported to be about 12 ppm, and 18-hr exposures to 3 ppm caused gross lung injury (407). But rats exercised 15 min/hr in an atmosphere containing

1 ppm ozone died after about 6 hr (517). Another report states that the $LC_{50}$ for a 4-hr exposure ranged from 1.4 to 10.5 ppm (575).

Repeated 4-hr exposures of animals to 2.4 ppm resulted in lung pathology (408), and 1 ppm 6 hr/day and 5 days a week caused bronchitis and bronchiolitis (566). On the other hand, animals subjected to a pre-exposure to sublethal concentrations of ozone could subsequently tolerate higher concentrations than unconditioned animals (517,575). This tolerance applied to other irritant gases (565).

Stokinger has reviewed the various mechanisms which may be involved in ozone intoxication (564).

In spite of its toxicity and rather wide distribution, very few serious cases of occupational ozone intoxication have been reported. One incident involved a crane operator who worked over a tank into which ozone was being transferred (313). Severe coughing and headache were the chief symptoms.

A man exposed in a test chamber to between 1 and 2 ppm of ozone for 2 hr developed chest pains, followed 2 days later by a cough which persisted for 2 weeks. A reduction in vital capacity was noted (226).

Pulmonary function studies of a group of welders exposed to 0.2–0.3 ppm of ozone revealed no impairment attributable to the exposure (662).

a. DETERMINATION IN AIR

Analysis of air for ozone has been studied intensively due in part to its importance in atmospheric pollution (see chapter by Lodge and Pate in this volume). A problem in ozone analysis is the difficulty of preparing known concentrations. Many procedures rely on the assumption that the reaction of ozone is stoichiometric:

$$O_3 + 2HI = H_2O + I_2 + O_2$$

This reaction is the basis of the majority of the methods proposed for ozone determination. The concentration of iodide and pH of solution affect the results materially. Saltzman and Gilbert, who studied these factors in detail, recommend a neutral 1% potassium iodide reagent (499). Alkaline iodide has been used to reduce the blank correction (542), but recovery is less than stoichiometric.

The free iodine liberated by ozone may be measured volumetrically or by determining the ultraviolet absorption of the solution at 352 m$\mu$.

Other oxidizing agents, such as chlorine and $NO_2$, interfere to varying degrees with the iodometric determination of ozone, as do reducing agents, such as $SO_2$, and even dust (499).

Other methods depend on the oxidation of dyestuffs (such as sodium diphenylamine sulfonate, 1% in 0.02% $HClO_4$ solution (49)), or fluorescent compounds.

A procedure based on the oxidation of NO, with subsequent determination of $NO_2$, has been described (498). Infrared and ultraviolet absorption methods have been suggested, but are not widely used (234).

A "fuel cell" containing bromide and a carbon electrode has been described for recording ozone in air concentrations (249). In contrast to electrometric devices containing iodide, weakly oxidizing gases would not interfere. A device based on the release of krypton 85 from a quinol clathrate when it is oxidized by ozone has been proposed for the determination of this gas in air (268). Also the rate of aging of specially prepared rubber has been employed as a means of estimating ozone concentration (661).

### 3. Hydrogen Sulfide ($H_2S$)

Hydrogen sulfide is an odorous gas, boiling at $-60°C$, which in high concentrations paralyzes the respiratory center and can therefore be classed as an asphyxiant. In somewhat lower concentrations irritation of the lower respiratory passages may occur, and even smaller amounts can cause conjunctivitis or keratitis (eye irritation). The odor of $H_2S$ does not provide a good warning, since the olefactory senses rapidly become accustomed to even high concentrations.

Workers have been overcome, in some instances fatally, where concentrations of $H_2S$ in the range of 500–1000 ppm apparently existed. Conjunctivitis develops more slowly and has been reported in rooms where the concentration was 10–20 ppm, or even less.

#### a. Determination in Air

The reaction of $H_2S$ with heavy metal salts to form black or colored precipitates is used in devices for air analysis. Indicator tubes or papers may contain lead or silver salts. A satisfactory chemical method is to pass the air through a neutral cadmium chloride solution, add standard iodine and acid, and back-titrate the excess iodine (159).

### 4. Sulfur Dioxide ($SO_2$)

Sulfur dioxide, a gas which boils at $-10°C$, is formed when sulfur or compounds containing sulfur are burned. Its effects in low concentrations have been studied extensively in connection with its presence in polluted atmospheres.

Concentrations in excess of 10 ppm are strongly irritating, and some irritation occurs between 5 and 10 ppm. Such concentrations are normally not dangerous, however, and, unlike hydrogen sulfide, $SO_2$ has good warning properties. Nevertheless, numerous fatalities from lung injury have resulted when workers were trapped in areas of high concentration.

According to Anderson, workers exposed regularly to concentrations of $SO_2$ up to 25 ppm and occasionally higher showed no adverse effects (15), but Shalpe reported that chronic exposures to concentrations measured between 2 and 36 ppm appeared to cause a significantly higher incidence of symptoms of respiratory disease (526). In a review of the literature, Greenwald concludes that there is no good evidence of chronic effects from concentrations below 5 ppm, but that 10 ppm is too high for continued exposure (224).

### a. DETERMINATION IN AIR

A simple method for determining $SO_2$ in the 1–10 ppm range is to pass the air through standard iodine solution containing several per cent (e.g., 25) KI. If excess iodide ion is not present, iodine will be lost. The iodine remaining is back-titrated with dilute thiosulfate. Other reducing gases interfere (159,446).

The West and Gaeke method involves collection in sodium tetrachloromercurate ($HgCl_2$ + NaCl solution), with development of color with $p$-rosaniline hydrochloride formaldehyde reagent (640). Addition of dimethyl formamide makes the color more intense (283).

A method depending on the color developed by a solution of ferric ion and 1,10-phenantholine has been described (555).

Absorption of $SO_2$ in dilute hydrogen peroxide and estimation of the acid formed has been used for determination of concentrations as low as 0.01 ppm (292).

Measurement of changes in electroconductivity has been employed chiefly in automatic recording instruments for the measurement of low concentrations of $SO_2$. A critical review of methods of $SO_2$ determination has been written by Hochheiser (261).

### 5. Sulfuric Acid ($H_2SO_4$)

Sulfuric acid and its anhydride sulfur trioxide are strongly irritating to the nose and throat. Mists of sulfuric acid are often present in battery charging rooms, as well as in certain chemical plants.

### a. DETERMINATION IN AIR

Since sulfuric acid is present in air chiefly as a mist, the sample may be collected in an impinger, on a filter paper, or even with the electric precipitator. Determination of free acid or sulfate ion may be used for the analysis.

## F. HALOGENS AND HALOGEN COMPOUNDS

### 1. Fluorine $(F_2)$

In practice fluorine is usually present in the air in conjunction with hydrogen fluoride. Although animal experiments have indicated a high degree of toxicity (562), workers exposed to concentrations averaging nearly 1 ppm (including some HF) reportedly had fewer respiratory complaints than unexposed workers (368).

#### a. DETERMINATION IN AIR

Use of a krypton 85 quinol clathrate, which releases [85]K when oxidized, has been suggested as a method for determining fluorine in air (268). Other strongly oxidizing gases ($ClO_2$, $NO_2$, $O_3$) interfere.

Methods depending on the determination of fluoride suffer from interference by HF.

### 2. Hydrogen Fluoride (HF)

Hydrofluoric acid (bp 19.4°C), although a weak acid, is highly irritating in the vapor and liquid states. Concentrated aqueous solutions can cause severe and painful burns on contact with the skin, and dilute solutions (as little as 3%) may produce delayed burns (442). Injection of calcium gluconate has been found effective in the treatment of such burns (46,131,641).

#### a. DETERMINATION IN AIR

HF can be absorbed in dilute NaOH solution and fluoride determined by the methods described for solid fluorides (q.v.).

### 3. Chlorine $(Cl_2)$

Chlorine (bp −35°C) is an irritant to the respiratory passages and has been used as a war gas. An incident in which a number of persons in a subway station were affected by chlorine gas from a leaking cylinder has been described by Chasis et al. (92). Symptoms observed included burning of the eyes, cough, substernal pain, and respiratory distress. Tracheobronchitis, pulmonary edema, and pneumonia developed in several patients.

### a. Determination in Air

The *o*-tolidine method used for determining chlorine in water is frequently employed for chlorine in air (551). The color developed by passage of a given volume of air containing chlorine is compared with permanent standards of dichromate solution or measured on a colorimeter. Other reagents for oxidants, such as potassium iodide, can also be used for determination of chlorine.

## 4. Hydrogen Chloride (HCl)

Hydrochloric acid is primarily an irritant of the upper respiratory passages, but fatal lung injury has been reported from single massive exposures. Chronic effects may include some erosion of the teeth.

### a. Determination in Air

Air containing HCl may be passed through dilute alkali and the chloride determined, or chloride may be determined by back-titration after absorption in standard NaOH. Alternatively water may be used as absorbent and the conductivity or acidity measured to determine the quantity of HCl.

## 5. Chlorine Dioxide ($ClO_2$)

Chlorine dioxide is a strongly oxidizing and highly irritating gas (bp 9.9°C). Rats repeatedly exposed to 10 ppm died with symptoms of bronchitis and bronchopneumonia. However, 0.1 ppm had no ill effect on either animals or workers. Men subjected occasionally to somewhat higher concentrations suffered respiratory distress, "bubbling" sounds in chest, and eye and nasal discharge (118). Slight bronchitis was observed in a small group of workers occasionally exposed to concentrations of $ClO_2$ somewhat above 0.1 ppm (212).

### a. Determination in Air

$ClO_2$ may be absorbed in neutral KI solution, with reduction to chlorite. The free iodine formed can be determined volumetrically. Upon acidification the chlorite is further reduced, hence $ClO_2$ can be determined in the presence of chlorine (208).

## 6. Chlorine Trifluoride ($ClF_3$)

This gas (bp 11.5°C) has been found highly toxic to animals. Six months of repeated exposure to about 1 ppm resulted in the death of dogs from pneumonia; and rats, while less severely affected, showed signs of pulmonary edema (270).

### a. DETERMINATION IN AIR

Absorption in 10% NaOH, followed by determination of chloride ion, has been used to measure the concentration of $ClF_3$ present in animal experiments (269).

## 7. Bromine (Br$_2$)

In spite of the irritating and corrosive properties of bromine (bp 59°C), relatively few cases of bromine intoxication have been reported in the literature.

### a. DETERMINATION IN AIR

The o-tolidine method suggested for chlorine can be used for the determination of bromine (159). Absorption in 10% KOH solution, followed by oxidation of the bromide and hypobromite to bromate with hypochlorite, removal of excess hypochlorite with formate, and iodometric determination of the bromate has been suggested (551).

## 8. Iodine (I$_2$)

Iodine vapor is reportedly somewhat more irritating than bromine, especially to the upper respiratory passages.

### a. DETERMINATION IN AIR

Iodine can be collected in 5% KI solution or in a solvent such as toluene and determined by ultraviolet absorption (117). If mercuric bromide is added to the reagent, the o-tolidine method may be used (299).

## 9. Phosgene (COCl$_2$)

Phosgene, or carbonyl chloride (bp 8.3°C) was one of the more effective poison gases used in World War I. It affects primarily the alveoli and smaller bronchioles of the lung, and pulmonary edema is the usual result of heavy exposure. CT values in excess of 180 ppm $\times$ min resulted in deaths in rats (474). Chronic exposure to relatively low concentrations has reportedly caused emphysema of the lungs (201).

Phosgene is used in organic synthesis and is also formed from the decomposition of various organic chloride vapors. Trichloroethylene vapor, when subjected to short uv light in the presence of air, forms relatively large amounts of phosgene (178). The thermal decomposition of such vapors is prone to produce HCl rather than phosgene, but the latter gas has been demonstrated in toxic concentrations where methylene chloride vapor was present in a room with a kerosene heater (207).

### a. DETERMINATION IN AIR

In the absence of interfering substances, phosgene can be absorbed in alcoholic (or even aqueous) KOH and the chloride formed by hydrolysis measured. HCl and $Cl_2$ can be removed by prior passage through suitable absorbents, e.g., pumice saturated with KI and $Na_2S_2O_3$ (207).

An iodometric method based on the reaction of phosgene with sodium iodide in acetone has been described (434) and a gas chromatograph method has been proposed (462).

The reaction of phosgene with aniline to form diphenyl urea has been used for phosgene determination. If high concentrations are present, the diphenyl urea can be measured gravimetrically. In concentrations of hygienic significance (below 1 ppm), the diphenyl urea can be determined by ultraviolet spectrophotometry, either directly (114) or after extraction with a mixture of hexane and pentanol (115).

Absorption of phosgene in $p$-nitrobenzyl pyridine (0.02% in diethylphthalate) followed by colorimetric determination has also been proposed (339).

Linch et al., after an extensive review of proposed methods, concluded that 4.4'-bis(diethylamino) benzophenone in $o$-dichlorobenzene was the most satisfactory reagent from the standpoint of specificity and sensitivity (362). It was used as a colorimetric detector, preferably by the gas titration technique.

## IV. ELEMENTS

### A. BERYLLIUM

Beryllium disease has received extensive study since 1943 and the literature has been reviewed by Tepper et al. (587). No cases of beryllium poisoning have been observed in miners handling beryl ore. A variety of ailments, however, ranging from dermatitis to severe respiratory illnesses have been reported among workers engaged in the extraction of the ore and others handling fluorescent powders containing beryllium (612). An acute pneumonitis may develop rapidly from a single heavy exposure or over a period of time if smaller amounts of beryllium are inhaled. The disability is usually of relatively short duration, although it sometimes terminates fatally. Eisenbud et al. reported that cases occurred invariably when exposure was in excess of 0.1 mg and consistently if exposure was greater than 1 mg per cubic meter of air (153).

Chronic berylliosis is a serious disease. The first well-documented cases in the United States were reported by Hardy and Tabershaw (239) and were in the fluorescent lamp industry where phosphors containing beryllium were used. Development of the disease proceeded gradually without signs of symptoms for a few months or years and was frequently progressive in severity and of long duration. It was characterized clinically by a pulmonary insufficiency, resulting from pathological changes in the lungs. The latent development of the disease frequently made it difficult to obtain reliable information about the occupational environment during the period of exposure. It appears that any operation in which beryllium particles are produced that are fine enough to reach the lower respiratory tract is potentially hazardous. Cases have been reported from the grinding of alloys containing as little as 2% beryllium (552,587).

Neighborhood or nonoccupational cases have appeared in communities near industrial plants processing beryllium. Ten cases were reported within a ¾-mile radius of a plant where outside air was found to contain less than 1 $\mu$g of beryllium per cubic meter of air, with a probable range from 0.01 to 0.1 $\mu$g (155). Additional cases are mentioned by Lieben and Metzner (359). Handling contaminated clothing appeared to be important in some, but not all, of these cases.

Air testing is the most effective way to assess beryllium exposure. Determination of beryllium in the urine is not a reliable index of exposure. Dutra found beryllium in the urine of most patients with acute pneumonitis, but only 5 of 14 patients with the chronic disease had detectable amounts (150). The rate of excretion of beryllium is a function not only of the quantity of this element in the body, but also of the solubility of the particles of beryllium which have been inhaled. Klemperer and co-workers found 1.2–8.3 $\mu$g/day was excreted by healthy workers in a beryllium extraction plant, but a daily excretion of less than 1.0 $\mu$g in urine from workers exposed to insoluble beryllium silicates (323). The excretion rate is slow, and beryllium may still be found in the urine several years after cessation of exposure.

## 1. Beryllium Analysis

Three general methods are employed for the determination of microquantities of beryllium: colorimetric, fluorometric, and spectrographic.

The minimum useful range for colorimetric analyses is usually 1–10 $\mu$g, but fluorometric procedures, particularly those using morin (penta hydroxyflavone), will easily detect submicrogram quantities. These methods, however, are not specific for beryllium, so some scheme for removing or masking interfering elements must be employed. Spectrographic methods, on the other hand, provide specificity to the analysis and a generally higher sensitivity than is obtained with the chemical tests, but they require an expensive initial installation and have the usual drawbacks of spectrographic analysis.

### a. DETERMINATION IN AIR

Samples may be collected on filter paper, by impinger and electrostatic precipitation, as well as on glass fiber and millipore filters. The method of treatment of samples varies, depending on the collecting medium, but most frequently involves wet ashing or low-temperature ignition followed by solution of the sample (533,631).

Morin procedures for analysis of beryllium in air are described by several authors. Welford and Harley (637) remove interfering metals from the digested sample with oxine (8-quinolinol) and precipitate the beryllium in sodium hydroxide with an aluminum carrier. The limit of beryllium detection with morin is 0.005 $\mu$g. Walkley (631) precipitates beryllium from the digested sample with ammonium hydroxide in the presence of an aluminum carrier. Strong sodium hydroxide is used to dissolve the precipitate. KCN is added to complex interfering ions and beryllium is measured from its fluorescence with morin. Concentrations as low as 0.004 $\mu$g/ml (0.02 $\mu$g per sample) can be determined. Sill and coworkers (533) eliminate various separation steps in their general procedure when air samples do not exceed 10 mg. By virtue of the high sensitivity obtained by this procedure, Sill limits sample volumes taken for analysis to not over 20 liters of air and measures beryllium concentrations well below the maximum permissible level. Filter paper is wet ashed with sulfuric and nitric acids. Sodium sulfate is evaporated to a pyrophosphate fusion. The cake is boiled and filtered if necessary. An aliquot of filtrate equivalent to 20 liters of air is taken, and the beryllium morin fluorescence is developed and measured as described under urinalysis.

If high sensitivity in the analysis is not required, colorimetric methods may be employed. These have been reviewed by Sandell (502). Procedures using eriochrome cyanine R (260), $p$-nitrophenyl azoorcinol (255), fast sulphon black F (73), and chrome azurol S (537) are mentioned as additional references.

### b. DETERMINATION IN BIOLOGICAL SAMPLES

Biological specimens from individuals exposed to beryllium usually contain only small amounts of the element and usually require taking rather large samples for analysis. Urine and tissue samples, except lungs with an appreciable amount of silica, can be wet ashed with nitric and sulfuric acids. Dry ashing can also be employed, but any meta- and pyrophosphate must be dissolved before proceeding with the analysis, or loss of beryllium will occur (98,322).

Chemical analyses of beryllium in biological samples usually measure the fluorescence with morin. Klemperer and co-workers in their procedure remove calcium after digesting the sample by addition of ammonium sulfate (322). The beryllium is precipitated with iron phosphate. Interfering ions are removed by electrolysis with a mercury cathode. A final collection of beryllium is made by ammonia precipitation using aluminum as a carrier. The beryllium is measured from its fluorescence in alkaline solution with morin stabilized with sodium stannite. Reportedly levels of the order of 0.05 $\mu$g can be detected. An average recovery of 80% was obtained, most of the loss occurring during the coprecipitation steps.

Laitinen and Kivalo (338) modified Klemperer's procedure and improved the recovery of beryllium appreciably. They used bismuth to precipitate phosphate without any significant coprecipitation of trace quantities of beryllium. Hydrous ferric oxide was employed as a collecting agent, and versene was used to prevent coprecipitation of calcium. Toribara and Chen (590) and Toribara and Sherman (591) used a semi-dry ashing procedure in determining beryllium in large samples of urine. They found it unnecessary to use a preliminary gathering step for beryllium and removed most of the interfering cations by electrolysis. Final separation of beryllium was carried out by extraction with acetyl acetone, and they reported an average recovery of 99.9%.

The most extensive study of the morin procedure was made by Sill et al. (532,533). When carried out with great care, this procedure brings the limit of the morin test down to the order of 0.0004 $\mu$g of beryllium, making it as sensitive as the spectrographic methods. Beryllium is separated from urine with ammonium hydroxide. Organic matter in the precipitate is destroyed with nitric and perchloric acids. Calcium sulfate is precipitated by the addition of sulfuric acid. EDTA is used to complex interfering ions and beryllium is extracted with a chloroform mixture of acetyl acetone. The alkalinity of the solution for development of beryllium fluoresecnce with morin is controlled with a sodium hydroxide and piperidine buffer. Diethylenetriaminepentaacetic acid and triethanol-amine are employed to eliminate the oxidation of morin. Exciting wave-lengths are entirely in the visible region, thus eliminating errors caused by colorless ions that absorb in the ultraviolet. A new combination of primary and secondary filters increases the ratio of net beryllium fluores-cence to blank fluorescence.

An important step in reliable estimation of minute quantities of beryl-lium by spectrographic methods is the preparation of the samples, and this is discussed in various publications on the subject (98,435,449).

## B. ZINC

In comparison with many heavy metals, zinc and its compounds are of relatively low toxicity. The chief harmful effect of zinc on the health of workers is metal fume fever, caused usually by inhalation of fumes of zinc oxide resulting from various melting, welding, and cutting processes. The symptoms include fever, chills, nausea, and vomiting, but recovery is ordinarily complete in 24–48 hr. After an initial attack immunity is usually acquired, which is lost after a few days without exposure.

A number of deaths and several cases of respiratory illness resulted from the inhalation of high concentrations of zinc chloride fume, released accidentally from a screening smoke generator in a confined space (168).

### 1. Determination in Air

Because of their relatively low toxicity, highly sensitive methods of analysis are not needed for the measurement of zinc fumes in air. Sam-ples can be collected on filter papers or by means of the electrostatic precipitator and dissolved in dilute acid. Analysis can be carried out nephelometrically with ferrocyanide, by the polarograph (340), color-imetrically with dithizone (416) or other organic reagents (406,438), or fluorometrically (298).

### 2. Determination in Urine

Urinalysis for zinc is not commonly used as a means of measuring exposure, but studies of zinc in urine have been made by Vallee and others, using dithizone (307) and atomic absorption (198) techniques of analysis.

## C. CADMIUM

The vapor pressure of cadmium at its melting point is high, and any process involving the melting of cadmium or its alloys may give off harmful amounts of fume. If slightly overheated, cadmium metal will ignite and evolve large quantities of smoke containing cadmium oxide.

The effects of acute exposure to cadmium fumes are similar to those from phosgene, consisting of injury to the lung with symptoms typically occurring 12 hrs or more after the exposure. Death from pulmonary edema may result. Acute poisoning has been reported from the inhalation of cadmium fumes from annealing cadmium-plated rivets (67), cutting or welding cadmium alloys or cadmium-coated metal (99,167), cadmium spraying (8), and melting and brazing with a cadmium–silver alloy (44).

Repeated exposure to lower concentrations of cadmium fume or dust over a prolonged period may cause ill health characterized by progressive shortness of breath, and the appearance in the urine of a low molecular weight protein (193). A high incidence of proteinuria was found in a battery plant where concentrations of cadmium oxide dust ranged from 3 to 15 mg per cubic meter of air (194). In a plant where cadmium alloys were cast and concentrations of cadmium fume did not exceed 0.27 mg/m³ except for brief periods (not over 20 min a day), proteinuria was found, especially in workers with 15 years or more exposure (48). Some evidence of poor health, including anemia, was found in a plant where concentrations of cadmium fume averaged about 0.1 mg/m³ (238). Another eport, however, records no evidence of intoxication in a refinery where concentrations as high as 6 mg/m³ of fume and 17 mg/m³ of cadmium oxide dust were found (463).

Cadmium is excreted rather slowly and apparently unevenly. Urinary cadmium concentrations between 0.0 and 0.8 mg/day (48) and 0.01–0.6 mg/liter (541) have been reported in workers suffering from cadmium intoxication. Cadmium was present in the urine of one worker 10 years after leaving his job (48), and battery workers autopsied 3–9 years after their exposure showed significant amounts of cadmium in the kidney, liver, and pancreas (195).

The cadmium content of normal urine is 0.01 mg/liter or less and in blood, less than 0.005 mg/100 g (288).

### 1. Determination

Urine, blood, and other biological samples taken for cadmium analysis are usually wet digested in a nitric–sulfuric acid mixture. Dry ashing at 500°C is not satisfactory since loss of cadmium occurs (100).

Air samples may be collected on paper, glass, or millipore filters by impinger or electrostatic precipitator. Treatment of the sample depends upon the collecting medium, but consists usually of acid leaching or wet digesting. Several methods are available for cadmium analysis, the most frequently employed being those using dithizone. Church reports a mixed color method for analysis of air and biological samples (100). Extraction of cadmium and other metals is made from a slightly alkaline solution with a chloroform solution of dithizone. Stripping the chloroform layer with acid leaves most interfering metals behind. A second dithizone extraction is made from a citrated buffered solution, and the cadmium dithizonate is measured colorimetrically.

Saltzman's modification of the dithizone procedure provides a more complete isolation of cadmium and comprises the basis of the cadmium procedure recommended by the American Conference of Governmental Industrial Hygienists (10,493). Cadmium is extracted from a strongly alkaline solution which contains a small amount of cyanide to complex large amounts of most interfering metals without affecting the cadmium. Acid stripping of the chloroform layer and a reextraction with dithizone from a highly alkaline solution isolates cadmium from all other methods except thallium. Colorimetric measurements are made at 518 m$\mu$, and sensitivity of 0.05 $\mu$g of cadmium in a volume of 15 ml is obtained.

Cadmium analyses by polarography and spectrography have been described by Cholak and Hubbard (97). Although these methods are not subject to interferences from other metals, they are not as sensitive as the dithizone procedures. Atomic absorption analysis, on the other hand, is highly sensitive and measures levels as low as 0.0004 $\mu$g/ml (198).

## D. MERCURY

The primary effects of chronic mercury poisoning are on the central nervous system, with tremor of the extremities the most noticeable symptom. Mental disturbances may also occur. Gingivitis and kidney injury are less frequently observed. At one time a common source of mercury intoxication was found in the felt hat industry, since mercuric nitrate was used as a carroting agent to promote felting of rabbit fur. At present mercury-carroted fur is rarely used in this country; but mercury, because of its unique properties, finds many industrial applications. In addition organic mercury compounds, some of them highly toxic, are used as fungicides and antifouling agents.

When inhaled, mercury vapor is largely retained by the respiratory passages and rapidly absorbed into the blood stream. Many mercury compounds, however, and metallic mercury itself, are also absorbed through the unbroken skin.

Normal urine contains only a trace of mercury, of the order of 0.01 mg/liter. Slightly elevated values can sometimes be traced to recent amalgam tooth fillings or mercurial ointments or other medication. Workers exposed to mercury may excrete relatively large amounts in the urine, 1 or 2 mg/liter being quite common, and concentrations as high as 8 mg/liter have been observed (159). Atmospheric mercury vapor in concentrations approximating the threshold limit value (0.1 mg/m³) have been found to result in average urinary mercury levels of the order of 0.25–0.35 mg/liter (319,415). The correlation of mercury intoxication with excretion rate is erratic. Continued excretion in excess of 0.25 mg/liter is believed by many to represent a harmful exposure, however (42,342).

Alkyl mercury compounds in general are considered to be more toxic than inorganic mercury. Exposures to such compounds resulting in urinary mercury levels exceeding 0.05 mg/liter are undesirable, if not definitely hazardous (4,369).

### 1. Determination in Air

The darkening of paper coated with selenium sulfide at slightly above room temperature has been used as a semiquantitative method for the measurement of mercury vapor in air (159). Relatively long sampling periods are necessary to detect concentrations of hygienic interest.

Several instruments depending on the direct measurement of ultraviolet light absorption have already been described (p. 20). Adaptation of these units to analyze integrated air samples has been proposed. One procedure involves collection in acid permanganate solution, concentration on a cadmium sulfide pad, and release of the mercury vapor by heating (410). Another method uses filter pads impregnated with iodine for collection of the sample (246).

A unique radiochemical method has been proposed in which the air is passed through a solution of radioactive mercuric chloride. The mercury vapor interchanges with the radioisotope and the latter is collected on hopcalite and measured on a scintillation counter (376).

Most of the above methods are designed primarily for determination of mercury vapor. Mercury-bearing dusts can be sampled by the usual dust collection techniques, but if mercury vapor is present as well, special reagents are needed. One procedure uses an iodine–potassium iodide solution (25). The amount of mercury present is estimated by observing the color produced by the addition of copper sulfate and sodium sulfite. Since the reaction results in a precipitate, the determination must be made visually by comparison with standards containing from 2 to 10 μg of mercury.

Procedures involving dithizone have also been described. Acid permanganate (65) and iodide–iodine solutions are suggested as collecting media (10). Methods involving condensation of mercury vapor with dry ice or liquid air have been tried, but are not especially well adapted for hygienic air analysis.

## 2. Determination in Urine and Biological Samples

The destruction of organic material prior to analysis for mercury must be done with care, otherwise mercury will be lost through volatilization. Dry ashing methods cannot be used, and wet digestion procedures are best done under reflux condensers. Cold oxidation with permanganate has been recommended, and some methods employ partial oxidation only with chlorate and hydrochloric acid (159).

Dithizone procedures for mercury are less satisfactory than for many of the heavy metals, due in part to relative lack of sensitivity (to about 1 μg). Various techniques have been followed for isolating mercury, including complexing with bromide (10), ion exchange separation followed by thiourea elution (332), and use of EDTA to complex interfering substances (76).

The micrometric method first described by Stock and Lux (568) has been used with some success in the authors' laboratory, primarily for urinalysis. Following partial oxidation of organic matter, the solution is electrolyzed and the mercury deposited on a copper wire. The wire is heated in a glass tube and the mercury volatilized and collected in a capillary. Upon addition of alcohol and centrifugation, the mercury coalesces to form a single drop, the diameter of which is measured using a microscope fitted with an eyepiece micrometer. In the hands of a skilled worker this method is highly sensitive and quite precise (569).

The ultraviolet photometric methods described under determination of mercury in air have been adapted to analysis of biological materials. The mercury is collected either by means of a cadmium sulfide pad (410) or by dithizone extraction (296). The mercury is volatilized by heating, and the vapor is measured with an ultraviolet photometer. A sensitivity of 0.001 μg of mercury is claimed.

## E. THALLIUM

Thallium is one of the most toxic of the heavy metals, from the standpoint of both acute and chronic poisoning. Animal experiments indicate an $LD_{50}$ of the order of 5–30 mg/kg when administered by intraperitoneal injection or ingested (136). Many cases of human intoxication have been reported, the majority resulting from medicinal use of thallium salts, especially as a depilatory. Relatively little industrial thallium poisoning has been recorded. A few incidents have occurred among pesticide workers who handled thallium rodenticides, and cases have been reported among metal refinery workers and in chemical plants (470).

### 1. Determination in Urine

Thallium can be separated from many other metals after digestion by extraction of thallic chloride or bromide with ether or other organic solvents. After reduction with iodide the free iodine can be determined colorimetrically (1), or thallium bromide can be reacted directly with methyl violet or a similar basic dye and determined colorimetrically after extraction with amyl acetate (77,293).

Polarographic (654) and flame spectrophotometric (552) methods have also been described for the determination of thallium in urine.

Jacobs found that thallium workers excreted up to 0.2 mg/liter of the metal, while no detectable amount was present in the urines of controls (293).

Air analysis for thallium involves collection on filter paper or other particulate collector, followed by one of the above procedures (77,341).

## F. LEAD

Although occupational lead poisoning in its severest form is now seen only rarely in the United States, the incidence of milder cases is still high enough to warrant designating lead as the most important elemental industrial poison.

Lead in the form of dust or fume enters the body primarily through the lungs, but some is also absorbed from swallowed dust. While soluble lead compounds are most rapidly absorbed, all except the highly insoluble substances, such as lead sulfide and chromate, readily cause industrial poisoning. Tetraethyl and tetramethyl lead, used as antiknock agents in motor fuels, can be absorbed through the skin, but a greater danger lies in inhalation of the vapor.

Plumbism occurs in many industries and results from many different processes. The smelting and refining of lead and the manufacture of storage batteries involve many operations with high concentrations of lead dust or fume. The spraying of lead metal and lead paint, the sanding and grinding of lead and solder, and the pouring of leaded iron or steel are inherently highly hazardous. Harmful exposures may also result from lead burning, oxy-gas cutting of lead painted steel, melting, pouring and grinding of bronze alloys, and the mixing and weighing of powders of lead compounds (159).

Brush painting, soldering, printing, and the melting and pouring of lead and its common alloys do not usually produce a serious lead hazard. Relatively few problems from lead absorption have been encountered in the use of leaded gasoline (312). Handling concentrated tetraethyl lead solutions is dangerous, however, as is the cleaning of tanks used for gasoline storage (86).

The symptoms of lead intoxication include colic, gastrointestinal disturbances, anemia, weakness in wrists and legs, and central nervous system effects. Encephalopathy from lead frequently occurs among children, but is now rarely seen in occupational poisoning except when organic (alkyl) lead has been absorbed. The toxicities of tetraethyl and tetramethyl lead are due to their lead content, but because of their fat-soluble characteristics they localize in nerve tissue, and poisoning is therefore essentially a central nervous system intoxication (86).

Lead is a normal constituent of body tissues and fluids. The blood-lead content ranges from 0.01 to 0.05 mg per 100 g, 95% or more being found in the erythrocytes. The normal range of lead in urine is usually given as 0.01–0.08 mg/liter, with a mean of 0.03 mg. Any increase in lead absorption results in a prompt elevation of lead in the urine, followed later by a smaller increment in the blood. When the exposure is terminated, the blood and urine lead levels gradually return to normal, a process which may take a few weeks to more than a year, depending on the quantity of lead retained and the time over which the retention took place (312).

Studies have indicated that workers exposed 40 hr a week to the TLV of lead dust or fume, 0.2 mg per cubic meter of air, will excrete on the average about 0.2 mg of lead per liter of urine (159). Most workers excreting less than 0.3 mg/liter do not develop lead poisoning, but levels above 0.4 mg/liter are usually associated with symptoms of plumbism.

The threshold value for lead in blood, on the other hand, is quite sharp. Kehoe states that the upper limit of safe exposure is just below 0.08 mg of lead per 100 g of blood. Levels of 0.08 mg and above are said to be compatible with lead intoxication (403).

In poisoning from organic lead, a striking difference is observed in the distribution of lead from that induced by inorganic compounds. Blood lead levels may be slightly elevated, but the concentrations in urine are higher than would result from a corresponding exposure to inorganic lead because the organic compounds are more rapidly excreted (130). Furthermore, the toxicity of tetraethyl lead is substantially greater than that of inorganic lead compounds; mild symptoms may occur when the urinary lead level is only 0.15 mg/liter. In severe poisoning excretion is at a level of 0.3 mg/liter or more (86).

One of the earliest signs of increased lead absorption is an increase in urinary coproporphyrin, resulting from interference with porphyrin synthesis (378). This effect is not observed in alkyl lead poisoning, but is nearly always present in intoxication by inorganic lead.

Delta aminolevulinic acid (ALA) is an intermediate in the biosynthesis of porphyrins. Lead appears to be specific in its capability to prevent the utilization of ALA, and determination of the latter compound in urine is reportedly an even more sensitive test for early lead intoxication than analysis for coproporphyrin. Normal urine contains less than 11 mg ALA per liter, and concentrations up to 120 mg/liter may be found in the urine of workers with lead colic (95,229). Normal serum ALA values as high as 26 $\mu$g/100 ml have been reported, but the mean is considerably lower. Subjects with lead poisoning have had values as high as 128 $\mu$g/100 ml of serum (96,491). Both serum and urinary ALA may remain elevated for many months following episodes of plumbism.

### 1. Determination in Air

Kits for field determination of lead are available commercially, but are not sufficiently sensitive for general industrial hygiene use. A method developed by Amdur and Silverman is based on the reaction of lead with tetrahydroxyquinone (9). The sample is collected on filter paper to which the reagent is added.

Conventional air sampling procedures for lead dust may employ the standard impinger, filter paper, or electrostatic precipitator. A single impinger does not collect lead fume completely, but with two impingers in series a tolerable efficiency is achieved. The sample is dissolved in dilute acid and the lead determined by any of several suitable methods.

A semi-micro method involving precipitation of lead chromate and iodometric determination has been employed, but this procedure has been generally discarded in favor of polarographic or colorimetric methods. Polarographic procedures for lead in air have been described by Levine (351), Dubois and Monkman (142), and others and appear to be generally more precise than colorimetric methods.

The reagent of choice for the microdetermination of lead is diphenylthiocarbazone (dithizone). Titrimetric, monocolor, and mixed-color procedures have been described. In monocolor methods lead is extracted from alkaline cyanide solution with a chloroform or carbon tetrachloride dithizone solution. The excess dithizone in the extractant is removed by shaking with an ammonia–cyanide solution, facilitating measurement of the red lead dithizonate color. Careful control of pH is necessary to remove all the free dithizone without decomposing the metal dithizonate (41,294).

Mixed-color methods in which the lead dithizonate is determined in the presence of excess dithizone are more frequently employed. The U.S. Public Health Service procedure, which is designed for the analysis of air and biological samples, has been accepted as a recommended procedure of the American Conference of Governmental Industrial Hygienists (10,310). After suitable preparation of the sample, a double extraction of lead as the dithizonate from alkaline cyanide solution separates it from all interfering metals except bismuth and thallium. Many procedures utilize a single extraction, especially for air samples where interferences are at a minimum.

Tetraethyl and tetramethyl lead can be collected by means of iodine crystals (361). After dissolving the iodine in potassium iodide, sodium sulfite is added and the lead determined by dithizone.

## 2. Determination in Urine

The dithizone procedure is most widely used for urinalysis for lead. Attempts to extract lead directly from untreated urine have met with little success. The urine may be evaporated to dryness and ignited at red heat without loss of lead. Wet digestion with nitric, sulfuric, and perchloric acids is a more popular treatment.

In the majority of urine samples lead can be separated from the bulk of organic matter by coprecipitation. If urine is made strongly alkaline, lead is carried down completely with the precipitate of calcium phosphate (172). After dissolving in acid, the lead is extracted by dithizone solution.

The authors have used a modification of the Ross and Lucas method, involving coprecipitation with calcium oxalate at a pH of 4–5 (485). The precipitate is treated with perchloric acid until the oxalate is destroyed, followed by any suitable dithizone procedure. This method has the advantage of eliminating phosphate, which tends to interfere with the dithizone extraction. One difficulty encountered in this procedure has been the presence of traces of sulfide in the sodium cyanide used. Freshly prepared sodium cyanide solutions apparently precipitated lead sulfide, preventing its extraction by dithizone. Aging of the cyanide for a few weeks resulted in oxidation of the sulfide and eliminated this difficulty (157).

Coprecipitation procedures are not suitable for urines containing EDTA, although the Ross and Lucas method works with other chelating agents, such as penicillamine and DTPA (diethylene triamine penta-acetic acid). Some authorities believe that in certain other urines lead is not completely recovered by coprecipitation, possibly because of the presence of natural chelating agents. The authors' experience has provided no evidence to substantiate such a theory. Interference by EDTA can be eliminated by using an ashing or digestion method or by substituting chromium for lead in the EDTA chelate and then coprecipitating (159).

Separation of lead from urine by means of ion exchange resin has also been described (256). After eluting the resin column with acid to remove the lead, determination is made by any appropriate method.

A partial digestion of urine with acid followed by extraction of the lead as iodide with methyl isopropyl ketone has been proposed (394). Final determination is with dithizone.

Spectrographic and atomic absorption methods have been utilized for lead in urine, but to date limited success has been achieved except after preliminary digestion and/or separation steps have been carried out.

### 3. Determination in Blood

Analysis of blood for lead is complicated by its high iron content. This interference is overcome, in the dithizone method, by liberal use of hydroxylamine hydrochloride. Spectrographic methods have also been employed for lead in blood (335).

### 4. Measurement of Coproporphyrin in Urine

Rapid analysis of urine for coproporphyrin is frequently performed by a modification of the DeLangen-Ten Berg procedure, in which urine is acidified with acetic acid and extracted with ether (343). The coproporphyrin is determined by measurement of its red fluorescence in the ether layer.

A more precise method has been described by Schwartz and co-workers (518). The urine is extracted with ethyl acetate after addition of acetic acid. The coproporphyrin is then extracted from the solvent layer by means of dilute hydrochloric acid and the fluorescence of this solution at 595 m$\mu$ measured using exciting light of 400 m$\mu$. The analysis can also be done by measuring the absorption of light at 402 m$\mu$.

### 5. Measurement of Delta Aminolevulinic Acid (ALA)

A rapid procedure is given by Shuster which depends upon reaction with picric acid (531). Interference is caused by urinary porphobilinogen. Mehani avoids this interference by passing the sample through an ion exchange resin (400). ALA passes through the resin and is determined colorimetrically with picric acid.

## G. VANADIUM

Vanadium poisoning has occurred in mining and milling of vanadium ore, production of vanadium compounds, and cleaning of boilers and heat exchangers fired with residual oils of high vanadium content.

The most important effects of exposure to vanadium dust are acute irritation of the eyes and upper respiratory tract. In severe cases bronchopneumonia may develop. Responses are generally acute, but not fatal, and do not usually appear until a day or more after exposure. Animal studies indicate that vanadium is a systemic poison, but evidence to support this is meager (655). It is generally felt that chronic vanadium intoxication has not been established (355), and vanadium is not a serious cumulative poison. Absorption occurs primarily through the respiratory tract. It disappears rapidly from the lungs and passes into the general circulation (538). Elimination of vanadium from the body is also rapid, most of it occurring through the kidneys during the first 24 hr after absorption (314,581). The amount present in the urine or blood at any time depends largely upon intensity and duration of exposure and the time interval between cessation of exposure and collection of the sample.

Heavy dust exposure in workers processing vanadium-bearing ore was reported by Vintinner and co-workers (618). The vanadium content of the air where ore was being processed ranged up to 59 mg/m$^3$ (average 12.8). The mean and maximum blood vanadium levels of workers were 0.041 and 0.09 mg/100 ml. No correlation was found with exposure.

There was some relationship with urinary vanadium values, however. The median and maximum values for the exposed workers were 0.041 and 0.298 mg/liter. Blood and urine values of controls did not exceed 0.06 mg per 100 ml and per liter, respectively.

Several reports appear in the literature of vanadium inhalation by men engaged in cleaning oil-fired boilers and heat exchangers (60). Vanadium is found in most crude oils in amounts ranging from traces to over 0.1% (398). Atmospheric concentrations encountered in this work ranged from about 40 (538) to nearly 100 mg per cubic meter of air (649). Vanadium forms up to 20% of the deposit on some turbine tubes and is found in exhausts to the atmosphere. Effects of exposure noted were nasal catarrh, nosebleed, cough, wheezing, dyspnea, sneezing, eye watering, and sore throats. A few cases of pneumonitis, emphysema, and blackening of the tongue and teeth have also been reported.

A reduction in the cystine content of hair and fingernails occurs in animals and men absorbing vanadium (419,420). The analysis is considered a highly sensitive test of vanadium action reflecting alteration in body metabolism. A 1% decrease in cystine content from the 10% value considered normal is believed significant. In workers whose urinary vanadium averaged 0.03 mg/liter, a mean cystine content of 8.4% was found. Urinary concentrations of 0.01–0.03 mg of vanadium per liter were reported for exposures considered borderline, and 0.03 to 0.3 mg/liter where exposures were excessive.

Low levels of vanadium absorption have also been shown to significantly lower serum cholesterol (354). In the plant studied only one air sample exceeded the threshold limit and the others were about half this value. Urinary vanadium ranged from 0.006 to 0.160 mg (average 0.046 mg) per liter.

### 1. Determination

Air can be sampled with the electrostatic precipitator or with the standard large impinger containing a 10% solution of nitric acid, and the vanadium content can be determined by the method outlined below.

The most frequently utilized procedure for vanadium determination in blood, urine, and other biological products is that of Talvitie (578). Not more than 5 g of blood or 50–150 ml of urine are prepared by wet ashing. An initial extraction of the digest at pH 9.4 with a chloroform solution of 8-quinolinol is made to remove any iron. The aqueous layer is adjusted to pH 4.0 with phthalate buffer and extraction of vanadium with 8-quinolinol in chloroform solution is made. Measurement of the magenta black color is made at 550 mμ. This method permits determination of vanadium in the range of 1–50 μg.

For the cystine analysis (420), 30 mg of fingernail is cleaned and defatted with acetone and water washes and is hydrolyzed with hydrochloric acid overnight at 124–126°C. Bromphenol indicator is brought to a greenish purple with 5 $N$ NaOH and the acidity is restored with dilute hydrochloric acid. An aliquot of the hydrolyzate is allowed to react first with 5% NaCN in 1 $N$ NaOH for 10 min, and then 2% aqueous solution of 1,2 naphthoquinone-4-sodium sulfonate is added. After addition of 10% $Na_2SO_3$ in 0.5 $N$ NaOH, the solution is allowed to remain in the dark for half an hour. Finally 5 $N$ NaOH and 2% $Na_2S_2O_4$ in 0.5 $N$ NaOH are added. Readings are taken on a photoelectric colorimeter using filter 54 within 3–10 min.

## H. ARSENIC

Systemic poisoning from industrial use of arsenic and its organic compounds is relatively uncommon. The injuries most frequently observed from the handling of arsenic trioxide and soluble arsenites and arsenates are dermatitis and irritation of the upper air passages, including ulceration and perforation of the nasal septum (159). Evidence of cutaneous cancer resulting from occupational exposure to arsenic has been reported by some (253) and disputed by others (546).

Arsine, the gaseous hydride of arsenic, is a powerful hemolytic poison. Hemoglobinuria may appear as early as 4 hr after an acute exposure (371), but is more typically delayed for 2 or 3 days. Anuria and pulmonary edema are observed in the most serious acute cases, while jaundice and anemia comprise the outstanding symptoms in chronic poisoning (68).

Arsenic is excreted quite rapidly in the urine, but after prolonged absorption elevated urinary arsenic levels may persist for some time. In one study of a smelting plant, the average level of arsenic in urine was 0.8 mg/liter, with some values as high as 4 mg (452). While local effects of arsenic were observed, there were no symptoms of systemic intoxication. On the other hand, hospitalized patients suffering from arsine poisoning have had urinary arsenic levels between 0.3 and 1.5 mg/liter (453). The authors have studied three nonfatal cases of arsine poisoning, with urine levels, about 3 days after exposure, of 1, 1, and 2 mg/liter.

The arsenic content of "normal" urine is less than 0.1 mg/liter, but following ingestion of lobster and certain other seafoods, concentrations as high as 1 mg/liter have been found (512).

Hair and nails usually contain less than 0.1 mg and 0.35 mg/100 g, respectively, while the normal arsenic content of blood is below 0.05 mg/100 g. In cases of arsenic poisoning the arsenic concentration in these materials may be increased tenfold or more. Arsenic concentrations of 3 mg/100 g in hair and 8 mg in fingernails have been reported (250).

## 1. Determination

Dusts and mists of arsenic and its oxide derivatives can be collected by any of the usual dust sampling procedures. Arsine can be estimated by drawing the air through silver nitrate or mercuric bromide impregnated paper and comparing the color with that produced by known concentrations. Hydrogen sulfide, if present, can be removed with lead acetate paper, but other reducing gases may interfere. For more accurate results a bubbler containing an oxidizing solution (e.g., permanganate) should be used and the sample analyzed by one of the following procedures.

Biological samples are commonly prepared by digestion with hot nitric and sulfuric acid. The elaborate precautions sometimes recommended to prevent loss of arsenic by volatilization have been reported to be unnecessary (409).

The well-known Gutzeit method has the advantages of specificity, simplicity, and sensitivity, but close adherence to a uniform procedure is required to obtain reproducible results. The recommended method of the American Conference of Governmental Industrial Hygienists is a modification of the procedure originally introduced by Vasak and Sedivec (10,614). Arsine is liberated from the sample by reaction of zinc and acid and is bubbled into a solution of silver diethyldithiocarbamate in pyridine, producing a red color which is measured with a colorimeter. Hydrogen sulfide is removed by a plug of glass wool treated with lead acetate. If an excess of chloride is used, stibine will not be given off if antimony is present. This method is considerably more precise than the Gutzeit techniques. Its application to urinalysis has been described by Roddy and Wallace (479).

In the molybdenum blue method, pentavalent arsenic is reacted with molybdate to form a stable blue color. Arsenic trichloride can be distilled over from digested samples and then oxidized (277), or a distillate may be obtained in which arsenic is in the pentavalent form by adding potassium bromide to a sulfuric acid digest (374). Finally arsine can be generated and trapped in sodium hypobromite which effects the necessary oxidation (295).

## I. ANTIMONY

Acute antimony poisoning has been reported following the ingestion of its salts in instances of homicide, suicide, and accident. The most characteristic symptom was violent and continuous vomiting, accompanied by profuse diarrhea, muscle weakness, and collapse. A fatal dose may cause death within a few hours to a few days (171). Many deaths have also been reported following antimony therapy (377).

Bradley and Fredrick reported liver and kidney damage in animals after intraperitoneal injection of inorganic antimony compounds (51). Using antimony trioxide fume, Nau and co-workers (424) produced inflammation and hemorrhages in the lungs as well as fatty degeneration of the liver and spleen.

Acute occupational poisoning is relatively rare, although severe exposures have apparently occurred. No serious effects were observed in a plant manufacturing antimony trioxide where exposure resulted in a daily fecal excretion of antimony from 10 to 98 mg per person (433). Many chronic symptoms have been noted. Workers exposed to antimony trisulfide (66) experienced upper respiratory irritation, pulmonary inflammation, systemic reactions, and skin lesions. Other symptoms reported were persistent nausea, occasional vomiting, diarrhea, fainting, albuminuria, loss of appetite, and loss of weight (123).

Renes (468) gives extensive exposure data on smelters processing antimony sulfide and experiencing chronic antimony poisoning. Antimony excretion from traces to 600 mg per liter of urine were reported, and air concentrations averaged about 11 mg/m$^3$. Several workers voided urine discolored with albumin.

There is evidence that antimony has specific effects on cardiac function. When administered to dogs, antimony was found to produce an irreversible progressive decrease in myocadial contractile force (31). Browning (61) described clinical symptoms including bradycardia, cardiac arrhythmias, and electrocardiographic S-T segment changes. A high incidence of positive cardiographic alterations was found in antimony metal foundry workers (325). Brieger et al. (58) reported 8 deaths in a group of 125 workers in an abrasive factory attributable to antimony on clinical and electrocardiographic evidence.

Most antimony compounds used industrially are only slightly soluble in water. Antimony metal appears to be more toxic than the sulfides and oxides, presumably because of its greater solubility in the gastrointestinal tract (424). It is rapidly eliminated from the body in 2 or 3 days (123) and symptoms of poisoning disappear when elimination is complete.

Stibine, antimony hydride, is a highly toxic gas. Similar to arsine in action, its primary effect is blood and liver damage. Early signs of poisoning include headache, nausea, and hemoglobinuria a few hours after exposure. Death occurs within a few hours at 100 ppm (171). Stibine is formed when nascent hydrogen comes in contact with metallic antimony or with a soluble antimony compound. It is liberated during the charging of storage batteries (240) and when certain drosses are heated with water or acids (128). Stibine incidents are either uncommon or unrecognized, due partly to its instability and to the fact that it is not formed as readily as arsine.

## 1. Determination

Several methods are available for analysis of antimony (390), but those most commonly used in industrial hygiene employ Rhodamine B. Pentavalent antimony in aqueous hydrochloric acid reacts with Rhodamine B to form a colored complex extractable in several organic solvents and is measured at 565 m$\mu$. One to 2 $\mu$g in 10 ml of final solution can be detected.

The American Conference of Governmental Industrial Hygienists published a procedure for antimony in air samples and biological materials (10). Air samples may be taken with an electrostatic precipitator, on filter paper, or with the impinger. Biological specimens and air samples are wet ashed in a sulfuric–nitric acid mixture. Care must be exercised to keep the quantity of sulfuric acid constant, since its concentration affects the color intensity of the antimony-Rhodamine B complex (191).

Oxidation of antimony samples with a sulfuric–nitric acid mixture frequently fails to convert the metal completely to the desired pentavalent form required to give the reaction with Rhodamine B. Satisfactory results are obtained by introducing sodium sulfite or, preferably, perchloric acid in the latter part of the digestion (384). After cooling, hydrochloric and phosphoric acids and Rhodamine B solution are added. The antimony–Rhodamine B complex formed is extracted in benzene or other organic solvent (636), and the intensity of the color is measured at 565 m$\mu$.

Stibine in air can be determined rapidly and semiquantitatively by comparing the darkening on silver nitrate paper exposed for a given length of time with that produced by known amounts of the hydride.

As little as 0.1 ppm is detectable in 5 min. This reaction is not specific since other hydrides produce similar discolorations. More precise results are obtained with a method using Rhodamine B (636). Stibine is collected in a bubbler containing a 6% acid solution of mercuric chloride. Antimony is oxidized to the pentavalent form with ceric sulfate and then reacted with Rhodamine B. The color complex formed is extracted from the aqueous layer with benzene and measured at 565 m$\mu$. Stibine in quantities of less than 1 $\mu$g is measurable.

## J. CHROMIUM

Hexavalent chromium (chromate) is highly irritating and toxic. The main effects among workers are dermatitis and ulceration and perforation of the nasal septum, and the most common cause of these latter conditions is chromic acid mist, resulting from chrome plating (320). Inhalation of high concentrations of chromic acid has reportedly caused severe and prolonged pulmonary disease (404).

A number of investigators have reported an abnormally high incidence of lung cancer in workers exposed to chromates, especially in plants processing chromite ore, where a variety of trivalent and hexavalent chromium compounds are handled (19,43,379,380).

The distribution of chromium in human lung tissue and in experimental animals has been discussed by Baetjer and co-workers (20). Chromates are much more active biologically than chromic salts. Some authorities aver that dermatitis from chrome-tanned leather (and glue made therefrom) is due to trivalent chromium (192,413,414), while others hold that hexavalent chromium is present and the offending agent (501).

The average blood and urine contents of "normal" persons are reported to be 2.6 $\mu$g/100 g and 3.8 $\mu$g/liter, respectively (288).

### 1. Determination in Air

Dusts and mists containing chromium can be collected by the usual methods for particulates. Determination is most frequently made with s-diphenylcarbazide, which reacts with chromate to give a red color. If relatively large amounts of hexavalent chromium are present, the sample is conveniently collected in the impinger and the resulting solution treated directly with reagent. A field method employing filter papers impregnated with diphenyl carbazide has been described for determining chromic acid in air (535). To determine total chromium, the sample is oxidized with sodium peroxide (37) or other suitable oxidizing agent and then measured colorimetrically or with the polarograph (609).

## 2. Determination in Biological Media

Several writers have described methods for determining chromium in urine, blood, and lung tissue. Following ashing of the sample, the chromium is oxidized with hypobromite (20,227) or sodium bismuthate (608) and determined colorimetrically with s-diphenylcarbazide.

## K. SELENIUM

Soluble compounds of selenium are highly toxic, but industrial selenium poisoning is relatively rare. This is partly due to the fact that most major industrial uses involve selenium in the elemental form, which is relatively inert. Selenium fume, however, has been shown to be somewhat irritating and toxic (232).

Industrial exposures to selenium dioxide ($SeO_2$) have resulted in pneumonitis, followed by residual bronchitis (652), dyspnea, rales, wheezing, and headache (105), also sleeplessness, irritability, nervous cardiac disorders, loss of appetite, and nausea (331).

Hydrogen selenide ($H_2Se$) was fatal to animals in concentrations as low as 3 ppm (144). Pneumonitis and changes in the liver and spleen were observed. Fifteen parts per million were intolerable to men, causing eye and nasal irritation but 3 ppm was not irritating. One group of 5 cases of selenosis, believed due to $H_2Se$ given off from an etching ink, have been described. The symptoms included nausea, vomiting, metallic taste, bad breath, dizziness, lassitude, and fatigability. Air tests indicated concentrations below 0.2 ppm, and urinary selenium levels below 0.15 mg/liter were found (64).

Selenium oxychloride ($SeOCl_2$) is vesicant as well as highly toxic (143).

## 1. Determination

Dusts and fumes of selenium and its solid compounds can be sampled by suitable filters or impingers. Hydrogen selenide requires a bubbler with an oxidizing reagent, such as iodine or bromine solution. Iodometric methods can be employed for the determination of $SeO_2$ (reduction with KI) or $H_2Se$ (oxidation by standard $I_2$ solution).

Estimation of selenium by measurement of the intensity of the red color of colloidal elemental selenium is a specific micro-method for this element. As a reducing agent sulfur dioxide, sometimes in combination with hydroxylamine, is commonly used. The method is sensitive to about 5 μg of selenium in 10 ml of test solution and has been utilized for analysis of both air and urine (159).

Greater sensitivity and accuracy can be achieved by a colorimetric reaction with 3,3'-diaminobenzidine (94). The reaction takes place with selenite at a pH below 3. The solution is adjusted to pH 6–7 with ammonia and is extracted with toluene. The yellow color of the toluene is measured. Various modifications of this test have been described, cheifly in connection with the analysis of foods and vegetation for selenium.

## L. TELLURIUM

Although tellurium compounds are toxic and fatal intoxications resulting from accidental ingestion have been reported (309), relatively few cases of industrial poisoning have been recorded. The outstanding symptom of tellurium absorption is a garliclike odor imparted to the breath and sweat. In some instances relatively mild complaints of headache, epigastric distress, and metallic taste have been noted.

The amounts of tellurium needed to produce unpleasant breath are quite small. Amdur found less than 0.02 mg/liter of Te in the urines of affected workers (7). Our laboratory studies of milder cases failed to reveal detectable amounts of urinary tellurium. Steinburg and co-workers found 0.01–0.06 mg/liter of tellurium in urine and 0.001–0.01 mg per cubic meter of air where workers were affected (553).

## 1. Determination

Air samples of Te and its solid compounds can be collected on filter paper or by the impinger or electric precipitator. Tellurium in solution as tellurite can be reduced to a colloidal form by stannous chloride and the amount estimated visually or by light absorption in a colorimeter (17).

A modification of this method, designed especially for urine analysis, involves extraction of the urine with an $n$-amyl alcohol–ether mixture, after wet ashing, removal of selenium by distillation with HBr, and addition of iodide. The solvent is evaporated, and the residual tellurium salt is dissolved and reduced by stannous chloride and determined photometrically (235). The method gave excellent results in amounts of 50 μg/liter and was sensitive to lower concentrations.

## M. URANIUM

Because of its importance in the nuclear industry, as well as in the manufacture of nuclear explosives, the toxic properties of uranium have been extensively studied. According to Hodge, uranium in the body is highly toxic, producing a characteristic histological injury in the kidney (262). It is poorly absorbed, however, and many workers have been heavily exposed to both soluble and insoluble uranium dusts and fumes with only a few mild cases of kidney damage resulting therefrom (154).

With natural uranium the chemical toxicity creates a greater hazard than the radioactivity. Uranium enriched in the isotope $^{235}$U may present a radiation hazard, however, primarily due to the presence of the relatively short-lived $^{234}$U. Such hazards and their measurement are beyond the scope of this chapter and will not be further considered.

### 1. Excretion

Following exposure to soluble uranium, there is an immediate increase in urinary uranium, but normally the concentration falls off rapidly. Thus a worker who excreted 10 mg/liter the day after exposure had only 0.1 mg/liter 8 days later; another excretion of 1 mg/liter fell off to 0.1 mg/liter in 3 days (364). Because of the rapid excretion some authorities recommend collection of samples after the weekend holiday. Where the exposure is relatively constant, a preshift urine level of 30 $\mu$g of uranium per liter has been reported as equivalent, on the average, to an atmospheric concentration of 50 $\mu$g/m$^3$ (243). When the airborne uranium was collected in a two-stage sampler, which separated the dust into "respirable" and "nonrespirable" fractions, the urinary uranium concentration (night-time samples) was nearly three times the concentration of "respirable" dust and about one-half to one-third the total dust concentration (values calculated as micrograms per liter and micrograms per cubic meter, respectively) (181.) The uranium content of normal urine is reportedly between 0.03 and 0.3 $\mu$g/liter (638).

### 2. Determination in Air

Uranium dust and fume can be collected on filter paper and determined by alpha counting with a suitable proportional or scintillation counter, or the fluorometric method described below for urinalysis can be used, after dissolving the uranium with acid (366). In the latter case other collecting devices, such as the impinger and electrostatic precipitator, can be employed.

### 3. Determination in Urine

The fluorescence imparted to solid sodium fluoride by the presence of trace amounts of uranium has been utilized for the determination of submicrogram amounts of this metal, particularly in urine. The usual procedure is to place a small sample of urine in a shallow platinum dish, evaporate to dryness, add solid sodium fluoride, heat to fusion for a prescribed period, cool, and measure the fluorescence of the dish of sodium fluoride when illuminated with ultraviolet light (366,607).

Factors affecting the sensitivity and reliability of the fluorophotometric method have been discussed by several authors. Some recommend a sodium fluoride–sodium carbonate fusion mixture (460), while others prefer a sodium–lithium fluoride preparation (88) in place of pure sodium fluoride.

For analysis of the urine of unexposed individuals, Welford and co-workers concentrated the uranium by means of an ion exchange resin, followed by electrolysis with a mercury cathode (638). This procedure is necessary to isolate the uranium from other inorganic constituents in relatively large volumes of urine.

A method for separation of enriched uranium from urine by means of liquid ion exchange has been described (72).

### N. FLUORIDE

The toxicology of fluoride has been studied extensively, due primarily to its wide distribution in nature and the resultant exposure of large segments of the public. Davis, in a review of the literature of animal experiment data, states that in acute poisoning the central nervous system is affected early (124). Absorbed fluoride is rapidly removed from soft tissues, being excreted in the urine and deposited in the bone. While it has been speculated that its affinity for calcium may be a clue to the toxicity of fluoride, the mechanism of toxic action of this element has not yet been determined.

Inhalation of fluoride dust and fumes has caused irritation of nasal passages and nosebleed (647). Concentrations were of the order of 10 mg/m³. Roholm, in a study of Danish cryolite workers, reported that acute gastric symptoms, loss of appetite, nausea, and vomiting were the most frequent complaints (483). Shortness of breath was a common symptom, as were rheumatic attacks and pains or stiffness in joints.

Examination of bones by X-ray revealed signs of diffuse osteosclerosis, with calcification of ligaments and restriction of mobility in the columna and thorax. The fluoride content of bone ash was around 10%, compared with less than 1% in controls.

Later studies showed heavily exposed workers to be excreting around 16 mg of F per liter of urine (251). Princi concluded that workers could tolerate without harm fluoride absorption leading to a daily excretion of 5–8 mg (464), but others consider 4 mg/liter the limit for safe exposure (129) if bone changes are to be avoided.

## 1. Determination in Air

Samples may be collected with the impinger, or on filters if gaseous fluorides are absent. It has been shown that the fumes from magnesium foundries, where fluoride fluxes are used, are largely particulate (647). The sample can be concentrated and steam distilled from perchloric acid and the fluoride titrated with thorium with an alizarin indicator [Willard and Winter method (645)]. Use of an ion exchange resin to eliminate the distillation has been suggested (426).

A portable continuous analyzer for gaseous fluorides, based on the increased electrolysis in a cell with platinum and aluminum electrodes in the presence of fluoride, has been described by Howard and Weber (275). The electrolyte is 6% acetic acid containing a wetting agent and 0.1 mg of fluoride per liter. An automatic recorder, utilizing the color change produced by the action of fluoride on the green iron-ferron (8-hydroxy-7-iodo-5-quinoline-sulfonic acid) complex has also been described (2).

A method which avoids distillation but is reportedly suitable for insoluble, as well as soluble, fluorides has been described by Setterlind and Geishecker (525). The sample is taken in dilute NaOH (0.002 $N$) in an impinger, and an aliquot is mixed with a solution of zirconyl nitrate and alizarin red S. After standing overnight the color is read and compared with a standard curve.

## 2. Determination in Urine

Urine can be dry ashed, after addition of CaO, and the residue dissolved in perchloric acid and steam distilled and the fluoride determined by the Willard and Winter method described above (645). Many efforts have been made to eliminate the distillation procedure. Most have involved either use of ion exchange resins or microdiffusion techniques.

Talvitie and Brewer describe two modifications of an ion exchange method, in which fluoride is separated from urine without ashing (580). The methods differ primarily in the reagents used for elution of fluoride from resin, sodium hydroxide in one case and a dilute solution of beryllium in the other. Final determination is carried out colorimetrically with zirconium-eriochrome cyanine R solution. The latter procedure was used by Dubois and co-workers with minor modifications (141). The authors also developed an electrometric method, based on the depolarization of a rotating aluminum electrode by fluoride, which was used to determine fluoride in raw urine.

Rowley and Farrah describe a micro-diffusion method utilizing 1 ml of urine and 2 ml of perchloric acid, carried out at 50°C. The HF is absorbed in NaOH and determined colorimetrically (174,488). A modification of this procedure has been outlined by Cumpston and Dinman (116).

## O. MANGANESE

Manganese poisoning has been reported most frequently in mining and smelting operations, but has also occurred in iron and steel manufacturing, dry cell battery plants, and in other industries which use manganese in quantity (397). Manganese is present in many welding-rod coatings, but excessive concentrations of Mn fume result from welding only under conditions of very poor ventilation.

Manganese primarily affects the central nervous system (466). Symptoms may include gait and speech disturbances, tremors, masklike face, uncontrollable laughing, and similar manifestations (121,446,480). Other effects of manganese inhalation include bronchitis, bronchopneumonia and blood changes (315). The onset of symptoms may occur after 1 or 2 months of work, but more frequently after 1 or 2 years of manganese exposure, and rarely after as long as 10 years (480,514). The clinical signs may disappear in time if the worker is removed from further exposure before his condition reaches an advanced stage.

Particle size is an important factor in determining the rate of absorption, as well as the concentration in the air (122). Although the manganese content of the blood of exposed workers is variable, blood analysis appears to be the best biochemical test for determining manganese absorption.

Flinn and associates found a high incidence of manganese poisoning in an ore-crushing plant where atmospheric concentrations exceeded 30 mg of manganese per cubic meter of air (184). Rodier noted levels of 100–900 mg of manganese per cubic meter of air in Moroccan mines, where he found 150 cases of poisoning, most of them among pneumatic drill operators (480). Davies reported a high incidence of pharyngitis, bronchitis, and pneumonia among workers exposed to manganese dioxide dust in concentrations ranging up to about 30 mg/m³ (121,122). No systemic poisoning was noted. Kesic and Hauser observed manganese intoxication in workers exposed to concentrations between 7 and 63 mg/m³, but at levels between 3 and 9 mg/m³ the incidence was low (315).

The blood levels of manganese in affected Cuban miners described by Penalver ranged from 7 to 47 $\mu$g/100 ml (446). Another group of miners who developed manganese poisoning after 6–24 months' exposure showed blood manganese levels between 3 and 82 $\mu$g/100 ml (573). Urinary manganese concentrations were low. Most authorities have considered the kidneys to play a relatively small role in the elimination of absorbed manganese (472,620); the liver is considered more important, since manganese is carried in the bile to the gastrointestinal tract and eliminated in the feces (480). On the other hand, urinary manganese levels as high as 48 mg/liter (184) and even higher (480) have been reported among manganese-exposed workers.

## 1. Determination in Air

Dusts and fumes are collected with the electrostatic precipitator or standard impinger. After dissolving in nitric acid containing a small amount of sulfuric acid, the sample is evaporated, phosphoric acid added, and the manganese oxidized to permanganate by means of periodate. The smallest amount detectable by this procedure is about 10 $\mu$g (10).

## 2. Determination in Biological Material

Manganese can be determined in fractional microgram amounts by using 4,4-tetramethyldiaminotriphenylmethane as the color reagent (202). The method is applicable to some biological samples, but not to urine or other materials that contain large amounts of salts, especially phosphates. Dry ashing appears to be preferable to wet digestion when this procedure is used. The 4,4-tetramethyldiaminotriphenylmethane is oxidized at 80°C by permanganate in the presence of phosphoric and nitric acids, and the color developed is measured at 470 m$\mu$. In a modification of this procedure the color development step is carried out at room temperature and maximum absorption is measured at 610 m$\mu$ (47).

The procedure described for manganese in air can be applied to urine samples, but unless large volumes are taken the sensitivity is relatively low.

## P. COBALT

Although it is not considered a toxic metal, dusts containing cobalt are believed to have caused serious lung disease in a number of workers in the tungsten carbide industry, both in this country (405) and in Europe (35,333). The effects of cobalt dust have been compared to those of beryllium oxide.

Animals exposed for 30 min to cobalt hydrocarbonyl [$HCo(CO)_4$] and its decomposition products showed gross lung damage and many developed pulmonary edema at concentrations of the order of 100 mg of cobalt per cubic meter of air (439). Cobalt metal dust has been found irritating to lungs of animals (506).

### 1. Determination in Air

Keenan and Flick found it necessary to fuse dust samples obtained in the tungsten carbide industry with potassium peroxydisulfate in order to recover all the cobalt (311). Determination was colorimetric with nitroso R salt. Simpler methods of solution with acid and determination by thiocyanate have been found reasonably satisfactory when other types of cobalt dust were involved (159).

### 2. Determination in Biological Material

After dry ashing or wet digestion, Hubbard and co-workers remove iron with cupferron and then complex the cobalt with sodium diethyl-dithiocarbamate and extract with chloroform (278). Saltzman has described a similar procedure, using 1-nitroso-2-naphthol for complexing the cobalt (495). Both procedures involve evaporating the chloroform, dissolving the residue in nitric acid, and making the final determination with Nitroso R salt.

## Q. NICKEL

Dermatitis from contact with nickel salts and sometimes from metallic nickel is the disease most commonly associated with this element (182,383). There is some evidence that inhalation of nickel fume or finely divided nickel dust will cause pneumonitis. Also, the increasd incidence of lung cancer and the marked incidence of nose cancer among workers in nickel refineries has been attributed by some authorities to breathing the dust of nickel compounds (135,412).

The most hazardous nickel compound, however, is the carbonyl [$Ni(CO)_4$], a volatile liquid the vapors of which are highly toxic (317). Repeated exposures to nickel carbonyl have caused respiratory cancers and pulmonary lesions in animals (572). Workers accidentally exposed to nickel carbonyl for relatively brief periods experienced dizziness, headache, nausea, and vomiting, followed by cough, shortness of breath, and other respiratory symptoms. Some of the more seriously affected became irrational, and two fatal cases had terminal convulsions. Autopsy indicated serious lung injury (571).

Analysis of lung sections from nickel workers with lung cancer have shown about 0.1 mg of nickel (100 ppm) per gram of dried lung (651).

### 1. Determination in Air

The dusts of nickel and its compounds can be collected by any suitable filter or impinger and the nickel determined by dimethylglyoxime. Many methods have been proposed for nickel carbonyl, but most are insufficiently sensitive to measure concentrations near the threshold limit (0.001 ppm). Brief and co-workers suggest collection in dilute HCl, neutralization and reaction with alpha-furildioxime, and extraction of the colored complex with chloroform (55).

### 2. Determination in Urine

A method for determination of nickel in urine without ashing has been described (412). After precipitation of phosphate with calcium, dimethylglyoxime is added and the complex extracted with chloroform. For the determination the chloroform is extracted with acid, citrate and ammonia are added, and the nickel is determined colorimetrically with dimethylglyoxime. Workers with significant exposure excreted 0.4–1 mg of nickel per liter of urine, while normal urine contained about 0.04 mg/liter.

Imbus and co-workers, on the other hand, found about 0.01 mg/liter in the urine of unexposed persons and a mean of 4 $\mu$g of nickel per 100 g of blood (288).

### R. OSMIUM

Although it is one of the more refractory members of the platinum group of metals with a melting point of 2700°C, osmium is readily oxidized to the volatile tetroxide. So far as is known, metallic osmium is not harmful, but the vapors of $OsO_4$ (mp 45°C, bp 100°C) are extremely toxic and irritating. Eye effects featuring a "halo around lights," with other disturbances in vision and signs of irritation, were the outstanding symptoms of human exposure. Sometimes headaches and bronchial symptoms were also noted (396).

Animal experiments indicate that severe pulmonary symptoms may result from inhalation of $OsO_4$ vapor, and, in fact, one human death from this cause has been reported. $OsO_4$ is used widely as a stain for biological specimens.

### 1. Determination in Air

McLaughlin and co-workers collected a spray containing osmium on a filter paper, converted the osmium to the tetroxide by digesting with nitric acid, and distilled off the $OsO_4$, which was determined colorimetrically with thiourea (396). The thiourea reaction has been further studied by Allen and Beamish (6).

Presumably $OsO_4$ vapor could be collected directly in an appropriate aqueous solution, possibly in water alone, and then determined by the thiourea reaction.

A polarographic method, sensitive to about 0.1 $\mu$g/per milliliter of osmium, has been described (328).

## S. PLATINUM

In view of the relatively small number of workers involved in the refining of platinum, a remarkable number of reports of respiratory disease among them have been published. The findings vary from nasal irritation to severe or full-fledged asthmatic attacks (285,306,388,478,503). Dermatitis, eczema, urticaria, and photophobia have also been mentioned as occurring. Nearly all authorities agree that the soluble platinum salts (ammonium or sodium chloroplatinate) were the responsible agents and that the dust of metallic platinum is relatively innocuous.

In one study atmospheric concentrations of platinum salts ranged from 2 to 20 $\mu$g/m$^3$ in most areas, with levels as high as 960 and 1700 $\mu$g/m$^3$ at certain operations (285).

### 1. Determination in Air

Collection on filter paper followed by separation as the thallium chloroplatinate and colorimetric determination of platinum after reduction to platinum chloride with stannous chloride has been described (285). A spectrophotographic method has also been reported (187).

## V. HYDROCARBONS AND HALOGENATED HYDROCARBONS

### A. ALIPHATIC HYDROCARBONS

#### 1. Paraffins

The saturated hydrocarbons are obtained mainly from natural gas and petroleum. Methane and ethane are simple asphyxiants. Propane and ethane have, in addition, anesthetic properties. The compounds from pentane to octane are liquids which are fat solvents and primary skin irritants. Their vapors possess some narcotic and irritating effects which increase with the higher homologs, but are nevertheless of a low order. With some of these compounds the margin of safety between narcotic and fatal concentrations appears to be very small. Paraffins above octane are not sufficiently volatile to be considered normally as vapor hazards.

The paraffins are found chiefly in the form of mixtures. Different groups derived from crude petroleum oil are ordinarily classed according to their volatility. In addition to paraffins, which predominate, there are varying quantities of naphthenes, olofins, and members of the benzene series. Variation will occur according to the source of the crude oil, the degree and method of refining, and the temperatures at which the cuts are made. Naptha is a general term applied to various mixtures of these petroleum hydrocarbons, but usually limited to those with boiling ranges between 40 and 230°C. Typical naphthas and boiling ranges include petroleum ether, 40–60°C, rubber solvent naphtha, 38–150°C, lacquer diluent, 95–135°C, V.M. and P naphtha, 105–165°C; and stoddard solvent or mineral spirits, 150–205°C. Gasoline covers a boiling range of 60–120°C and is likely to contain more naphthenes and branched-chain hydrocarbons; kerosine boils at a higher range, 150–250°C, and may contain as much as 25% aromatic hydrocarbons.

#### 2. Olefins

Ethylene and some of its homologs are used in manufactured gas to give illuminating power. Little is known about them, but effects of ethylene do not differ greatly from the paraffins. It acts as an anesthetic and can be an asphyxiant, as would be propylene and the butylenes. Other toxic effects have not been reported from industrial exposures. The diolefins (butadiene, isoprene, etc.) are more irritating than paraffins or monoolefins of the same volatility. Repeated exposures were found to affect the bone marrow in experimental animals (621).

### 3. Acetylene

The most toxic effect of acetylene is its narcotic action. Problems from its use may be encountered from phosphine and other toxic substances that may be present as impurities in some commercial grades of acetylene.

### 4. Naphthenes

Cyclopropane has been used as an anesthetic, but neither it nor its derivatives are important industrial hazards. Cyclohexane sometimes serves as a substitute for benzene and toluene in solvents. Prolonged exposures of animals have produced slight degenerative changes in liver and kidney (600), but no intoxication from industrial applications has been reported.

### 5. Analysis

Aliphatic hydrocarbons mentioned in this section are detected usually through their property of flammability. Portable methane detectors and combustible gas indicators properly calibrated give sufficiently accurate results for most purposes. These instruments are discussed in the section on direct reading methods. A much more sensitive instrument is the portable flame ionization meter. This unit provides a continuous detection of combustible hydrocarbons at levels of a few parts per million.

Adsorption methods are suitable for heavily contaminated workroom air. The sample is obtained by passing a measured volume of air, freed from water and carbon dioxide, over silica gel or activated charcoal in weighed U-tubes. The additional weight after sampling is considered due to adsorbed organic vapor.

Other instruments that find application in hydrocarbon analysis are the interferometer, gas chromatograph, infrared spectrometer, and the Haldane or Orsat gas apparatus.

Butadiene can also be determined colorimetrically (81). The method is not generally applicable to routine field work, however. It is based on the complete oxidation of butadiene by iodine pentoxide at 200°C, with the liberation of iodine which is measured by suitable means. The reaction is not specific for butadiene, since a variety of other organic compounds also give this reaction.

Acetylene may be analyzed by precipitation of copper acetylide in an ammoniacal solution of cuprous chloride (279). Levels as low as

10 ppb collected on a column of silica gel and heated in a solution of ammoniacal cuprous chloride can be measured by the depth of the color produced on the gel. In addition to acetylene, any alkyne in which the triple bond occurs at the end of the chain can be analyzed by this method.

## B. BENZENE

An acute benzene exposure may produce irritation of the respiratory tract and narcosis. The effects from a single incident may not be any more serious than a similar exposure to many other solvents. However, repeated exposures to even moderate concentrations have caused blood changes which frequently develop into anemia (166,286). If absorption of benzene is allowed to continue, damage to the blood-forming mechanism becomes irreversible and death results from an infection predisposed by this condition.

With good reason, benzene has one of the worst reputations of all the industrial solvents. Its employment as a raw material frequently does not involve a serious health hazard because enclosed processes are used. Most problems from its use have occurred from its presence in lacquer compositions used in dope formulations employed in the manufacture of artificial leather, from its use as a solvent for rubber, and from its application as a paint remover where atmospheric contamination was not well controlled. The majority of fatal poisonings have occurred where exposures, when known, were 200 ppm or higher, but concentrations below 100 ppm also involve a substantial hazard (50,221,236). Studies in rubber coating plants have indicated that concentrations of the order of 25 ppm are rarely associated with blood dyscrasias (436).

In recent years benzene has been largely eliminated from many formerly common industrial uses. It still appears frequently, however, in certain petroleum naphthas, and handling substantial quantities of these solvents containing as little as 2.5% benzene can produce significant benzene concentrations in workroom air.

Benzene is rapidly absorbed through the lungs and equilibrium with the concentration in the air occurs within 30–60 min. Accumulation in tissues occurs in proportion to their fat content (458). In experiments on man an average of 46% of the benzene inhaled from a 5-hr exposure to 100 ppm was retained (513). Of the retained benzene, 12% was exhaled unchanged. Blood levels disappeared rapidly when exposure ceased. Urine excretion accounted for elimination of 0.1–0.2% over a long and irregular period. An average of 28.8% of the absorbed benzene was excreted in the urine as phenol, 2.9% as catechol, and 1.1% in the form of quinol (585). Excretion of phenol and catechol was highest during the first 24 hr, but quinol excretion lasted 48 hr. In workers exposed daily to benzene, phenol levels for all practical purposes returned to normal or near-normal overnight. Other minor metabolites included hydroxyquinol and mercapturic and muconic acids. A small amount was found to undergo complete metabolism to carbon dioxide and appeared in the expired air.

Phenols are excreted in the urine conjugated with sulfuric acid or glucuronic acid. Normally inorganic sulfates comprise 85–95% of the total sulfates in the urine. Within a few hours after benzene exposure individuals will show an increase of organic sulfate at the expense of the inorganic sulfate portion (658). An average sulfate ratio of 70% in a sample taken at the end of the work day is said to correspond to an exposure of 35 ppm (158). Because of individual variation in organic sulfate excretion, lower levels of benzene can easily go undetected.

Measurement of total phenol in urine is a more direct and sensitive test for benzene absorption. The apparent phenol content of normal urine ranges from 5 to 50 mg/liter, depending in part on whether a method specific for phenol or a procedure affected by other phenolic compounds is used. Urine samples taken at the end of work have been reported to contain 100 mg/liter at 15 ppm benzene (23) and about 200 mg/liter at 25 ppm (436), while the 24-hour excretion of phenol by workers exposed to 25 ppm (for 8 hr) has been given as 100 mg (586).

Analysis of solvents and air samples for benzene is an important industrial procedure, and, accordingly, several methods of analysis have been employed. Most frequently used are procedures based on measurement of the colorimetric reaction of its dinitro derivative with methyl ethyl ketone and ultraviolet spectrophotometry.

## 1. Determination in Solvents

Lacquers, cements, and dopes taken for benzene analysis are first steam distilled to separate the solvent. They can then be subjected to general procedures for solvent analysis in which the benzene is separated by fractional distillation and identified by refractive index, density, boiling point, and chemical tests (10,159).

## 2. Determination in Air

### a. NITRATION

Several modifications of the method of nitration developed by Smyth (543) and the colorimetric analysis of dinitrobenzene with butanone by Schrenk and co-workers (511) are available for benzene analysis.

Air samples taken at a rate of 20–30 ml/min can be introduced directly into a bubbler containing fuming nitric acid and concentrated sulfuric acid (159). Alternatively the sample can be collected in an evacuated 250-ml sampling bottle or on silica gel and nitrated in the laboratory. The silica gel contained in a U-tube is immersed in hot water (80–90°C) and aerated into the acid mixture. The acid is diluted and neutralized with sodium hydroxide and extracted with butanone. Color development occurs when a concentrated solution of sodium hydroxide is added to the butanone. Measurement is made photometrically at 530 mμ. As little as 0.001 mg of benzene may be determined with an accuracy of about 5% in the range of 0.01–0.06 mg. Aliphatic solvents do not as a rule interfere, but chlorobenzene, xylene, and toluene also produce a color, although much less intense than that of an equal amount of benzene. The addition of acetic acid and other reagents to remove interferences in the benzene analysis has been attempted with varying success (134).

### b. Ultraviolet Spectrophotometry

Samples are most conveniently collected by adsorption on silica gel. The benzene is readily desorbed by a polar solvent, such as ethyl or isopropyl alcohol (160). Alternatively the gel can be wet with water and then extracted with a suitable aliphatic hydrocarbon, such as cyclohexane, heptane, and isooctane (of spectrographic grade) (373). For some purposes solvents such as propyl acetate or ethylene dichloride can be used, but they are less suitable optically than the lower alcohols and paraffin hydrocarbons.

Benzene has absorption peaks at 244, 249, 255, and 261 mμ. If the extractant volume is 25 ml, 1–2 ppm can be detected when a 50-liter air sample is taken. Other aromatics, such as toluene and xylene, interfere, but if not present in excess, absorption measurements can be made at two or more wavelengths and the concentration of each determined by solving simultaneous equations. Or benzene can be separated from higher aromatics by fractional distillation, using carrier solvents such as cyclohexane and heptane (160).

### c. Indicator Tubes

Hubbard and Silverman (276) developed an indicator tube utilizing the color resulting from the reaction of sulfuric acid and formaldehyde with benzene. Since then, many other tubes have become available commercially. Some of these can measure benzene at the MAC (25 ppm), but for the most part this level is close to the lower sensitivity limit of the device. Discretion must be used, since errors in the field have been found to be well over 150% in some instances for readings at 25 ppm (242).

### 3. Determination in Urine

#### a. URINE SULFATE RATIO

Urine samples must be taken near the end of the exposure period or at least within 2 hr after exposure, since levels return to normal fairly rapidly. Inorganic sulfate is determined in acidified urine by precipitation with barium chloride. Total sulfate is found by gently boiling an equal volume of acidified urine and then adding barium chloride. The precipitates are weighed and results are expressed as the percentage of inorganic to total sulfate in the sample analyzed (159,658). Ratios of inorganic to total sulfate below about 80% indicate probable benzene absorption.

Several modifications of the basic sulfate procedure appear in the literature. Benzidine has been used to precipitate the sulfate, which after isolation is dissolved, and the sulfate is determined by titration (263). Gerarde hastened the hydrolysis of organic sulfate by autoclaving the sample and used pressure filtration to collect the precipitated sulfate (206). Lewis dissolved the barium sulfate with a known amount of ammoniacal EDTA and determined the excess EDTA by titration (357).

#### b. PHENOL

Deichmann and Schafer attempted to isolate phenol from biological samples by solvent extraction and also by precipitation of interferences, but both procedures required further separation steps (127). Walkley found that phenol could conveniently be recovered from urine by steam distillation with a minimum carryover of interferences (632). Ten milliliters of urine acidified with dilute sulfuric acid was steam distilled with collection of 50 ml of distillate. For analysis a modification of the Theis and Benedict method is used (587). Sodium acetate, $p$-nitroaniline (diazotized with sodium nitrite before use) and sodium carbonate are added to an aliquot of distillate in this order. The color produced is compared with a blank at 525 m$\mu$. Sensitivity is about 4 mg phenol per liter of urine when a 10-ml aliquot of distillate is used. A normal range of 15–50 mg/liter was found. $p$-Cresol, which appears normally in urine, does not seriously interfere since the color formed has the intensity of only one-tenth of an equivalent amount of phenol. Measurements on unexposed individuals showed occasional higher values due to the ingestion of certain medication. There was no increase in urinary phenol after exposure to low concentrations of toluene or xylene.

Gibbs reagent, 2,6 dichloroquinone-chloroimide, gives somewhat lower results and appears to be more specific for phenol, but is critical in regard to pH adjustment and time of color development.

Best results appear to be obtained with the reaction of 4-aminoantipyrene with phenols in the presence of potassium ferricyanide (164). The pH was found to be the most critical variable and color intensity varied somewhat with time. A satisfactory procedure is to add an aliquot of steam distillate, a sodium acetate–sodium carbonate buffer (pH 10.5–11.0), 4-aminoantipyrine reagent, and potassium ferricyanide (438). The color produced is read at 500 m$\mu$ after exactly 5 min. Sensitivity is about 5 $\mu$g in 10 ml of distillate. p-Cresol does not give a positive test, and catechol, another phenolic constituent of normal urine, is also unreactive. The normal urinary content found by using this method ranges from 5 to about 25 mg/liter with an average of 18 mg/liter.

Gas chromatography has also been employed for phenol analysis in urine (348,611). The phenol in each case must be hydrolyzed before it is added to the column for separation. Levels of phenols as low as 1 mg per liter of urine can be detected. Normal phenol content in urine was lower than that found by chemical methods. For males, averages of 7.5 and 8.6 mg/liter were found. Levels in women were even lower.

## C. TOLUENE

The chemical and physical properties of toluene closely resemble those of benzene, but benzene's toxic action on blood-forming organs is nearly absent. Toluene is not a bone marrow poison, but some slight temporary lymphocytosis has been found in experimental toluene exposure studies (624). One report of enlarged livers (determined by palpation) among painters appears in the literature (222), but these involved toluene exposures that were excessive, reaching levels as high as 1100 ppm. No other symptoms or serious illness were observed, however. Toluene is a mildly irritating solvent with a strong narcotic effect. At levels of 200 ppm signs of drowsiness, mild headache, and even impaired coordination may appear (624).

Toluene is poorly absorbed through the skin and its main avenue of entrance from industrial exposures is through the lungs. Blood accumulation is rapid and increases with its concentration in the air. After an 8-hr exposure to 200 ppm, blood levels have been found to range from 0.41 to 0.73 mg %, but rapidly disappear in 2 hr. Within a few hours 16–20% of an absorbed dose is exhaled. Roughly 80% is oxidized to benzoic acid, which in turn combines with available glycine to form hippuric acid and is eliminated in the urine (163,497). Excretion is rapid and levels return to normal usually overnight.

Von Oettingen and co-workers in extensive fume chamber studies of human subjects found that hippuric acid excretion roughly paralleled the intensity of toluene exposure (628). An average of 1.2 g of hippuric acid per day was found for each 100 ppm of toluene in the test atmosphere. The actual amount was possibly somewhat higher than this, since some loss of sample usually occurred in the early procedures for hippuric acid analysis.

It has been deduced from von Oettingen's data that 3.0–5.0 g of hippuric acid per liter of urine would be expected in samples collected during the last few hours of an 8-hr exposure to 200 ppm of toluene (159).

At this writing there are only two reports available regarding hippuric acid excretion in industrial workers exposed to toluene. One, by Ogata et al. on Japanese subjects, covers only one plant and includes less than 10 workers where exposures were of 3-hr duration (431). One worker exposed to 160 ppm of toluene excreted 1.93 g of hippuric acid in an end-of-shift sample. For another group of workers exposures ranged from 150 to 250 ppm, and hippuric acid excretion averaged 1.46 g/liter.

A more extensive study was carried out in 12 rubber coating and leather finishing plants by Pagnotto and Lieberman (437). Toluene levels ranged to nearly 200 ppm. For 200-ppm exposures, urinary hippuric acid excretion at the end of the work day was expected to average about 7.0 g/liter or result in a hippuric acid/creatinine ratio of 5.0.

The normal hippuric acid content of urine varies considerably since it is largely derived from benzoic acid or precursors of this product found in man's diet. From one laboratory a range between 0.4 and 1.4 g/liter was found (437). The average level most frequently mentioned is approximately 0.8 g/liter (241), although a much lower value of 0.18 g/liter was reported by Ogata et al. (431). Hippuric acid excretion in end-of-shift samples for even moderate exposures to toluene greatly exceeds the normal range.

## 1. Determination in Air

In general, toluene analysis can be performed by the methods used for benzene. Most frequently mentioned are the colorimetric reaction of its dinitro derivative with methyl ethyl ketone (159), and toluene analysis by ultraviolet spectrophotometry (120,160,373).

For the colorimetric analysis, air samples are collected for 10–30 min. in fuming nitric acid at a rate of about 0.1 liter/min, using a special fritted bubbler or U-tube filled with glass beads. The nitrated sample is extracted with methyl ethyl ketone after dilution with water, and color development is achieved by making the solution strongly alkaline. Measurement is made at 560 m$\mu$. Benzene and other homologs which also undergo this reaction interfere.

Alternatively, toluene can be collected on silica gel at a rate of 1–3 liters/min, thus permitting a larger sample to be obtained and also avoiding the handling of acid solutions in the field. Since toluene is not quantitatively removed by aerating the gel as described for benzene, nitrating acid is added directly to it. The reaction products are washed off with water and the rest of the analysis is performed as outlined above. The sensitivity of the test is approximately 1 ppm in a 25-liter air sample.

Ultraviolet spectrophotometric methods for toluene analysis are simpler to perform. Air samples can be collected directly in alcohol or on silica gel and desorbed with alcohol or isooctane and water. Absorption is measured at the 269-m$\mu$ peak, and amounts of 50 $\mu$g or less per/milliliter of solution can easily be determined. Aliphatic solvents do not usually interfere, but other aromatics do.

## 2. Determination in Urine

Many procedures are available for hippuric acid analysis. Early methods that depended on precipitation and crystallization to separate hippuric acid from urine are reviewed by Ellman et al. (162). These were macro-procedures that were tedious to perform, and quantitative results were not always obtained.

Recent procedures are more easily carried out, but are not specific for hippuric acid. Best results are obtained with those providing some preliminary separation of the hippuric acid before the analysis is performed.

Two direct methods are the fluorometric procedure of Ellman et al., which measures the fluorescence of hippuric acid in 70% sulfuric acid, and the method of Umberger (606), based on measuring the color produced from the reaction of hippuric acid dissolved in pyridine with benzene sulfonyl chloride.

Gaffney and co-workers (200) separated hippuric acid from urine by paper chromatography, sprayed the paper with p-dimethyl amino benzaldehyde, and heated it to form a colored azolactone. The spot was eluted with methyl alcohol and read on a colorimeter.

Ogato et al. (431) extracted hippuric acid from urine with an alcohol–ether mixture, spotted it on paper, and then used the reagent employed by Gaffney to form the azolactone. Quantitative results were obtained by comparing the colored spots obtained with standards similarly prepared.

Two spectrophotometric procedures are available. Elliot (161) employed an ion exchange resin column to separate hippuric acid from the major constituents of the urine. Uric acid is not removed by the resin, thus a correction must be made for its presence in the ultraviolet spectrophotometry analysis. Pagnotto and Lieberman make a separation of hippuric acid from normal constituents of urine, including uric acid, with an isopropyl alcohol–diethyl ether mixture. Measurement at 230 m$\mu$ on the ether layer is made by ultraviolet absorption analysis (437).

## D. STYRENE

Styrene has narcotic powers comparable to those of toluene and xylene, but is more strongly irritating. Animals exposed repeatedly to 1300 ppm gave evidence of respiratory and eye irritation, and some deaths occurred (205). Human subjects find concentrations of 200 ppm objectionable and irritating to the throat and eyes. Workers have complained of headache, fatigue, drowsiness, nervousness, etc. (324), and of nausea, vomiting, and loss of appetite (482).

### 1. Determination

Styrene can be readily determined by ultraviolet spectrophotometry, after absorption in a suitable solvent or adsorption on silica gel followed by extraction with alcohol. Or it can be nitrated with an $HNO_3$–$H_2SO_4$ mixture and the resulting yellow color measured. Absorption in carbon tetrachloride is suggested when this technique is employed (487).

Styrene is metabolized in part to hippuric acid and determination of this compound in the urine has been suggested as a method of estimating recent exposure.

## E. HIGHER AROMATIC AND CYCLIC HYDROCARBONS

### 1. Xylene

Xylene, or dimethylbenzene, exists in three forms, *ortho*, *meta*, and *para*. Commercial xylene usually contains all three isomers, with the *meta* form in greatest abundance, and in addition smaller amounts of ethylbenzene, trimethylbenzene, and other related compounds. It is found in mixtures with toluene and other solvents used in paints, lacquers, cellulose sprays, and rubber cements.

Exposure studies on animals indicated that xylene produced slight liver and kidney damage and hyperplasia of the bone marrow. The blood effect was much less than that produced by the same amount of benzene (32). The irritant and narcotic effects of xylene are pronounced. There is also evidence of circulatory disorder in human exposure. In some cases where blood pathology was found, the absence of benzene in the solvent mixture employed was not established (62).

## 2. Ethylbenzene

Ethylbenzene was developed commercially for use as an antiknock agent, especially in airplane fuels. It is used as a source of styrene and is found as a constituent of commercial solvent mixtures.

Industrial exposure to ethylbenzene has not produced any apparent systemic damage. However, it has markedly irritative effects on the skin and eyes, which serve as a warning of dangerous concentration.

Inhalation studies on human subjects indicate that about half the inhaled ethylbenzene is retained. The main metabolite is mandelic acid. An average excretion of 500 mg per liter of urine was obtained after an 8-hr exposure to 50 ppm of ethylbenzene (24).

## 3. Cumene

Cumene, isopropylbenzene, is used as a diluent or thinner for paints and enamels. It is strongly narcotic, but its volatility is low. Animal studies have shown it capable of producing fatty changes and congestion in the liver and kidneys (639). No ill effects from its use have been reported in humans.

## 4. Tetrahydronaphthalene

Tetrahydronaphthalene, or tetralin, has a powerful solvent action. Coupled with its slow rate of evaporation, it has been found quite useful as a solvent for oils, fats, and waxes and as a substitute for turpentine in shoe polishes, oil paints, and lacquers.

The principal pathological changes in animals were in the kidney, liver, lung, and blood (79). Such findings have not been observed in man, but significant exposure results in impartation of a green color to the urine.

## 5. Turpentine

Turpentine is a volatile oil obtained from various species of pine. It is not a definite chemical substance, but a mixture of hydrocarbons. Various grades of these solvents are available. American steam-distilled turpentine consists of 70–90% alpha- and beta-pinene, 10% dipentene, and other hydrocarbons. It is used principally as a solvent in paints and varnishes and is also employed in the manufacture of sealing waxes, shoe polishes, and other products.

The low volatility of turpentine ordinarily prevents it from constituting a vapor hazard. It is, nevertheless, an irritant chiefly affecting the eyes, lungs, and skin. It has a stimulating, followed by a paralyzing, effect on the central nervous system and injurious effects on the liver and kidneys (62).

Turpentine can be absorbed through the skin. Elimination takes place largely through the kidneys, with the turpentine partly unchanged and partly conjugated with glucuronic acid. The urine acquires an odor resembling that of violets.

## 6. Analysis of Higher Aromatic Hydrocarbons

Methods applicable to hydrocarbons in general may be employed for the aromatic hydrocarbons, including the use of the combustible gas indicator, interferometer, gas chromatograph, and equilibrated silica gel or activated charcoal. In addition, analysis can be performed with aromatic hydrocarbon detectors and ultraviolet spectroscopy.

Xylene, ethylbenzene, and cumene vapors can be analyzed by nitration and subsequent color formation in alkaline butanone similar to the procedure described for benzene. Determination can also be made by passing these vapors into a sulfuric acid–formaldehyde mixture and measuring the depth of color reaction (276). This test is applicable to benzene and other aromatic hydrocarbons. Naphthalene vapor interferes by producing a black film on the surface of the reagent.

For turpentine analysis, samples are collected in alcohol and an aliquot is reacted in an acidified solution of vanillin (291). It can also be determined by measuring the color intensity produced by turpentine in concentrated sulfuric acid (659). Acetone and methyl ethyl ketone will react with vanillin to give a pink color, but benzene and benzine will not interfere in either of these procedures. Since turpentine is not a pure substance, standards must be prepared with material obtained from the sampling site.

## F. CHLORINATED ALIPHATIC HYDROCARBONS

These compounds, because of their excellent solvent properties, low flammabilities, and wide range of volatility, find extensive use in industry. Toxicologically they are much more active than the corresponding hydrocarbons. Some appear to have no toxic activity except a narcotic effect, while others may produce severe injury to the liver, kidneys, and other organs. In many instances such injuries have not been reported in humans, possibly because enough severe exposures have not occurred.

### 1. Methyl Chloride

Poisoning from methyl chloride has resulted chiefly from the use of this gas as a refrigerant. Chronic and subacute exposures principally affect the central nervous system, producing symptoms resembling drunkenness or inebriation. In acute poisoning gastrointestinal disturbances and pulmonary congestion may be observed. The onset of symptoms is often delayed, but they may persist for several hours after exposure has ceased. Animal studies have shown that severe exposure can produce damage to the kidneys, liver, and heart, but these findings have not been reported in cases of human poisoning (626).

### 2. Methylene Chloride

Dichloromethane, or methylene chloride, is used for paint stripping and in other applications where a nonflammable solvent of high volatility is required. It is considered the least toxic of the chlorinated methanes, but has fairly strong narcotic powers. A fatal case resulting from very heavy exposure was reported by Moskowitz et al. (417).

### 3. Chloroform

Chloroform is widely known as an anesthetic, but findings of liver injury and cardiac sensitization have caused a lessening of its use for this purpose during recent years (62). No such effects have been observed from its limited industrial use as a solvent. Chloroform is rapidly absorbed when inhaled and is eliminated chiefly through the lungs, although a portion may be metabolized and excreted in the urine (626).

## 4. Carbon Tetrachloride

The numerous cases of carbon tetrachloride poisoning, resulting from its use as a solvent or from accidental ingestion, have given this compound the reputation of being one of the most harmful of the common solvents (159,626). Acute exposures will produce depression of the central nervous system, gastrointestinal disturbances, and damage to liver, kidneys, and lungs. Chronic poisoning from relatively mild exposures leads to loss of appetite and tendency to nausea and vomiting, with evidence of liver and kidney injury (356).

Carbon tetrachloride has been widely used as a fire extinguisher, fumigant, and solvent. It has been largely replaced by tetrachloroethylene as a dry cleaning agent primarily because of its toxicity. Fatal cases have been reported from relatively brief exposures to concentrations estimated at a few hundred parts per million parts of air. Typically the early symptoms are comparatively mild, but become more intense, and death may not occur until 6–14 days after the incident. Alcohol markedly exacerbates the effects of carbon tetrachloride, and several fatal poisonings have occurred in workers who drank heavily, while others who were equally exposed were only slightly affected (429). Chronic poisoning has been reported from repeated exposure to concentrations of the order of 45–100 ppm (245,308) and even lower (159).

Animal experiments have shown that most of the absorbed carbon tetrachloride is eliminated unchanged from the lungs (626). The desorption, however, takes place over a long period of time. Some metabolism occurs, since carbon dioxide from labeled carbon tetrachloride has been detected in the breath of animals, as well as in a nonvolatile fraction in the urine (559).

## 5. Ethyl Chloride

This gas is used to some extent as a refrigerant and also as an anesthetic, but controversy over its effect on the respiratory and circulatory functions has limited its employment for the latter purpose. It is one of the less toxic of the common chlorinated hydrocarbons.

## 6. Ethylene Dichloride

This compound, 1,2-Dichloroethane, is used in various cleaners and as a solvent for certain plastics. Like carbon tetrachloride it is capable of causing injury to lungs, liver, and kidneys. In addition it has been found to cause cloudiness and deformation of the cornea in animals, but no human cases have been reported (626). The effects of continued absorption of small amounts are similar to those from carbon tetrachloride, but higher concentrations of ethylene dichloride can be tolerated.

### 7. Ethylidine Chloride

1,1-Dichloroethane is less widely used than its isomer ethylene dichloride. It also appears to lack the toxic action of the latter solvent on liver and kidneys.

### 8. Methyl Chloroform

1,1,1-Trichloroethane, or methyl chloroform, is a cold cleaner and solvent for oils, tars, and waxes. The chief effect of inhalation of its vapor is depression of the central nervous system, since it has a minimal potential for causing liver and kidney damage (592). Consideration has been given to its use as an anesthetic, but it does not appear to be highly effective, and in some cases ventricular fibrillation may develop from its use (558). Industrial deaths have been reported from this solvent, but they involved tank exposures with grossly excessive concentrations. Because of its low toxicity and vapor pressure and solvent power close to that of carbon tetrachloride, it has been widely employed as a substitute for the latter solvent for many purposes.

Animal studies show that 99% of absorbed methyl chloroform is eliminated via the respiratory tract, while 1% appears in the urine as the glucuronide of 2,2,2-trichloroethanol (231). Humans exposed to 500 ppm showed concentrations of 22 ppm in the breath which dropped off slowly, being at detectable levels for more than 20 hr (561).

### 9. 1,1,2-Trichloroethane

This compound, which is not widely used, is considered much more toxic than its isomer methyl chloroform. It has been compared to carbon tetrachloride in its toxic effects (290), but no reports of human poisonings are available.

### 10. Tetrachloroethane

1,1,2,2-Tetrachloroethane (acetylene tetrachloride) is usually considered the most toxic of the chlorinated hydrocarbon solvents. Numerous reports of poisioning from industrial sources have been reviewed by von Oettingen (626). Mild intoxication will produce symptoms of gastrointestinal irritation and central nervous system depression. In more severe cases the predominant symptoms arise from its action as a hepato- and hemolytic poison, producing yellow atrophy of the liver and destruction of bone marrow cells. Illness has been reported in workers apparently exposed to concentrations below 10 ppm (159).

Tetrachloroethane has been employed as a cleaner, and during World War I it was widely used as a solvent for cellulose acetate and a coating for the fabric wings of airplanes. Many of the problems with its use occurred at that time.

### 11. Pentachloroethane

This liquid is used as a solvent and chemical intermediate. It has a strong narcotic action and may also cause damage to liver, lungs, and kidneys. No human cases of intoxication are known.

### 12. Hexachloroethane

Hexachloroethane is a solid which has been used as an anthelmintic in veterinary medicine and an ingredient of chemical smokes. Its toxicity has not been fully studied, but it appears to present relatively little hazard if handled with reasonable precautions.

### 13. Vinyl Chloride

Vinyl chloride is a gas used primarily as a monomer in plastic manufacture. It has a low order of toxicity and appears to be principally a central nervous system depressant. Although some fatal intoxications have occurred in workers who entered tanks where vinyl chloride was present, the fire and explosion hazard is the most important problem usually associated with its handling.

### 14. Vinylidine Chloride

1,1-Dichloroethylene is a basic monomer for a number of thermoplastic polymers. In the presence of oxygen it reacts to form a peroxide which is violently explosive (626).

### 15. Dichloroethylene

Commercial 1,2-dichloroethylene consists of a mixture of two stereo-isomers, the *cis* and *trans* forms. It has been employed as a solvent and intermediate, but does not have wide industrial usage. The major response to inhalation of the vapor is central nervous system depression.

## 16. Trichloroethylene

Trichloroethylene is used to some extent in dry cleaning shops and finds general use as an industrial solvent. It is most widely employed for the degreasing of metal parts.

The effects of acute trichloroethylene exposure are related primarily to the central nervous system. Chronic exposures may produce neurological symptoms, impairment of vision, and intolerance to alcohol. Kidney and liver involvement were mentioned in early reports (570), but no toxic effects on the kidney have resulted from experimental studies using purified trichloroethylene (125), and liver damage reports are based largely on abnormal findings in liver function tests.

Trichloroethylene is readily absorbed through the mucous membranes, and to some extent, through the skin, but ordinarily the most important absorption results from inhalation of the vapor. Blood levels reach a maximum after a few hours of exposure, but disappear rapidly when exposure is terminated. About 20% of the absorbed dose is eliminated in the expired air, following a steep rate of decline (560). The major portion of the absorbed trichloroethylene is metabolized to trichloroethanol and trichloroacetic acid. These compounds, amounting to 40–50% and 20–30%, respectively, of the absorbed dose, appear in the urine soon after exposure starts (584). The former reaches a maximum concentration within a few hours after cessation of exposure, but the level of trichloroacetic acid rises more slowly and the maximum may not occur for 24–48 hr (27,548).

Attempts to correlate trichloroacetic acid excretion with trichloroethylene exposure have yielded varying results (189,217). A review of all these data indicates that an exposure to 100 ppm of trichloroethylene will result in a trichloroacetic acid level in the urine of 300–350 mg/liter. Trichloroethanol determination in urine to evaluate trichloroethylene absorption has not been widely employed, due in part to the difficulty of the procedure. It has been suggested, however, that this metabolite might be a better index of exposure than trichloroacetic acid (584).

## 17. Tetrachloroethylene

This compound, commonly known as perchloroethylene, is widely used in dry cleaning and, to a lesser extent, in metal degreasing. While the major response to inhalation of this solvent is its effect on the central nervous system, some animal studies have indicated that the liver and kidneys are affected following repeated exposures (290). Abnormal serum protein and liver function tests were reported in a small group of workers exposed intermittently, but repeatedly, to concentrations of tetrachloroethylene vapor of the order of 300 ppm (110). There was also a case of cirrhosis of the liver.

Little is known of the metabolic fate of tetrachloroethylene. It is partially eliminated through the lungs, but is also converted in part to an unidentified water-soluble metabolite (28).

## 18. Propylene Dichloride

1,2-Dichloropropane is used as a solvent and fumigant. It has narcotic properties and in high concentrations may cause injury to the liver and other organs, as seen from animal studies (248). No observations of such injury to humans from industrial use have been reported.

## 19. Allyl Chloride

3-Chloropropene is used as a chemical intermediate. It is highly toxic and irritating, causing injury to the lungs, liver, and kidneys of exposed animals (290).

## 20. Chloroprene

2-Chlorobutadiene is used in the manufacture of synthetic rubber. It is a highly toxic compound, capable of causing lung, liver, and kidney damage, injury to the male reproductive organs, anemia, and loss of hair (627).

## 21. Determination of Chlorinated Hydrocarbons

### a. In Air

Air analysis methods for chlorinated hydrocarbons depend for the most part on measurement of organic chloride, or on semispecific group reactions (Fujiwara test).

### (1) Field Methods

The halide leak detector, based on the Beilstein test, is useful for detecting leaks and providing a very rough indication of high concentrations of chlorinated hydrocarbon vapors. The Davis halide meter, utilizing the same principle, provides results sufficiently accurate for most industrial hygiene purposes. Flame ionization instruments have been used, as well as combustible gas indicators, in the case of flammable vapors, such as those of vinyl chloride.

Indicator tubes have been developed for some of the more common chlorinated hydrocarbons. As previously indicated, these are of limited accuracy and varying reliability. The Kitagawa tubes for trichloroethylene have given fairly good results in the authors' laboratory.

### (2) Thermal Decomposition Methods

In a typical combustion apparatus for field sampling of organic chlorides, the air is passed through a red-hot quartz tube containing a platinum foil catalyst. Practically all the organic vapor is converted to carbon dioxide, water, and hydrochloric acid, with traces of free chlorine. The latter gases are absorbed in a bubbler containing alkali or sodium arsenite. The amount of chloride is determined by a Volhard titration or other suitable method (582). These devices are capable of a high degree of accuracy, but since they are cumbersome, fragile, and present a fire hazard, they are not satisfactory for many sampling situations.

### (3) Sodium Reduction

The sodium reduction procedure adopted by the American Conference of Governmental Industrial Hygienists has been found quite satisfactory. Air samples are collected on silica gel and extracted with secondary butyl or isopropyl alcohol. The chlorinated hydrocarbon in the eluate is completely hydrolyzed by refluxing with metallic sodium (10), and the chloride content is determined by titration or other conventional methods. The test is limited by the sensitivity of the titration in the presence of an excess of sodium salts.

### (4) Hydrolysis

Many chlorinated hydrocarbons can be partially (in a few cases, completely) hydrolyzed by refluxing in an alcoholic solution of potassium hydroxide. A simpler modification of the procedure provides for incubating a solution of the organic chloride in isopropyl alcohol overnight at 50°C with a few pellets of potassium hydroxide (170). Yields of 80–90% have been reported for carbon tetrachloride and chloroform and almost exactly 50% for trichloroethylene and ethylene dichloride (159). Some compounds, such as methylene chloride and tetrachloroethylene, hydrolyze poorly and erratically under these conditions.

### (5) Fujiwara Reaction

The Fujiwara reaction provides a sensitive colorimetric means of analysis for many of the chlorinated hydrocarbons containing more than one chlorine atom attached to the same carbon atom. The air sample may be collected in alcohol, pyridine, or acetone, or a grab sample can be taken. Color is developed by heating the sample in alkaline pyridine. Several modifications have been proposed. The more recent practice is to use 20% alkali and heat to 60–70°C, since higher alkalinity and heat depress the color formation (523,635). Procedures have been given for carbon tetrachloride, chloroform, trichloroethylene, and ethylene dichloride (551). The reaction is said to go at room temperature with trichloroethylene (550).

An interesting modification of the Fujiwara procedure involves discharging the color with acetic acid after cooling, followed by addition of a benzidine–formic acid reagent which causes the formation of a violet color. The sensitivity of this modification is reportedly five times that of the conventional Fujiwara procedure (360).

## b. In Biological Samples

### (1) Breath

Studies on human subjects have shown that measurement of chlorinated hydrocarbon vapors in expired air is a useful method for essessing exposure to many of these substances. One technique is to sample in saran bags and analyze by gas chromatography. If the solvent is not known, identification by means of infrared spectroscopy may be possible. Decay curves for carbon tetrachloride, methyl, chloroform, tetrachloroethylene, and trichloroethylene have been prepared (560). Another procedure described is collection in toluene, with determination by the Fujiwara reaction (459).

### (2) Blood

Analysis of blood for chlorinated hydrocarbons is not a common industrial hygiene practice, partly because the unchanged solvent rapidly disappears from the blood stream. It is possible to remove the more volatile solvents by distillation or aeration or to extract the blood with carbon disulfide or other suitable solvents. In the case of trichloroethylene, determination of trichloroethanol or trichloroacetic acid by methods similar to those described for urine analysis may be carried out.

### (3) Urine

The amounts of unchanged chlorinated solvent in urine following exposures of the magnitude typical in industry are too small to be determined readily. The metabolic products of trichloroethylene, however, are present in sufficient quantity to provide a useful index of exposure to this solvent. A typical procedure for determination of trichloroacetic acid consists of adding 0.1–0.2 ml of urine to an alkaline pyridine mixture and heating to 60–70°C in a water bath for 20 min. The color developed in the pyridine layer is measured at 537 or 370 m$\mu$ (196). Greater sensitivity can be achieved by discharging the color with acetic acid and measuring the violet color produced by the addition of benzidine–formic acid reagent as described above (360) (see Fujiwara reaction).

Analysis of urine for the more abundant metabolite trichloroethanol has not been widely employed because early procedures were tedious. It has been reported that free and conjugated trichloroethanol, upon heating for 5 min at 70°C in a sulfuric acid dichromate solution, is converted quantitatively to trichloroacetic acid (619). Analysis of the resulting solution by the Fujiwara test gives the total amount of both metabolites. An alternate method that does not use pyridine depends on separating the free and combined trichloroethanol by distillation, heating the distillate with alkali, and measuring the formaldehyde which is formed (385).

## G. FLUOROHYDROCARBONS

The toxicity of fluorine compounds is given extensive treatment in a review by Pattison (443). Compounds possessing a $\omega$-fluorine atom attached to an unbranched carbon chain show an alternation of toxic properties in various homologous series. The most toxic members are frequently those having an even number of carbons and capable by natural detoxication mechanisms of being metabolized to highly toxic fluoroacetic acid.

Most perfluoroalkanes have a low order of toxicity. In completely halogenated chlorofluoroalkanes of the methane and ethane series (Freons), toxicity decreases with increasing fluorine content and increases with increasing chlorine content. At sufficiently high concentrations a number of them will affect the central nervous system and produce narcosis and lung congestion, but no organic injury. Liquid fluorocarbons are important as high-temperature lubricants. Freons are extensively employed as refrigerants and aerosol propellants.

Octafluorocyclobutane is a gas at room temperature and is used as a food propellant. Animal studies have shown it to have a low order of toxicity (103).

The presence of a double bond in polyfluoroalkenes is associated in general with greater physiological activity than the corresponding alkanes. Perfluoroisobutylene and hexafluoropropylene are pulmonary irritants found as decomposition products of Teflon. Hexafluoropropylene can also cause renal injury.

Teflon is a nontoxic polytetrafluoroethylene polymer, also known as Fluon. Dust from resins formed by this compound is reported to be inert. Heating Teflon at 380°C and above gives rise to noxious fumes containing hydrogen fluoride, carbonyl fluoride, and various fluorocarbons, including the toxic perfluoroisobutylene and hexafluoropropylene which produced acute pulmonary irritation and injuries to brain, liver, and kidneys in animal studies (597,663).

The chief difficulty encountered by industrial workers is known as polymer fever, with symptoms similar to those of metal fume fever, from exposures to Teflon heated above 340°C (563). In a plant where 7 cases of polymer fever were reported, urinalyses showed increased fluorine content and air tests for fluorine showed 3.5 mg/m³ of Fluon (530).

## 1. Determination in Air

Direct field analysis can be made using the Davis Halide Meter on the basis of the chloride content of the molecule. The sensitivity of this instrument for these substances is low. The flame ionization meter can be used for low concentrations.

Marcali and Linch reviewed methods for the determination of unsaturates and found conventional techniques not applicable for accurate analysis of perfluoroalkenes; infrared, Raman, and ultraviolet procedures lacked sufficient sensitivity for air analysis (382). They reported, however, that certain compounds containing difluorinated terminal unsaturates adjacent to a carbon that contains halogens reacted in methanol with a mixture of pyridine and piperidine to produce a stable yellow color. Samples for perfluoroisobutylene (PFIB) and hexafluoropropene (HFP) were collected at sampling rates up to 0.1 cfm in two midget impingers in series containing methanol and cooled to −30 to −40°C. Color developed after the addition of pyridine, and piperidine was measured at 412 m$\mu$. A 0.1-ft³ air sample detected 0.1 ppm of PFIB and 0.02 ppm of HFP. The addition of acetic acid to the methanol solution inhibits color formation of PFIB and permits the determination of HFP alone. Other similar alkenes will react to give color in this test, but of much lower intensities.

A field method is given by the same authors for PFIB and HFP in which the reagents are combined in the sampling tube and collection is made at room temperature. Color comparisons are made visually with potassium dichromate standards.

Specific methods for PFIB and HFP using gas chromatography can also be employed (78).

## H. BROMOHYDROCARBONS

Substitution of bromine for chlorine in a simple aliphatic compound produces a marked increase in density, boiling point, and toxicity. While the narcotic and hepatoxic properties are frequently similar, central nervous system effects and respiratory tract irritation are usually more pronounced from organic bromides than from the corresponding chlorides. These differences are reflected in the threshold limit values for a number of common aliphatic bromides and chlorides, listed in Table IV.

Because of their high cost, as well as toxicity, bromohydrocarbons are seldom employed as solvents, but find considerable application as fumigants and some use as fire extinguishing agents.

### 1. Methyl Bromide

Methyl bromide is widely known as a fumigant and a fire extinguishing agent. It is a highly toxic substance with a characteristic delayed insidious action. Skin contact produces serious burns. Inhalation of the gas rapidly fatigues the sense of smell; thus dangerous concentrations may be built up without sufficient warning.

The symptoms from an acute exposure may be delayed from 30 min to several hours and may include malaise, headache, visual disturbance, nausea, vomiting, and convulsions (626). Damage to the kidney, brain, and other organs may occur. In fatal cases the immediate cause of death is frequently lung congestion associated with circulatory failure. The effects from exposure to lower concentrations vary in intensity and are

TABLE IV
Threshold Limits for Organic Bromides and Chlorides

| Chloride | TLV, ppm | Bromide | TLV, ppm |
|----------|----------|---------|----------|
| $CH_3Cl$ | 100 | $CH_3Br$ | 20 |
| $CH_2Cl_2$ | 500 | $CH_2ClBr$ | 200 |
| $CF_2Cl_2$ | 1000 | $CF_2Br_2$ | 100 |
| $C_2H_5Cl$ | 1000 | $C_2H_5Br$ | 200 |
| $CH_2ClCH_2Cl$ | 50 | $CH_2BrCH_2Br$ | 25 |
| $CHCl_2CHCl_2$ | 5 | $CHBr_2CHBr_2$ | 1 |

most frequently referable to the central nervous system. Recovery is usually slow, and sometimes permanent damage to the central nervous system occurs.

Absorption of methyl bromide usually takes place through the lungs. Skin penetration is not considered important. There is a partial breakdown of methyl bromide in the system to nonvolatile bromide readily detectable in the blood. Excretion of methyl bromide appears to be predominantly through the lungs (29) and this occurs promptly (406). Blood bromide remains elevated for some time, hence complete elimination of bromide in the urine is also prolonged and has been known to take several weeks (101).

Numerous cases of methyl bromide poisoning are reviewed by von Oettingen (626). Thirty-four cases were reported in a date-packing plant where concentrations ranged from 100 to 500 ppm (300). Two other cases with one fatality occurred in a fire extinguisher filling plant (595). The methyl bromide concentration in the workroom was at times as high as 390 ppm. A blood bromide of 211 mg % was found in the fatal case and 50 mg % in the other. Poisoning was also found to occur at much lower levels of exposure, less than 35 ppm, in a group of workers engaged in the preparation of sealed glass ampoules containing methyl bromide (632). Additional cases caused by a leak in a fire extinguisher system were reported. The blood bromides in two men who died were 9.2 and 8.3 mg %, and the urinary bromide level in one of these men was 92 mg/liter. In two individuals who survived, blood bromide levels remained at 6.9 mg % for 12 days and fell to practically zero after 30 days (101).

Blood bromide levels in normal individuals range from 0 to 1.5 mg %. The level at which bromide effects become noticeable is uncertain, but Irish states that in the absence of inorganic bromide derived from ingested medication, levels of 15–20 mg % would lead to severe reactions (290).

## 2. Determination in Air

For a rapid check of methyl bromide leakage the halide torch or halide leak detector can be employed. More sensitive and quantitative direct reading instruments are the Davis halide meter and flame ionization detector.

Chemical methods of analysis most frequently involve hydrolysis of the methyl bromide with a subsequent determination of the bromide. Methyl bromide can be determined by adsorption on silica gel chilled with Dry Ice followed by hydrolysis with KOH in isopropyl alcohol at 50°C, as described in the procedure for chlorinated hydrocarbons. Recovery of the methyl bromide is substantially complete (159).

Busbey and Drake collected methyl bromide in air sampling bulbs and hydrolyzed the sample with heat in a special saponification apparatus using alcoholic potassium hydroxide (69). After removal of the alcohol by distillation, the bromide was oxidized to bromate by sodium hypochlorite and analyzed by iodometric titration (329). With a 2-liter air sample, 2 ppm of methyl bromide is detectable.

Stenger et al. found that methyl bromide decomposed in ethanolamine at room temperature in 15 min. (554). The bromide was determined by the Volhard titration if large concentrations of methyl bromide were present or by the bromate oxidation procedure if small amounts were anticipated.

Blinn and Gunther obtained air samples by drawing air through two series-connected scrubbers containing 5% alcoholic KOH (45). Hydrolysis of the methyl bromide at room temperature was seen to be complete in 2 hr, and the analysis was made by titration with $AgNO_3$.

Williams passed air samples through a quartz tube heated at 950–1000°C and absorbed the combustion products in dilute sodium hydroxide (648). Bromide analysis was performed by the Kolthoff–Yutzy method (329).

A colorimetric procedure for bromide determination is employed by Turner (605) which could be adapted to methyl bromide analysis. The bromide is oxidized to bromine in a sulfuric acid solution of potassium persulfate. Rosaniline is added and pentabromorosaniline is formed. It is extracted in benzyl alcohol and measured photometrically at 585 m$\mu$. Less than 5 $\mu$g of bromide per sample can be determined without interference from chloride.

### 3. Bromide Analysis in Body Fluids

For a rapid bromide analysis of biological fluids the gold chloride method can be employed (53). The protein is removed by precipitation with trichloroacetic acid and gold chloride is added to the filtrate. The color produced is compared with standards. This procedure is not suitable for concentrations below 25 mg per 100 ml of blood.

A more quantitative analysis requires that the organic matter be destroyed. This can be accomplished by alkaline ashing with potassium nitrate. The bromide is oxidized to bromate and determined by iodometry (353). The determination can also be done colorimetrically by the formation of pentabromorosaniline as described in the preceding section.

## 4. Monochlorobromomethane

This compound, known commonly as methylene chlorobromide, is an effective fire-extinguishing agent and has been considered as a replacement for carbon tetrachloride in this field. The primary hazard from inhalation of the vapor is anesthesia. Little information is available regarding its toxicity in man; but Svirbely et al. (574), Torkelson et al. (593), and others have shown from animal data that acute toxicity of methyl chlorobromide is high. However, this substance has only a slight tendency to cause liver damage or other organic injury from either acute or chronic exposure. A significant amount of hydrolysis of the compound occurs in the system resulting in an accumulation of inorganic bromide in the blood.

## I. CHLORINATED AROMATIC HYDROCARBONS

## 1. Dichlorobenzene

$p$-Dichlorobenzene is most widely known as a moth deterrent. The vapor is painful to the eyes and has a negligible irritating action on the skin. Liver and kidney damage has been produced in animals, but the concentrations employed were higher than an average man would tolerate (264). Berliner reported cataracts in humans exposed to its vapors (40), but this effect was not found in studies by Pike and others (451). Hollingsworth et al. reported only eye and nose irritation in workers handling $p$-dichlorobenzene from 8 months to 25 years (264).

A single oral dose of $p$-dichlorobenzene given to rabbits was metabolized 35% to 2,5-dichlorophenol, 6% to 2,5-dichloroquinol, and to conjugates of glucuronide and ethereal sulfates (650). Inhalation of the vapor by workers handling $p$-dichlorobenzene resulted in an excretion of chlorinated phenols that reached a maximum at the end of the work day. After an initial rapid decline, elimination continued for several days. A worker exposed to an average of 50 ppm of $p$-dichlorobenzene in his work day excreted about 140 mg of dichlorophenol per liter of urine at the end of the shift (438).

The acute effects of $o$-dichlorobenzene are similar to those of $p$-dichlorobenzene (75). Animals showed irritation and definite kidney and liver damage. According to Browning, however, its use in industry has produced little or no intoxication, either acute or chronic (62). No indication of injury was noted by Hollingsworth and co-workers in a group of workers where exposures were as high as 44 ppm (average 15 ppm) (266). The authors' laboratory found no ill effects except irritation of the eyes and respiratory passages from intermittent exposures to 100 ppm in a wool-fulling plant (159). o-Dichlorobenzene is metabolized to dichlorophenols, dichlorocatechols, and dichlorophenyl mercapturic acid (650).

### a. DETERMINATION IN AIR

Dichlorobenzene can be determined by combustion or sodium reduction, followed by titration of the chloride as described for other chlorinated hydrocarbons (10,582), by infrared analysis after collection in carbon disulfide (487), and by ultraviolet spectrometry at 281 m$\mu$ following collection on silica gel and desorption overnight with isopropyl alcohol (438).

### b. DETERMINATION OF PHENOLIC METABOLITES IN URINE

An aliquot of urine collected at the end of the work shift after p-dichlorobenzene exposure is acidified and steam distilled as described for phenol in the benzene section (p. 111). Total phenols can be determined using diazotized p-nitroaniline or Gibbs reagent (2,6-dichloroquinonechloroimide).

The method of choice for measuring the metabolites of p-dichlorobenzene employs 4-amino antipyrine, also described in the benzene section. The reaction is pH sensitive. Dichlorophenols give no color at pH 10.4, but at pH 8.0 they are quantitatively determined with other phenols. It is necessary to make two analyses on each distillate, and the net difference is reported as 2,5-dichlorophenol (438).

The analysis can also be done by extraction of the distillate with cyclohexane or heptane and measurement of the difference in absorption at 284 and 287 m$\mu$. Little interference from phenol is encountered since its peaks occur at lower wavelengths.

## 2. Chlorinated Naphthalenes

The tri- to the octachloronapthalenes are solid waxy materials. Commercial preparations are usually mixtures of more than one derivative. The higher chlorinated compounds are frequently used in combination with chlorinated diphenyls. Chlorinated naphthalenes are employed as dielectric media, insulation in electric condensers, and impregnating electric wire insulation. Wire insulation uses molten wax or the compounds dissolved in an organic solvent. The wet product is dried in an oven, during which dangerous fumes are given off. Absorption of these fumes is primarily by inhalation and, to a lesser extent, through the skin.

In World War I, German authors described "perna" disease as a special form of chloracne caused by perchloronaphthalene. This problem is commonly observed in handling chlorinated naphthalenes. Several writers have also reported that the penta- and hexachloronaphthalenes produced acute yellow atrophy of the liver which proved fatal in a number of cases (138,183). Air analyses in a plant where 2 such deaths had occurred revealed from 1 to 2 mg of chloronaphthalene per cubic meter of air (159).

Studies in animals showed no significant storage of polychloronaphthalene, nor was any significant amount excreted in urine following exposures to these substances (104). An increase in ethereal sulfate in urine was observed, however.

### a. Determination in Air

Chlorinated naphthalenes can be determined by combustion followed by measurement of the chloride with silver nitrate by titration or nephelometry (582), and by the sodium reduction procedure for chlorinated hydrocarbons.

Air samples can also be passed through spectrograde heptane or isooctane chilled at 0°C to prevent evaporation of the collecting solvent or through silica gel and desorbed with isopropyl alcohol. Absorbance is measured in the ultraviolet region. Absorption peaks are found toward higher wavelengths as the chloride content of the compound increases. Since commercial products are mixtures, standards should be made with samples obtained from the testing site.

## 3. Chlorinated Diphenyls

Chlorodiphenyls are used extensively for insulating electric wire and impregnation of dielectrics. Enough information is available to indicate that some of these compounds cause liver injury. Treon and co-workers found from animal studies that a product consisting chiefly of pentachlorodiphenyl would produce liver damage (598). Trichlorodiphenyl or Arochlor 1242, however, had little effect on various animals studied, even at levels approaching saturation.

A study of human industrial exposures indicated no evidence of toxic effects from mixed chlorodiphenyls where concentrations ranged as high as 10 mg/m³. Average concentrations were much lower, however. Fumes at the maximum level were unbearably irritating (159).

### a. Determination in Air

Methods mentioned in the preceding section on chlorinated naphthalenes are generally applicable to chlorinated diphenyl analysis. The ultraviolet absorption is at shorter wavelengths, however, and less characteristic than for the chlorinated naphthalenes.

# VI. COMPOUNDS OF CARBON, HYDROGEN, AND OXYGEN

## A. ALCOHOLS

### 1. Methanol

Many cases of fatal intoxication and blindness have resulted from the ingestion of methyl alcohol. A number of similar industrial poisonings occurred when wood alcohol was one of the few volatile solvents in common use (62) and excessive exposures were frequent.

Sayers et al. exposed dogs to 400–500 ppm of methanol for over a year with no evidence of intoxication (505). Modern industrial experience has indicated that workers are not seriously affected by concentrations of 200 ppm and probably can tolerate 500 ppm or even higher (159). A case of chronic poisoning resulting from exposure to between 1200 and 8000 ppm of methanol has been reported. Marked diminution of vision and liver enlargement were noted, but the vision improved when exposure was discontinued (284).

#### a. DETERMINATION IN AIR

Methanol vapor can be absorbed in water in a bubbler or impinger and oxidized with permanganate to formaldehyde, and the latter determined colorimetrically with Schiff's reagent (481) or chromotropic acid (177). If a single bubbler is used, not more than 10 liters of air should be sampled for each 10 ml of water absorbent. This limits the sensitivity of the test. Greater volumes of air can be sampled and better sensitivity attained if two bubblers in series are used and/or the absorbing liquid is chilled.

#### b. DETERMINATION IN URINE

Methanol in urine can be separated by distillation, after addition of sulfuric acid and subsequent determination by the methods outlined above. Only a small fraction of the methanol absorbed is excreted unchanged in the urine: 1% according to Leaf and Zatman (347), even less according to data from the authors' laboratory (159).

### 2. Ethyl Alcohol

Ethyl alcohol is not considered a toxic solvent, although inhalation of high concentrations will result in the usual symptoms of alcohol absorption.

### a. Determination in Air

A general method for determination of water-soluble alcohol vapors is to pass the air through water and then oxidize with standard dichromate, determining the excess iodometrically.

## 3. Propyl Alcohol

The propyl alcohols, while more toxic than ethanol, usually present a minor vapor hazard when used as solvents. Mild irritation and narcotic effects may result from exposure to relatively high concentrations.

## 4. n-Butanol

In comparison with the lower alcohols, butanol is quite irritating, particularly to the eyes (106). While some studies have indicated eye effects below 100 ppm (576), an extensive investigation by Sterner et al. (556) resulted in the conclusion that no eye injuries or symptoms were observed at 100 ppm. Corneal inflammation and other eye effects were noted at concentrations of 200 ppm.

### a. Determination in Air

The dichromate oxidation method used for ethyl alcohol may be employed for n-butanol. Since butanol is only partly soluble in water, it is logical to collect the vapor on silica gel and then extract with water, rather than using water directly as absorbent.

## 5. Allyl Alcohol

Compared with the saturated alcohols, allyl alcohol is extremely irritating and toxic. Animals exposed repeatedly to 7 ppm showed evidence of liver and kidney injury, but 2 ppm caused no detectable damage (594). Workers moderately exposed suffered from lachrymation, retrobulbar pain, photophobia, and blurring of vision, but recovered within 48 hr. Skin absorption resulted in deep pain (146).

### a. Determination in Air

Absorption in water followed by coulometric bromination has been mentioned as a suitable method for determination of allyl alcohol vapor in concentrations of hygienic interest (594).

### 6. Ethylene Chlorohydrin

Ethylene chlorohydrin is a powerful renal, hepatic, nerve, and vascular poison (213). Numerous fatal cases have been reported, most of them involving kidney, liver, and brain damage (71,132). In nonfatal cases nausea is the predominant symptom.

#### a. DETERMINATION IN AIR

Ethylene chlorohydrin is water soluble and can be collected in aqueous NaOH. The resulting solution is heated and the chloride formed by hydrolysis measured (132). Determination by the Fujiwara color reaction, after absorption in a pyridine–water mixture, has also been described (551).

### B. ALDEHYDES

### 1. Formaldehyde

Formaldehyde is an irritating gas, especially to the eyes, which may be affected at concentrations below 5 ppm. Tolerance is frequently developed, and some workers can stand concentrations approaching 10 ppm without complaints. Irritation of the upper respiratory passages may occur at such levels. Dermatitis often results from formaldehyde solutions and is possibly caused by the gas as well.

#### a. DETERMINATION IN AIR

Absorption in water followed by colorimetric determination with Schiff's reagent is a simple method for the determination of formaldehyde in concentrations of a few parts per million in air. Busch and Berger found that addition of 1% methanol to the water improved the stability of the formaldehyde solution formed (70). Their studies indicated that collection with the midget impinger was about 74% efficient. Rayner and Jephcott found a similar efficiency when the standard impinger with 0.005 $N$ HCl was used for sampling (465).

Chromotropic acid is reportedly sensitive to smaller concentrations of formaldehyde than is Schiff's reagent (392).

The recommended method of the American Conference of Governmental Industrial Hygienists involves collection in sodium bisulfite solution and titration of excess bisulfite and then of the sulfite released when the solution is made slightly alkaline (10,215).

Adsorption on silica gel followed by development of color on addition of a freshly prepared solution of $p$-phenylinediamine containing 2% hydrogen peroxide has been proposed as a general procedure for aldehydes in air (280).

Absorption of formaldehyde in a 0.25% solution of 2-hydrazinobenzothiazole in 6 $N$ HCl followed by addition of ferricyanide, dimethylformamide, and 10% KOH solution has also been recommended (504), and a silica gel tube procedure using the same reaction has been described.

## 2. Acrolein

The unsaturated aldehyde acrolein is much more toxic and irritating than the simple saturated aldehydes. Exposure of 4 hr to 8 ppm was sufficient to cause deaths among rats (544). Because of the intense irritation of eyes and nose from low concentrations, acrolein has been used as a warning agent in methyl chloride in refrigerators; higher concentrations will cause edema of the lungs.

### a. DETERMINATION IN AIR

While many of the general methods for aldehydes will determine acrolein, lack of specificity is a drawback when other less toxic aldehydes may be present. Because of its limited solubility in water, sampling for acrolein is something of a problem. Collection in cold ethyl alcohol or an alcoholic solution of 4-hexyl-resorcinol, mercuric chloride, and trichloroacetic acid has been proposed. The blue color produced is measured at 605 m$\mu$ (109).

A polarographic method, using adsorption on silica gel, has also been suggested (613).

## C. KETONES

### 1. Ketene

Ketene is a highly toxic gas, similar to phosgene in its effects. As little as 12 ppm was fatal to animals after 2 weeks of daily 6-hr exposures (596). The deaths were delayed and featured pulmonary edema.

### a. DETERMINATION IN AIR

Absorption in alkaline hydroxylamine (10% NaOH and 10% $NH_2OH \cdot Cl$) followed by treatment with acid ferric chloride and colorimetric determination of the ferric acetohydroxamic complex has been recommended for the measurement of ketene in air (133,402). Acetic anhydride and acetates interfere, but can be partially removed by absorption in a solvent such as toluene (133).

## 2. Acetone

Acetone is one of the least toxic organic solvents, but represents a serious fire hazard due to its great volatility. High concentrations have some narcotic effect, and mild irritation of the mucous membranes is noted at somewhat lower levels. While chronic effects (bronchitis and gastric disturbances) have been reported (441), they are not frequently observed. The toxic action of acetone has been discussed in detail by Haggard et al. (230).

### a. DETERMINATION IN AIR

Acetone can be collected in water or on silica gel followed by water extraction. The volume of air which can be sampled with a given volume of water or gel is limited due to the high vapor pressure of acetone. For collection in water, two bubblers in series and cooling is suggested to increase the sampling efficiency.

The iodoform reaction, with standardized iodine solution and NaOH, followed by titration of excess iodine (after acidification) is a reasonably satisfactory method for the determination of acetone (159). Acetaldehyde and other methyl ketones interfere.

An alternative method involves collection in freshly prepared 1% hydroxylamine hydrochloride solution, neutralized to brom cresol green end point. The acetone reacts to form a ketoxime and HCl, and the latter can be titrated with standard alkali (159). This procedure, the Morasco method, is a general method for ketones.

The absorption of acetone in the ultraviolet (maximum at 265 m$\mu$) is sufficiently strong to permit the measurement of relatively high concentrations in the absence of interfering substances (274).

## 3. Methyl Ethyl Ketone, Methyl Isobutyl Ketone, Methyl Butyl Ketone

These ketones are somewhat more toxic and irritating than acetone, but are not considered important health hazards. Workers exposed to moderate concentrations sometimes complain of headaches, throat irritation, and even nausea, but no definite evidence of chronic poisoning has been reported.

### a. DETERMINATION IN AIR

The methods outlined for acetone can be used for the higher methyl ketones. Due to their lower solubility in water, however, collection should be on silica gel or in a suitable reagent (e.g., hydroxylamine hydrochloride). If extraction of silica gel with water results in a cloudy solution, isopropyl alcohol has been suggested as a collection medium for determination by ultraviolet absorption (12).

## 4. Mesityl Oxide

Mesityl oxide (methyl isobutenyl ketone) is distinctly more toxic than the saturated ketones. Concentrations as low as 12 ppm may cause some irritation of the nose and eyes; at 25 ppm pulmonary discomfort may result. Animal experiments have shown damage to liver, lungs, and kidneys from prolonged exposure (528).

### a. DETERMINATION IN AIR

Any of the general methods for ketones can be used for mesityl oxide. The iodoform reaction reportedly gives a 70% yield with this ketone (427). The sensitivity of this method can be increased by extracting the iodoform produced with chloroform and measuring the uv absorption of the extract. Mesityl oxide itself has an absorbance peak at 314 m$\mu$, compared with peaks around 270 m$\mu$ for the saturated ketones (12).

## 5. Quinone

Many cases of eye injury have been reported among workers exposed to quinone ($OC_6H_4O$) vapor and hydroquinone dust (432,557).

### a. DETERMINATION IN AIR

Absorption in isopropyl alcohol and colorimetric determination after reaction with phloroglucinol in potassium hydroxide has been used to measure quinone vapor in air (432).

## D. ETHERS AND OXIDES

## 1. Diethyl Ether

In spite of its reputation as one of the safest inhalation anesthetics, ether is considered a disagreeable industrial solvent. Its use is frequently associated with complaints of headache and other nonspecific symptoms. Serious ill effects are not commonly reported. From the fire and explosion standpoint, ether is one of the most dangerous solvents.

### a. DETERMINATION IN AIR

The combustible gas indicator is frequently used for the estimation of ether vapor concentrations. A method based on oxidation by chromic

acid and subsequent measurement of excess chromate has been described
(551). A 4% solution of potassium dichromate in nitric acid mixed with
an equal volume of concentrated sulfuric acid is employed as absorbing
liquid.

## 2. 1,4-Dioxane

Although animal studies based on single exposures indicated dioxane
to be of only moderate toxicity (657), its use in a rayon plant under
conditions of heavy exposure resulted in a number of fatal intoxications
(22). Subsequent animal studies confirmed the severe toxic effect on
the kidneys and liver of this solvent (173).

A case has also been reported where a worker exposed for a week
to dioxane in a concentration averaging 470 ppm was fatally stricken
with liver, kidney, and brain involvement (301). While many authorities
consider dioxane a solvent of no unusual toxicity, as indicated by its
relatively liberal threshold limit value, the deaths resulting from its
use suggest otherwise.

### a. DETERMINATION IN AIR

A chromate oxidation method for the determination of dioxane vapors
in air has been described (93). Other water-soluble solvents would
interfere.

## 3. Tetrahydrofuran

This solvent does not appear to possess any peculiar toxic properties.
A method for determination in air, based on its reaction with phenan-
thraquinone in concentrated sulfuric acid, with subsequent colorimetric
measurement at 660 m$\mu$, has been described (147).

## 4. $\beta\beta'$ Dichloroethyl Ether

This is one of the more toxic solvents. Single 8-hr exposures to concentrations in excess of 40 ppm caused serious respiratory symptoms in
animals, while deaths resulted from 200–300 ppm levels (510).

### a. DETERMINATION IN AIR

Dichloroethyl ether is readily hydrolyzed by alcoholic KOH. The usual
methods for chlorinated hydrocarbons can be used.

## 5. Ethylene Oxide

Primarily this is considered only as an irritating gas, but repeated
exposure to 200–400 ppm affected the vital organs of animals and caused

death through lung injury (265,297). Severe injury to the eyes and skin result from contact with water solutions of ethylene oxide.

### a. DETERMINATION IN AIR

Absorption in 0.025 $N$ $H_2SO_4$ containing 600 g $MgBr_2 \cdot 6H_2O$ per liter has been used as a method of collection. Ethylene oxide combines with hydrobromic acid, and the amount of acid remaining is measured by titration with standard alkali (267). For efficient absorption the solution should be chilled during sampling (551).

## E. ETHER ALCOHOLS

The monoalkyl ethers of ethylene glycol, commonly known as Cellosolves, are useful solvents with relatively high boiling points. Because of their low volatilities, occupational exposures to high concentrations are not common. A number of incidents involving chronic intoxication by 2-methoxyethanol (methyl Cellosolve) have been reported, however. Neurological symptoms predominated, but blood changes were observed in some workers (220,664).

Animal experiments have indicated ethyl and butyl Cellosolves to be as toxic as the methyl ether, but few cases of human intoxication have been recorded.

### 1. Determination in Air

Because of their miscibility with water and low vapor pressures, the Cellosolves can be collected from relatively large volumes of air. In the absence of interfering substances, determination by chromate oxidation is feasible. A differential oxidation method has been used for determining methyl Cellosolve in the presence of methyl and ethyl alcohols (159).

## F. ESTERS

The most important esters in industry are the acetates, especially those of the alcohols from methyl through hexyl, and some of the Cellosolves. The vapors of the alkyl acetates are mildly narcotic and irritating, increasingly so as molecular weights and boiling points increase. Hydrolysis may occur in the body, hence any special toxic properties of the parent alcohol (e.g., methanol from methyl acetate) are assumed to be inherent in the ester.

### 1. Determination in Air

The esters may be collected in ethyl alcohol (preferably chilled) or on silica gel which is then extracted with alcohol. The ester may be hydrolyzed by refluxing with a known amount of standard NaOH and the excess titrated with standard acid (159), or the solution can be reacted with alkaline hydroxylamine and the color developed with ferric ion (after acidification) measured (551).

This method is a general one for acetates. If several are present, gas chromatographic methods may be useful. The authors have been able to measure methyl Cellosolve acetate in the presence of ethyl acetate by collection on silica gel followed by aeration with moist air, which removes the ethyl acetate, but not the higher boiling water-soluble ester.

## 2. Determination in Urine

The urine of workers exposed to substantial concentrations of methyl acetate has been found to contain methanol in amounts comparable to those found in the urines of workers with equivalent methanol exposure.

## VII. ORGANIC COMPOUNDS OF NITROGEN AND SULFUR

### A. ALIPHATIC AMINES

### 1. Alkyl Amines

The simple aliphatic amines are strongly irritating to the eyes and respiratory passages. Repeated exposure to as little as 50 ppm of mono-, di-, or tri-ethylamine resulted in marked irritation of the cornea and lung tissue of animals (57). Diisopropylamine was fatal to animals in concentrations of 260 ppm after a number of 7-hr exposures. (602)

The effects of human exposures include headache and flushing of the face from butylamine in concentrations of the order of 5 ppm (13) and nausea and vomiting from cyclohexylamine (634).

#### a. DETERMINATION IN AIR

The amines can be absorbed in standard acid and the excess back-titrated with dilute alkali. A more sensitive colorimetric method, involving absorption in acidified isopropanol and reaction with ninhydrin, has been described for n-butyl amine (507) and would presumably work for other primary amines.

### 2. Ethylene Diamine

Ethylene diamine and related compounds, such as diethylene triamine, are primarily skin irritants and sensitizers rather than inhalation hazards.

### 3. Ethyleneimine

This compound is much more toxic than comparable alkyl amines. Exposure to 25 ppm for 8 hrs was fatal to some animals, but 10 ppm caused no deaths (82). The effects included kidney necrosis as well as lung injury.

#### a. DETERMINATION IN AIR

Absorption in 0.01 $M$ potassium acid phthallate followed by colorimetric determination with $\gamma$-(4-nitrobenzyl) pyridine has been suggested (165).

## B. AROMATIC AMINES

In contrast to the aliphatic amines, most of the various amino derivatives of aromatic compounds are systemic poisons rather than irritants.

### 1. Aniline

The chief symptom of aniline intoxication is cyanosis, resulting from the formation of methemoglobin in the blood. Absorption of liquid and even vapor through the skin occurs readily.

In early stages of methemoglobinemia, no ill effects are noted. Later, headache may develop. Cyanosis is reportedly recognizable with about 15% methemoglobin (233). Dogs showed no effects from 26 weeks of daily 6-hr exposures to 5 ppm aniline; rats, however, developed some methemoglobin (430).

#### a. DETERMINATION IN AIR

Aniline vapor may be collected by passing the air through a suitable bubbler containing dilute acid. After diazotization, the solution is made alkaline and coupled with H Acid (159), or Chicago Acid (330), and determined colorimetrically.

An alternative method is measurement of uv absorption at 254 m$\mu$ (pH 1) or 282 m$\mu$ (pH 9) (273). Or the ultraviolet fluorescence (at 340 or 360 m$\mu$) when activated by light at 280 or 290 m$\mu$ can be used for the micromeasurement of aniline in solution at pH 9 (273).

#### b. DETERMINATION IN URINE

Measurement of diazotizable metabolites of aniline in urine has been suggested as a method of estimating absorption (254). The method of analysis is essentially that used for the determination of sulfanilamide and involves coupling with $N$ (1-naphthyl) ethylenediamine hydrochloride (52). Determination of *p*-amino-phenol in urine has also been proposed as a means of measuring aniline absorption (455).

## 2. Benzidine

A high incidence of bladder tumors has been observed among workers exposed for a number of years to benzidine (29,85). Absorption through the skin was found to be relatively more important than inhalation of the dust in a plant studied by Meigs et al. (401).

### a. DETERMINATION IN URINE AND AIR

Benzidine can be determined by measuring the yellow color developed by chloramine-T in acid solution. Urine is extracted with ether or acetone–alcohol at pH 8.5 (211,519). The greater part of the benzidine excreted, however, was converted to 3-hydroxybenzidine (521). This was determined by measuring the yellow color produced by nitrous acid (520).

Other aromatic amines interfere to some extent with both of the above tests.

## 3. Naphthylamine

Beta-Napthylamine is considered the most active bladder carcinogen of the common dye intermediates, being the first such compound to produce bladder tumors in animals (126). The alpha isomer is less potent, and some authorities consider that tumors in workers exposed to the commercial product are caused by beta-napthalene impurity.

### a. DETERMINATION IN AIR

Absorption in 10% acetic acid followed by reaction with diazotized sulfanilic acid reagent and measurement of the color has been recommended for the determination of air-borne naphthylamine (289). Due to differences in the rates of reaction, the alpha and beta isomers can be estimated separately, if present in comparable quantities. To determine 0.01 mg per cubic meter of air of beta-naphthylamine, an air sample of 750 liters per 10 ml of absorbing liquid is needed.

## 4. Pyridine

While pyridine has a very disagreeable odor, it is not usually considered a highly toxic compound. Repeated exposures to 100 ppm reportedly caused nausea, headache, and nervous symptoms (13). Mild central nervous system injury was reported in a plant where concentrations ranged from 6 to 12 ppm (583).

### a. Determination in Air

A method based on the color developed with cyanogen bromide in the presence of benzidine has been described. The sample is collected with acetic acid and a sensitivity of 1 $\mu g/ml$ is reported (169). Measurement of uv absorption after collection in dilute sulfuric acid in alcohol has also been recommended (13).

### 5. 2-Aminopyridine

Inhalation of 2-aminopyridine resulted in severe headache and nausea after 5 hr in a concentration probably of the order of 5 ppm (634). Colorimetric determination, after absorption in water, by reaction with quinone in alcoholic acetic acid has been described.

### C. NITROPARAFFINS

Commercially 2-nitropropane is the most important of the nitroparaffins. Studies have shown it to damage the livers of cats in concentrations of 330 ppm upon repeated exposure. Slight changes were observed at 85 ppm; other animals were more resistant (601).

The authors have investigated a number of complaints of nausea, headache, and other symptoms in workers exposed to relatively low concentrations (539). A fatality has been reported in a worker engaged in painting the inside of a tank with a coating containing 2-nitropropane (203). The chief pathological finding was liver injury.

The toxicities of other nitroparaffins (nitromethane, nitroethane, and 1-nitropropane) appear to be similar to that of 2-nitropropane. The vapors of these compounds would seem more hazardous than those of the majority of common alcohols, esters, ketones, and hydrocarbons used as solvents.

### 1. Determination in Air

The nitroparaffins can be collected by adsorption on silica gel and then removed by a suitable solvent, such as alcohol. A colorimetric method employing ferric chloride has been described (522). This procedure is better suited to the primary compounds than to 2-nitropropane and other secondary derivatives. A method specific for secondary nitroparaffins consists of absorption in concentrated sulfuric acid followed by treatment with resorcinol and measurement of the color (303,304).

A colorimetric method for primary nitroparaffins involving coupling with $p$-diazobenzenesulfuric acid has also been described (108).

## D. NITROAROMATICS

### 1. Nitrobenzene

The chief toxic effect of nitrobenzene, as well as several other aromatic nitrocompounds, is cyanosis caused by formation of methemoglobin. Headache is a common symptom, but the blue color of skin, nails, and lips may be present in the absence of subjective complaints. In fatal cases, many of which have occurred in the past, death is usually due to respiratory failure. According to von Oettingen, late or chronic effects of nitrobenzene poisoning may include cardiac disturbances, liver damage, and anemia (622).

It is probable that absorption of the liquid through the skin, rather than inhalation of vapor, is the most frequent cause of occupational nitrobenzene poisoning.

#### a. DETERMINATION IN AIR

Due to its low volatility, nitrobenzene vapors can be efficiently collected by absorption in a solvent such as alcohol. In the absence of interfering substances, determination by uv absorption (at 260 m$\mu$) may be carried out (272). Other methods involve reduction to aniline with zinc amalgam or dust and coupling with R Salt (551) or Chicago Acid (330).

#### b. DETERMINATION IN URINE

Nitrobenzene is partially converted to $p$-nitrophenol and, according to some authorities, $p$-aminophenol, both of which are excreted in the urine. These can be determined after hydrolysis with acid and extraction with solvent. A woman chronically exposed and who had headache, nausea, liver damage, and cyanosis showed both nitrophenol and aminophenol in the urine (287). Experimental subjects exposed to nitrobenzene excreted $p$-nitrophenol only, however (492).

### 2. Trinitrotoluene

TNT, the well-known military explosive, exhibits the toxic action of other aromatic nitrocompounds. It causes cyanosis, although it is not a powerful methemoglobin-forming agent. A yellow discoloration of the skin and hair and dermatitis have been frequently observed in TNT workers. The most serious effects, however, are liver damage (toxic jaundice) and aplastic anemia. Twenty-two deaths from these causes were reported in munitions workers in this country during World War II (393), and twenty-seven cases of aplastic anemia (15 fatal) occurred in Great Britain during the same period (113).

As with other aromatic amino and nitro compounds, absorption through the skin, as well as inhalation of dust and fume, can lead to intoxication.

### a. DETERMINATION IN AIR

Collection in a mixture of cyclohexane and methyl ethyl ketone containing KOH in suspension, with estimation of the red color produced, has been described (551). Or the dust may be sampled with an impinger containing isopropyl alcohol; the TNT reduced with titanium trichloride, diazotized, and coupled with dimethyl alpha-naphthylamine; and the color measured (451). Other colorimetric methods recommended include collection in diethylaminoethanol (214) or absorption in Cellosolve followed by addition of alkali (372).

### b. DETERMINATION IN URINE

Metabolites of TNT in urine can be estimated by extraction with ether and observation of the color developed with alcoholic KOH, or by diazotization and coupling with alpha-naphthylamine, with final toluene extraction (452,547).

## 3. Tetryl (Trinitrophenylmethylnitramine)

The high explosive tetryl is a powerful skin irritant, and dermatitis is common in plants where it is handled in quantity. Other effects are yellow coloration of skin and hair and irritation of the upper respiratory passages and eyes.

Although the majority of authorities find no convincing evidence of systemic intoxication from tetryl, complaints of nausea, vomiting, headache, and similar symptoms were frequently noted (38,180,421), and some cases of illness, with liver damage the predominant symptom, have been described in workers exposed to tetryl dust (237,603).

### a. DETERMINATION IN AIR

The color produced by absorption in diethylaminoethanol has been suggested as a means of analysis of air-borne tetryl dust (318). Absorption in dilute HCl and visual comparison of the color produced by addition of alkali with that of standards has also been employed (159). The color fades rapidly.

## E. ORGANIC NITRATES

### 1. Nitroglycerin and Nitroglycol

The organic nitrates most widely used are the high explosives nitroglycerin, or glycerol trinitrate $[C_3H_5(NO_3)_3]$, and nitroglycol, or ethylene glycol dinitrate $[C_2H_2(NO_3)_2]$. The major physiological effect of these compounds is to reduce the blood pressure, and nitroglycerin is employed as a drug for this purpose. Occupational exposures are frequently associated with severe headaches, sometimes accompanied by nausea and vomiting. Tolerance is often acquired (54,625).

A number of fatal heart attacks, many occurring during the weekend or on Monday morning, have been reported in explosives plant workers exposed to nitroglycol and nitroglycerin. Carmichael and Lieben recorded eleven such cases over a period of 5 years in an exposed population of 125 (80). They noted a total of 46 other cases in the literature.

The effects on workers of the mixture of these nitrates appear to be more pronounced than those of nitroglycerin alone. This may be due to the greater volatility of nitroglycol (vp 0.045 mm at 20°C, compared with about 0.0005 mm for nitroglycerin) (660). On the other hand, there is evidence that skin absorption is a major avenue of intoxication by these compounds (152).

#### a. DETERMINATION IN AIR

No practicable specific method for nitroglycol in the presence of nitroglycerin (or vice versa) has been reported. Several procedures based on determination of the nitrate groups have been proposed. One involves collection by freezing, solution in acetone which is allowed to evaporate, and determination of the residual nitrate by means of phenoldisulfonic acid (188). Another method uses collection in triethyleneglycol and addition of m-xylenol and concentrated sulfuric acid, resulting in nitration of the xylenol. After dilution with water the nitroxylenol is distilled off into alkali and the color intensity determined (656). Collection in alcohol followed by hydrolysis to nitrite and determination of the latter by diazotizing sulfanilic acid and coupling with 1-naphthylamine has been used (152,471).

## 2. Other Nitrates

Animal studies of *n*-propyl nitrate (473) and mixed amyl nitrates (599) indicate moderate toxicities, with methemoglobin formation the major feature. Human exposure to the latter material resulted in nausea and headache. Analysis was by uv absorption (599) or nitration of thymol (473).

### F. NITRILES

### 1. Acrylonitrile ($CH_2$=CH—CN)

Acrylonitrile, a liquid boiling at 76°C, is the most widely used compound of this class. It is quite toxic, repeated exposures to 30–40 ppm being fatal to dogs (653); other animals were more resistant (145). Some authorities hold that the toxic effects of acrylonitrile are essentially cyanide poisoning (56), but others believe that different mechanisms are important (375).

Acute intoxication results in anoxia and respiratory paralysis. Chronic effects noted in workers are suggestive of liver damage and include nausea, vomiting, and headache (653).

#### a. DETERMINATION IN AIR

In the absence of interfering substances, acrylonitrile can be absorbed in cold water and the uv absorbance (at 210 m$\mu$) determined (56). Absorption in 0.001 $N$ $KMnO_4$ solution containing NaOH and telluric acid until a given degree of color change is produced has been recommended (210).

#### b. DETERMINATION IN BLOOD AND URINE

The thiocyanate contents of blood serum and urine have been shown to be increased following exposure to acrylonitrile. Urine is treated with albumin tungstate reagent and acid and filtered, and ferric nitrate added to the filtrate. The decrease in color caused by addition of mercuric nitrate is a measure of the thiocyanate concentration. Smoking increases the thiocyanate content of these fluids, which is usually negligible in nonsmokers (346).

### G. DIMETHYLFORMAMIDE [$HCON(CH_3)_2$]

DMF appears to be a liver poison, repeated exposures to concentrations of the order of 100 ppm producing damage to this organ in animals

(102,387). Workers with dimethylformamide have complained of head-ache and loss of appetite, and shown some evidence of liver injury (386,467).

## 1. Determination in Air

Collection in dilute acid, hydrolysis with alkali, steam distillation of the dimethylamine formed, and titration with dilute acid has been used for the determination of DMF (102). Absorption in water, reaction with alkaline hydroxylamine, and colorimetric determination with ferric chloride has also been proposed (39).

## H. ISOCYANATES

### 1. Tolylene Diisocyanate [$CH_3C_6H_3(OCN)_2$]

Tolylene diisocyanate (TDI) vapor is strongly irritating to the respiratory passages. The literature through 1961 includes reports of 318 cases of TDI intoxication among workers making or processing poly-urethane foam, finishes, or molded materials (63). The clinical signs include dry cough, cyanosis, conjunctivitis, and bronchitis, and with further exposure the characteristic pattern of bronchial asthma may develop. At least one fatal case has been reported (516).

#### a. DETERMINATION IN AIR

Absorption in a dilute mixture of acetic and hydrochloric acid followed by addition of sodium nitrate, sulfamic acid, and N-naphthylethylene diamine and measurement of the color produced has been employed for determining TDI vapor in concentrations of hygienic significance (381). A less sensitive method depends on the yellow color produced in a solution of sodium nitrite in Cellosolve when air containing TDI vapor is passed through (540).

### 2. Other Isocyanates

A number of other diisocyanates, as well as some monisocyanates, have found industrial use, but less commonly than TDI. All are irritants, and the hazard produced depends to a considerable extent on the volatility. MDI (methylene-bis-4-phenylisocyanate) is one of the best known and appears to be as toxic as TDI, but less hazardous because of its lower vapor pressure.

A modification of the Marcali method (for TDI) suitable for determination of MDI has been described (225).

## I. SULFUR COMPOUNDS

### 1. Carbon Disulfide ($CS_2$)

Extremely flammable, due to its great volatility and low ignition temperature, and highly toxic, carbon disulfide is little used at the present time as a solvent. Exposures result chiefly from its employment as a raw material in the manufacture of viscose rayon.

The effect of carbon disulfide are primarily on the nervous system. Hysteria, mental fatigue, and sleepiness were the prevailing symptoms in 148 cases reported in Poland (440). Headache, a feeling of pins, needles, and cold in the feet, and nausea were also reported. Concentrations as high as 300 ppm, and others ranging from 30 to 125 ppm were measured.

In 100 cases which occurred in Italy, polyneuritis was the commonest finding (616). Gastric disturbances, headaches, vertigo, sexual weakness, and tremors were noted. The greatest incidence was in an area where concentrations averaged 300 ppm, but mild cases resulted between 60 and 100 ppm.

In this country cyclic psychotic episodes, accompanied by hallucinatory phenomena, were noted as sequelae in 6 cases (216). In 2 other cases, where neuropsychiatric manifestations predominated, air analyses indicated concentrations of carbon disulfide slightly above 20 ppm (321). Three mild cases were reported in which recovery occurred, two from difficulties in walking and one from mental depression requiring a stay in a sanitarium (30). In this group of workers no trouble was observed at concentrations below 30 ppm. In another group exposed to levels of carbon disulfide between 2 and 26 ppm, no definite signs of intoxication were noted (489).

An extensive study with animals led to the theory that carbon disulfide reacts with amino acids and protein to form complexing groups which chelate heavy metals (copper and zinc), resulting in a harmful interference with metabolism (107).

### a. Determination in Air

The yellow color developed by carbon disulfide with diethylamine in the presence of copper salts forms the basis of a highly sensitive analytical method. The reagent and absorbing medium may consist of a 0.1% solution of diethylamine in alcohol containing 2% triethanolamine and 0.005% copper acetate (617), or a 1% solution of diethylamine in 2-methoxyethanol containing 0.1% copper acetate (411). In the latter case a drying agent in the absorption train before the absorber is recommended. Relatively small volumes of air are needed for production of color of adequate intensity for accurate measurement.

An automatic continuous recorder based on this reaction has been described (642).

### b. Determination in Biological Specimens

Free $CS_2$ can be separated from blood or urine by aeration and determined by the diethylamine copper reaction. It is also present in the breath in small amounts following exposure.

Metabolites of carbon disulfide in the urine may be measured by their catalytic action on the reaction of sodium nitride and iodine (615). One milliliter of urine, 0.2 ml of sodium dihydrogen phosphate (110 g in 100 ml water), and 1 ml of a solution of 0.1 $N$ iodine containing 3% sodium azide are mixed and the time required for decolorization measured. An empirical interpretation of the results has been developed.

## VIII. MINERAL AND ORGANIC DUSTS

The majority of minerals and solid mixtures of organic material (vegetable and animal fiber, etc.) are not toxic in a systemic sense. Inhalation of the dusts of such materials, however, may eventually impair the functioning of the respiratory system. The effects vary from simple foreign body reactions, or mechanical loading of the lungs with inert material, to irreversible fibrosis of lung cells and cancer.

As a rule, the concentrations of these dusts in air are not measured chemically. Methods of determination include counting, light scattering or absorption, and gravimetric measurement of total particulate matter. Since particle size is often a critical factor, measurements of this property, or fractionation of the dust cloud into different size groups, is a frequent procedure.

### A. SILICA

By far the most important mineral dust, from the standpoint of occupational disease, is quartz, the crystalline form of silica most widespread in nature. Quartz dust is markedly more pathogenic than the dust of combined silica (silicates) or even amorphous silica. The dusts of cristobalite and tridymite, other crystalline forms of silica, have physiological effects comparable to those of quartz, but are much less frequently encountered.

Silicosis is defined by the American Public Health Association as a "disease due to breathing air containing silica ($SiO_2$) characterized anatomically by generalized fibrotic changes and the development of miliary nodulation in both lungs, and clinically by shortness of breath, decreased chest expansion, lessened capacity for work, absence of fever, increased susceptibility to tuberculosis . . ." (139).

Typically silicosis develops slowly and usually affects middle-aged or older workers. Cases have resulted from less than 12 months' exposure, however. In spite of a vast amount of research, the reason for this reaction of the lung tissue to particles of quartz (and not to combined or amorphous silica) is unknown.

The threshold limit for quartz dust in air has been established as about 2.5 million particles per cubic foot (88 particles per cubic centimeter) of air, measured by the "standard light-field counting method." Since most dusts do not consist of pure quartz, a formula for the threshold limit (TLV) based on the *free* silica content of the dust is commonly employed:

$$\text{TLV} = \frac{250}{(\%\ \text{quartz} + 5)}\ \text{million particles per cubic foot of air}$$

This formula is applicable only when the other ingredients of the dust are classed as "inert." The TLV for dust containing no free silica becomes: $250/5 = 50$ mppcf.

## 1. Determination of Free Silica in Parent Rock or Settled Dust

### a. Chemical Methods

In mechanical mixtures of quartz, or other forms of free silica, and nonsiliceous materials, determination of total silica by conventional methods is an adequate procedure for industrial hygiene purposes. If combined silica (silicate) is present, however, special methods must be employed. These are usually based on selective solution of silicates by various reagents, such as fluosilicic acid, fluoboric acid (338), phosphoric acid (148,577,579), and potassium pyrosulfate. Under proper conditions finely divided particles (below 200 mesh) of most silicates are dissolved, while quartz is attacked much more slowly.

The phosphoric acid method is based on the fact that ortho phosphoric acid (85%) forms soluble complexes with silicic acid and many metal oxides. Upon boiling, the acid is concentrated further and additional heating results in the formation of pyrophosphoric acid. When heated to a temperature of 230–245°C, silicates are decomposed and dissolved, leaving a residue of quartz, which is washed with HCl and then with water until acid-free, filtered, ignited and weighed.

The chief difficulty with the method results from the need to closely control the temperature during the solution process. After a temperature of 230°C is attained, the heating should not be continued beyond 15 min, since appreciable solution of quartz can occur. Although relatively few other mineral substances will survive this treatment, the residue should be tested for purity petrographically or by solution in hydrofluoric acid.

This method has also been used for the analysis of air-borne dust samples (579) by spectrophotometric determination of silica as molybdo-silicic acid.

### b. PETROGRAPHIC METHODS

Particles of quartz can be distinguished from those of other materials by determination of certain optical properties (186,484,646). These methods require a high degree of skill and experience on the part of the analyst if reliable results are to be achieved. Persons without previous training in petrographic techniques often find them difficult, tedious, and unreliable.

### c. X-RAY DIFFRACTION METHODS

The characteristic X-ray diffraction pattern of quartz is used for its detection and estimation in minerals (21). The simplest method requires visual comparison or densitometer measurement of the intensity of lines on photographic film. By replacing the X-ray film with a goniometer, direct readings of the X-ray intensities at various angles can be made and the percentage of quartz more accurately determined (326).

Edwards has compared X-ray diffraction, phosphoric acid, and a petrographic staining method for the determination of quartz in minerals and has concluded that the last-named was preferable, especially in field situations (151).

## 2. Determination in Air

### a. COUNTING METHODS

Unlike most chemical hazards, silica dust in air is commonly determined by counting. In this country the standard method involves collection with the impinger, followed by counting the number of particles in an aliquot of the sample in a Sedgwich-Rafter, Dunn, or hemocytometer cell. A microscope with a 16-mm 10-power objective lens is commonly used (91). Alternatively a microprojector can be employed (59).

Samples may also be collected directly on microscope slides using the thermal precipitator or cascade impactor. Or membrane filters may be employed for sampling and the dust counted directly, after addition of immersion oil (139).

Grab samples of air for dust counting purposes may be taken with the konimeter, or Bausch and Lomb or Owens' jet dust counter. Correlation of the results obtained by such devices with those secured by continuous sampling methods has not been especially good.

### b. GRAVIMETRIC METHODS

Gravimetric determination of silica dust collected by the usual sampling devices is not considered an appropriate procedure for evaluating the hazard from silica dust, since undue importance is given to the presence of a few large particles. Devices which remove the heavier particles of dust, however, and permit measurement (by weighing) of only the fine dust have been developed. One such device is the hexhlet, in which settling chambers remove all of the less physiologically active fraction of the dust. The fine particles are collected in a filter and determined by weighing (252). The conicycle is another selective gravimetric air-borne dust sampler (84).

### c. DIRECT READING METHODS

The particle counters and similar devices described in Section II are designed primarily for measurement of silica and other mineral dusts.

### 3. Determination in Tissue

Measurement of the silica content of lung tissue is a frequent procedure, especially in autopsy material where pneumoconiosis appears to be present. After dry ashing and treatment with acids, total silica can be determined chemically, preferably after X-ray diffraction examination for the estimation of quartz. The total silica content of normal dried lung tissue is usually 0.12% or less (139). Severe silicosis results in a level of 1% or more, with a total lung content of 3 g of quartz. With slight silicosis 1 g of quartz may be present (423).

### B. ASBESTOS

Asbestos is a term applied to several fibrous complex magnesium silicates. Its dust causes a serious lung disease quite distinct from silicosis. There is some evidence that, in contrast to silica, the large fibers may be more important than very fine asbestos dust in causing lung fibrosis (a view which is not universally shared). This observation has led to a theory that asbestosis is a mechanical, rather than chemical effect, since the chemical properties of the asbestos minerals do not appear to differ in any significant way from those of many other silicates.

Tuberculosis is not as frequent a complication of asbestosis as of silicosis, but a markedly increased incidence of lung cancer in workers with asbestosis (and asbestos workers) has been reported (16,149).

### 1. Determination in Air

The standard method for determination of asbestos dust is collection with the impinger and light field counting, using the same technique as with silica dust. Frequently fibers, defined as particles with diameters of 5 $\mu$ or less and at least four times as long, are counted separately, in addition to the usual fine particles (18).

### 2. Asbestos Bodies

A.bestos bodies are symmetrical, club-shaped golden-brown structures, usually 3–5 $\mu$ thick and 20–50 $\mu$ long. They are characteristically found in the lungs and sputum of workers with asbestosis, but also may be detected in healthy asbestos workers (344) and even in persons with no occupational exposure (87). They are believed to result from the absorption of protein, together with endogenous iron, on a core of asbestos fiber.

### 3. Asbestos in Lungs

The mineral content of dried lung in cases of asbestosis was found by Knox and Beattie to range from 3 to 8 mg/g. The post-exposure survival time, as well as the extent of exposure, appeared to be a factor in determining this value (327).

## C. OTHER MINERAL DUSTS

The dusts of a number of silicates, such as talc, soapstone, and mica, have been reported to cause lung disease, although the effects are typically less serious than those resulting from inhalation of free silica and asbestos dust. The more soluble dusts, such as limestone and dolomite, are relatively harmless.

Inert insoluble dusts, such as coal, silicon carbide, and aluminum oxide, can cause some impairment of lung function if large amounts are inhaled for prolonged periods, but the effects are nonspecific. These dusts are usually determined by the same methods that are used for silica dusts.

## D. ORGANIC DUSTS

Inhalation of raw cotton or jute dust can lead to a transient fever similar to that resulting from zinc fumes. Byssinosis is a more serious disease of cotton mill workers, causing more prolonged impairment of lung function. Other organic dusts, such as from grain, hay, or even wood, may contain spores of fungus, which can cause respiratory disease of varying degrees of intensity.

In general, organic dusts are determined gravimetrically after collection on suitable filter papers.

## REFERENCES

1. Ackerman, H. H., *J. Ind. Hyg. Toxicol.,* **30,** 300 (1948).
2. Adams, D. F., *Anal. Chem.,* **32,** 1312 (1960).
3. Adley, F. E., and C. P. Skillern, *Amer. Ind. Hyg. Assoc. J.,* **19,** 233 (1958).
4. Ahlmark, A., *Brit. J. Ind. Med.,* **5,** 117 (1948).
5. Aldrich, W. N., *Analyst,* **69,** 262 (1944).
6. Allan, W. J., and F. E. Beamish, *Anal. Chem.,* **24,** 1608 (1952).
7. Amdur, M. L., *J. Occupational Med.,* **3,** 386 (1947).
8. Amdur, M. L., and R. A. Caputi, *Ind. Med. Surg.,* **22,** 561 (1953).
9. Amdur, M. O., and L. Silverman, *Arch. Ind. Hyg. Occupational Med.,* **10,** 152 (1954).
10. American Conference of Governmental Industrial Hygienists, *Manual of Analytical Methods,* Cincinnati, 1958.
11. American Conference of Governmental Industrial Hygienists, *Documentation of Threshold Limit Values,* Cincinnati, 1965.
12. American Industrial Hygiene Association, *Analytical Abstracts,* Detroit, 1965.
13. American Industrial Hygiene Association, *Hygienic Guide Series,* Detroit, 1960.
14. American Public Health Association, *Standard Methods for Examination of Water and Sewage,* 8th ed., 1936.
15. Anderson, A., *Brit. J. Ind. Med.,* **7,** 82 (1950).
16. Anderson, J., and F. A. Campagna, *Arch. Environ. Health,* **1,** 27 (1960).
17. Anderson, W. L., and H. E. Peterson, *U.S. Bur. Mines, Rept. of Invest.* **6201** (1963).
18. Asbestos Textile Institute, *Determining Asbestos Dust Concentrations.* Pompton Lakes, N.J., 1964.
19. Baetjer, A. M., *Arch. Ind. Hyg. Occupational Med.,* **2,** 487 (1950).
20. Baetjer, A. M., C. Damron, and V. Budacz., *Arch. Ind. Health,* **20,** 136 (1959).
21. Ballard, J. W., H. I. Oshry, and H. Schrenk, *U.S. Bur. Mines, Rept. Invest.,* **3520** (1940).
22. Barber, H., *Guy's Hospital Rept.,* **84,** 267 (1934).

23. Bardodej, Z., *Cesk. Hyg.*, 5, 39 (1960).
24. Bardodej, Z., and E. Badodejova, *Cesk. Hyg.*, 6, 537 (1961).
25. Barnes, E. C., *J. Ind. Hyg. Toxicol.*, 28, 257 (1946).
26. Barnes, E. C., and G. W. Penney, *J. Ind. Hyg. Toxicol.*, 20, 259 (1938).
27. Barrett, H. M., J. G. Cunningham, and J. H. Johnston, *J. Ind. Hyg. Toxicol.*, 21, 479 (1939).
28. Barrett, H. M., and J. H. Johnston, *J. Biol. Chem.*, 127, 765 (1938).
29. Barsotti, M., and E. C. Vigliani, *Arch. Ind. Hyg. Occupational Med.*, 5, 234 (1952).
30. Barthelemy, H. L., *J. Ind. Hyg. Toxicol.*, 21, 141 (1939).
31. Baruch, B. B., and N. L. Stephans, *Amer. Ind. Hyg. Assoc. J.*, 26, 404 (1965).
32. Batchelor, J. J., *Amer J. Hyg.*, 7, 276 (1927).
33. Beatty, R. L., "Methods for Detecting and Determining Carbon Monoxide," *U.S. Bur. Mines Bull.*, 557 (1955).
34. Beatty, R. L., L. B. Berger, and H. H. Schrenk, *U.S. Bur. Mines Rept. Invest.*, 3687 (1943).
35. Beck, A. O., M. D. Kipling, and J. C. Heather, *Brit. J. Ind. Med.*, 19, 239 (1962).
36. Beckman, A. O., J. D. McCullough, and R. A. Crane, *Anal. Chem.*, 20, 674 (1948).
37. Belth, S. M., E. Kaplan, and C. E. Couchman, *Arch. Environ. Health*, 1, 311 (1961).
38. Bergman, B. B., *Arch. Ind. Hyg. Occupational Med.*, 5, 10 (1952).
39. Bergman, F., *Anal. Chem.*, 24, 1367 (1952).
40. Berliner, M. L., *Arch. Ophthalmol.*, 22, 1023 (1939).
41. Bessman, S. P., and E. C. Layne, Jr., *J. Lab. Clin. Med.*, 45, 159 (1955).
42. Bidstrup, P. L., J. A. Bonnell, O. G. Harvey, and S. Locket, *Lancet*, 195-II, 856.
43. Bidstrup, P. L., and R. A. M. Case, *Brit. J. Ind. Med.*, 13, 260 (1956).
44. Blejer, H. P., *Ind. Med. Surg.*, 35, 362 (1966).
45. Blinn, R. C., and F. A. Gunther, *Anal. Chem.*, 21, 1289 (1949).
46. Blunt, C. P., *Ind. Med. Surg.*, 33, 869 (1964).
47. Bolton, N. E., J. D. Cavender, and V. T. Stack, Jr., *Amer. Ind. Hyg. Assoc. J.*, 23, 319 (1962).
48. Bonnell, J. A., *Brit. J. Ind. Med.*, 12, 181 (1955).
49. Bovee, H. H., and R. J. Robinson, *Anal. Chem.*, 33, 1115 (1961).
50. Bowditch, M., and H. B. Elkins, *J. Ind. Hyg. Toxicol.*, 21, 321 (1939).
51. Bradley, W. R., and W. G. Fredrick, *Ind. Med.* 10, *Ind. Hyg. Sect* 2, 15 (1941).
52. Bratton, A. C., and E. K. Marshall, *J. Biol. Chem.*, 128, 537 (1939).
53. Bray, W. E., *Clinical Laboratory Methods*, 4th ed., Mosby, St. Louis, 1945.
54. Bresler, R. R., *Ind. Med. Surg.*, 18, 519 (1949).
55. Brief, R. S., F. S. Venable, and R. S. Ajemian, *Amer. Ind. Hyg. Assoc. J.*, 26, 72 (1965).
56. Brieger, H., H. F. Rieders, and W. A. Hodes, *Arch. Ind. Hyg. Occupational Med.*, 6, 128 (1952).
57. Brieger, H., and W. A. Hodes, *Arch. Ind. Hyg. Occupational Med.*, 3, 287 (1951).
58. Brieger, H., C. W. Semisch, J. Stasney, and D. A. Piatnek, *Ind. Med. Surg.*, 23, 521 (1954).

59. Brown, C. E., and H. H. Schrenk, *U.S. Bur. Mines, Inform. Circ.*, **7026** (1938).
60. Browne, R. C., *Brit. J. Ind. Med.*, **12**, 57 (1955).
61. Browning, E., *Toxicity of Industrial Metals*, Butterworth, London, 1961.
62. Browning, E., *Toxicology of Industrial Organic Solvents*, Chemical Publishing Co., New York, 1953.
63. Brugsch, H. G., and H. B. Elkins, *New Engl. J. Med.*, **268**, 353 (1963).
64. Buchan, R. F., *Occupational Med.*, **3**, 439 (1947).
65. Buckell, M., *Brit. J. Ind. Med.*, **8**, 181 (1951).
66. Bulmer, F. M. R., and J. H. Johnston, *J. Ind. Hyg. Toxicol.*, **30**, 26 (1948).
67. Bulmer, F. M. R., H. E. Rothwell, and E. R. Frankish, *Can. Publ. Health J.*, **29**, 19 (1938).
68. Bulmer, F. M. R., H. E. Rothwell, S. S. Pollack, and D. W. Stewart, *J. Ind. Hyg. Toxicol.*, **22**, 111 (1940).
69. Busbey, R. L., and N. L. Drake, *Ind. Eng. Chem., Anal. Ed.*, 390 (1938).
70. Busch, H. W., and L. B. Berger, *U.S. Bur. Mines, Rept. Invest.*, **4531** (1949).
71. Bush, A. F., H. K. Abrams, and H. V. Brown, *J. Ind. Hyg. Toxicol*, **31**, 352 (1949).
72. Butler, F. E., *Anal. Chem.*, **37**, 340 (1965).
73. Cabrera, A. M., and T. S. West, *Anal. Chem.*, **35**, 311 (1963).
74. Calvert, S., and W. Workman, *Amer. Ind. Hyg. Assoc. J.*, **22**, 318 (1961).
75. Cameron, G. R., J. C. Thomas, S. A. Ashmore, J. L. Buchan, E. H. Warren, and A. W. McKenny, *J. Pathol. Bacteriol.*, **44**, 281 (1937).
76. Campbell, E. E., and B. M. Head, *Amer. Ind. Hyg. Assoc. Quart.*, **16**, 275 (1955).
77. Campbell, E. E., M. F. Milligan, and J. A. Lindsey, *Amer. Ind. Hyg. Assoc. J.*, **20**, 23 (1959).
78. Campbell, R. H., and J. Gudzinowicz, *Anal. Chem.*, **33**, 842 (1961).
79. Cardani, A., *Med. Lavoro*, **33**, 145 (1942).
80. Carmichael, P., and J. Lieben, *Arch. Environ. Health*, **7**, 424 (1963).
81. Carpenter, C. P., C. B. Schaffer, C. S. Weil, H. F. Smyth, Jr., *J. Ind. Hyg. Toxicol.*, **26**, 69 (1944).
82. Carpenter, C. P., H. F. Smyth, Jr., and C. B. Schaffer, *J. Ind. Hyg. Toxicol.*, **30**, 2, (1948).
83. Carson, T. R., M. S. Rosenholtz, F. T. Wilinski, and M. H. Weeks, *Amer. Ind. Hyg. Assoc. J.*, **23**, 457 (1963).
84. Carver, J., G. Nagelschmidt, S. A. Roach, C. E. Rossiter, and H. S. Wolff, *Mining Eng.*, **21**, 601 (1962).
85. Case, R. A. M., M. E. Hosker, D. B. McDonald, and J. T. Pearson, *Brit. J. Ind. Med.*, **11**, 75 (1954).
86. Cassells, D. A. K., and E. C. Dodds, *Brit. Med. J.*, **2**, 681 (1946).
87. Cauna, D., R. S. Totten, and P. Gross, *J. Amer. Med. Assoc.*, **192**, 371 (1965).
88. Centanni, F. A., A. M. Ross, and M. A. DeSesa, *Anal. Chem.*, **28**, 1651 (1956).
89. Chambers, L. A., *Amer. Ind. Hyg. Assoc. Quart.*, **15**, 290 (1954).
90. Channell, K., and R. J. Hanna, *Arch. Ind. Health*, **6**, 386 (1963).
91. Chapman, H. M., and R. C. Ruhf, *Amer. Ind. Hyg. Assoc. Quart.*, **16**, 201 (1955).
92. Chasis, H., J. A. Zapp, J. H. Bannon, J. L. Whittenberger, J. Helm, J. J. Doheny, and C. M. MacLeod, *Occupational Med.*, **4**, 152 (1947).

93. Chemodanova, L. S., *Gigiena Sanit.*, **13**, 31 (1948); cited in *Chem. Abstr.*, **43**, 8976 (1949).
94. Cheng, K. L., *Anal. Chem.*, **28**, 1738 (1956).
95. Chiesura, T., and F. Brugnone, *Lavoro Umana*, **19**, 507 (1962).
96. Chiesura, T., and F. Brugnone, *Med. Lavoro*, **54**, 88 (1963).
97. Cholak, J., and D. M. Hubbard, *Ind. Eng. Chem., Anal. Ed.*, **16**, 333 (1944).
98. Cholak, J., and D. M. Hubbard, *Anal. Chem.*, **20**, 73 (1948).
99. Christensen, F. C., and E. C. Olson, *Arch. Ind. Health,* **16**, 8 (1957).
100. Church, F., *J. Ind. Hyg. Toxicol.*, **29**, 34 (1947).
101. Clarke, C. A., C. G. Rowarth, and H. E. Holling, *Brit. J. Ind. Med.*, **2**, 17 (1945).
102. Clayton, J. W., J. R. Barnes, D. B. Hood, and G. W. H. Schepers, *Amer. Ind. Hyg. Assoc. J.*, **24**, 144 (1963).
103. Clayton, J. W., M. A. Delaplane, and D. B. Hood, *Amer. Ind. Hyg. Assoc. J.*, **21**, 383 (1960).
104. Cleary, R. V., J. Maier, and G. H. Hitchings, *J. Biol. Chem.*, **127**, 403 (1939).
105. Clinton, M., Jr., *J. Ind. Hyg. Toxicol.*, **29**, 225 (1947).
106. Cogan, D. G., and W. M. Grant., *Arch. Ophthalmol.*, **33**, 106 (1945).
107. Cohen, A. E., L. D. Scheel, J. F. Kopp, F. R. Stockell, R. G. Keenan, J. T. Mountain, and H. J. Paulus, *Amer. Ind. Hyg. Assoc. J.*, **20**, 303 (1959).
108. Cohen, I. R., and A. P. Altshuller, *Anal. Chem.*, **31**, 1638 (1959).
109. Cohen, I. R., and A. P. Altshuller, *Anal. Chem.*, **33**, 726 (1961).
110. Coler, H. R., and H. R. Rossmiller, *Arch. Ind. Hyg. Occupational Med.*, **8**, 227 (1953).
111. Comstock, C. G., L. H. Lawson, E. A. Greene, and F. W. Oberst, *Arch. Ind. Hyg. Occupational Med.*, **10**, 476 (1954).
112. Conner, W. D., and J. S. Nader, *Amer. Ind. Hyg. Asso. J.*, **25**, 291 (1964).
113. Crawford, M. A. D., *Brit Med. J.*, **2**, 430 (1954); abstr. in *Arch. Ind. Health,* **12**, 442 (1955).
114. Crummett, W. B., *Anal. Chem.*, **28**, 410 (1956).
115. Crummett, W. B., and J. D. McLean, *Anal. Chem.*, **37**, 424 (1965).
116. Cumpston, A. G., and B. D. Dinman, *Amer. Ind. Hyg. Assoc. J.*, **26**, 461 (1966).
117. Custer, J. J., and S. Natelson, *Anal. Chem.*, **28**, 1475 (1956).
118. Dalhamm, T., *Arch. Ind. Health,* **15**, 101 (1957).
119. Dambrauskas, T., and H. H. Cornish, *Amer. Ind. Hyg. Assoc. J.*, **23**, 151 (1962).
120. Dambrauskas, T., and W. A. Cook, *Amer. Ind. Hyg. Assoc. J.*, **24**, 568 (1963).
121. Davies, T. A. L., *Brit. J. Ind. Med.*, **3**, 111 (1946).
122. Davies, T. A. L., and H. E. Harding, *Brit. J. Ind. Med.*, **6**, 82 (1949).
123. Davis, P. A., *Rubber Age*, **27**, 367 (1930).
124. Davis, R. K., *J. Occ. Med.*, **3**, 593 (1961).
125. Defalque, R. J., *Clin. Pharmacol. Therap.*, **2**, 665 (1961).
126. Deichmann, W. B., and J. L. Radomski, *Ind. Med. Surg.*, **32**, 161 (1963).
127. Deichmann, W. B., and L. J. Schafer, *Amer. J. Clin. Pathol.*, **12**, 129 (1942).
128. Dernehl, C. U., F. M. Stead, and C. A. Nau, *Ind. Med.*, **13**, 361 (1944).
129. Derryberry, O. M., M. D. Bartholomew, and R. B. L. Fleming, *Arch. Environ. Health,* **6**, 503 (1963).
130. Detreville, R. T. P., H. W. Wheeler, and T. Sterling, *Arch. Environ. Health,* **5**, 532 (1962).

131. Dieffenbacher, P. F., and J. H. Thompson, *J. Occupational Med.*, **4**, 325 (1962).
132. Dierker, H., and P. G. Brown, *J. Ind. Hyg. Toxicol.*, **26**, 277 (1944).
133. Diggle, W. M., and J. C. Gage, *Analyst*, **78**, 473 (1953).
134. Dolin, B. H., *Anal. Chem.*, **15**, 242 (1943).
135. Doll, R., *Brit. J. Ind. Med.*, **15**, 217 (1958).
136. Downs, W. L., J. K. Scott, L. T. Steadman, and E. A. Maynard, *Amer. Ind. Hyg. Assoc. J.*, **21**, 399 (1960).
137. Drinker, C. K., *Carbon Monoxide Asphyxia*, Oxford Univ. Press, New York, 1938.
138. Drinker, C. K., M. F. Warren, and G. A. Bennett, *J. Ind. Hyg. Toxicol.*, **19**, 283 (1937).
139. Drinker, P., and T. Hatch, *Industrial Dust*, McGraw-Hill, New York, 1954.
140. Drinker, P., R. M. Thomson, and S. M. Fitchet, *J. Ind. Hyg.*, **5**, 162 (1923).
141. Dubois, L., J. L. Monkman, and T. Teichman, *Amer. Ind. Hyg. Assoc. J.*, **23**, 157 (1963).
142. Dubois, L., and J. L. Monkman, *Amer. Ind. Hyg. Assoc. J.*, **25**, 485 (1964).
143. Dudley, H. C., *U.S. Publ. Health Rept*, **53**, 94 (1938).
144. Dudley, H. C., and J. W. Miller, *J. Ind. Hyg. Toxicol.*, **33**, 470 (1941).
145. Dudley, H. C., T. R. Sweeney, and J. W. Miller, *J. Ind. Hyg. Toxicol*, **24**, 255 (1942).
146. Dunlap, M. K., J. K. Kodama, J. S. Wellington, H. H. Anderson, and C. H. Hine, *Arch. Ind. Health*, **18**, 303 (1958).
147. Dupont, de Nemours & Co., *Physiological Properties of Tetrahydrofuran*, Wilmington, Delaware.
148. Durkan, T. M., *J. Ind. Hyg. Toxicol.*, **28**, 217 (1946).
149. Dutra, F. R., and J. D. Carney, *Arch. Environ. Health*, **10**, 416 (1965).
150. Dutra, F. R., J. Cholak, and D. M. Hubbard, *Amer. J. Clin. Pathol.*, **19**, 229 (1949).
151. Edwards, G. H., *Amer. Ind. Hyg. Assoc. J.*, **26**, 532 (1965).
152. Einert, C., W. Adams, R. Crothers, H. Moore, and F. Ottoboni, *Amer. Ind. Hyg. Assoc. J.*, **24**, 435 (1964).
153. Eisenbud, M., C. F. Berghout, and L. T. Steadman, *J. Ind. Hyg. Toxicol.*, **30**, 281 (1948).
154. Eisenbud, M., and J. A. Quigley, *Arch. Ind. Health*, **14**, 12 (1956).
155. Eisenbud, M., R. C. Wanta, C. Dustan, L. T. Steadman, and B. S. Wolf, *J. Ind. Hyg. Toxicol.*, **31**, 282 (1941).
156. Elkins, H. B., *J. Ind. Hyg. Toxicol.*, **28**, 37 (1946).
157. Elkins, H. B., *Amer. Ind. Hyg. Assoc. J.*, **14**, 109 (1953).
158. Elkins, H. B., *Arch. Ind. Hyg. Occupational Med.*, **9**, 212 (1954).
159. Elkins, H. B., *The Chemistry of Industrial Toxicology*, 2nd ed., Wiley, New York, 1959.
160. Elkins, H. B., L. D. Pagnotto, and E. M. Comproni, *Anal. Chem.*, **34**, 1797 (1962).
161. Elliott, H. C., Jr., *Anal. Chem.*, **29**, 1712 (1957).
162. Ellman, G. L., A. Brukhalter, and J. Ladou, *J. Lab. Clin. Med.*, **57**, 813 (1961).
163. El Masri, A. M., J. N. Smith, and R. T. Williams, *Biochem. J.*, **64**, 50 (1956).
164. Emerson, E., *J. Org. Chem.*, **8**, 417 (1943).
165. Epstein, J., R. W. Rosenthal, R. J. Ess, *Anal. Chem.*, **27**, 1435 (1955).

166. Erf, L. A., and C. P. Rhoads, *J. Ind. Hyg. Toxicol.,* **21,** 421 (1939).
167. Evans, D. M., *Brit. Med. J.,* **1,** 173 (1960).
168. Evans, E. H., *Lancet,* **249,** 368 (1945).
169. Fabre, R., R. Truhaut, and H. Herbert., *Ann. Pharm. France,* **8,** 773 (1950); abstr. in *Arch. Ind. Hyg. Occ. Med.,* **4,** 290 (1951).
170. Fahy, J. P., *J. Ind. Hyg. Toxicol.,* **30,** 205 (1948).
171. Fairhall, L. T., and F. L. Hyslop, *Publ. Health Rept. (U.S.) Suppl.,* **195,** (1947).
172. Fairhall, L. T., and R. G. Keenan, *J. Amer. Chem. Soc.,* **63,** 3076 (1941).
173. Fairley, A., E. C. Linton, and A. H. Ford-Moore, *J. Hyg.,* **34,** 486 (1934).
174. Farrah, C. H., *Amer. Ind. Hyg. Assoc. J.,* **25,** 55 (1964).
175. Feinsilver, L., J. A. Perregrino, and C. J. Smith, Jr., *Amer. Ind. Hyg. Assoc. J.,* **20,** 26 (1959).
176. Feldstein, M., J. D. Coons, H. C. Johnson, and J. E. Yocum, *Amer. Ind. Hyg. Assoc., J.,* **20,** 374 (1959).
177. Feldstein, M., and N. C. Klendshoj, *Anal. Chem.,* **26,** 932 (1954).
178. Ferry, J. J., and G. B. Ginther, *Amer. Ind. Hyg. Assoc. Quart.,* **13,** 196 (1952).
179. First, M. W., and L. Silverman, *Arch. Ind. Hyg. Occupational Med.,* **7,** 1 (1953).
180. Fischer, C. N., and H. D. Murdock, *Ind. Med.,* **15,** 428 (1946).
181. Fischoff, R. L., *Amer. Ind. Hyg. Assoc. J.,* **26,** 26 (1965).
182. Fisher, A. A., and A. Shapiro, *J. Amer. Med. Assoc.,* **161,** 717 (1956).
183. Flinn, F. B., and N. E. Jarvik, *Amer. J. Hyg.,* **27,** 19 (1938).
184. Flinn, R. H., P. A. Neal, and W. B. Fulton, *J. Ind. Hyg. Toxicol.,* **23,** 374 (1941).
185. Flury, F., and F. Zernik, *Schädliche Gase,* Springer, Berlin, 1931.
186. Foster, W. D., *U.S. Bur. Mines, Rept. Invest.,* **4573** (1949).
187. Fothergill, S. J. R., D. F. Withers, and F. S. Clements, *Brit. J. Ind. Med.,* **2,** 99 (1945).
188. Foulger, J. H., *J. Ind. Hyg. Toxicol.,* **18,** 127 (1936).
189. Frant, R., and J. Westendorp, *Arch. Ind. Hyg. Occupational Med.,* **1,** 308 (1950).
190. Fraser, D. A., *Amer. Ind. Hyg. Assoc. J.,* **18,** 139 (1957).
191. Freedman, L. D., *Anal. Chem.,* **19,** 502 (1947).
192. Fregert, S., and H. Rorsman, *Arch. Dermatol.,* **90,** 4 (1964).
193. Friberg, L., *J. Ind. Hyg. Toxicol.,* **30,** 32 (1948).
194. Friberg, L., *Acta Med. Scand.,* **138** (Suppl. 240), (1950).
195. Friberg, L., *Arch. Ind. Health,* **16,** 27 (1957).
196. Friedman, P. J., and J. R. Cooper, *Anal. Chem.,* **30,** 1674 (1958).
197. Fristrom, G. R., L. Bennett, and W. G. Berl, *Anal. Chem.,* **31,** 1696 (1959).
198. Fuwa, K., and B. L. Vallee, *Anal. Chem.,* **35,** 942 (1963).
199. Gaensler, E. A., J. B. Cadigan, M. F. Ellicott, R. H. Jones, and A. Marks, *J. Lab. Clin. Med.,* **49,** 945 (1957).
200. Gaffney, G. W., K. Schreur, N. Ferrante, and K. Altman, *J. Biol. Chem.,* **206,** 695 (1954).
201. Galdston, M., J. A. Luetscher, W. T. Longcope, and N. L. Ballich, *J. Clin. Invest.,* **26,** 169 (1947).
202. Gates, E. M., and G. H. Ellis, *J. Biol. Chem.,* **168,** 537 (1947).

203. Gaultier, M., P. E. Fournier, P. Gervais, and C. Sicot, *Arch. Maladies Professionnelle,* **25,** 425 (1964).
204. Geischecker, D., and A. N. Setterlind, *What's New in Industrial Hygiene,* **7,** 12 (1950).
205. Gerarde, H. W., *Toxicology and Biochemistry of Aromatic Hydrocarbons,* Elsevier, 1960.
206. Gerarde, H. W., *Amer. Ind. Hyg. Assoc. J.,* **21,** 511 (1960).
207. Gerritsen, W. B., and C. H. Buschmann, *Brit. J. Ind. Med.,* **17,** 187 (1960).
208. Giertz, H. W., *Träkemi,* **6,** 77 (1951); cited by Dalhamm, see ref. 118.
209. Gill, W. E., *Amer. Ind. Hyg. Assoc. J.,* **21,** 87 (1960).
210. Gisclard, J. B., D. B. Robinson, and P. J. Kuczo, Jr., *Amer. Ind. Hyg. Assoc. J.,* **19,** 43 (1958).
211. Glassman, J. M., and J. W. Meigs, *Arch. Ind. Hyg. Occupational Med.,* **4,** 519 (1951).
212. Gloemme, J., and K. D. Lundgren, *Arch. Ind. Health,* **16,** 168 (1957).
213. Goldblatt, M. W., and W. E. Chrisman, *Brit. J. Ind. Med.,* **1,** 207 (1944).
214. Goldman, F. H., and D. E. Rushing, *J. Ind. Hyg. Toxicol.,* **25,** 164 (1943).
215. Goldman, F. H., and H. Yagoda, *Ind. Eng. Chem., Anal. Ed.,* **15,** 377 (1943).
216. Gordy, S. T., and M. Trumper, *J. Amer. Med. Assoc.,* **110,** 1543 (1938).
217. Grandjean, E., R. Münchinger, V. Turraan, P. A. Haas, H. K. Knoepfel, and H. Rosenmund, *Brit. J. Ind. Med.,* **12,** 131 (1955).
218. Gray, E. L., *Arch. Ind. Health,* **19,** 479 (1959).
219. Green, H. L., and H. H. Watson, Medical Council of Privy Council, Special Reprint 199, His Majesty's Stationery Office, London, 1935.
220. Greenburg, L., M. R. Mayers, L. J. Goldwater, W. J. Burke, and S. Moskowitz, *J. Ind. Hyg. Toxicol.,* **20,** 134 (1938).
221. Greenburg, L., M. R. Mayers, L. J. Goldwater, and L. R. Smith, *J. Ind. Hyg. Toxicol.,* **21,** 395 (1939).
222. Greenburg, L., M. R. Mayers, H. Heimann, and S. Moskowitz, *J. Amer. Med. Assoc.,* **118,** 573 (1942).
223. Greene, S. A., and H. Pust, *Anal. Chem.,* **30,** 1039 (1958).
224. Greenwald, I., *Arch. Ind. Hyg. Occupational Med.,* **10,** 455 (1954).
225. Grim, K. E., and A. L. Linch, *Amer. Ind. Hyg. Assoc. J.,* **25,** 285 (1964).
226. Griswold, S. S., L. A. Chambers, and H. L. Motley, *Arch. Ind. Health,* **15,** 108 (1957).
227. Grogan, C. H., H. J. Cahnmann, and E. Lethco, *Anal. Chem.,* **27,** 983 (1955).
228. Gussman, R. A., R. Dennis, and L. Silverman, *Amer. Ind. Hyg. Assoc. J.,* **23,** 480 (1962).
229. Haeger, B., *Lancet,* **1958-II,** 606 (1958).
230. Haggard, H. W., L. A. Greenburg, and J. M. Turner, *J. Ind. Hyg. Toxicol.,* **26,** 133 (1944).
231. Hake, C. L., T. B. Waggoner, D. N. Robertson, and V. K. Rowe, *Arch. Environ. Health,* **1,** 101 (1961).
232. Hall, R. H., S. Laskin, P. Frank, E. A. Maynard, and H. C. Hodge, *Arch. Ind. Hyg. Occupational Med.,* **4,** 458 (1951).
233. Hamblin, D. O., *Industrial Hygiene and Toxicology,* Vol. 2, F. A. Patty, Ed., Interscience, New York, 1963.
234. Hangst, P. H., E. R. Stephens, W. E. Scott, and R. C. Doerr, *Anal. Chem.,* **33,** 1113 (1961).

235. Hanson, C. K., *Anal. Chem.*, **29**, 1204 (1957).
236. Hardy, H. L., and H. B. Elkins, *J. Ind. Hyg. Toxicol.*, **30**, 96 (1948).
237. Hardy, H. L., and C. C. Maloof, *Arch. Ind. Hyg. Occupational Med.*, **1**, 545 (1950).
238. Hardy, H. L., and J. B. Skinner, *J. Ind. Hyg. Toxicol.*, **29**, 321 (1947).
239. Hardy, H. L., and I. R. Tabershaw, *J. Ind. Hyg. Toxicol.*, **28**, 197 (1946).
240. Haring, H. E., and K. G. Compton, *Trans. Electrochem. Soc.*, **68**, 283 (1935).
241. Hawk, P. B., B. Oser, and W. H. Summerson, *Practical Physiological Chemistry*, 12th ed., Blackiston Co., Toronto, 1947, p. 738.
242. Hay, E. B., *Amer. Ind. Hyg. Assoc. J.*, **25**, 386 (1964).
243. Heatherton, R. C., and J. A. Huesing, Symposium on Occupational Health Experiences and Practices in the Uranium Industry, U.S. Atomic Energy Commission, 1958, p. 69.
244. Heimann, H., *J. Ind. Hyg. Toxicol.*, **28**, 142 (1946).
245. Heimann, H., and C. B. Ford, *N.Y. Ind. Bull.*, **20**, 209 (1941).
246. Hemeon, W. C. L., and C. F. Haines, *Amer. Ind. Hyg. Assoc. J.*, **22**, 75 (1961).
247. Henderson, Y., and Haggard, H. W., *Noxious Gases*, 2nd ed., Reinhold, New York, 1943.
248. Heppel, L. A., P. A. Neal, B. Highman, and V. T. Porterfield, *J. Ind. Hyg. Toxicol.*, **30**, 189 (1948).
249. Hersch, P., and R. Deuringer, *Anal. Chem.*, **35**, 897 (1963).
250. Heyman, A., J. B. Pfeiffer, Jr., R. W. Willett, and H. M. Taylor, *New Engl. J. Med.*, **254**, 401 (1956).
251. Heyroth, F. E., *Industrial Hygiene and Toxicology*, Vol. 2, F. A. Patty, Ed., Interscience, New York, 1963, p. 841.
252. Higgins, R. I., and P. Dewell, *Brit. Cast Iron Res. Assoc. J.*, **8**, 425 (1960).
253. Hill, B. A., and E. L. Fanning, *Brit. J. Ind. Med.*, **5**, 1 (1948).
254. Hill, D. A., *Arch. Ind. Hyg. Occ. Med.*, **8**, 347 (1953).
255. Hill, U. T., *Anal. Chem.*, **30**, 521 (1958).
256. Hill, W. H., F. H. Hengstenberg, and C. E. Sharpe, *Amer. Ind. Hyg. Assoc. J.*, **19**, 330 (1958).
257. Hill, W. H., and M. S. Johnston, *Anal. Chem.*, **27**, 1300 (1955).
258. Hill, W. H., H. J. Kuhns, J. M. Merrill, B. J. Palm, J. Seal, and U. Urquiza, *Amer. Ind. Hyg. Assoc. J.*, **21**, 231 (1960).
259. Hill, W. H., J. M. Merrill, E. C. Montiegel, B. J. Palm, J. Schmitt, and M. Schulte, *Arch. Ind. Health*, **17**, 210 (1958).
260. Hisler, R. A., H. M. Donaldson, and C. W. Schwenzfeier, *Amer. Ind. Hyg. Assoc. J.*, **22**, 280 (1961).
261. Hochheiser, S., "Methods of Measuring and Monitoring Atmospheric Sulfur Dioxide," Publ. Health Service Publication, 999-AP-6 (1964).
262. Hodge, H. C., *Arch. Ind. Health*, **14**, 43 (1956).
263. Hoffman, W. S., and B. Osgood, *Am. J. Clin. Pathol.*, **15**, 293 (1945).
264. Hollingsworth, R. L., V. K. Rowe, F. Oyen, H. R. Hoyle, and H. C. Spencer, *Arch. Ind. Health*, **14**, 138 (1956).
265. Hollingsworth, R. L., V. K. Rowe, F. Oyen, D. D. McCollister, and H. C. Spencer, *Arch. Ind. Health*, **13**, 217 (1956).
266. Hollingsworth, R. L., V. K. Rowe, F. Oyen, T. R. Torkelson, and E. M. Adams, *Arch. Ind. Health*, **17**, 180 (1958).

267. Hollingsworth, R. L., and V. F. Waling, *Amer. Ind. Hyg. Assoc. Quart.,* **16,** 52 (1955).
268. Hommel, C. O., F. J. Brousaides, and R. L. Bersin, *Anal. Chem.,* **34,** 1608 (1962).
269. Horn, H. J., and R. J. Weir, *Arch. Ind. Health,* **12,** 515 (1955).
270. Horn, H. J., and R. J. Weir, *Arch. Ind. Health,* **13,** 340 (1956).
271. Hosey, A. D., H. H. Jones, and H. E. Ayer, *Amer. Ind. Hyg. Assoc. J.,* **21,** 491 (1960).
272. Houghton, J. A., *Amer. Ind. Hyg. Assoc. J.,* **22,** 296 (1961).
273. Houghton, J. A., and G. Lee, *Amer. Ind. Hyg. Assoc. J.,* **21,** 219 (1960).
274. Houghton, J. A., and G. Lee, *Amer. Ind. Hyg. Assoc. J.,* **22,** 296 (1961).
275. Howard, O. H., and C. W. Weber, *Amer. Ind. Hyg. Assoc. J.,* **23,** 48 (1962).
276. Hubbard, B. L., and L. Silverman, *Arch. Ind. Hyg. Occ. Med.,* **2,** 49 (1950).
277. Hubbard, D. M., *Ind. Eng. Chem., Anal. Ed.,* **13,** 915 (1941).
278. Hubbard, D. M., F. M. Creech, and J. Cholak, *Arch. Environ. Health,* **13,** 190 (1966).
279. Hughes, E. E., and R. Gordon, Jr., *Anal. Chem.,* **31,** 94 (1959).
280. Hughes, E. E., and S. G. Lias, *Anal. Chem.,* **32,** 707 (1960).
281. Hughes, J. G., and A. T. Jones, *Amer. Ind. Hyg. Assoc. J.,* **24,** 164 (1963).
282. Hughes, J. P. W., R. Baron, D. H. Buckland, M. A. Cooke, J. D. Craig, D. P. Duffield, A. W. Grosart, P. W. J. Parkes, and A. Porter, *Brit. J. Ind. Med.,* **19,** 83 (1962).
283. Huitt, H. A., and J. P. Lodge, *Anal. Chem.,* **36,** 1305 (1964).
284. Humperdinck, K., *Arch. Gewerbepathol. Gewerbehyg.,* **10,** 569 (1941); cited by E. V. Henson, *J. Occupational Med.,* **2,** 497 (1960).
285. Hunter, D., R. Milton, and K. M. A. Perry, *Brit. J. Ind. Med.,* **2,** 92 (1945).
286. Hunter, F., *J. Ind. Hyg. Toxicol.,* **21,** 331 (1931).
287. Ikeda, M., and A. Kila, *Brit. J. Ind. Med.,* **21,** 20 (1964).
288. Imbus, H. R., J. Cholak, L. H. Miller, and T. Sterling, *Arch. Environ. Health,* **6,** 286 (1963).
289. International Union of Pure and Applied Chemistry, Recommended Method, 1958.
290. Irish, D. D., *Industrial Hygiene and Toxicology,* 2nd ed., Vol. 2, F. A. Patty, Ed., Interscience, New York, 1963.
291. Jacobs, M. B., *Analytical Chemistry of Industrial Poisons, Hazards and Solvents,* Interscience, New York, 1949.
292. Jacobs, M. B., *The Chemical Analysis of Air Pollutants,* Interscience, New York, 1960.
293. Jacobs, M. B., *Amer. Ind. Hyg. Assoc. J.,* **23,** 411 (1962).
294. Jacobs, M. B., and J. Herndon, *Amer. Ind. Hyg. Assoc. J.,* **22,** 372 (1961).
295. Jacobs, M. B., and J. Nagler, *Ind. Eng. Chem., Anal. Ed.,* **14,** 442 (1942).
296. Jacobs, M. B., S. Yamaguchi, L. J. Goldwater, and H. Gilbert, *Amer. Ind. Hyg. Assoc. J.,* **21,** 475 (1960).
297. Jacobson, K. H., E. B. Hackley, and L. Feinsilver, *Arch. Ind. Health,* **13,** 237 (1956).
298. Jensen, R. E., and R. T. Pflaum, *Anal. Chem.,* **38,** 1268 (1966).
299. Johnannesson, J. K., *Anal. Chem.,* **28,** 1475 (1956).
300. Johnstone, R., *Ind. Med.,* **14,** 495 (1945).
301. Johnstone, R. T., *Arch. Ind. Health,* **20,** 445 (1959).

302. Jones, A. T., R. C. Jones, and E. O. Longley, *Amer. Ind. Hyg. Assoc. J.* **25**, 376 (1964).
303. Jones, L. R., *Amer. Ind. Hyg. Assoc. J.*, **24**, 11 (1963).
304. Jones, L. R., and J. A. Reddick, *Anal. Chem.*, **24**, 1533 (1952).
305. Jones, R. H., M. F. Ellicott, J. B. Cadigan, and E. A. Gaensler, *J. Lab. Clin. Med.*, **51**, 553 (1958).
306. Jordi, A., *Schweiz. Med. Woschr.* **81**, 1117 (1951); abstr. in *Arch. Ind. Hyg. Occupational Med.*, **5**, 500 (1952).
307. Kägi, J. H. R., and B. L. Vallee, *Anal. Chem.*, **30**, 1951 (1958).
308. Kazantzis, G., and R. R. Bomford, *Lancet*, **1960-I**, 360.
309. Keall, J. H. H., N. H. Martin, and R. E. Turnbridge, *Brit. J. Ind. Med.*, **3**, 175 (1946).
310. Keenan, R. G., D. H. Byers, B. E. Saltzman, and F. L. Hyslop, *Amer. Ind. Hyg. Assoc. J.*, **24**, 481 (1963).
311. Keenan, R. G., and B. M. Flick, *Anal. Chem.*, **20**, 1238 (1948).
312. Kehoe, R. A., *Industrial Hygiene and Toxicology*, 2nd ed., Vol. 2, F. A. Patty, Ed., Interscience, New York, 1963.
313. Kelley, F. J., and W. E. Gill, *Arch. Environ. Health*, **10**, 517 (1965).
314. Kent, N. L., and C. A. McCance, *Biochem. J.*, **35**, 837 (1941).
315. Kesic, B., and V. Hausler, *Arch. Ind. Hyg. Occupational Med.*, **10**, 336 (1954).
316. Ketchman, N. H., *Amer. Ind. Hyg. Assoc. J.*, **23**, 127 (1962).
317. Kincaid, J. F., J. S. Strung, and F. W. Sunderman, *Arch. Ind. Hyg. Occupational Med.*, **8**, 48 (1953).
318. Kinosian, J. R., and B. R. Hubbard, *Amer. Ind. Hyg. Assoc. J.*, **19**, 453 (1958).
319. Kleinfeld, M., J. Messite, C. Kooyman, and L. J. Goldwater, *Arch. Environ. Health*, **3**, 676 (1961).
320. Kleinfeld, M., and A. Rosso, *Ind. Med. Surg.*, **34**, 242 (1965).
321. Kleinfeld, M., and I. R. Tabershaw, *J. Amer. Med. Assoc.*, **159**, 677 (1955).
322. Klemperer, F. W., and A. P. Martin, *Anal. Chem.*, **22**, 828 (1950).
323. Klemperer, F. W., A. P. Martin, and J. van Riper, *Arch. Ind. Hyg. Occupational Med.*, **4**, 251 (1951).
324. Klimková-Deutschová, E., *Arch. Gewerbepathol. Gewerbehyg.*, **19**, 35 (1960); abstr. in *Bull. Hyg.*, **37** (8), 811 (1962).
325. Kluck, I., and L. Ulrich, *Pracovni Lekar.*, **5**, 236 (1960).
326. Klug, H. P., L. Alexander, and E. Kummer, *J. Ind. Hyg. Toxicol.*, **30**, 166 (1948).
327. Knox, J. F., and J. Beattie, *Arch. Ind. Hyg. Occupational Med.*, **10**, 23 (1954).
328. Kolthoff, I. M., and E. P. Parry, *Anal. Chem.*, **25**, 188 (1953).
329. Kolthoff, I. M., and H. Yutzy, *Ind. Eng. Chem., Anal. Ed.*, **9**, 75 (1937).
330. Koniecki, W. B., and A. L. Linch, *Anal. Chem.*, **30**, 1134 (1958).
331. Konigkeit, G., *Z. Ges. Hyg. Ihre Grenzgebiete*, **8**, 350 (1962); abstr. in *Bull. Hyg.*, **37** (10), 1029 (1962).
332. Kopp, J. F., and R. G. Keenan, *Amer. Ind. Hyg. Assoc. J.*, **24**, 1 (1963).
333. Kühne, W., *Arch. f. Gewerbepathol. Gewerbehyg.*, **19**, 633 (1962); abstr. in *Bull. Hyg.*, **38**, 650 (1963).
334. Kuhns, L. J., R. F. Forsyth, and J. F. Masi, *Anal. Chem.*, **28**, 1750 (1956).
335. Kumler, K., and T. P. Schreiber, *Amer. Ind. Hyg. Assoc. Quart.*, **16**, 296 (1955).
336. Kusnetz, H. L., *Amer. Ind. Hyg. Assoc. J.*, **21**, 340 (1960).

337. Kusnetz, H. L., B E. Saltzman, and M. E. Lanier, *Amer. Ind. Hyg. Assoc. J.,* **21,** 361 (1960).

338. Laitenen, H. A., and P. Kivalo, *Anal. Chem.,* **24,** 1467 (1952).

339. Lamouroux, A., *Mem. Poudres,* **38,** 383 (1956); cited by Rinehart and Hatch, ref. 474.

340. Landry, A. C., *J. Ind. Hyg. Toxicol.,* **29,** 168 (1947).

341. Landry, A. C., *Amer. Ind. Hyg. Assoc. J.,* **21,** 407 (1960).

342. Lane, R. E., *Brit. Med. J.,* **1,** 978 (1954).

343. de Langen, C. D., and J. A. ten Berg, *Acta. Med. Scand.,* **130,** 37 (1948).

344. Lanza, H. A., *Pneumoconioses,* Greene and Stratton, New York, 1963.

345. Lawther, P. J., and J. N. Apthorp, *Brit. J. Ind. Med.,* **12,** 326 (1955).

346. Lawton, A. H., T. R. Sweeney, and H. C. Dudley, *J. Ind. Hyg. Toxicol.,* **25,** 13 (1943).

347. Leaf, G., and L. J. Zatman, *Brit. J. Ind. Med.,* **9,** 19 (1952).

348. Lebbe, J., J. P. Lafarge, and R. A. Menarde, *Arch. Mal. Prof.,* **27,** 565 (1966).

349. Lester, D., *J. Ind. Hyg. Toxicol.,* **26,** 61 (1944).

350. Levaggi, D. A., and M. Feldstein, *Amer. Ind. Hyg. Assoc. J.,* **25,** 64 (1964).

351. Levine, L., *J. Ind. Hyg. Toxicol.,* **27,** 171 (1945).

351a. Levine, L., and Fahy, J., *J. Ind. Hyg. Toxicol.,* **27,** 217 (1945).

352. Levinskas, G. J., M. R. Paslian, and W. R. Bleckman, *Amer. Ind. Hyg. Assoc. J.,* **19,** 46 (1958).

353. Levinson, S. A., and R. P. MacFate, *Clinical Laboratory Diagnosis,* 3rd ed., Lea and Febiger, Philadelphia, 1946.

354. Lewis, C. E., *Arch. Ind. Health,* **19,** 419 (1959).

355. Lewis, C. E., *Arch. Ind. Health,* **19,** 497 (1959).

356. Lewis, C. E., *J. Occupational Med.,* **3,** 82 (1961).

357. Lewis, D. A., *Analyst,* **87,** 566 (1962).

358. Lieben, J., J. A. Dattoli, and V. M. Vought, *Arch. Environ. Health,* **12,** 331 (1966).

359. Lieben, J., and F. Metzner, *Amer. Ind. Hyg. Assoc. J.,* **20,** 494 (1959).

360. Liebman, K. C., and J. D. Hindman, *Anal. Chem.,* **30,** 1674 (1958).

361. Linch, A. L., R. B. Davis, R. F. Stalzer, and W. F. Anzilotti, *Amer. Ind. Hyg. Assoc. J.,* **25,** 81 (1964).

362. Linch, A. L., S. S. Lord, Jr., K. A. Kubitz, and M. R. DeBrunner, *Amer. Ind. Hyg. Assoc. J.,* **26,** 465 (1965).

363. Line, W. R., and P. W. Aradnine, *Ind. Eng. Chem., Anal. Ed.,* **9,** 60 (1937).

364. Lippmann, M., *Arch. Ind. Health,* **20,** 225 (1959).

365. Lodge, J. P., Jr., E. R. Frank, and J. Ferguson, *Anal. Chem.,* **34,** 702 (1962).

366. Los Alamos Scientific Laboratories Analytical Procedures, L.A. 1858 (1955).

367. Lowe, H. J., and G. Freeman, *Arch. Ind. Health,* **16,** 523 (1957).

368. Lowry, T. L., and L. M. Schuman, *J. Amer. Med. Assoc.,* **162,** 153 (1956).

369. Lundgren, K. D., and A. Swensson, *J. Ind. Hyg. Toxicol.,* **31,** 190 (1949).

370. Lyon, J. S., *J. Occupational Med.,* **4,** 199 (1962).

371. Macauley, D. B., and D. A. Stanley, *Brit. J. Ind. Med.,* **13,** 217 (1956).

372. Mackay, J., K. W. Holmes, and R. E. Wilson, *Brit. J. Ind. Med.,* **15,** 126 (1958).

373. Maffett, P. A., T. F. Doherty, and J. L. Monkman, *Amer. Ind. Hyg. Assoc., Quart.,* **17,** 186 (1956).

374. Magnuson, H. J., and E. B. Watson, *Ind. Eng. Chem., Anal. Ed.*, **16**, 339 (1944).
375. Magos, L., *Brit. J. Ind. Med.*, **19**, 283 (1962).
376. Magos, L., *Brit. J. Ind. Med.*, **23**, 230 (1966).
377. Mainzer, F., and M. Krause, *Trans. Royal Soc., Trop. Med. Hyg.*, **33**, 405 (1940).
378. Maloof, C. C., *Arch. Ind. Hyg. Occupational Med.*, **1**, 296 (1950).
379. Mancuso, T. F., *Ind. Med. Surg.*, **20**, 393 (1951).
380. Mancuso, T. F., and W. C. Hueper, *Ind. Med. Surg.*, **20**, 358 (1951).
381. Marcali, K., *Anal. Chem.*, **29**, 552 (1957).
382. Marcali, K., and A. L. Linch, *Amer. Ind. Hyg. Assoc. J.*, **27**, 360 (1966).
383. Marcussen, P. V., *Brit. J. Ind. Med.*, **17**, 65 (1960).
384. Maren, T. H., *Anal. Chem.*, **19**, 487 (1947).
385. Marshall, E. K., Jr., and A. H. Owens, Jr., *Bull. Johns Hopkins*, **95**, 1 (1954).
386. Massmann, W., *Zentr. Arbeitmed. Arbeitschutz*, **5 & 6**, 207 (1955).
387. Massmann, W., *Brit. J. Ind. Med.*, **13**, 51 (1956).
388. Massmann, W., and H. Opitz, *Zentr. Arbeitmed. Arbeitschutz*, **4**, 1 (1954); abstr. in *Arch. Ind. Health*, **11**, 78 (1955).
389. Massmann, W., and D. Sprecher, *Arch. Gewerbepathol. Gewerbehyg.*, **14**, 208 (1956).
390. Matulis, R. M., and J. C. Guyon, *Anal. Chem.*, **37**, 1391 (1965).
391. May, K. R., *J. Sci. Instr.*, **22**, 187 (1945).
392. Maynard, W. E., *Amer. Ind. Hyg. Assoc. Quart.*, **15**, 217 (1954).
393. McConnell, W. J., and R. H. Flinn, *J. Ind. Hyg. Toxicol.*, **28**, 76 (1946).
394. McCord, W. M., and J. W. Zemp, *Anal. Chem.*, **27**, 1171 (1955).
395. McFarland, R. A., *Amer. Ind. Hyg. Assoc. J.*, **24**, 209 (1963).
396. McLaughlin, A. I. G., R. Milton, and K. M. A. Perry, *Brit. J. Ind. Med.*, **3**, 185 (1946).
397. McNally, W. D., *Ind. Med.*, **4**, 581 (1935).
398. McTurk, L. C., C. H. W. Hirs, and R. E. Eckardt, *Ind. Med. Surg.*, **25**, 29 (1956).
399. Medlin, W. L., *Anal. Chem.*, **32**, 632 (1960).
400. Mehani, S., *Brit. J. Ind. Med.*, **21**, 78 (1964).
401. Meigs, J. W., R. M. Brown, and L. J. Sciarini, *Arch. Ind. Hyg. Occ. Med.*, **4**, 533 (1951).
402. Mendenhall, R. M., *Amer. Ind. Hyg. Assoc. J.*, **21**, 211 (1960).
403. Meyers, G. B., *Ind. Med. Surg.*, **25**, 4 (1956).
404. Meyers, J. B., *Arch. Ind. Hyg. Occupational Med.*, **2**, 742 (1950).
405. Miller, C. W., M. W. Davis, A. Goodman, and J. P. Wyatt, *Arch. Ind. Hyg. Occupational Med.*, **8**, 453 (1953).
406. Miller, D. P., and H. W. Haggard, *J. Ind. Hyg. Toxicol.*, **25**, 423 (1943).
407. Mittler, S., D. Hedrick, M. King, and A. Gaynor, *Ind. Med. Surg.*, **25**, 301 (1956).
408. Mittler, S., M. King, and B. Burkhardt, *Arch. Ind. Health*, **15**, 191 (1957).
409. Monkman, J. L., and L. Dubois, *Amer. Ind. Hyg. Assoc. J.*, **23**, 327 (1962).
410. Monkman, J. L., P. A. Maffett, and T. F. Doherty, *Amer. Ind. Hyg. Assoc. Quart.*, **17**, 418 (1956).
411. Morehead, F. F., *Ind. Eng. Chem., Anal. Ed.*, **12**, 373 (1940).
412. Morgan, J. G., *Brit. J. Ind. Med.*, **17**, 209 (1960).

413. Morris, G. E., *Arch. Ind. Health,* 11, 368 (1955).

414. Morris, G. E., *Arch. Dermatol.,* 78, 612 (1958).

415. Moskowitz, S., *N.Y. Dept. Labor Monthly Rev.,* 29, 17 (1950).

416. Moskowitz, S., and W. J. Burke, *J. Ind. Hyg. Toxicol.,* 20, 457 (1938).

417. Moskowitz, S., and H. Shapiro, *Arch. Ind. Hyg. Occ. Med.,* 6, 116 (1952).

418. Moss, R. H., C. F. Jackson, and J. Seiberlich, *Arch. Ind. Hyg. Occupational Med.,* 4, 53 (1951).

419. Mountain, J. T., L. L. Delker, and H. E. Stokinger, *Arch. Ind. Hyg. Occupational Med.,* 8, 406 (1953).

420. Mountain, J. T., F. R. Stockell, and H. E. Stokinger, *Arch. Ind. Health,* 12, 494 (1955).

421. Murray, H. M. L., R. W. Prunster, and R. D. Anderson, "Tetryl Dermatitis," Tech. Report No. 2, Ind. Welfare Div., Dept. of Labour & Natl. Service, Australia, 1944.

422. Nader, J. S., G. C. Ortman, and M. T. Massey, *Amer. Ind. Hyg. Assoc. J.,* 22, 42 (1961).

423. Nagelschmidt, G., *Amer. Ind. Hyg. Assoc. J.,* 26, 1 (1965).

424. Nau, C. A., C. V. Dernehl, and H. H. Sweets, *J. Ind. Hyg. Toxicol.,* 27, 256 (1945).

425. Nelson, J. P., and A. J. Milein, *Anal. Chem.,* 29, 1665 (1957).

426. Nielson, J. P., and A. D. Dangerfield, *Arch. Ind. Health,* 11, 61 (1955).

427. Nogare, S. D., T. O. Norris, and J. Mitchell, *Anal. Chem.,* 23, 1473 (1951).

428. Nomura, T., *J. Sci. Labor (Japan),* 109 (Feb. 1956).

429. Norwood, W. D., P. A. Fuqua, and B. C. Scudder, *Arch. Ind. Hyg. Occ. Med.,* 1, 90 (1950).

430. Oberst, F. W., E. B. Hackley, and C. C. Comstock, *Arch. Ind. Health,* 13, 379 (1956).

431. Ogata, M., K. Sugiyam, and H. Moriyasu, *Acta Med. Okayama,* 16, 283 (1962).

432. Oglesby, F. L., J. H. Sterner, and B. Anderson, *J. Ind. Hyg. Toxicol.,* 29, 74 (1947).

433. Oliver, T., *Brit. Med. J.,* 1, 1094 (1933).

434. Olsen, J. C., and G. E. Ferguson, *Ind. Eng. Chem., Anal. Ed.,* 3, 189 (1931).

435. O'Neil, R. L., *Anal. Chem.,* 34, 781 (1962).

436. Pagnotto, L. D., H. B. Elkins, H. G. Brugsch, and J. E. Walkley, *Amer. Ind. Hyg. Assoc. J.,* 22, 417 (1961).

437. Pagnotto, L. D., and L. M. Lieberman, *Am. Ind. Hyg. Assn. J.,* 28, 129 (1967).

438. Pagnotto, L. D., and J. E. Walkley, *Amer. Ind. Hyg. Assoc. J.,* 26, 137 (1965).

439. Palmes, E. D., N. Nelson, S. Laskin, and M. Kuschner, *Amer. Ind. Hyg. Assoc. J.,* 20, 453 (1959).

440. Paluch, A., *J. Ind. Hyg. Toxicol.,* 30, 37 (1948).

441. Parmeggiani, L., and C. Sassi, *Med. Lavoro,* 45, 431 (1954); abstr. in *Arch. Ind. Health,* 11, 444 (1955).

442. Paterson, J. D., *Brit. J. Ind. Med.,* 56, 301 (1956).

443. Pattison, F. L. M., *Toxic Alipatic Fluorine Compounds,* Elsevier, Amsterdam, 1959.

444. Patty, F. A., *Industrial Hygiene and Toxicology, II,* 609, Interscience, New York, 1949.

445. Patty, F. A., and G. M. Petty, *J. Ind. Hyg. Toxicol.* 23, 129 (1941).

446. Pearce, S. J., and H. H. Schrenk, *U.S. Bur. Mines, Rept. Invest.*, **4282** (1948).
447. Penalver, R., *Ind. Med. Surg.*, **24**, 1 (1955).
448. Peters, J. P., and D. D. Van Slyke, *Quantitative Clinical Chemistry, II: Methods*, Williams & Wilkins, Baltimore, 1932.
449. Peterson, C. E., G. A. Welford, and J. H. Harley, *Anal. Chem.*, **22**, 1197 (1950).
450. Pfitzer, E. A., and J. M. Seals, *Amer. Ind. Hyg. Assoc. J.*, **20**, 392 (1959).
451. Pike, M. H., *J. Mich. Med. Soc.*, **43**, 581 (1944).
452. Pinto, S. S., and J. P. Fahy, *J. Ind. Hyg. Toxicol.*, **24**, 24 (1942).
453. Pinto, S. S., and C. M. McGill, *Ind. Med. Surg.*, **22**, 281 (1953).
454. Pinto, S. S., S. J. Petronella, D. R. Johns, and M. F. Arnold, *Arch. Ind. Hyg. Occupational Med.*, **1**, 437 (1950).
455. Pinto, S. S., and W. L. Wilson, *J. Ind. Hyg. Toxicol.*, **25**, 381 (1943).
456. Piotrowski, J., *J. Hyg., Epidemiol., Microbiol. Immunol.*, **1**, 23 (1957).
457. Platte, J. A., and V. M. Marcy, *Anal. Chem.*, **31**, 1226 (1959).
458. Polis, R. D., L. B. Berger, and H. H. Schrenk, *U.S. Bur. Mines, Rept. Invest.*, **3785**, (1944).
459. Porteous, J. W., and R. T. Williams, *Biochem. J.*, **44**, 46 (1949).
460. Powell, J. F., *Brit. J. Ind. Med.*, **2**, 142 (1945).
461. Price, G. R., R. J. Feretti, and S. Schwartz, *Anal. Chem.*, **25**, 322 (1953).
462. Priestley, L. J., F. E. Critchfield, N. H. Ketcham, and J. D. Cavender, *Anal. Chem.*, **37**, 70 (1965).
463. Princi, F., *J. Ind. Hyg. Toxicol.*, **29**, 315 (1947).
464. Princi, F., *J. Occupational Med.*, **2**, 92 (1960).
465. Rayner, A. C., and C. M. Jephcott, *Anal. Chem.*, **33**, 627 (1961).
466. Reinhart, W. H., J. M. Dallavalle, W. B. Fulton, and A. E. Dooley, *U.S. Publ. Health Bull.*, **247** (1940).
467. Reinl, W., and H. J. Urban, *Arch. Gewerbepathol. Gewerbehyg.*, **21**, 333 (1965).
468. Renes, L. E., *Arch. Ind. Hyg. Occupational Med.*, **7**, 99 (1953).
469. Rice, E. W., *Arch. Ind. Hyg. Occupational Med.*, **6**, 487 (1952).
470. Richeson, E. M., *Ind. Med. Surg.*, **27**, 607 (1958).
471. Rider, B. F., and M. G. Mellon, *Ind. Eng. Chem., Anal. Ed.*, **18**, 96 (1946).
472. Rieman, C. K., and A. S. Minot, *J. Biol. Chem.*, **45**, 133 (1920).
473. Rinehart, W. E., R. C. Garbers, E. A. Greene, and R. M. Stouffer, *Amer. Ind. Hyg. Assoc. J.*, **19**, 80 (1958).
474. Rinehart, W. E., and T. Hatch, *Amer. Ind. Hyg. Assoc. J.*, **25**, 545 (1965).
475. Ringold, A., J. R. Goldsmith, H. E. Helving, R. Finn, and F. Schulte, *Arch. Environ. Health*, **5**, 308 (1962).
476. Ripley, D. L., J. M. Clingenpeel, and R. W. Hurn, *Intern. J. Air, Water Pollution*, **8**, 455 (1964); abstr. in *J. Occupational Med.*, **7**, 173 (1965).
477. Robbie, W. A., and P. J. Leinfelder, *J. Ind. Hyg. Toxicol.*, **27**, 136 (1945).
478. Roberts, E. A., *Arch. Ind. Hyg. Occupational Med.*, **4**, 549 (1951).
479. Roddy, T. C. Jr., and S. M. Wallace, *Amer. J. Clin. Pathol.*, **36**, 373 (1961).
480. Rodier, J., *Brit. J. Ind. Med.*, **12**, 21 (1955).
481. Rogers, G. W., *J. Ind. Hyg. Toxicol.*, **27**, 224 (1945).
482. Rogers, J. C., and C. C. Hooper, *Ind. Med. Surg.*, **26**, 32 (1957).
483. Roholm, K., *Fluorine Intoxication*, H. K. Lewis & Co., Ltd., London, 1937.
484. Ross, H. L., and F. W. Sehl, *Ind. Eng. Chem., Anal. Ed.*, **7**, 32 (1935).
485. Ross, J. R., and C. C. Lucas, *J. Biol. Chem.*, **3**, 285 (1935).

486. Roush, G., Jr., *J. Occupational Med.*, **1**, 46 (1959).
487. Rowe, V. K., G. J. Atchison, E. N. Luce, and E. M. Adams, *J. Ind. Hyg. Toxicol.*, **25**, 348 (1943).
488. Rowley, R. J., and G. H. Farrah, *Amer. Ind. Hyg. Assoc. J.*, **23**, 314 (1960).
489. Rubin, H. H., and A. J. Arieff, *J. Ind. Hyg. Toxicol.*, **27**, 123 (1945).
490. Rushing, D. E., *Amer. Ind. Hyg. Assoc. J.*, **23**, 383 (1962).
491. Saita, G., and L. Moreo, *Med. Lavoro*, **54**, 183 (1963).
492. Salmowa, J., J. Piotrowski, and U. Neuhorn, *Brit. J. Ind. Med.*, **20**, 41 (1963).
493. Saltzman, B. E., *Anal. Chem.*, **25**, 493 (1953).
494. Saltzman, B. E., *Anal. Chem.*, **26**, 1949 (1954).
495. Saltzman, B. E., *Anal. Chem.*, **27**, 284 (1955).
496. Saltzman, B. E., *Anal. Chem.*, **33**, 1100 (1961).
497. Saltzman, B. E., *Amer. Ind. Hyg. Assoc. J.*, **23**, 112 (1962).
498. Saltzman, B. E., and N. Gilbert, *Amer. Ind. Hyg. Assoc. J.*, **20**, 379 (1959).
499. Saltzman, B. E., and N. Gilbert, *Anal. Chem.*, **31**, 1914 (1959).
500. Saltzman, B. E., and A. L. Mendenhall, Jr., *Anal. Chem.*, **36**, 1300 (1964).
501. Samitz, M. H., S. Katz, and S. Gross, *J. Occupational Med.*, **2**, 435 (1960).
502. Sandell, E. B., *Colorimetric Methods for the Determination of Traces of Metals*, Interscience, New York, 1959.
503. Sauerwald, P., *Z. Hyg. Ihre Grenzgebiete*, **7**, 738 (1961); abstr. in *Bull. Hyg.*, **37**, 462 (1962).
504. Sawicki, E., and T. R. Hauser, *Anal. Chem.*, **32**, 1434 (1960).
505. Sayers, R. R., W. P. Yant, H. H. Schrenk, J. Chornyak, S. J. Pearce, F. A. Patty, and J. G. Linn, *U.S. Bur. Mines, Rept. Invest.*, **3617** (1942).
506. Schepers, G. W. H., *Arch. Ind. Health*, **12**, 127 (1955).
507. Scherberger, R. F., G. P. Happ, F. A. Miller, and D. W. Fassett, *Amer. Ind. Hyg., Assoc. J.*, **23**, 127 (1962).
508. Scherberger, R. F., F. A. Miller, and D. W. Fassett, *Amer. Ind. Hyg. Assoc. J.*, **21**, 471 (1960).
509. Scholander, P. F., and F. J. W. Roughton, *J. Ind. Hyg. Toxicol.*, **24**, 218 (1942).
510. Schrenk, H. H., F. A. Patty, and W. P. Yant, *U.S. Publ. Health Rept.*, **48**, 1389 (1933).
511. Schrenk, H. H., S. J. Pearce, and W. P. Yant, *U.S. Bur. Mines, Rept. Invest.* **3287** (1935).
512. Schrenk, H. H., and L. Schreibeis, Jr., *Amer. Ind. Health Assoc. J.*, **19**, 225 (1958).
513. Schrenk, H. H., W. P. Yant, S. J. Pearce, F. A. Patty, and R. R. Sayers, *J. Ind. Hyg. Toxicol.*, **23**, 20 (1941).
514. Schuler, P., H. Oyanguren, V. Maturova, A. Valenzuela, E. Cruz, V. Plaza, E. Schmidt, and R. Haddad, *Ind. Med. Surg.*, **26**, 167 (1957).
515. Schulte, J. H., *Arch. Environ. Health*, **7**, 524 (1963).
516. Schürmann, D., *Deut. Med. Wochschr.*, **80**, 1661 (1955).
517. Schwartz, L., L. Tulipan, and D. J. Birmingham, *Occupational Diseases of the Skin*, 3rd ed., Lea & Febiger, Philadelphia, 1957.
518. Schwartz, S., L. Zieve, and C. J. Watson, *J. Lab. Clin. Med.*, **37**, 843 (1951).
519. Sciarini, L. J., and J. A. Mahew, *Arch. Ind. Health*, **11**, 420 (1955).
520. Sciarini, L. J., and J. W. Meigs, *Arch. Ind. Health*, **18**, 521 (1958).
521. Sciarini, L. J., and J. W. Meigs, *Arch. Environ. Health*, **2**, 423 (1961).

522. Scott, E. W., and J. F. Treon, *Ind. Eng. Chem., Anal. Ed.,* **12,** 189 (1940).
523. Seto, T. A., and M. O. Schultz, *Anal. Chem.,* **28,** 1625 (1956).
524. Setterlind, A. N., *Amer. Ind. Hyg. Assoc. Quart.,* **14,** 113 (1953).
525. Setterlind, A. N., and D. Geishecker, *What's New in Industrial Hygiene,* **5,** 6 (Oct. 1948).
526. Shalpe, I. O., *Brit. J. Ind. Med.,* **21,** 69 (1964).
527. Shaver, C. G., and A. R. Riddell, *J. Ind. Hyg. Toxicol,* **29,** 147 (1947).
528. Shell Chemical Corp. Toxicity Data Sheet: *Mesityl Oxide,* New York, 1957.
529. Shepherd, M., *Anal. Chem.,* **19,** 77 (1947).
530. Sherwood, R. J., *Trans. Assoc. Ind. Med. Off.,* **5,** 10 (1955); abstr. in *Arch. Ind. Health,* **13,** 292 (1956).
531. Shuster, L. *Biochem. J.,* **64,** 101 (1956).
532. Sill, C. W., and C. P. Willis, *Anal. Chem.,* **31,** 598 (1959).
533. Sill, C. W., C. P. Willis, and J. K. Flygare, Jr., *Anal. Chem.,* **33,** 1671 (1961).
534. Silverman, L., in *Encylopedia of Instrumentation for Industrial Hygiene,* University of Michigan, 1956, p. 17.
535. Silverman, L., and J. F. Ege, Jr., *J. Ind. Hyg. Toxicol.,* **29,** 136 (1947).
536. Silverman, L., and G. R. Gardner, *Amer. Ind. Hyg. Assoc. J.,* **26,** 97 (1965).
537. Silverman, L., and M. E. Shideler, *Anal. Chem.,* **31,** 152 (1959).
538. Sjoberg, S. G., *Arch. Ind. Health,* **11,** 505 (1955).
539. Skinner, J. B., *Ind. Med.,* **16,** 441 (1947).
540. Skonieczny, R. F., *Amer. Ind. Hyg. Assoc. J.,* **24,** 17 (1963).
541. Smith, J. C., and J. E. Kench, *Brit. J. Ind. Med.,* **14,** 240 (1957).
542. Smith, R: G., and P. Diamond, *Amer. Ind. Hyg. Assoc. Quart.,* **13,** 235 (1952).
543. Smyth, H. F., Jr., *J. Ind. Hyg.* **11,** 338 (1929).
544. Smyth, H. F., Jr., *Amer. Ind. Hyg. Assoc. Quart.,* **17,** 144 (1956).
545. Sneddon, I. B., *Brit. Med. J.,* **1,** 1448 (1955).
546. Snegiriff, L. S., and O. M. Lombard, *Arch. Ind. Hyg. Occupational Med.,* **4,** 199 (1951).
547. Snyder, R. K., and W. F. Von Oettingen, *J. Amer. Med. Assoc.,* **123,** 202 (1943).
548. Soucek, B., and D. Vlachova, *Brit. J. Ind. Med.,* **17,** 60 (1960).
549. Srbova, J., and J. Teisinger, *Prakt. Lekar,* **4,** 41 (1952).
550. Stack, V. T., Jr., D. E. Forrest, and K. K. Wahl, *Amer. Ind. Hyg. Assoc. J.,* **22,** 184 (1961).
551. Stafford, N., C. R. N. Strouts, and W. V. Stubbings, *The Determination of Toxic Substances in Air,* Heffer, Cambridge, 1956.
552. Stavinoah, W. B., and J. B. Nash, *Anal. Chem.,* **32,** 1695 (1960).
553. Steinburg, H. H., S. C. Massari, A. C. Miner, and R. Rink, *J. Ind. Hyg. Toxicol.,* **24,** 183 (1942).
554. Stenger, V. A., S. A. Shrader, and A. W. Beshgetoor, *Ind. Eng. Chem. Anal. Ed.,* **11,** 121 (1939).
555. Stephens, B. G., and F. Lindstrom, *Anal. Chem.,* **36,** 1308 (1964).
556. Sterner, J. H., H. C. Crouch, H. F. Brockmyre, and M. Cusak, *Amer. Ind. Hyg. Assoc. Quart.,* **10,** 53 (1949).
557. Sterner, J. H., F. W. Oglesby, and B. Anderson, *J. Ind. Hyg. Toxicol.,* **29,** 60 (1947).
558. Stewart, R. D., *J. Occupational Med.,* **5,** 259 (1963).

559. Stewart, R. D., H. H. Gay, D. S. Erley, C. L. Hake, and J. E. Peterson, *J. Occupational Med.,* **3,** 586 (1961).
560. Stewart, R. D., H. H. Gay, D. S. Erley, C. L. Hake, and J. E. Peterson, *Amer. Ind. Hyg. Assoc. J.,* **23,** 167 (1962).
561. Stewart, R. D., H. H. Gay, D. S. Erley, C. L. Hake, and A. W. Schaffer, *Amer. Ind. Hyg. Assoc. J.,* **22,** 252 (1961).
562. Stokinger, H. E., et al., Natl. Nuclear Energy Series, Manhattan Project, Tech. Sec., Div. VI, 1. Part II, 1021 (1949).
563. Stokinger, H. E., *Occupational Health,* **13,** 88 (1953).
564. Stokinger, H. E., *Arch. Environ. Health,* **10,** 719 (1965).
565. Stokinger, H. E., and L. D. Scheel, *Arch. Environ. Health,* **4,** 327 (1962).
566. Stokinger, H. E., W. Wagner, and O. G. Dobrogorski, *Arch. Ind. Health,* **16,** 514 (1957).
567. Stokinger, H. E., W. Wagner, and P. G. Wright, *Arch. Ind. Health,* **14,** 158 (1956).
568. Stock, A., and H. Lux, *Z. Angew. Chem.,* **44,** 200 (1931).
569. Storlazzi, E., and H. B. Elkins, *J. Ind. Hyg. Toxicol.,* **23,** 459 (1941).
570. Stuber, K., *Arch. Gewerbepathol. Gewerbehyg.,* **2,** 398 (1931).
571. Sunderman, F. W., and J. F. Kincaid, *J. Amer. Med. Assoc.,* **155,** 889 (1954).
572. Sunderman, F. W., J. F. Kincaid, A. J. Donnelly, and B. West, *Arch. Ind. Health,* **16,** 480 (1957).
573. Suzuki, Y., K. Nishiyama, M. Doi, T. Hirose, and H. Shibata, *Tokushima J. Exptl. Med.,* **7,** 124 (1960).
574. Svirbely, J. L., B. Highman, W. C. Alford, and W. F. Von Oettingen, *J. Ind. Hyg. Toxicol.,* **29,** 382 (1947).
575. Svirbely, J. L., and B. E. Saltzman, *Arch. Ind. Health,* **15,** 111 (1957).
576. Tabershaw, I. R., J. P. Fahy, and J. B. Skinner, *J. Ind. Hyg. Toxicol.,* **26,** 328 (1944).
577. Talvitie, N. A., *Anal. Chem.,* **23,** 623 (1951).
578. Talvitie, N. A., *Anal. Chem.,* **25,** 604 (1953).
579. Talvitie, N. A., *Amer. Ind. Hyg. Assoc. J.,* **25,** 169 (1964).
580. Talvitie, N. A., and L. W. Brewer, *Amer. Ind. Hyg. Assoc. J.,* **21,** 287 (1960).
581. Talvitie, N. A., and W. D. Wagner, *Arch. Ind. Hyg. Occupational Med.,* **9,** 414 (1954).
582. Tebbens, B. D., *J. Ind. Hyg. Toxicol.,* **19,** 204 (1937).
583. Teisinger, J., *Czech. Med. J.,* **39,** (Oct. 17, 1947) abstr. in *J. Ind. Hyg. Toxicol.,* **30,** 58 (1948).
584. Teisinger, J., *Prakt. Lekar.,* **15,** 48 (1963).
585. Teisinger, J., V. Bergerova, and J. Kudrna, *Prakt. Lekar,* **4,** 175 (1952).
586. Teisinger, J., and V. Bergerova-Fiserova, *Arch. Mal. Prof.,* **16,** 221 (1958).
587. Tepper, L. B., H. L. Hardy and R. I. Chamberlin, *Toxicity of Beryllium Compounds,* Elsevier, Amsterdam, 1961.
588. Theis, R., and S. R. Benedict, *J. Biol. Chem.,* **61,** 67 (1924).
589. Thomas, M. D., J. A. MacLeod, R. C. Robbins, R. C. Goettelman, R. W Eldridge, and L. H. Rogers, *Anal. Chem.,* **28,** 1810 (1956).
590. Toribara, T. Y., and P. S. Chen, Jr., *Anal. Chem.,* **24,** 539 (1952).
591. Toribara, T. Y., and R. E. Sherman, *Anal. Chem.,* **25,** 11 (1953).
592. Torkelson, T. R., F. Oyen, D. D. McCollister, and V. K. Rowe, *Amer. Ind. Hyg. Assoc. J.,* **19,** 353 (1958).

593. Torkelson, T. R., F. Oyen, and V. K. Rowe, *Amer. Ind. Hyg. Assoc. J.*, **21**, 275 (1960).

594. Torkelson, T. R., M. A. Wolf, F. Oyen, and V. K. Rowe, *Amer. Ind. Hyg. Assoc. J.*, **20**, 224 (1959).

595. Tourangeau, F. J., and S. R. Plasmondon, *Can. J. Publ. Health*, **26**, 362 (1945).

596. Treon, J. F., et al., *J. Ind. Hyg. Toxicol.*, **31**, 209 (1949).

597. Treon, J. F., J. W. Cappell, H. E. Sigmon, K. V. Kitzmiller, F. R. Heyroth, W. J. Younker, and J. Cholak, *Amer. Ind. Hyg. Assoc. Quart.*, **16**, 187 (1955).

598. Treon, J. F., F. P. Cleveland, E. E. Larson, R. W. Atchley, and R. T. Denham, *Amer. Ind. Hyg. Assoc. Quart.*, **17**, 204 (1956).

599. Treon, J. F., F. P. Cleveland, and J. Duffy, *Arch. Ind. Health*, **11**, 290 (1955).

600. Treon, J. F., W. E. Crutchfield, and K. V. Kitzmiller, *J. Ind. Hyg. Toxicol.*, **25**, 323 (1943).

601. Treon, J. F., and F. R. Dutra, *Arch. Ind. Hyg. Occ. Med.*, **5**, 52 (1952).

602. Treon, J. F., H. Simon, K. V. Kitzmiller, and F. E. Heyroth, *J. Ind. Hyg. Toxicol.*, **31**, 142 (1949).

603. Troup, H. B., *Brit. J. Ind. Med.*, **3**, 20 (1946).

604. Truhaut, R., and G. LeMoan, *Occupational Health Rev.*, **14**, 4 (1962).

605. Turner, W. J., *Ind. Eng. Chem, Anal. Ed.*, **14**, 599 (1942).

606. Umberger, C. J., and F. T. Fiorese, *J. Clin. Chem.*, **9**, 91 (1963).

607. U.S. Atomic Energy Commission, AECU-4024, Chemical Methods for Routine Bioassay, Rochester, New York, 1958.

608. Urone, P. F., and H. K. Anders, *Anal. Chem.*, **22**, 1317 (1950).

609. Urone, P. F., M. L. Druschel, and H. K. Anders, *Anal. Chem.*, **22**, 472 (1950).

610. Van der Horst, A., and J. van Duijn, *Nature*, **206**, 87 (1965).

611. Van Haaften, A. B., and S. T. Sie, *Amer. Ind. Hyg. Assoc. J.*, **26**, 52 (1965).

612. Van Ordstrand, H. S., R. Hughes, and M. G. Carmody, *Cleveland Clinic Quart.*, **10**, (1943).

613. Van Sandt, W. A., R. J. Graul, and W. J. Roberts, *Amer. Ind. Hyg. Assoc. Quart.*, **16**, 221 (1955).

614. Vasak, V., and V. Sedivec, *Chem. Listy*, **46**, 341 (1952).

615. Vasak, V., M. Van Eeck, and B. Kimelova, *Prakt. Lekar.*, **15**, 145 (1963).

616. Vigliani, E. C., *Brit. J. Ind. Med.*, **11**, 235 (1954).

617. Viles, F. J., *J. Ind. Hyg. Toxicol.*, **22**, 188 (1940).

618. Vintinner, F. J., R. Vallenas, C. E. Carlin, R. Weiss, C. Macher, and R. Ochoa, *Arch. Ind. Health*, **12**, 635 (1955).

619. Vlachova, D., *J. Hyg. Epidemiol. Mikrobiol. Immunol. (Prague)* **1**, 225 (1957).

620. Von Oettingen, W. F., *Physiol. Review* **15**, 175 (1935).

621. Von Oettingen, W. F., *U.S. Publ. Health Serv. Bull.*, **255** (1940).

622. Von Oettingen, W. F., *U.S. Publ. Health Serv. Bull.*, **271** (1941).

623. Von Oettingen, W. F., *U.S. Publ. Health Serv. Bull.*, **272** (1941).

624. Von Oettingen, W. F., P. A. Neal, D. D. Donahue, J. L. Svirbely, H. D. Baernstein, A. R. Monaco, P. J. Valaer, and J. L. Mitchell, *U.S. Public Health Serv. Bull.*, **279** (1942).

625. Von Oettingen, W. F., *Natl. Inst. Health Bull.*, **186** (1946).

626. Von Oettingen, W. F., The Halogenated Hydrocarbons: Toxicity and Potential Dangers, *U.S. Pub. Health Serv. Publ.*, **414** (1955).

627. Von Oettingen, W. F., W. C. Hueper, W. Deichmann, and F. H. Wiley, *J. Ind. Hyg. Toxicol.*, **18**, 240 (1936).

628. Von Oettingen, W. F., P. A. Neal, and D. D. Donahue, *J. Amer. Med. Assoc.*, **118**, 579 (1942).

629. Wade, H. A., H. B. Elkins, and B. P. W. Ruotolo, *Arch. Ind. Hyg. Occupational Med.*, **1**, 81 (1950).

630. Wagner, W. D., B. R. Duncan, P. C. Wright, and H. E. Stokinger, *Arch. Environ. Health*, **10**, 455 (1965).

631. Walkley, J. E., *Amer. Ind. Hyg. Assoc. J.*, **20**, 241 (1959).

632. Walkley, J. E., L. D. Pagnotto, and H. B. Elkins, *Amer. Ind. Hyg. Assoc. J.*, **22**, 362 (1961).

633. Watrous, R. M., *Ind. Med.*, **11**, 575 (1942).

634. Watrous, R. M., and H. W. Schultz, *Ind. Med. Surg.*, **19**, 317 (1950).

635. Webb, F. J., K. K. Kay, and W. E. Nichol, *J. Ind. Hyg. Toxicol.*, **27**, 249 (1945).

636. Webster, S. H., and L. T. Fairhall, *J. Ind. Hyg. Toxicol.*, **27**, 183 (1945).

637. Welford, G. A., and J. Harley, *Amer Ind. Hyg. Assoc. Quart.*, **13**, 232 (1952).

638. Welford, G. A., R. S. Morse, and J. S. Alercio, *Amer. Ind. Hyg. Assoc. J.*, **21**, 68 (1960).

639. Werner, H. W., R. C. Dunn, and W. F. Von Oettingen, *J. Ind. Hyg. Toxicol.*, **26**, 264 (1944).

640. West, P. W., and G. C. Gaeke, *Anal. Chem.*, **28**, 1816 (1956).

641. Wetherhold, J. M., and F. P. Shepherd, *J. Occupational Med.*, **7**, 193 (1965).

642. White, B. E., and W. R. Calvert, *J. Ind. Hyg. Toxicol.*, **23**, 196 (1941).

643. Whitman, N. E., and A. E. Johnston, *Amer. Ind. Hyg. Assoc. J.*, **25**, 464 (1964).

644. Wilding, J. L., W. J. Smith, P. Yevich, M. S. Sicks, S. G. Ryan, and C. L. Punte, *Amer. Ind. Hyg. Assoc. J.*, **20**, 284 (1959).

645. Willard, H. H., and O. B. Winter, *Ind. Eng. Chem., Anal. Ed.*, **5**, 7 (1933).

646. Williams, C. R., *J. Ind. Hyg. Toxicol.*, **19**, 44 (1937).

647. Williams, C. R., *J. Ind. Hyg. Toxicol.*, **24**, 277 (1942).

648. Williams, D., *Ind. Eng. Chem., Anal. Ed.*, **17**, 295 (1945).

649. Williams, N., *Brit. J. Ind. Med.*, **9**, 50 (1952).

650. Williams, R. T., *Detoxication Mechanisms*, 2nd ed., Wiley, New York, 1959.

651. Williams, W. J., *Brit. J. Ind. Med.*, **15**, 235 (1958).

652. Wilson, H. M., *North Carolina Med. J.*, **33**, 73 (1962); abstr. in *J. Am. Med. Assoc.* **180**, 173 (1962).

653. Wilson, R. H., and W. E. McCormick, *Ind. Med.* **18**, 243 (1949).

654. Winn, G. S., E. L. Godfrey, and K. W. Nelson, *Arch. Ind. Hyg. Occupational Med.*, **6**, 14 (1952).

655. Wyers, H. *Brit. J. Ind. Med.*, **3**, 177 (1946).

656. Yagoda, H., and F. H. Goldman, *J. Ind. Hyg. Toxicol.*, **25**, 440 (1943).

657. Yant, W. P., H. H. Schrenk, F. A. Patty, and C. P. Waite, *U.S. Pub. Health Rept.*, **45**, 2023 (1930).

658. Yant, W. P., H. H. Schrenk, and F. A. Patty, *J. Ind. Hyg. Toxicol.*, **18**, 349 (1936).

659. Yates, M. T., and S. Levenson, *Navy Med. Bull., Washington*, **41**, 1138 (1943).

660. Yee, H. T., L. B. Fosdick, and H. G. Bourne, *Amer. Ind. Hyg. Assoc. J.*, **20**, 45 (1959).

661. Young, W. A., D. B. Shaw, and D. V. Bates, *Aerospace Med.*, **33**, 311 (1962).

662. Young, W. A., D. B. Shaw, and D. V. Bates, *Arch. Environ. Health,* **7,** 337 (1963).
663. Zapp, J. A., *Arch. Environ. Health,* **4,** 335 (1962).
664. Zavon, M., *Amer. Ind. Hyg. Assoc. J.,* **24,** 36 (1963).

## SUPPLIERS OF AIR ANALYSIS INSTRUMENTS

1. American Systems, Inc., Hawthorne, California.
2. Bacharach Industrial Instrument Co., Pittsburgh, Pennsylvania.
3. Beckman Instruments, Inc., Fullerton, California.
4. Cole-Parmer Instrument & Equipment Co., Chicago, Illinois.
5. Davis Co., Inc., Newark, 4, New Jersey.
6. Engineering Specialties Co., Madeira, Ohio.
7. Mast Development Co., Davanport, Pennsylvania.
8. Mines Safety Appliances Co., Pittsburgh, Pennsylvania.
9. Modern and Classical Instruments, Livermore, California.
10. Phoenix Precision Instrument Co., Philadelphia, Pennsylvania.
11. Royco Instruments, Menlo Park, California.
12. Sunshine Scientific Instruments, Philadelphia, Pennsylvania.
13. Tracer Lab Division, Laboratory for Electronics, Waltham, Massachusetts.

# ODORS

By Amos Turk, *Department of Chemistry, The City College of the City University of New York, New York*

**Contents**

## I. DEFINITIONS. SCOPE OF ODOR MEASUREMENTS

### A. ODOR SENSATIONS

The scope and applications of odor measurements are frequently confused by the various meanings of the word *odor*. *Odor* is defined either

177

as (a) the perception of smell, referring to the experience, or (b) that which is smelled, referring to the stimulus. The word *odorant* is preferred for the latter meaning. The experience of smell, moreover, can be taken either to mean any perception that results from nasal inspiration or to refer only to sensations perceived via the receptors of the olfactory epithelium, an area of about 2.5 cm² within the upper nasal cavity. An odorant that is sensed only by the olfactory receptors (for example, air containing 0.01 ppm of vanillin) is said to be psychologically "pure." An odorant that stimulates both the olfactory receptors and other sensitive areas (common chemical irritation) is said to be psychologically "impure"; an example is air containing 50 ppm of propionic acid. The common chemical sense includes feelings of pain, heat, and cold, which are not unique to the nasal areas. This concept of psychological purity does not imply anything about chemical composition.

Differences between psychologically pure and impure odors are neglected in many odor measurements, especially in industrial hygiene and community air pollution applications, where irritants and stenches are grouped together as objectionable atmospheric contaminants that ought to be removed. Furthermore, it is not always operationally feasible to make distinctions among odors based on degrees of psychological purity. In establishing sensory measurement scales, however, it is important to recognize that "irritating odor" is not necessarily an extension in magnitude of "strong odor," but refers to a different type of sensation. From this point of view, the former description may be represented as a point on a scale of irritation, whereas the latter is a point on a "pure" odor intensity scale. Also, the changes in odor quality or character that sometimes accompany changes in odorant concentrations may be related to shifts in sensory receptor mechanisms.

## B. ODOROUS SUBSTANCES

Strictly speaking, the odorant that stimulates smell in man is always an air-borne gas, vapor, or aerosol (20,34) that is inspired into the nasal cavity through either the nose or the mouth. The odorant generally originates from a solid, a liquid, or a concentrated gas that is called the *odor source*. Thus, a garbage dump, an open solvent vat, and a stream of odorized natural gas leaking from a valve are all odor sources. The dispersal of an odor source into the atmosphere is accompanied by dilution and also, frequently, by fractionation (change in relative concentrations of components) and by chemical change, such as decomposition or oxidation. Odorants are therefore not always reliably characterized by the composition of the sources from which they originate. Methods of dispersal include evaporation, desorption, condensation to produce an aerosol, diffusion, convection, or a combination of these. As an example, a mixture of phenol and water vapors may be discharged to the atmosphere by vaporization of an aqueous phenol solution that is heated in an industrial process incidental to resin formation. The discharged vapors, on cooling in the outdoor atmosphere, recondense to form a mist composed of droplets of aqueous phenol solution; this aerosol is dispersed by wind currents. On further dilution, the droplets evaporate again and are more widely dispersed by wind and diffusion. Air containing a sufficient concentration of phenol in vapor form or in a mixture of vapor and aerosol phases is odorous; the sensation in both cases is the recognizable phenolic odor quality.

Most gases and vapors that are not one of the "normal" components of air ($O_2$, $N_2$, $H_2O$, $CO_2$, and the noble gases) are odorous in some ranges of concentration. Apparent exceptions are $H_2$ and $CO$. Some solids and liquids have vapor pressures so low that the maximum equilibrium concentrations that can exist in air at temperatures tolerable to man may be too dilute to smell. Such substances can nonetheless be odor sources if they are dispersed into the atmosphere as aerosol particles, condensation nuclei, or other molecular aggregates that do not represent equilibrium between vapor and solid or liquid phases.

## II. ODOR SOURCES

### A. CONFINED SOURCES

A vented storage tank being filled with liquid ethyl acrylate from a delivery truck discharges to the atmosphere a volume of air saturated with the acrylate vapor at the prevailing temperature of the liquid. A system of this type is a simple example of a confined odor source: the location, molecular aggregation, composition, concentration, and volumetric discharge of the source can be quantitatively specified. Such definite characterizations facilitate the establishment of relationships between the odor source and the odor measurements made in the community. In general, an odor source may be said to be confined when its rate of discharge to the atmosphere can be measured and when the atmospheric discharge is amenable to representative sampling and to physical or chemical processing for purposes such as odor abatement. For meteorological diffusion calculations (27), the location where the odor is discharged into the atmosphere is assumed to be a point in space.

The characterization of a confined odor source should include (a) the volumetric rate of gas discharge (gas volume/time), (b) the temperature at the point of discharge, (c) the moisture content, (d) the location, elevation, and the area and shape of the stack or vent from which the discharge is emitted, and (e) a description of the state of aggregation (gas, mist, etc., including particle size distribution) of the discharge. Such information is useful when meteorological factors relating to odor reduction by dispersion and dilution are being evaluated. The characterization of an odor source in terms of chemical composition will depend on what relationships are to be established between sensory and chemical measurements. If there are no technical or legal uncertainties concerning the source of a given community odor, a detailed chemical analysis of the source is not needed; instead, a comparative method of appraising the effect of control procedures will suffice. On the other hand, chemical characterization may be helpful in tracing a community odor to one of several alleged sources, in relating variations in odor from a given source to changes in process conditions, or in appraising the effectiveness of chemical procedures that are designed for odor abatement.

The direct sensory characterization of a confined odor source is frequently impossible because extremes of temperature or of concentration of noxious components make the source intolerable for human exposure. Suitable methods of dilution and cooling for sensory evaluation of odor sources are described in Section IV on sampling.

### B. UNCONFINED SOURCES

A drainage ditch discharges odorous vapors to the atmosphere along its length. The composition of the contents of the ditch changes from

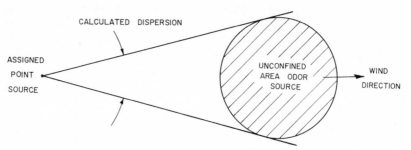

Fig. 1. Assignment of dispersion to unconfined odor source.

place to place and the rate of discharge of odorants to the atmosphere is affected by wind and terrain. No single air sample is likely to be representative of the odor source at the time the sample is taken. Such a configuration is an unconfined odor source. Other examples are garbage dumps, settling lagoons, and chemical storage areas. An unconfined source may be represented by an imaginary emission point for the purpose of meteorological diffusion calculations. Such assignment may be made on the basis that, if all the odor from the unconfined area were being discharged from the "emission point," the dispersion pattern would just include the unconfined source. Figure 1 is a schematic illustration of this procedure.

## III. SAMPLING FOR ODOR MEASUREMENTS

### A. PURPOSES OF SAMPLING PROCEDURES

In the case of community nuisance odors, sensory judgments are usually made from evidence gained on direct exposure of the judges to the odorous atmosphere in question. Where outdoor odor intensities are low enough to be tolerable and where they vary from time to time in accordance with atmospheric turbulence, changes in wind direction, and changes in the odor source, it is much better for the judges to expose themselves directly to the atmosphere rather than to a previously collected sample. When wind direction oscillates over a few degrees of arc, an observer at a distance of, say, 500–3000 ft from an odor source may have to wait for periods of several minutes between exposures to perceptible odor levels. He is, in effect, making a measurement with each sniff, without being fatigued during the times that he is not detecting odor. It would be economically prohibitive to collect samples that would be represented by all the experiences that an observer could have merely by remaining in one location for an hour. An observer may also move about from place to place in an area of suspected odor, either by foot or automobile, and spend most of his time making judgments at locations where the odor levels are highest. There are some instances, however, in which it is advantageous to collect a sample of odorant before presenting it for sensory measurements. Such instances occur when (a) the odorant must be diluted, concentrated, warmed, cooled, or otherwise modified before people can be exposed to it, (b) it is necessary to have a uniform sample large enough to be presented to a number of judges, (c) the samples must be transported to another location where sensory evaluations are made.

## B. SAMPLING WITHOUT CHANGE OF CONCENTRATION
### (GRAB SAMPLING)

A grab sample places a volume of odorant at barometric pressure into a container from which it can subsequently be presented to judges for evaluation. Grab sampling of odorants is subject to some severe limitations: (a) If the odorant is hot, condensation may occur on cooling. The condensate will probably contain odorous material at the expense of the concentration in the gas phase. (b) During the time between collection and evaluation, odorous material may be sorbed on the walls of the container or on particulate matter in the air sample. (c) Chemical changes may alter the odorant.

Containers for grab sampling should therefore be inert to the odorant material and should have a large volume-to-surface ratio. If the odorant being sampled is not at ambient temperature, the investigator must assure himself that condensation will not occur on cooling.

Grab sampling is carried out by allowing the air to fill an evacuated or collapsed container or to displace a fluid from a container. Suitable materials of construction may include stainless steel, glass, and plastics such as Mylar, Teflon, and Saran (11,12). Any container, however, together with its auxiliary tubing and equipment such as air moving devices, must be tested for suitability for the odorant in question, especially with regard to extraneous background odor and to depletion of sample by adsorption or absorption effects.

When the grab sample is to be evaluated, it must be expelled from the container into the space near the judge's nose. This expulsion may be effected by displacement of the sample with another fluid or by collapsing the container. The following example is given as an illustration of grab sampling.

*Example 1.* A sampling probe of 1 in. diameter Teflon tubing is mounted so that its inlet end is close to the surface of a fat skimming tank in a rendering plant. A blower of suitable capacity draws air through the probe and discharges it into a collapsed Mylar bag of about 2-ft³ capacity. The sampling procedure is repeated under different conditions of residence time of the fat in the tank. The samples are then removed to a suitable test room where a panel of judges can appraise them by sensory measurements such as those elaborated in Section IV.

## C. SAMPLING WITH DILUTION

Dilution procedures for sampling odor sources such as oven exhausts can reduce concentrations and temperatures to levels suitable for human exposure without permitting condensation of the odorant material. The dilution ratio must be specified; it can be determined on the basis of either pressure or volume:

$$\text{Dilution ratio} = \frac{\text{Volume of sample after dilution}}{\text{Volume of sample before dilution}}$$

(Pressure is constant; temperature is irrelevant.)

$$\text{Dilution ratio} = \frac{\text{Total pressure of sample in container after dilution}}{\text{Partial pressure of odorant in container}}$$

The container is rigid; the temperature must be constant or appropriate correction of pressure must be made according to Amontons' law, $P \propto$ absolute temperature.)

The material of choice for dilution sampling of hot odor sources in stainless steel. A suitable device is a 1000 in.[3] stainless steel tank (Fig. 2), fitted with a flow control inlet valve (shown with handle removed), a constant differential type flow controller (Moore Products Company, Model 63SU), and two brass or stainless steel bellows seal valves, one between the flow controller and the tank and the other at the opposite end of the tank. Before use in sampling, the tank is evacuated, and the inlet valve is adjusted to the desired flow rate, as indicated on a flowmeter (not shown in the figure). A convenient rate for many applications is one that fills the tank to within about 75% of its capacity over a 20-min interval. Once the adjustment is made, the handle is removed from the inlet valve and its stem is sealed with wax so as

Fig. 2. Constant flow sampling tank.

to insure against accidental tampering; the tank is then reevacuated and the two seal valves are closed. For sampling, it is necessary to open only the seal valve between the flow controller and the tank and to record the time during which the odorant is being sampled. The total volume of sample will be equal to the time of sampling multiplied by the flow rate through the inlet valve. The flow controller assures that this rate will be constant over the sampling period if the tank is not filled beyond about 75% of its capacity. As an alternate method, the flow control system is omitted and the end opposite the sampling probe is fitted with a vacuum gage; the partial pressure of the odorant is then the difference between the vacuum readings before and after sampling. The method is further illustrated by the following example.

*Example 2.* A direct-flame afterburner is to be used to deodorize an oven exhaust that contains malodorous lacquer solvent fumes. The afterburner discharge is to be evaluated to determine what flame temperature and residence time are needed to effect complete deodorization. The odor can be adequately characterized even after a 100 to 500-fold dilution. Discharge temperatures are around 1100°F (590°C). For sampling, a stainless steel tank fitted with a length of stainless steel tube probe is evacuated to a pressure of 100 torr. The steel probe is inserted in the burner discharge and a sample is drawn into the tank until the pressure reaches 110 torr. At this point the temperature of the gas mixture in the tank is 28°C. The tank is now pressurized with odor-free air to 2.00 atm (1.52 × 10³ torr). The final temperature is 22°C. The dilution ratio then is

$$\frac{1.52 \times 10^3 \text{ torr}}{(110 - 100) \text{ torr} \dfrac{(273 + 22)}{(273 + 28)}} = 155$$

The diluted sample in the tank is then removed to a test room where judges can draw samples for sniffing simply by opening the valve. A sequence of samples taken from afterburner discharges under different temperatures and flame detention times can be used for tests to ascertain the conditions necessary for deodorization.


## D. SAMPLING WITH CONCENTRATION

A dilute odorant may have to be concentrated before it can be adequately characterized by chemical analysis. Such circumstances are likely to arise when a community malodor is to be traced to one or more possible sources. The ratio of concentrations between the odor source and the odorant outdoors where it constitutes a nuisance may be in the range of $10^3$–$10^5$. Under such circumstances the comparison of the odorant with the alleged source is greatly facilitated if the concentration is increased to approximate that of the source. Comparative examinations of infrared spectra or gas chromatograms then become much more informative. The most widely used methods of concentration are freeze-out trapping and adsorptive sampling. Absorptive sampling is sometimes used, but less frequently.

## 1. Freeze-Out Sampling

In freeze-out sampling (6,29) the odorant air stream is passed through a cold trap that freezes and holds the odorous substances but does not retain the major nonodorous components. Unfortunately, the trap retains water. The coldest permissible refrigerant is usually liquid air (liquid nitrogen, bp −196°C, may condense oxygen in the trap, thus creating a hazard of pressurization when the trap is sealed and the refrigerant is removed). The trap should accommodate the relatively large quantity of ice that is collected and a filter for the aerosol matter that is usually formed. The designs of Shepherd et al. (29) and Turk et al. (36), illustrated in Fig. 3, both provide these features. Freeze-out sampling for odorants is advantageous because interactions among the concentrated components are minimized at low temperatures. A serious disadvantage is the icing of practically all the water in the air being sampled. Of course, a desiccant can be placed before the cold trap, but the desiccant may absorb or absorb odorous matter and invalidate the sampling (24).

## 2. Adsorptive Sampling

In adsorptive sampling (6,10,38) the odorant air stream is passed through a bed of activated carbon, silica gel, or (much less frequently) some other adsorbent to concentrate the odorous material. Activated carbon is advantageous because it adsorbs organic matter in preference to water, and excessive aqueous dilution of the collected odorant therefore does not occur (39). Activated carbon is so retentive to most odorous matter, however, that recovery may be difficult. Desorption of the odorant from the carbon *in vacuo* into a cold trap is effective, but may involve isomerization or other chemical changes (36,37). Solvent extraction of the odorant is a less drastic method, but may yield much less recovery (8). When the degree of concentration needed is small enough

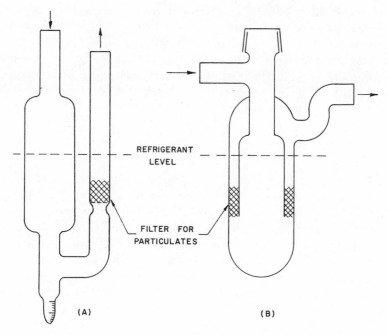

REFRIGERANT
LEVEL

FILTER FOR
PARTICULATES

(A)                    (B)

Fig. 3. Freeze out traps; (A) Turk; (B) Shepherd.

and the ambient air is dry enough so that water collection is not a serious problem, silica gel may be used in place of carbon, with the advantage that milder conditions for odorant recovery can be used (1,3,9).

## 3. Absorptive Sampling

It is sometimes advantageous to concentrate and hold an odor sample easily and with minimum manipulation of equipment. If the concentration factor need not be known precisely, it may be convenient to use an odorless solvent, like mineral oil, carried on a relatively inert material like absorbent cotton. A wad of such absorbent material may be suspended in an odorous space and subsequently removed for odor evaluation.

Absorbing bubblers are seldom used for odor sampling because collection is usually inefficient and not worth the trouble.

## IV. SENSORY ODOR MEASUREMENTS

### A. SENSORY ATTRIBUTES OF ODOR

An odor can be characterized by its intensity, its quality, its absolute threshold, and its affective tone, or pleasant–unpleasant dimension. It is important to relate any program of sensory odor measurements to realistic analytical objectives. For example, if the odor from a landfill operation is to be controlled by masking agents, it is irrelevant to appraise odor intensities or threshold levels; a more appropriate measurement would describe the changed odor quality or character and would assay its acceptability to the people in the community. On the other hand, a nonselective method of odor reduction, like ventilation or activated carbon adsorption, may well be monitored by measurements of intensity or by threshold dilution techniques.

### 1. Odor Intensity

Odor intensity is the magnitude of the stimulus produced when a person (or animal) is exposed to an odorant. A number of investigators (25) have studied neural responses of organisms to odorants, but it is important to understand that electrophysiological signals, even if it were convenient to monitor them routinely from human subjects, are not direct expressions of subjective experience. The magnitude of an odor stimulus is therefore measured along an intensity scale (called a psychophysical scale) whose reference points consist of standard odorants. The composition of the odor reference standards should be known and reproducible. Because odor, like other sensations, is a power function of the stimulus (30), it is appropriate for the concentrations of the reference odor standards to be disposed along some exponential scale; the scale most frequently used is based on log 2. The procedure is illustrated by the following example.

*Example 3.* The intensity of a series of phenolic odors is to be measured. The reference standards are the vapor phases in equilibrium with a log 2 concentration series of phenol solutions in water. The solutions are listed in Table I. About 25–30 ml (1 fl oz) of each solution is placed in a 4-oz polyethylene squeeze bottle. A judge sniffs the odor standard when he squeezes the bottle to expel about half (50 ml) the vapor phase in equilibrium with any given solution. Instructions are given to the judges as follows: "The samples lined up in front of you all contain solutions of phenol in water. They differ from each other in odor strength,

TABLE I

Phenol Odor Reference Standards

| Dilution no. | Concentration of phenol in water |
|:---:|:---|
| 1 | 5% by weight at 20°C $= C_1$ |
| 2 | $\frac{1}{2} C_1 = C_1 \times 2^{-1}$ |
| 3 | $\frac{1}{4} C_1 = C_1 \times 2^{-2}$ |
| — | — |
| — | — |
| — | — |
| $n$ | $C_1 \times 2^{1-n}$ |

the most intense odor is on the left, and the intensity gradually gets less from sample to sample towards the right. Be cautious in sniffing the strong odors. The last bottle on your right has so little phenol odor that it may not be detectable at all. You are to judge the phenol odor intensity of the unknown sample by picking the standard solution that matches it most closely."

The odor standards need not match the quality of the odors being measured. Phenol itself will serve as a standard for other phenolic odors, such as those of cresols and xylenols. There is evidence (7) that the standard odor may be radically different in quality from that being measured, but we do not know to what extent such divergence is disadvantageous.

Judges may make subjective estimates of magnitude between points that are represented by reference standards. It is also possible for a judge to estimate intensity ratios that are based on only one reference point (14). Thus, a judge may estimate that a given phenolic odor is five times as strong as that of a standard phenol odorant. Measurements set up in this way are called *ratio scales*.

The upper limit to the number of meaningful points on an odor intensity scale should not exceed the number of just perceptible differences that a judge can perceive between the lowest and highest detectable concentrations of the odorant. For most odorants this number is approximately 30. At the other extreme, a scale may have as few as two points; a measurement on such a scale amounts to a paired comparison of intensity between two odorants.

Some odor intensity scales are not anchored in specific reference standards at all, but instead are defined by descriptions like "slight," "moderate," "strong," and "extreme." Such adjectives are actually implied reference standards because an odor judge, even without instructions, will refer to his experience. Thus, for example, a fragrant odor of "moderate" intensity may be taken to mean the typical odor level in a florist shop. Such scaling can be grossly imprecise.

## 2. Odor Quality

The quality of an odor is its character described in terms of resemblance to some other odor. Descriptions of quality include words like "fragrant," "putrid," "musky," and "phenolic." If a general description of odor qualities could be set up, it would be possible to describe any odor in terms of a number of primary odor standards. Attempts of this sort include Henning's odor prism (21), Foster's odor wheel (16), the Crocker-Henderson system (13), and Amoore's classification (4). Taking the Crocker-Henderson system as a simple example, odors are classified according to four primary qualities: fragrant, acidic, burnt, and caprylic (goaty or rancid). Each quality is also rated on an odor intensity scale from 0 (none) to 8 (strongest). Thus, acetic acid is described by the numer 3803, which implies that the odor is moderately fragrant, highly acidic, not burnt, and mildly caprylic. Systems of this type, though they date from 1895 or earlier and are described in standard psychological texts, have not become useful methods of odor measurement. No conceptual system has yet been devised which accurately predicts odor quality from the chemical composition of the odorant, or vice versa, or explains the detailed mechanism of odor perception. As a result, the odor quality classifications are largely empirical and are usually compromises between high specificity, which requires many reference qualities, and convenience, which implies that the reference qualities should be few and universally recognized.

An empirical approach that does not entail any assumptions concerning primary odor types can be realized by using specific odor quality descriptors that are represented by odor quality reference standards (33). In this method, the group of odors to be judged is defined in terms of a few (usually three to eight) qualities that seem reasonable in the light of subjective associations and chemical analysis. The selections are made by people who are familiar both with the odors in question and with the analytical findings, even though the latter may be incomplete. Then an odor quality reference standard is made up to represent each quality description. The chemicals used in a reference standard represent the best choice available on the basis of odor, stability, lack of toxicity, and correspondence with constituents that are known or suspected to exist in the odorant. Each reference standard may then be expanded into a dilution scale using a suitable odorless diluent (see Sect. IV-C). For convenience, and in order not to overload the judges' capacity for yielding informative responses, the number of points on the dilution scale should correspond to the following relationship:

No. of quality stds. × no. of intensity stds/quality ≈ 12–36.

Then an odor to be appraised may be described in terms of intensities of the various qualities by proper matching with the reference standards, as in the Crocker-Henderson system. Such a description is called a *quality–intensity profile*. The procedure is illustrated by the following example:

*Example 4.* Diesel exhaust is to be appraised in terms of its quality intensity profile (33). It is found that the odor can be characterized in terms of four descriptors; burnt/smoky, oily, pungent/acid, and aldehydic/aromatic. The odor quality reference standards are made up of the following components: *burnt,* oil of cade (Juniper tar), guaiacol, carvacrol, and acetylenedicarboxylic acid; *oily,* n-octylbenzene; *pungent/acid,* crotonic acid and propiolic acid; *aromatic/aldehydic,* a mixture of aromatic hydrocarbons and aromatic and aliphatic aldehydes. Each reference standard is diluted in mineral oil, with benzyl benzoate added if necessary for solubilization, to four different concentrations representing different levels of intensity. The resulting kit of 16 reference standards is used as a basis for quality–intensity profiling of diesel exhaust odors.

## 3. Dilution and Threshold Measurements

The odor threshold is the minimum concentration at which an odorous substance can be distinguished from odor-free air (*detection threshold*) or at which its quality can be recognized (*recognition threshold*). The latter is the higher value. Odor threshold levels depend on the nature of the substance and on the sensitivity of the judge. The "$n\%$ threshold" is the concentration at which the odor can be detected (or recognized) by $n\%$ of the population.

Threshold data can be used to predict the conditions under which a given substance will be odorous or odorless. Such predictions provide a basis for calculating (*a*) the degree of dilution, by ventilation or outdoor dispersal, that is needed to deodorize a given odor source, (*b*) the proportion of odorant that must be removed from a space, by methods such as activated carbon adsorption, to effect deodorization, (*c*) the quantity of a substance that must be injected into a space to odorize it, or (d) the volume of air that can be odorized by a given quantity of substance. Threshold concentrations are *not*, however, measures or reliable predictors of odor intensity at suprathreshold levels.

The threshold values reported in the literature are scattered over wide ranges, for example, $3.2 \times 10^{-4}$ to 10 p.p.m. for pyridine (2). This variance reflects the fact that threshold concentrations are frequently so low that analytical, calibration, or other errors are large. The threshold level, $C_t$, is often measured by quantitative dilution of a given volume, $V$, of odorant of known concentration, $C$. Then

$$C = W/V \quad \text{and} \quad C_t = W/V_t$$

where $W$ is the quantity of odorant and $V_t$ is the volume of sample after it is diluted to threshold level.

Dividing and solving for $C_t$,

$$C_t = CV/V_t$$

The same procedure can be applied to characterize an odorant or odor source of unknown concentration. Then the *threshold dilution ratio* is given by $V_t/V = C/C_t$. This ratio, also called the *threshold odor number*, or the *odor pervasiveness* (32), can be used as a basis for the same calculations as those previously cited for the odor threshold concentration. Likewise, the threshold dilution ratio is *not* a measure of suprathreshold odor intensity.

A related unit, somewhat sweepingly called the *odor unit*, is defined as 1 ft³ of air at the odor threshold (5). A cubic foot of odorant that must be diluted to $n$ ft³ to reach the odor threshold level is said to contain $n$ odor units. The *odor concentration* of an odorant is then expressed in terms of "odor units per cubic foot." This nomenclature is unfortunate in that the meaning of "concentration" is foreign to chemical usage, but it will be recognized that it is identical with the threshold dilution ratio, with volumes being expressed in cubic feet.

Dilution methods have been described by several workers (5,19,23,26); the general principles are explained in Section III-B. In the light of the gross variances in odor threshold data, it must be assumed that nominal dilution factors, calculated from ratios of volumes or flow rates in a dilution system, are unreliable. An absolute method for establishing the reliability of a dilution method involves reconcentrating the odorant and verifying the reestablishment of the original concentration. The maximum error in such a procedure can be calculated on the following basis: Assume that an initial concentration of odorant, $C_i$, is sufficiently high so that it can be determined accurately by a reliable method of analysis.

The odorant is then diluted by a factor, $F_d$, that is nominally determined by volume or flow ratios in the system, to a lower concentration $C_d$. Now, using some method such as freeze-out trapping, the diluted odorant is reconcentrated by a factor, $F_r$, to recover a high concentration, $C_r$, which, like $C_i$, can be determined accurately. Now, the value for the concentration of the diluted odorant that is calculated wihout a confirming analysis from the applied dilution factor is

$$C_{d(\text{calc})} = C_i F_d$$

The reconcentrated value is

$$C_r = C_d F_r \quad \text{and} \quad C_d = C_r/F_r$$

Now, the error in measuring $C_d$ is

$$\text{Error (fractional)} = \frac{C_{d(\text{calc})} - C_d}{C_{d(\text{calc})}} = \frac{C_i F_d - C_r/F_r}{C_i F_d}$$

$$= 1 - \frac{C_r}{C_i F_d F_r}$$

If $F_d = 1/F_r$, that is, if the original concentration is nominally restored after dilution, then error $= 1 - C_r/C_i$. Note that in this calculation it is assumed that recovery of the diluted odorant is complete and that all the error lies in the dilution procedure. If some loss occurring during reconcentration is thus erroneously ascribed to the dilution, then the calculated dilution error is too high. There is no way to resolve this question except to state that the calculated error is a *maximum* value and that the real error therefore cannot be any greater than that obtained by this procedure. Turk et al. (35) have shown that a tracer gas like $SF_6$ can be used to explore inherent errors in a gas dilution system.

### 4. Odor Acceptability

Acceptability of an odor can be rated either on a hedonic (like–dislike) or an action basis.

A typical hedonic odor scale is verbally anchored with nine categories in a linear arrangement (Table I). For appraisal of community maladors, only the "dislike" half of the scale is appropriate. The panel moderator explains the test procedure to the judges and then defines the context in which the rating scale applies. For example, "The odor which you are about to test is a diluted exhaust from a diesel engine. Consider how you would rate this odor if you were outdoors and were exposed to the exhaust of a diesel vehicle. Mark your rating on the score sheet

TABLE I
Acceptability Scales

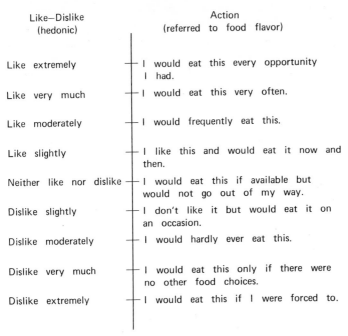

| Like–Dislike (hedonic) | Action (referred to food flavor) |
|---|---|
| Like extremely | I would eat this every opportunity I had. |
| Like very much | I would eat this very often. |
| Like moderately | I would frequently eat this. |
| Like slightly | I like this and would eat it now and then. |
| Neither like nor dislike | I would eat this if available but would not go out of my way. |
| Dislike slightly | I don't like it but would eat it on an occasion. |
| Dislike moderately | I would hardly ever eat this. |
| Dislike very much | I would eat this only if there were no other food choices. |
| Dislike extremely | I would eat this if I were forced to. |

accordingly." No other attempt is made to direct the judges' response. A new sheet is used for each test.

An action scale rates the judges' predicted behavior under some specified conditions of exposure to an odorant. Schutz (28) has described such a scale for food acceptance (Table I) and reports correlation coefficients up to 0.97 with hedonic scales.

# V. JUDGES FOR SENSORY MEASUREMENTS

## A. SELECTION OF HUMAN JUDGES

Candidates for a sensory odor panel that involve judgments other than acceptability should demonstrate (a) that they can discriminate among different odors at low or moderate levels of intensity and (b) that they can focus their attention on more than one odor quality or character in a given odor sensation. Practically all programs that involve discrimination among odorous materials of products demand sensory abilities of one or both of these types.

Three variables characterize the efficacy of a screening procedure:

(a) the cost, as determined by the number of sensory tests, (b) the proportion of potentially suitable candidates rejected by the screen, and (c) the proportion of potentially unsuitable candidates accepted by the screen. These variables are functionally dependent, that is, specification of any two determines the value of the third. Thus, if the screening procedure is to be economical and is to accept a large majority of the potentially able candidates, it will also be necessary to accept some predetermined proportion of the potentially unsuitable candidates. The unsuitable candidates can be subsequently eliminated during training sessions when their poor performance becomes apparent. Conversely, if an economical procedure is to screen out a large majority of the unsuitable candidates, it will also be necessary to lose some of the potentially able ones.

The experimental procedures previously described for sensory evaluation of materials can also be used to screen candidates for sensory judgment panels. It is somewhat advantageous, however, for a screening test to be complicated enough to result in easily observable differences in test behavior among competing candidates. The attentive panel moderator will gain rapid initial insight into the potential value of a candidate by careful observation of his performance. The specific items to which the panel leader should be attentive are: (a) *Speed.* The best behavior is purposeful and deliberate, neither excessively hasty nor too slow. (b) *Interest level.* The candidate should feel challenged and motivated. Candidates who find the work distasteful or uncomfortable should not be selected. (c) *Domination.* In group testing, the candidate should be helpful when asked, but should not try to push his opinions on others. (d) *Independence.* The candidate should be willing to consider the suggestions of others, but should not be influenced to change score against his own judgment. (e) *Honesty.* Candidates who try (successfully or not) to decode labels or peek under bottles should be rejected.

Wittes and Turk (40) have described several procedures for rapid selection of a panel of judges by screening of a relatively large number of candidates.

When judges are to be assigned to acceptability measurements, discriminatory abilities are not necessarily relevant. Instead, the judges should share the same likes and dislikes as the general population of interest. Panels of this type therefore consist of a large number of judges, perhaps several hundred, and they yield results that are interpreted as "consumer surveys." The methods of selection of such panels are not considered in this chapter.

## B. THE TRAINING OF JUDGES

The candidates that have been selected should repeat the screening procedures in order to become familiar with the conduct and execution of sensory testing. During the training, no errors are ignored. As soon as a trainee or group of trainees scores a test, the correct answers are disclosed, and the trainee repeats the exercise with attention focused on elimination of the error. If the test program will involve the use of odor reference standards, a set of standards should be made available to each panel member and he should be trained in the recognition and use of the standards until his performance reaches a satisfactory level.

## C. ENVIRONMENTAL CONDITIONS FOR SENSORY TESTING

A space for sensory testing should be free of competing distractions. In-and-out visits and socialization by nonparticipants should be restricted, except in the case of demonstration exercises. The area for preparation and coding of test samples or makeup and dilution of gas streams should be separated from the panel members and not visible to them. There should be no extraneous sounds related to sample preparation. Color schemes should be neutral and not striking.

The test area should be provided with some means for space odor control, especially for control of the odors introduced from the samples being tested. Such air cleaning may be accomplished by local exhaust of vapors from the test samples by general purification of the room air through a recirculating device (preferably an activated carbon unit), or by some combination of both methods. If a considerable volume of odorous exhaust air is spilled into the space during the conduct of the tests, then odor control by general recirculation through an air purifying device will be limited in its effectiveness (31). Hard-surfaced wall panels and asphalt tile flooring have been found to be low in background odor. If it is feared that highly odorous materials may contaminate the test space, the walls may be sprayed with an odorless, strippable, replaceable coating.

When the tests are to be conducted and reported on an individual basis without communication between judges, it is desirable to have separate booths or enclosures for the individual panel members. When the test is to be cooperative, with discussion and comparisons among the judges, then a conference table setup is convenient. The panel moderator or chairman should be able to communicate readily and conveniently with all the judges. The general atmosphere should be comfortable and relaxing, but attentive and serious.

Several simple rules for conduct should be imposed. No smoking, eating, or drinking that is not associated with tests should be allowed in the test area. Women should be discouraged from the use of perfumes or perfumed cosmetics just prior to a test session. A period of about $\frac{1}{2}$ hr or more should be interposed after smoking, eating a meal, or drinking coffee before participating in a test exercise.

## D. THE NUMBER AND ASSIGNMENT OF PANEL MEMBERS

There is no "magic number" of panel members. Many panels number 5 to 15 judges, and a number close to 10 is probably suitable for most sensory work that involves discrimination. A larger number of panelists should be available for testing, so that no interruptions need be caused by temporary absenteeism or personnel turnover. The panel members should not be divided, however, into "regulars" and "standbys." Some rotation scheme should be set up so that no trained panel member is allowed to go stale.

## VI. MATERIAL MEASUREMENTS OF ODORS. CORRELATIONS BETWEEN MATERIAL AND SENSORY MEASUREMENTS

Odorants, like other substances, are amenable to chemical analysis. In many cases such analysis is difficult and time consuming, because an odorant may be a complex mixture of many components in extremely high dilution in air or other carrier. Since the specific chemical and physical determinants of odor are not yet known, a chemical analysis of itself, no matter how complete, is not a measurement of odor. To correlate the chemical with the sensory properties of an odorant, it is necessary to assign odor intensity and quality attributes to the various components that the analyst has identified and possibly to consider interaction effects. Very few complex odorous substances have been carefully investigated in this way.

An example of an analytical investigation that offers sensory correlations is the identification of components of cucumber flavor by Forss and co-workers (15). A petroleum ether extract of cucumber distillate was gas chromatographed and the separated aldehydes were converted to their 2,4-DNPH derivatives for identification. Odor descriptions of some of the components are shown in Table II.

### TABLE II
#### Odors of Cucumber Components

| Component | Odor threshold concentration, ppm in water | Odor quality |
|---|---|---|
| 2-Nonenal | 0.0005–0.001 | Oily or tallowy near threshold concentration; cucumberlike at higher concentration |
| *trans, trans*-2,6-Nonadienal | 0.0005–0.001 | Oily or tallowy near threshold concentration; cucumberlike at higher concentration |
| *trans*-2-*cis*-6-Nonadienal | 0.00001 | Green or cucumberlike at all concentrations |

There is no specific recommended procedure for correlating chemical with sensory measurements of the properties of odorants. In general, chemical analysis and sensory evaluations are carried on side by side so as to guide the investigator in concentrating his efforts on those fractions or components that make the most significant contributions to odor (22). In some studies it is even possible to smell fractions directly as they emerge from the chromatograph (18). Of course, these remarks imply that the establishment of correlations between chemical and sensory measurements of a complex mixture is still a demanding, time-consuming mixture of science and art. Until the odorant properties of substances are better understood on a theoretical basis, this will continue to be the case.

### REFERENCES

1. Adams, D. F., R. K. Koppe, and D. M. Jungroth, *Tappi*, **43**, 602 (1960).
2. Adams, E. M., "Physiological Effects," in *Air Pollution Abatement Manual*, Manufacturing Chemists Association, Washington, D.C., 1951, Chap. 5.
3. Altshuller, A. P., T. A. Bellar, and C. A. Clemons, *Amer. Ind. Hyg. Assoc. J.*, **23**, 164 (1962).
4. Amoore, J. E., *Ann. N.Y. Acad. Sci.*, **116**, 457 (1964).
5. ASTM Method of Measurement of Odor in Atmosphere (Dilution Method) D 1391-57, in *ASTM Standards on Methods of Atmospheric Sampling and Analysis*, 2nd ed., American Society for Testing Materials, Philadelphia, 1962, pp. 40–43.
6. ASTM Recommended Practice for Sampling Atmospheres for Analysis of Gases and Vapors D 1605-60, in *ASTM Standards on Methods of Atmospheric Sampling and Analysis*, 2nd ed., American Society for Testing Materials, Philadelphia, 1962, pp. 44–46.
7. Beck, L. H., L. Kruger, and P. Calabresi, *Ann. N.Y. Acad. Sci.*, **58**, 225 (1954).
8. Brooman, D. L., and E. Edgerly, *J. Air Pollution Control Assoc.*, **16**, 25 (1966).

9. Campbell, E. E. and H. M. Ide, *Amer. Ind. Hyg. Assoc. J.*, **27**, 323 (1966).
10. Chiantella, A. J., W. D. Smith, M. E. Umstead, and J. E. Johnson, *Amer. Ind. Hyg. Assoc. J.*, **27**, 186 (1966).
11. Clemons, C. A., and A. P. Altshuller, *J. Air Pollution Control Assoc.*, **14**, 407 (1964).
12. Connor, W. D. and J. S. Nader, *Amer. Ind. Hyg. Assoc. J.*, **25**, 291 (1964).
13. Crocker, E. C. and L. F. Henderson, *Amer. Perfumer,* **22**, 325, 356 (1927).
14. Engen, T., *Ann. N.Y. Acad. Sci.*, **116**, 504 (1964).
15. Forss, D. A., E. A. Dunstone, E. H. Ramshaw, and W. Stark, *J. Food Sci.*, **27**, 90 (1962).
16. Foster, D., A New Method of Predicting the Qualities of Flavor Mixtures, Institute of Food Technologists, Jan. 1952.
17. Fraust, C. L., and E. R. Hermann, *Amer. Ind. Hygiene Assoc. J.* **27**, 68 (1966).
18. Fuller, G. H., R. Steltenkamp, and G. A. Tisserand, *Ann. N.Y. Acad. Sci.*, **116**, 711 (1964).
19. Gex, V. E. and J. P. Snyder, *Chem. Eng.*, **59**, No. 12, 200 (1952).
20. Goetz, A., *Intern. J. Air Water Pollution*, **4**, 168 (1961).
21. Henning, H., *Der Geruch*, 2nd Ed., Leipzig, 1924.
22. Kendall, D. A., and A. J. Neilson, *Ann. N.Y. Acad. Sci.*, **116**, 567 (1964).
23. Mateson, J. F., *J. Air Pollution Control Assoc.*, **5**, 167 (1955).
24. McKee, H. C., J. W. Rhoades and W. A. McMahon, paper presented at 136th National Meeting American Chemical Society, Atlantic City, New Jersey, Sept. 1959.
25. Moulton, D. G. and D. Tucker, *Ann. N.Y. Acad. Sci.*, **116**, 380 (1964).
26. Nader, John S., *Amer. Ind. Hyg. Assoc. J.*, **19**, 1 (1958).
27. Pasquill, F., *Atmospheric Diffusion,* Van Nostrand, Princeton, N.J., 1962.
28. Schutz, H. G., *J. Food Sci.*, **30**, 365 (1965).
29. Shepherd, M., S. M. Rock, R. Howard, and J. Stormes, *Anal. Chem.*, **23**, 1431 (1951).
30. Stevens, S. S., *Psychol. Rev.*, **64**, 153 (1957).
31. Turk, A., *ASHRAE J.*, **6**, 55 (Oct. 1963).
32. Turk, A., "Odor Measurement and Control," in *Air Pollution Abatement Manual,* Manufacturing Chemists' Association, Washington, D.C., 1960, Chap. 13.
33. Turk, A., *Selection and Training of Judges for the Sensory Evaluation of Odor Intensity and Character of Diesel Exhaust,* Public Health Service Publication No. 999-AP-32, 1967.
34. Turk, A., and K. Bownes, *Science,* **114**, 234 (1951).
35. Turk, A., S. M. Edmonds, H. Mark, and G. F. Collins, *Environmental Sci. Tech.*, Jan. 1968, p. 44.
36. Turk, A., J. I. Morrow, and B. E. Kaplan, *Anal. Chem.*, **34**, 561 (1962).
37. Turk, A., J. I. Morrow, S. H. Stoldt, and W. Baecht, *J. Air Pollution Control Assoc.*, **16**, 383 (1966).
38. Turk, A., H. Sleik and P. J. Messer, *Amer. Ind. Hyg. Assoc. Quart.*, **13**, 23 (1952).
39. Turk, A., and A. Van Doren, *Agr. Food Chem.*, **1**, 145 (1953).
40. Wittes, J., and A. Turk, "The Selection of Judges for Odor Discrimination Panels," in *Correlation of Subjective—Objective Methods in the Study of Odor and Taste,* American Society for Testing Materials, Spec. Tech. Public No. 440, 1967.

# ANALYSIS OF AIR FOR POLLUTANTS

By James P. Lodge, Jr., and John B. Pate, *National Center for Atmospheric Research, Boulder, Colorado**

## Contents

* Operated by the University Corporation for Atmospheric Research with sponsorship of the National Science Foundation. The mention of particular manufacturers or their products does not constitute an endorsement by the National Center for Atmospheric Research or the National Science Foundation.

**Contents** (*continued*)

# I. INTRODUCTION

## A. SCOPE

For most purposes, the definition of *air pollutants* is a subjective one, limiting the term to anthropogenic substances present in sufficient quantity to cause a human response, whether physiological, economic, or aesthetic. Chemically speaking, this definition is not a useful one, since it makes sulfur dioxide from a power plant a pollutant, while chemically identical sulfur dioxide from a volcano is not. It further implies that, below some threshold of concentration, sulfur dioxide ceases to be a pollutant; any similarity between this threshold and the threshold of chemical detection is fortuitous.

For purposes of this chapter, therefore, it is preferable to consider an entity called "pure air," consisting of nitrogen, oxygen, the noble gases, carbon dioxide, and water, either as a vapor or as droplets, and to consider anything else present in air for on appreciable length of time to be a pollutant. Such a definition has numerous shortcomings. It may easily be construed as a judgment that the presence of anything else in air renders it polluted and, hence, inferior. It opens to consideration a number of trace species not particularly susceptible to chemical determination, such as nitrous oxide, which this chapter will not treat in any detail. Despite these shortcomings, this definition delimits a group of substances which pose closely similar analytical problems from the chemists' viewpoint. Furthermore, the elementary gases have already been considered (Part II). Carbon dioxide is not frequently considered a pollutant, although it is of increasing concern today. It will be mentioned briefly. The subject of humidity, the measurement of the water vapor content of the air, is a major subject in itself, and has been arbitrarily excluded from this chapter.

The analytical chemist is perhaps more aware than most of the extreme diffuseness of the boundary between chemistry and physics. Nevertheless, this chapter will emphasize a consideration of what may reasonably be called chemical methods of analysis, which means that such clearly nonchemical techniques as odor perception will be omitted; methods which do not yield quantitative answers in terms of definable chemical entities will receive, at most, passing mention; and physical methods such as mass spectrometry will not be covered in depth.

## B. CLASSIFICATION OF POLLUTANTS

Of the numerous bases for classifying pollutants, only one is of operational importance for analytical purposes, and even it is more arbitrary than is sometimes realized. However, the physical state of the pollutant does deserve attention, because it has a bearing on the means used for collecting it.

If pollutants are clearly dispersed in air in a molecular state, the pollutant is said to be a gas, in contradistinction to the highly polymolecular aggregates of liquid or solid substances which are lumped together as aerosols. To define these terms may seem an unnecessary elaboration of the obvious, yet in practice these definitions engender as much perplexity as the convenience of the labels resolves. Many particules carry with them quantities of absorbed or absorbed "gas." Some systems for collecting these aerosols may also collect the "planetary atmospheres" which the particles carry with them. Are these species truly part of the aerosol or are they truly gases?

It has been computed that roughly ten molecules of sulfuric acid, if joined together from the gas phase, constitute a stable nucleus with more probability of growing by accumulation than of being disrupted by normal thermal agitation. Yet a particle of this size is smaller than many individual molecules and behaves towards most methods of collection more like a gas than like an aerosol. Here again the line of demarcation is not at all clear.

For reasons of organization, the convention of distinguishing between gases and aerosols (or particulates) will be retained here. The fact that the distinction is artificial is one of numerous *caveats* which must be borne in mind if the limitations of pollutant analysis are to be clearly understood.

## C. INHERENT DIFFICULTIES

The atmosphere with its load of pollutants constitutes a highly inhomogenous and dynamic mixture which, in its natural state, is virtually never in equilibrium and is infrequently in a steady state (38). Species which are completely incompatible with one another can co-exist for extended periods because of extreme dilution. The mixture is usually highly inconstant on a scale running the entire gamut from the microscopic to the macroscopic. As a result, the atmosphere may appear to the analyst to be a large-scale manifestation of Heisenberg's principle: the act of sampling invariably affects the sample. If the information desired is the elementary composition of the sample, sampling effects may be minimized to the point where they can generally be ignored. However, the analyst usually wishes to know the molecular composition of the pollutants. In such cases, it is frequently preferable to employ chemical means of collecting the species of interest. Such means properly consist of the promotion of a known chemical reaction which is fast, compared with the numerous unknown reactions possible among the other species present in the sample. The ultimate reaction product thus accumulates in proportion to the amount of original substance in the air and may be subsequently determined. ASTM Recommended Practice No. 1357–57 (13) states that "the collection, transfer, and transportation of samples without alteration or change from the condition and composition in which they existed in the atmosphere should be emphasized." Except in unusual circumstances, this is manifestly impossible. Experience has shown that more accurate and consistent results are obtained by sampling for specific substances using chemical methods which fix those substances for subsequent analysis, irrespective of the effect on other species present in the original sampled air.

The concentration of pollutants is usually sufficiently low that large air samples are required to permit the concentration of enough material for analytical purposes. The total diversity of species present in any sample is so great that all potential interfering substances must be assumed present until it is clearly proven otherwise. Analytical methods research in this field is thus largely a search for more sensitive and selective reagents or other analytical tools. Occasionally, success in this search can prove embarrassing. A few years ago the author witnessed the testing of a new instrument for detecting one particular pollutant. This instrument was sufficiently sensitive that its response was virtually instantaneous. There were some obvious inherent difficulties, but tests on synthetic mixtures showed the instrument to be generally acceptable. However, when it was tested on the natural atmosphere, it was found that the pollutant was so imperfectly mixed that the fluctuations in instrument response exceeded the writing rate of the recording potentiometer attached to the output, resulting in a completely ink-covered chart, a damaged recorder, and no data which could be interpreted. Once the apparently attractive feature of rapid response had been removed by adding a large mixing chamber to the intake line, thereby causing some loss of the pollutant to be measured, the instrument drew interpretable lines, but it had ceased to have any advantage over less sensitive methods. It was ultimately abandoned. The very minute syringe samples necessary for introduction into modern high sensitivity gas chromatographs may be subject to similar fluctuations which are less obvious, since the analytical system itself is not continuously sensitive to fluctuations.

## II. SAMPLING

It has been stated above that the act of sampling inevitably modifies the sample to some degree. It is therefore necessary in planning sampling operations to consider carefully the question which the final analysis is designed to answer. The case of the automatic analyzer of instantaneous response cited above is an extreme example of the typical misfit which can occur between the actual sampling device and the intent of the analysis; a properly formulated program could doubtless have used that analyzer in an unmodified form to obtain very useful information concerning the scale of turbulence in the environment. However, the unmodified instrument failed entirely to provide the information actually desired, which was the mean level of the pollutant averaged over a span of a minute or so, rather than a second.

There are, of course, many other ways in which misfits of scale may occur. Many devices will not collect submicron particles, and it is therefore useless to look for them in the sample. Some devices, as will be discussed later, have collection thresholds—concentrations below which the desired substances are not collected at all.

In addition, some techniques may be chemically inappropriate to the problem at hand. It is obviously impossible to count water-soluble particles if they are collected by impingement in water. It is less obvious, but nonetheless true, that a thick mat of collected particles on a filter may react with passing trace gases to yield a final sample very different in composition from the original air-borne particles. Such a mat also changes the retention characteristics of the filter toward fine particles. Sorbed species may be lost by being stripped off by passing air from particles collected on a filter.

It is axiomatic for chemists that no analysis can be better than the quality of the sampling. In no analytical area is this more painfully true than in air analysis.

## A. SAMPLING OF AEROSOLS

Lodge (128) has treated this subject extensively in a previous review. It will therefore be covered here only briefly.

### 1. Inertial

A large group of techniques for the separation of particles from gases may be referred to as *inertial*. These make use of the fact that the inertia of a particle is greater than that of an individual gas molecule. If the gas stream is constrained to change direction rapidly by collision with a barrier, the particles, depending on their size, will be in greater or lesser degree unsuccessful in following the air stream and will then deposit in some pattern on the barrier. Included in this category of devices are simple plates extended from rapidly flying aircraft to capture large particles (263), spider silk used for the same purpose (244), impactors in which an air stream accelerated by passage through a jet strikes against a closely spaced surface (153), and impingers in which the same sort of action occurs under the surface of a liquid (81). The liquid serves the dual purpose of constantly washing off the collecting surface and of providing more opportunity for collection, since any particles not collected are trapped in bubbles and may collide with the walls by Brownian motion before the bubbles burst. Inertial methods are adaptable to sampling from sizable volumes (116) and can be arranged to yield a sample classified as to particle size (126). The chief disadvantage of the method is that the necessary high relative velocity between particle and collecting surface may cause shattering or bounce-off and reentrainment of the particles (37).

### 2. Gravitational

Closely related to the inertial methods are the *gravitational* techniques, in which particles are induced to leave the air parcels in which they travel by gravity or by the induced gravity of a centrifugal field. Devices in this class range from simple quiescent sedimentation chambers (209) to elaborate centrifugal collectors, such as the Goetz "particle spectrometer" (80). Devices of this sort have several advantages: They can be designed so as to yield collections which are classified by apparent size, since the larger particles will sediment more rapidly than the smaller ones, other things being equal. Also, since the treatment of the particles is generally rather gentle, collection by this method has perhaps the least tendency either to add or remove sorbed layers or to lead to reaction after collection. The disadvantages lie in the sensitivity of all systems to small perturbations; ideal patterns of settling can be completely destroyed by electric charge phenomena or by slight convection in the sedimentation volume (209). Although gravitational collection can be designed to provide concentration data, the preponderant use of the method is in the determination of "fallout." This term is here used in its proper sense, meaning the rate of arrival of any species at the ground, measured in units of mass per unit area.

### 3. Gradient

In at least one sense, gravitational methods of sampling involve motion of the particles through a gravitational gradient. Nearly any gradient which can be induced in the atmosphere will cause a motion of particles with respect to it, giving rise to a large class of methods that can generally be characterized as *gradient* techniques. A large number of different types of gradients have been explored as possible means of collecting fine particles.

Electrophoresis, the motion of a charged particle in electrostatic field or gradient, is the basis of the electrostatic precipitator, widely used as an air cleaning device in air pollution control (260). It has also been used extensively in various forms and in the sampling of airborne particles (125). The method is highly efficient for submicron particles, with the efficiency decreasing as size increases. Its greatest advantage is that electrostatic forces can be made large, making the sampling process rapid and thus permitting the high sampling rates. All particles are charged before collection by passage through a corona discharge or, less frequently, a beam of ionizing radiation. The chief disadvantage is that either means of charging also generates substantial quantities of ozone, which may undesirably alter the chemical composition of the particles collected. Also, the collecting surface must be electrically conducting to some degree, which poses some limitations on the sampling substrate. Liu and co-workers (126a) have recently announced the development of a new precipitator design which appears to avoid both the requirement of electrical conductivity in the collecting substrate and of size discrimination in sampling.

Thermophoresis, as the name implies, is movement in a thermal gradient. In the thermal precipitator, the sampled air is drawn between a heated surface and a cold one. Particles tend to move down the thermal gradient and are thus collected on the cold surface. The chief advantage of the method lies in its nearly complete lack of size discrimination. However, thermal forces are weak, and very low sampling rates are necessary with this device. It can, therefore, only be used in very high particle concentrations or in experiments in which very long sampling times are not inconvenient (94).

Some studies have also been made of diffusophoresis [motion of particles in a vapor concentration gradient (211)] and photophoresis [motion under the influence of intense light (182)]. However, both of these forces are small compared with those above, and neither appears, at the moment, to be practical as a sampling method.

### 4. Diffusional

*Diffusional* methods are used for the smallest particles. These are entirely statistical processes based on the fact that, whenever a collecting surface and a small particle are brought near together, there is a finite probability that Brownian motion of the particle will bring the two into collision. Twomey and Severynse (245), among others, have used very closely spaced labyrinths of interleaving baffles as "diffusion batteries" to remove the finest particles—the so-called Aitken nuclei—from air. Since the efficacy of collection depends so strongly on the ratio of collecting surface to total volume, the diffusion battery is obviously of little use as a sampling device.

### 5. Sieving

The largest air borne particles may be collected by *sieving*. As the name implies, this consists simply of interposing in the path of the particles a mesh structure of some kind having holes smaller than the particle diameter. So far as air sampling is concerned, collection by pure sieving action is of little importance, unless insects are considered to be air pollutants.

### 6. Filtration

Collection by *filtration* (124), perhaps the most widely used single technique of removing particles from air, is also the most complex. Depending on the filter structure, sieving may have greater or lesser importance. It is certainly a major effect in sampling on membrane filters, which have small pore sizes. All filters have some depth, however, and the air is constrained to move through them in more or less tortuous paths. Thus, both diffusional and inertial collection also play roles of some consequence. Finally, many filters assume an electrostatic charge, so that electrophoretic mechanisms may also operate. Many filters, because of the interaction of the many mechanisms, display a characteristic size of maximum particle penetration, with higher efficiency for both larger and smaller particles. (See, e.g., 222a). An excellent code for the testing of high efficiency filters has been provided by the Verein Deutscher Ingenieure (129).

## B. SAMPLING OF GASES

With a very few exceptions to be discussed later, aerosols are sampled by removing them from the gas phase onto a solid surface or, less frequently, directly into a liquid. The means for doing so are varied and constitute the basis of the above classification of sampling methods. Since gases are continuous with the supporting medium by definition, techniques for collecting them are less varied, and, thanks to recent advances in analytical methods, such concentration steps may frequently be avoided.

### 1. Storage

The term *storage* is here used in the special sense of simply moving a portion of the ambient air into a container and closing it off there. No concentration of the sample occurs; it is merely isolated from its environment and may be transported to the laboratory for analysis. Storage is perhaps an inadequate name for this process, but no better one appears to exist. The more widely used term, *grab sampling*, is even less descriptive of a large number of methods clearly in this general class and should be restricted to small volume, rapidly collected storage samples. Where large samples are needed, the container may be a gas cylinder and the air sample may be forced into it under considerable pressure. Inert ingredients, such as the noble gases, can be analyzed very well in this way. However, reactions among the more active species are accelerated both by pressure and by the concomitant heating, so that the application of storage sampling under pressure is quite limited. Today its primary use appears to be in atmospheric studies of isotope abundances, which are unaffected by the possible chemical changes caused by compression.

Storage at atmospheric pressure may be in rigid containers which are initially evacuated or which are so designed that they can readily be flushed with the air to be sampled before being closed off (105). The requirements for inertness and rigidity in the container largely limits it to glass and stainless steel, although other materials may be used for specific purposes. Recently, increasing use has been made of nonrigid sampling containers, such as plastic bags (49) and even rubber bladders (2). The choice of material depends strongly on the pollutants to be collected and, in some cases, on the storage time between sampling and analysis. A number of materials have been evaluated against a broad spectrum of pollutants with varying success (3,44). The most widely used and the most generally applicable, appear to be Mylar, certain laminates, and fluorinated hydrocarbon materials, such as Tedlar [poly-(vinyl fluoride)]. The laminates have excellent characteristics protecting against loss by simple diffusion, but are generally insufficiently passive for the storage of highly reactive species, such as ozone and the nitrogen and sulfur oxides. The highly fluorinated films are the most inert, but are quite difficult to seal into bags which do not leak. Mylar appears to be a good general purpose compromise, though not as good as either of the other choices in the area in which each of the respective materials is best. Mylar has the added advantage of being extremely inelastic, so that if it is filled to a constant, slight overpressure, a bag will permit the collection of fairly reproducible volumes (25). The chief advantage of bags for sample collection is that they may be squeezed flat so as to minimize the need for flushing before filling. They also pose little or no resistance to being filled.

The development of high sensitivity gas chromatographs has greatly increased the popularity of storage sampling, since it makes possible the determinations of very low concentrations of many species in small volumes of air. The volumes needed are frequently so small that they may simply be drawn into a glass syringe and injected directly into the chromatograph (21,187). The syringe may be capped during transportation to the analytical laboratory. Syringe sampling has the great advantage of requiring a minimum number of transfers between the atmosphere and the analysis. Like the bag, it has the added advantage of having a minimum dead volume that must be flushed, together with an inherently defined sample volume. The chief disadvantage, aside from the fragility of the syringe, is the danger that the sample may be taken so rapidly as to be unrepresentative of the atmosphere generally.

## 2. Condensation

Low temperature condensation, sometimes called cryosampling, is an attractive method, but it has a number of shortcomings so far as atmospheric problems are concerned. In essence, it consists of drawing air through a trapping device which is cooled to a suitable low temperature. Many species will be present in air at such concentrations that they will condense out in the zone of reduced temperature and will thus be concentrated (48).

If the sampling trap is maintained at the temperature of liquid hydrogen, the air itself will be totally condensed. Where a large air sample is needed, the method probably introduces fewer artifacts than does storage sampling with compression. Certain precautions are obviously needed to handle such a sample, and, of course, neither hydrogen nor helium will be collected.

A more usual refrigerant for air pollution studies is liquid oxygen. The material is somewhat dangerous to handle, but liquid nitrogen cannot be used because its boiling point is sufficiently low that the trap would rapidly fill with liquid oxygen. However, if proper precautions are observed, a substantial sample comprising the moisture, the carbon dioxide, and an interesting cross section of the pollutants will be collected.

Aside from the hazard of handling liquid oxygen, the method has two principal shortcomings. The first of these is that this method has a threshold of collection. Roughly speaking, no substance will be collected unless its partial pressure in air exceeds the vapor pressure of the liquid or solid at the temperature of liquid oxygen. To clarify the issue, assume that a particular substance has, at that temperature, a vapor pressure of 1 $\mu$. If the collecting trap functions ideally and if the partial pressure in air is 100 $\mu$, the substance will be collected with 99% efficiency. If its partial pressure is 2 $\mu$, it will be collected wth 50% efficiency, and, finally, if its partial pressure is 1 $\mu$ or less, it will not be collected at all, irrespective of the design of the trap or the number of traps connected in series. The above is, of course, an oversimplification, since the collection will be a mixture and the equilibrium vapor pressure of the substance above the mixture will depend on the other substances present. However, it emphasizes the complexity of anticipating the efficiency of a cryosampling system.

Condensation also can result in large artifacts because it brings together reactive species in a highly concentrated form. Although the reaction rates may be small at the temperature of liquid oxygen, it is almost invariably necessary to increase the temperature to remove samples for analysis. Various means can obviously be devised to minimize such reaction, but it is a problem that must be met if this technique is used.

Generally speaking, the availability of analytical methods of greatly increased sensitivity has decreased the popularity of condensation sampling except for special research purposes.

### 3. Adsorption

The obvious shortcomings of condensation led to serious consideration of the possibilities of concentrating material on an adsorbent at an appropriate, frequently reduced temperature, presumably to be followed by either evacuation or flushing with an inert gas to remove oxygen and then, desorption at an elevated temperature. This idea was based upon two fundamental premises: first, that an entirely nonselective collector was desirable and, second, that it was necessary to concentrate a large amount of gaseous material. Numerous studies were made of the adsorption characteristics of a number of charcoals, aluminas, and other adsorbents (35,46,97,164,185,222,255). However, the need for concentrating gases and vapors has been greatly decreased by the development of highly sensitive gas chromatographic detectors and other techniques. Nonpolar species can generally be analyzed with high sensitivity and accuracy with the chromatograph, as most of them are organic and thus are detectable by flame ionization. Highly polar substances are, in general, impossible to desorb, and they are generally sufficiently reactive that it is simpler to collect them selectively and determine them colorimetrically.

Nearly all adsorbents have individual disadvantages in addition to the above general ones. Silica gel and alumina are excellent isomerization catalysts (4,255). Carbons tend to be almost too strongly adsorbent; desorption from them can be extremely difficult (33,156). Furthermore, some highly reactive gases attack carbon to produce additional artifacts. For example, ozone reacts to form carbon monoxide (22). Some adsorbents appear to catalyze surface reactions between sorbed species.

Taken all in all, the disadvantages of the method have led to a loss of interest in a totally nonselective collecting system. Adsorption sampling is still used, but for specific purposes. For example, carbon containing substantial amounts of bromine can be used to collect ethylene (241), which is a trifle difficult to detect otherwise. The resulting ethylene dibromide can be subsequently desorbed and detected gas chromatographically or by other appropriate means (157). The substantial selectivity of certain of the molecular sieve materials permits the separation of otherwise fairly intractable hydrocarbon mixtures (31,261).

Naughton and co-workers (164) desorbed samples collected on silica gel and analyzed them by gas chromatography in an elegant study of volcanic gases. Despite such occasional studies, the primary use of adsorbents today is in purifying air for experimental purposes, such as sample dilution, rather than in collecting samples.

## 4. Absorption

By far the most widely used method for collecting and concentrating the reactive pollutants is absorption, generally in aqueous media. Saltzman has given an excellent treatment to the kinetics of the process (196), and there have been both theoretical (40,62) and experimental (76) studies of the critical parameters involved in bubbling polluted air through a liquid collecting medium.

Whenever air containing trace impurities contacts a liquid surface, a complex of exchange mechanisms begins, whose rates and equilibrium positions depend on the usual parameters. For example, sulfur dioxide can be removed from air with more than 80% efficiency if a jet of air is merely directed at a water surface (162). Roughly equivalent efficiency is obtained in the reaction between ozone and potassium iodide solution in the Brewer ozone transmogrifier (32). The contact between air and solution is scarcely greater than that necessary for sulfur dioxide collection. On the other hand, absorption of nitrogen dioxide in aqueous media is very slow, so that several carefully designed bubblers in series may be necessary for substantially complete collection of nitrogen dioxide (197).

Absorption, then, is a process by which a component of the gas phase is transferred into the bulk of a liquid or solid phase. The transfer process is usually accompanied by a chemical reaction which fixes the absorbed species in its new state, making the transfer substantially irreversible. Selection of the appropriate chemical reaction can make the process specific for a single compound or a restricted group of compounds. In some cases, additional selectivity can be provided by selection of the means of contact between the gas and the absorbent.

Contact between gas and liquid is generally induced by one of three methods: ventilation, spraying, and bubbling. As it is used here, ventilation means the simple passage of the gas in a more or less defined path over the surface of the liquid. This method provides sufficient contact only for the most reactive gases. The sulfur dioxide analyzer of Nash (162) and the Brewer ozone transmogrifier (32) are both examples. In both cases, numerous interferences are avoided or minimized on purely kinetic grounds, since the interfering substances are less soluble in the aqueous reagents. Spray contactors are widely used in air cleaning, but the only conspicuous example in air sampling is the Crabtree-Kemp ozone apparatus (50). Here the sampled air is used to atomize the reagent, which strikes the opposing wall of the apparatus and runs down to join the pool of reagent which is then reatomized. This arrangement generates a great deal of reacting surface, but it is complex, requires a substantial pressure drop through the apparatus, and seems to have very little advantage over bubbling.

There appear to be as many devices for bubbling gas through liquid as there are investigators. With a few exceptions, the essential requirements for a bubbler are an apparatus which is reasonably durable and which provides the maximum ratio of sample flow rate to absorbent volume consistent with reasonably complete absorption of the gas under study. In addition, there may be special requirements; for example, some reagents tend to foam badly and require adequate free space to prevent foam from being carried into the rest of the sampling system.

The incoming gas stream is usually broken up into bubbles by a sintered glass (or occasionally plastic) disperser which is submerged in, or covered by, the absorbing liquid. The primary difference between bubblers is generally in the geometry of the outer container which holds the absorbent.

Numerous data support the idea that little is to be gained by attempting to generate very small bubbles by the use of fine frits. Apparently such phenomena as bubble coalescence largely negate any gain in bubble surface from an initially smaller size, and such a gain is more than offset by the increase in pressure drop through the finer frit. All available information indicates that more can be gained by increasing the contact time by making the height of liquid above the frit greater.

European scientists seem to prefer a large flat frit sealed into the bottom of the sampling vessel, while Americans prefer a thimble-shaped frit at the end of a tube which is introduced from the top (102,217). The former arrangement initially spreads the bubbles over a wider cross section, but the resulting structure is more fragile and more difficult to clean than the latter. The general tendency in the United States is to use a bubbler resembling a midget impinger with a glass frit in place of a nozzle (193) or a modification having a bulbular enlargement near the top of the outer vessel to serve as a bubble and spray trap (20). Wartburg et al. (252a) have proposed a convenient form of this sampler in which a plastic fitting replaces the ground joints. An unusual modification was suggested by Ehmert (60); it is a sort of reversed bubbler which is particularly adapted to using very small liquid volumes, down to 1 or 2 ml. This form was subsequently used by Bravo and Lodge (30) in their specific method for ozone.

Where longer reaction times are desirable, it is possible to space bubbles into a concurrent flow of liquid in a long, thin tube. One excellent example is a small device in which a fixed volume of base is conductimetrically titrated with air for the determination of atmospheric carbon dioxide (95). In this instance, the low air flow rate is no disadvantage since carbon dioxide concentrations are several orders of magnitude higher than those of most pollutants. Similar contactors have been used in a number of automatic monitoring instruments, but it appears that the contact is actually far longer than necessary and that the resulting devices may be more impressive than effective.

Solid absorption sampling can be divided into two general classes, which might well be called *passive* and *active*. Since building surfaces, vegetation, and many other objects are affected by simple transfer of the reacting species from air passing by rather than passing through, it was suggested many years ago that a suitable reacting surface merely exposed to the wind might be a better model of the actual effectiveness of pollutants in causing damage than one subjected to artificial ventilation. At least two devices arose from this philosophy. The oldest is certainly the "lead peroxide candle," a cylinder coated with a layer of lead dioxide and exposed in a shelter for an extended period of time (generally a month) (89,118,168). At the end of that time, the resulting sulfate was determined and found usually to relate to mean levels of sulfur dioxide in the environment during the sampling period. The use of various types of coated plates has been proposed to simplify sampler preparation (25a,98a). Similarly, paper impregnated with lime has been used as a passive collector for hydrogen fluoride (1). The primary advantages of these methods are extreme simplicity and low cost. However, the rate of uptake of the sampled pollutant is a function not only of concentration, but of ventilation rate, humidity, and the amount of sampled material already present. The degree to which these passive samplers actually model uptake rates by walls or vegetation has never been seriously investigated. In concept, the long-term cumulative rubber cracking test for ozone, devised by Haagen-Smit and Fox (84), is in somewhat the same category, although it is unclear whether actual absorption of ozone is involved.

A number of gas chromatographic column packings have been used for direct sampling (5,14,51,216,262), a technique first reported by Eggertsen and Nelsen (59a). Although such sampling superficially resembles adsorption techniques, absorption in the liquid phase is probably the dominant mechanism. The advantages are optimum contact, giving high collection efficiency, and portability. Reaction upon concentration is not necessarily avoided, however, since the sample presumably undergoes displacement rather than elution chromatography in the sampling column.

The use of packed beds or impregnated filters actively aspirated at a known rate, and thus properly called active sampling devices is becoming more widespread. Almost simultaneously, Huygen (100) and Pate and co-workers (174) published the first of respective series of papers dealing with gas sampling on chemically impregnated dry filters. Huygen's approach is somewhat more empirical than Pate's; however, both appear to have demonstrated the utility of this particular approach for some highly active substances. More recently, Okita and Lodge (167) have described a particularly simple system for collecting and estimating hydrogen sulfide.

Direct reaction of the filter material with the component to be sampled has been used in a few cases. An example is the use of glass fiber filters for direct sampling of hydrogen fluoride (170).

A system which appears to have great possibilities, but which has been little investigated, is sampling in packed beds of ion exchange resins (46). Dry or nearly dry systems are appealing since they generally avoid the necessity of taking fragile glassware and corrosive liquids into the field. There is also evidence to suggest that undesired reactions between collection and analysis may be minimized in the dry state, and there is little question that the shelf life of the collector prior to use is considerably greater than that of many liquid reagents. There is also every indication that dry systems can be made far more efficient than comparable liquid absorbers, at least in favorable situations. The main advantage is simplicity, especially when coupled with the elegant flow control system of Lodge and his collaborators (130). Solid sampling systems free the analyst in the field from most of the complexities that have led to lost samples in the past.

## III.  ANALYSIS

In the end, the selection of a sampling method must be made with an eye to the method of analysis to be used on the collected sample, which must, in turn, be dictated by the type of answers desired. It is time, therefore, to consider the analytical techniques available to the chemist, with some mention of the classes of sampling methods peculiarly adaptable to each.

## A. ANALYSIS OF AEROSOLS

Collected fine particles may be analyzed with either of two general aims in mind: (*1*) to determine the composition of the entire sample in terms of percentages of various atomic or molecular components or (*2*) to obtain information concerning the composition of individual particles. Different analytical techniques are involved in the two cases.

### 1. Bulk Methods

A question commonly raised in air pollution studies that can be answered by bulk analysis is the total content of the atmosphere, in units such as micrograms per cubic meter, of a particular metal. The general approach to such a case is to take as large a sample as possible, usually by electrostatic precipitation (125) or by filtration (200,248) on a substrate which presumably neither contains that metal nor contributes ions which interfere with its determination (77,173). The sample is then brought into solution and analyzed by means discussed in previous volumes. The analysis of such a sample differs from alloy analysis or mineral analysis only in the larger number of other species that may be present in comparable amounts.

When information concerning molecular composition is desired, more precautions must be taken in handling the sample, as it is relatively easy to introduce artifacts in the handling process (see Sect. II). The analytical problem is still fundamentally a classical one which can be transferred with relative ease from methods adopted to other types of samples. Thus, so far as the bulk analysis of collected particulate matter is concerned, there are no unique methods peculiar to air pollutants. Because the desired materials are generally a small component of a dilute system, the tendency is to use the most sensitive methods available. Gravimetric and titrimetric determinations are rarely made, colorimetric methods are by far the most popular, and there is increasing use of the particularly sensitive methods, such as fluorometry (207) and atomic absorption spectrometry. A recent review (256) stressed the potentialities of the ring oven method, probably correctly.

### 2. Single Particle Methods

Substantial information concerning the variation of chemical composition with particle size can be gained by sampling with a collector which classifies the particles according to size, such as the particle spectrometer or the cascade impactor. However, neither device is well adapted to taking large samples, so that very careful microchemical methods are necessary if either is to yield data of sufficient accuracy to be enlightening. At least in favorable circumstances, it is scarcely more difficult to analyze the individual particles. This involves microscopy and is undeniably tedious. However, it definitely provides information difficult to obtain by any other means. The three principal methods of single particle analysis are morphology, micrurgy, and microspot test techniques. These were the subject of a recent review by Lodge (128); the present discussion can therefore be less detailed except in the case of a few new developments.

Morphological identification consists essentially in the recognition of chemical species at sight. In the case of light microscopy, such recognition may be aided by the use of polarized light, by the precise measurement of various characteristic angles of crystal habit, and such ancillary tools as immersion liquids and dispersion staining (52). While the problem in its simplest terms is scarcely more difficult than the daily task of recognizing one's friends, the latter are acquired over a longer period of time and under more familiar circumstances than the acquaintance of some hundreds of chemical species. As a result, the method has not been widely used. It has become far more feasible with the publication of a manual of systematic identification (147).

Morphological identification with the electron microscope appears still more difficult, since such clues as color and birefringence are missing. However, Lodge and Frank (131) have shown that several species, particularly sulfuric acid and most phosphates, can be recognized at sight. Since most electron microscopes can also be used for electron diffraction, further identifications are also possible, as shown by the work of Kumai and Francis (114,115) on the identification of snowflake nuclei.

Micrurgy is simply the conduct of relatively simple identification reactions under the light microscope, usually with the aid of a more or less precise micromanipulator. The general techniques were thoroughly outlined in the classic treatise of Chamot and Mason (41). The specific application of these methods to the analysis of pollutant particles has been ably discussed by Cadle (39). Micrurgic techniques are applied to particles singly, frequently after morphological examination has given clues as to their composition. In many cases, if the initial identification is incorrect, further tests can be applied to the same particle, so long as the respective reagents are compatible. However, if large numbers of particles are to be examined, these techniques are extremely slow and fatiguing.

An alternative approach is to treat an entire collection with a reagent specific for a given ion in such a way that the resulting reaction remains localized in the vicinity of the particle which occasioned it. Particles not containing an ion being sought are ignored. Lodge (132) has termed this group of techniques "micro-spot tests." Two subclasses can be distinguished. In the first of these, pioneered by Seely (53,212), the particles are collected on a surface which already includes the specific reagent. Once the particles are collected on it, the reaction either proceeds immediately, as in Seely's methods cited above and a few others (68,154,249,251), or after extremely simple treatment, such as storage at high humidity (65,133). The obvious requirement is a medium which would hold the reagent, permit the reaction, and immobilize the reaction products. Gels such as gelatin are most widely used, although impregnated membrane filters are also applicable in some cases. Samples on gelatin are normally collected with impactors; the membrane filters serve as their own collection medium by simple filtration.

The obvious alternative is to make the collection first and add the reagent afterwards. Seely (213) accomplished this in gelatin collections by first coating the entire sample with a thin plastic layer through which appropriate reagents could pass by dialysis without serious danger of washing off the particles. Lodge (134,135) found the membrane filter a simpler substrate for this purpose, since the reagents were drawn rapidly through the pores from the reverse side by capillarity without enough free liquid reaching the surface to move the particles. Several additional methods were subsequently reported using the same approach (136,236,237), including two in which the final reaction spot was examined in the electron microscope (238,239). Farlow (66) found that some mixtures could be resolved in gelatin by a sort of differential precipitation chromatography, Tufts (240) used a variety of electrophoretic separation, and Turner (242,243) reported electrophoretic separations of extremely small quantities of mixtures, using as his substrate the layer of sorbed moisture on a clean microscope slide held in a moist chamber.

One particular potential of this class of methods which has been little explored lies in the possibility of identifying and measuring sorbed gases. The sole example to date is the method for particle-bound formaldehyde of Lodge and Frank (137). It is also the only microspot test for an organic substance. However, if the collecting medium can be impregnated with a specific reagent for either the identification or the retention of the sorbed gas or vapor in question, quite labile species can be subsequently identified and their amounts estimated. Lodge (132) has reviewed and discussed the quantitative aspects of these methods. It should be noted that the identification of radioactive particles by radio-autography is a closely related technique (183,186).

## B. ANALYSIS OF GASES

In a very real sense, the methods for the identification and measurement of atmospheric trace gases are more individual than the techniques for aerosols. This difference derives from the fact that the collection of aerosols is largely a function of size, although with some methods collection efficiency may also be affected by hygroscopicity and thus by chemical nature to that degree. Gases, on the other hand, differ so widely in their solubility and rate of solution, their vapor pressures from solution, their critical temperatures, etc. that there is considerable tendency to use quite different collecting devices, depending on the substance or class of substances which is of greatest interest. This is true even among the nominally nonselective sampling techniques. The use of such different sampling methods clearly demands a diversity of subsequent analytical techniques.

### 1. General or Nonselective Methods

In spite of the fact cited above that different sampling methods may favor the collection of individual compounds or classes of compounds, there is certainly a large class of analytical tools applicable to a broad spectrum of substances. In many respects, the problem here is analogous to the bulk analysis of aerosols; once a sample has been collected, the analytical problem is no longer peculiarly an air pollutant analysis problem. If the collected sample is primarily of hydrocarbon materials, the classical techniques of the petroleum chemist can be applied with little modification beyond a few precautions necessitated by the inevitable presence of at least traces of other substances. Thus, condensation samples can be analyzed by mass spectrometry (18), and, as mentioned previously, almost all types of nonselective collectors have been used to collect gas chromatographic samples (5,15,56,71,122). For a variety of obvious reasons, the most reactive atmospheric gases cannot be readily analyzed by these methods; they are either lost during collection, which is almost invariably the case with ozone, or they fail to move through the chromatographic column. Radioactive trace gases, such as the radon isotopes, may be concentrated by adsorption and subsequently desorbed and measured by standard low-level counting techniques (158,210). In some cases, direct counting without concentration may be possible (47).

For the most part, the nonselective methods are used for the less reactive and closely related compounds, such as homologous series of hydrocarbons and aldehydes. Depending on the nature of the substance, the most widely used analytical tool is certainly the gas chromatograph with either the flame ionization or electron capture detector.

## 2. Specific Techniques

The more polar trace gases, on the other hand, are collected almost entirely by absorption in specific collecting solutions. A substantial degree of specificity can be gained simply by optimizing the composition of these reagents. Generally speaking, the particular composition of the final analytical reagent must be adjusted to the nature of the collecting solution, and thus the analytical methods may well be said to be peculiar to air pollutant analysis, although some are borrowed from industrial hygiene practice.

It is well to reemphasize at this point that the analysis of trace gaseous pollutants with precision is a relatively new field. The years of experience which have been accumulated in the analysis of many other types of samples have not been accumulated by the air pollution chemist. Until recently it has been impossible to prepare truly accurate standard mixtures in a number of laboratories for the intercomparison of methods, and unanticipated interferences are still being found in some of the most established techniques. For all the above reasons, there is probably no single method in the discussion that follows which is not the subject of some controversy. Lodge (140) has recently reviewed methods of producing known test mixtures and has called attention to some recent advances which may make possible an increasing amount of interlaboratory testing of methods. Axelrod et al. (16c) subsequently developed one of Lodge's recommendations into a complete apparatus capable of delivering reasonably accurate concentrations down to 1 ppb. Thus, it can be expected that the next few years will see the resolution of a number of disagreements concerning the methods.

### a. Sulfur Dioxide

Three properties of sulfur dioxide may be used as the basis for its determination (91,92,106). Unfortunately, only one of these properties is in the least specific, and it suffers from interferences caused by side reactions.

Most of the early determinations were based on the acidity of sulfurous acid or of the sulfuric acid formed after mild oxidation. Generally speaking, these techniques involved direct collection either in water or in dilute acidified hydrogen peroxide (28). The change in acidity is measured by titration (60,82,91,230) or by measurement of the resulting change in conductivity (231,246). This latter method is still widely used and is the basis of several instruments (54,98,107,127,163,234). The technique is extremely simple, and manual determinations can be made with a minimum of equipment. In many environments it can also be considered fairly specific. However, this specificity results from the absence of potential interferences from the air rather than from any inherent selectivity in the method. Obviously, anything which can dissolve in water or weak acid to yield ions will be determined as sulfur dioxide. A prefilter can be used to remove soluble salts and sulfuric acid mist; however, many filter materials remove most of the sulfur dioxide (36a) and if it is permitted to collect any quantity of material, the resulting filter cake may remove sulfur dioxide as well. Hydrogen chloride, hydrogen fluoride, and other acidic gases will interfere in any case. Since nitrogen dioxide is only slowly soluble in water, its interference will depend on the particular method of collection, with more efficient collectors favoring its interference. Ammonia will cause negative interference by neutralizing hydronium ion, the most mobile species present. After oxidation by a peroxide collecting solution, sulfate has been determined by barium chloranilate (109). Lack of sensitivity and the difficulty described above in the removal of interference from particulate sulfate has limited the use of determinations of sulfur dioxide as sulfate.

A number of techniques have been built around the reducing properties of sulfur dioxide. It has been determined iodimetrically by titration of an iodine collecting solution with thiosulfate (74,123,233), by adding iodine to a starch–iodine collecting solution to match the original color (22,150), and by drawing the air sample through an iodine solution containing some starch until the blue color is just removed (110,178). In this sense, the standard iodine solution is titrated with air, and the total volume measured. Unfortunately, some small amount of iodine is invariably lost by evaporation into the passing air stream. This means that it is generally necessary to run a blank, if this can be arranged. It can be expected that the blank will be somewhat dependent on temperature. Iodometric titration after collection in sodium hydroxide solution has also been used (221,230). An instrument called the Titrilog was developed in which the passing sulfur dioxide was continuously titrated with colorimetrically generated bromine (151,160,215). Since the free bromine level is kept extremely low, aeration loss is minimized, and the technique should have some promise. The original instrument was designed for industrial hygiene levels of sulfur dioxide and not for air pollution. The system will be discussed in more detail later. There is no evidence yet that a stable instrument has been built, which is suitable for the low concentrations found in the ambient atmosphere, although some preliminary work in the author's laboratory is promising.

Generally speaking, these reductometric methods suffer positive interference from other reducing substances in the atmosphere, particularly hydrogen sulfide and some organics. By the same token, oxidizing agents reduce the apparent concentration of sulfur dioxide; ozone and organic peroxides generally interfere quantitatively, while the interference of nitrogen dioxide will again depend on the intimacy of contact between the air sample and the collecting solution. Free halogens are less common constituents of urban atmospheres, but will also interfere if present.

Sulfur dioxide collected in alkali has been determined polarographically after acidification (12,177). Kolthoff and Miller (111) found two waves which they postulated to be due to tautomeric forms of sulfurous acid; however, Polazzo (171) disagrees. The method is free of most interferences from which the other reductometric methods suffer, but a lack of sensitivity has prevented widespread use.

Conceivably, the lead peroxide candle method for estimating sulfur dioxide activity in the atmosphere should also be included as a reductometric method, since the reaction between lead dioxide and sulfur dioxide is clearly a redox reaction. The limitations of the method have already been discussed. Sulfuric acid also interferes, as does hydrogen sulfide.

Stephens (224) has reported a technique based on the reduction of iron (III) to iron (II) in the presence of thiocyanate. The method has some attractive features, but it appears to be nonstoichiometric and highly influenced by temperature. This feature makes it inconvenient for use in the field, and it appears to have been little used.

The only reaction of sulfur dioxide which can be said to be specific is its participation in the Schiff reaction, first proposed for use as a test for sulfite by Steigmann (223). Since the initial use of the reaction to determine atmospheric sulfur dioxide (113), a number of reagent compositions have been used (12,91,247). All suffered from the common problem of protecting collected sulfite from oxidation long enough to permit the final reaction. Sulfur dioxide was usually collected in alkali, and the resulting sulfite ion was usually converted with substantial efficiency to sulfate by oxygen during the sampling process. West and Gaeke (257) noted a suggestion by Feigl (69) that the sulfite complex with the tetrachloromercurate (II) ion was highly resistant to oxidation. The complex was initially thought to be disulfitomercurate (II), but subsequently proved to be dichlorosulfitomercurate (II) (165). Sulfite in this form is only slowly oxidized, even by so strong an agent as permanganate. However, it is still accessible to participate in the Schiff reaction. Numerous minor modifications have been made subsequently in the colorimetric reagent described by West and Gaeke (87,99,109a,175). It was shown that the interference of nitrogen dioxide could be eliminated by treatment with a number of substances, but that the best results appeared to be achieved with sulfamic acid (27,58,176,258,264). Ozone interferes slightly, but neither the mechanism of interference nor a completely satisfactory procedure for removing it have been reported. Hydrogen sulfide precipitates mercuric sulfide which must be removed from the collecting medium by centrifugation or filtering, and iron and a few other constituents of the particulate phase also cause undesirable side reactions. These can be removed by filtration of the incoming air, but sulfur dioxide may be lost onto any substantial filter cake. Scaringelli, Saltzman, and Frey (208) reported a set of modifications claimed to solve the remaining problems with the reagents. Although published critiques of this work are lacking, the authors have had difficulty in repeating these experiments, and it seems probable that the final word has not yet been said on the subject. Meanwhile, Axelrod et al. (16a) have reported a fluorometric approach to sulfur dioxide measurement which could possibly make the argument academic.

### b. HYDROGEN SULFIDE

There are three basic approaches to the determination of hydrogen sulfide. If sulfur dioxide can be removed and other interfering species are absent, hydrogen sulfide can be determined by the above reductometric methods for sulfur dioxide. The work of Okita and Lodge (167) indicates that sulfur dioxide can be quantitatively removed by a glass fiber filter impregnated with potassium carbonate. [Huygen (100) and Pate et al. (174) have discussed the collection of sulfur dioxide with this medium, but a final satisfactory analytical method has not been reported.]

Hydrogen sulfide forms strongly colored precipitates with a variety of heavy metals. Porous ceramic tiles soaked in lead acetate have been used as passive collectors, with a final estimation based on visual comparison (78). Sensenbaugh and Hemeon (214) drew air through impregnated filter paper tape in a tape sampling device and determined hydrogen sulfide by transmittance or reflectance photometry. Okita (167) showed that if membrane filters were substituted for the filter paper, and the filter subsequently was dissolved in a mixture of methanol, acetic acid, and methyl acetate, the lead sulfide formed a highly stable sol which could be determined spectrophotometrically. However, Okita's method has not yet been fully evaluated and appears to have a threshold of about 2 ppb. Sulfur dioxide interferes with all these methods, probably by oxidizing some of the sulfide to elemental sulfur. Ozone oxidizes lead sulfide to lead sulfate. Nitrogen dioxide causes some reduction in color intensity, probably by a similar reaction (201).

The method most nearly analogous in its inherent specificity to the West-Gaeke procedure for sulfur dioxide is the Jacobs, Braverman, and Hochheiser procedure for hydrogen sulfide (103). In this, the sulfide is trapped as a heavy metal salt in aqueous suspension, generally as cadmium sulfide. This is then reacted with $N,N$-dimethyl-$p$-phenylene-diamine in the presence of ferric chloride as a mild oxidizing agent to form the dye methylene blue, which is determined colorimetrically. The weak point in the method appears to lie in the collecting medium (17a,24). The same trace gases which attack lead sulfide can probably have adverse effects on cadmium sulfide. In any case, experience in the author's laboratory with the method has not been encouraging. The results appear erratic, and it seems evident that further research will be required before it can be treated as a referee method.

Axlerod and co-workers (16b) report an extremely sensitive method for hydrogen sulfide, featuring collection in alkali and subsequent determination by fluorescence quenching. These authors report that at sufficiently high alkali concentrations, the air oxidation of collected sulfide seems negligible. To date no independent studies have been reported that permit assessment of the correctness of this claim.

Feigl (70) has pointed out that virtually all sulfides, soluble or insoluble, catalyze the reaction between iodine and sodium azide, yielding as a visible product nitrogen gas, with the simultaneous discharge of the iodine color. So far as can be ascertained, this reaction has not been seriously investigated as a technique for determining hydrogen sulfide. Several papers have suggested the use of metal ions other than cadmium and lead (36,64,73,172), but there has been insufficient experience with these to permit a general evaluation.

### c. Nitrogen Oxides

Altshuller (6), among others, has pointed out that all the possible oxides of nitrogen probably exist to some slight degree in polluted atmospheres. Nitrous oxide naturally exists at a measurable concentration worldwide and has no known role in pollution chemistry. It is normally determined spectroscopically (220) or chromatographically (117a).

The only oxides of nitrogen which have been studied significantly in polluted atmospheres are nitric oxide and nitrogen dioxide. Most pollutant sources emit primarily the former; its accelerated conversion to the latter is one of the outstanding features of the atmospheric reaction chain loosely referred to as "photochemical smog."

Nitrogen dioxide, at atmospheric concentrations, is almost invariably determined by converting it to nitrite which is subsequently used to diazotize a primary aromatic amine. The resulting diazonium salt is then coupled with an appropriate aromatic compound to form a highly colored dye—the so-called Griess-Ilosvay reaction (19).

Two adaptations of this reaction are currently in use. Jacobs and Hochheiser (104) suggested collection in alkali, followed by acidification in the presence of sulfanilamide and $N$-(1-naphthyl)-ethylenediamine. Saltzman (197) collected directly in an acetic acid solution containing the same coupler, but with sulfanilic acid instead of sulfanilamide. Mueller and co-workers have exhaustively investigated the effects of modifying the amine, coupler, and reaction medium (112,159).

Unfortunately, neither reaction appears to be stoichiometric. The reaction

$$2NO_2 + H_2O \rightleftarrows HNO_2 + HNO_3$$

suggests that each mole of nitrogen dioxide should yield 0.5 mole of nitrite. Saltzman (197) showed, however, by comparing the color intensity produced by an accurately measured quantity of nitrogen dioxide with that from a standardized nitrite solution, that each mole of nitrogen dioxide was equivalent approximately to 0.72 moles of nitrite in his technique. Lodge et al. (139) described a brief series of experiments comparing the two methods. They found that if Saltzman's value for his method is assumed, the average of twelve determinations gives 0.52 for the Jacobs-Hochheiser method. They therefore suggested that this technique followed the stoichiometry suggested by the equation above. Stratmann and Buck (227) reported values much nearer unity, whereas Mueller and co-workers (159) obtained a 0.7 ratio. More recently, Hochheiser (90) has reported a far more extensive series of experiments comparing the methods in the field. He states that his data are still inconclusive, but that the conversion factors for the two methods appear very nearly equal. Meanwhile, there were isolated verbal reports supporting values for both methods running the full gamut from 0.5 to 1.0.

It appears that the question has been answered by the studies of Huygen (100a). He has shown that the apparent equivalence factor may be manipulated over a large range by changing the composition of the reagent solution, and has isolated the factors responsible for the nonintegral stoichiometry, including reduction of nitrogen dioxide to nitric oxide, nitration of the reagent, and poor collection efficiency. Huygen seems to have demonstrated that a reagent composition can be engineered deliberately to yield, reproducibly, an overall efficiency ranging from 0.5 or less up to substantially 1.0.

Meanwhile, the question of possible interference in the method from nitric oxide also appears unsettled. Since

$$NO + NO_2 + H_2O \rightleftarrows 2HNO_2$$

at least on paper, the presence of significant amounts of nitric oxide may increase the apparent equivalence factor between nitrogen dioxide and nitrite. The method of Saltzman and Gilbert (198) for ozone requires the determination of nitrogen dioxide in the presence of nitric oxide. Since Saltzman reported that the amount of excess nitric oxide had no effect on his results, it appears that his method does not suffer from this shortcoming. Gill (79) reported finding some effect on a method similar to the Jacobs-Hochheiser technique from excess nitric oxide at concentrations about ten times the normal atmospheric concentrations. The scatter in his data was considerable, and it is possible to question his conclusions, since no statistical tests of validity were applied. The matter is therefore still open to question, at least when the nitrogen dioxide is collected in alkali.

Interferences with these methods are not fully documented. Ozone gives a different color, which does not usually interfere in the determination (112,197). High concentrations of sulfur dioxide may interfere.

Nitric oxide is invariably determined by conversion to nitrogen dioxide. Two general approaches are used. In the first, nitrogen dioxide is collected in one or two bubblers in series, and the air thus freed of nitrogen dioxide is passed through the oxidation medium to a further bubbler containing the same reagent. Alternatively, parallel determinations are made, one bubbler measuring nitrogen dioxide and the other the sum of nitrogen dioxide and nitric oxide.

The oxidant first used was acidified potassium permanganate, apparently suggested first by Thomas and co-workers (232). Wartburg, Brewer, and Lodge (252) showed that this oxidation was more complete if an impinger with a rather large nozzle was used instead of a fritted bubbler to bring the sample stream in contact with the permanganate. Prolonged contact may result in oxidation to nitrate or some other side reaction. "Dry" glass fiber filters impregnated with acidified permanganate have also been used as an oxidation medium (63).

More recently, Ripley, Clingenpeel, and Hurn (192) reported excellent results with a "dry" oxidation medium consisting of glass fiber filter paper impregnated with a mixture of sodium dichromate and sulfuric acid. The sampled air is simply passed through a U-tube loosely packed with strips of the impregnated filter paper. This oxidation medium is rapidly inactivated by the vapors of the Saltzman reagent and, therefore, the parallel collection technique mentioned above should be used, nitric oxide being determined by difference. It is also affected by humidity (108).

In addition to the uncertainties involved in any determination of nitrogen dioxide, the measurement of nitric oxide involves uncertainties in the efficiency of oxidation. It is extremely difficult to prepare accurately known concentrations of nitric oxide. The general practice is therefore to prepare an approximately known concentration for test purposes and then to adjust the oxidation medium, whatever it may be, so as to give the largest possible answer. It is difficult to dilute nitric oxide in air rapidly enough to inhibit its oxidation to nitrogen dioxide, although the former gas is quite stable at concentrations as low as a fraction of a part per million. This problem may be obviated by dilution with pure nitrogen or argon, but the whole chemical sequence involved in the above reactions is sufficiently obscure to raise the question of whether atmospheric oxygen enters into the final analytical oxidation. The entire field of nitrogen oxide analysis is in serious need of further investigation and new ideas.

### d. Ozone and Other Oxidants

Ozone is normally determined in air through some manifestation of its oxidizing power. Unfortunately, most polluted atmospheres contain numerous other substances nearly as powerful, together with reductants such as sulfur dioxide which are entirely capable of coexisting with ozone in the gaseous state for protracted period. If other substances are present, therefore, most methods of determination will yield, instead of the absolute concentration of ozone, the algebraic sum of the concentrations of all the oxidants present, each multiplied by a coefficient (generally less than unity) representing the activity of the particular oxidant towards the specific reagent, and the concentrations of all reductants, each multiplied by a suitable negative coefficient. In polluted atmospheres, the resulting number, usually expressed as "oxidant concentration calculated as ozone," has been found somewhat useful empirically, but it always must be remembered that it is an abstraction created by (a) the particular mixture of oxidants and reductants, (b) the particular reagent used in the determination, and (c) the particular sampling technique employed. Attempts to intercompare various techniques have not been particularly fruitful, which is scarcely surprising, in view of the number of variables involved (228). The only serious attempt at resolution of a mixed system is that of Effenberger (59). Given the simplified system, ozone–chlorine–nitrogen dioxide, he showed that the stoichiometry of iodide oxidation varied differently for the three substances with pH. He determined reaction coefficients for the three substances and was thus able to determine all three in a mixture by using potassium iodide solution buffered at three different pH values.

However, the problem is even worse than the above would indicate. No clear proof exists that the reaction between ozone and potassium iodide, which is always taken as the standard, is really that indicated by the equation:

$$O_3 + 2KI + H_2O \rightarrow O_2 + 2KOH + I_2$$

at least at the concentrations experienced in the atmosphere. Saltzman and Gilbert (199) have offered some evidence to suggest that this is probably correct above about 0.05 ppm, but their proof cannot be considered unequivocal for reasons that will be discussed later.

Subject, then, to the limitation that the stoichiometry is only assumed, ozone in air can be determined by its oxidizing power if no interfering substances are present. The accepted standard method today appears to be the use of 2% aqueous potassium iodide buffered with phosphate to a pH of approximately 7 (102,219). Depending on the technique used to measure the resulting iodine concentration, other substances may be present in the reagent solution. While it is obviously possible to measure the resulting iodine titrimetrically, as well as by several other methods, most American authors use spectrophotometric determination at 352 m$\mu$.

An alkaline potassium iodide reagent (7,102) is also in use. The solution is acidified with the mixture of phosphoric and sulfamic acids just before analysis. This method gives consistent results after several days' storage and thus is preferred when measurements are taken in the field for subsequent analysis.

At least two authors (61,250) have used coulometric or amperometric techniques in the determination of liberated iodine. The results obtained are in substantial agreement with spectrophotometric measurements. If determinations are being made manually, there seems little from which to choose between the two techniques, since the spectrophotometer is more expensive, but can be used in more different determinations than the coulometer. As will be discussed later, however, the coulometric technique seems clearly preferable when the technique is incorporated into a monitoring instrument (152).

A number of dyes undergo oxidation–reduction reactions which may be utilized to determine air-borne oxidants (26,106). Phenolphthalein is readily reduced to phenolphthalin, which is colorless in alkaline solutions. A fairly broad spectrum of oxidants reoxidize this compound to give the characteristic pink color of the indicator dye (83). Determination by this and the previous method in the polluted atmosphere usually differs, since the reaction coefficients of the various oxidants with iodide ion are substantially different from those with phenolphthalin (143,229). The other dyestuffs which have been tested at various times as potential reagents seem to possess insufficient advantage over phenolphthalin to warrant discussion.

At least two instruments have been suggested for the specific determination of ozone based on the absorption spectrum of ozone in the air, no chemical transformations being explicitly involved. The long path instrument designed by Renzetti and co-workers (190,191) proved difficult to maintain, and the data obtained were apparently awkward to reduce to ozone concentrations. A fundamental difficulty lay in the fact that it was never proved that other compounds which absorbed in the same spectral region were not present in air. An instrument with a path length of only 25 cm, developed by Kruger (34), presented still more serious maintenance problems because of the enormous sensitivity to minute changes in light intensity demanded of the photocell.

Probably the earliest reaction claimed to be specific to ozone was the accelerated cracking of stressed rubber (29). The claimed specificity has never been disproved; however, the method is extremely awkward to apply, is quite subjective in evaluation, and has a substantial temperature coefficient. If labor is substantially less expensive than equipment, it can still be used with good results, provided that suitable precautions are taken and that a single technician is carefully "calibrated" against known ozone concentrations.

The method of Saltzman and Gilbert has been mentioned previously (198). It depends on the fact that the reaction between nitric oxide and ozone is substantially more rapid than that between nitric oxide and any other oxidant. The resulting nitrogen dioxide is determined by Saltzman's method, described above. It is thus subject to the uncertainties concerning the stoichiometry of the nitrogen dioxide–nitrite conversion. If Saltzman's figure of 0.72 for this factor is correct, then the method should be both specific and quite accurate, although not particularly convenient (88). It was by comparison with this technique that Saltzman found deviations from linearity in the potassium iodide method, as mentioned previously.

Bravo and Lodge (30) state that the ozonolysis of $p,p'$-dimethoxystilbene to anisaldehyde and anisic acid can be made quantitative and thus used as the basis of a method of determination, since anisaldehyde can be determined with great sensitivity by an adaptation of one of the color reactions of Sawicki and co-workers (202). They presented presumptive evidence to support this claim, as well as the claim that the method has no serious interferences. However, the method has not been evaluated in the field, and conclusive evidence to support the claimed stoichiometry is still missing. Hauser and Bradley (86), by substituting 1,2-di-(4-pyridyl)ethylene for the dimethoxystilbene, are able to work with less corrosive solvents and largely preserve the specificity of the method. Bergshoeff (22a) ran a comparison of these two methods with a number of others, including a modified potassium iodide technique in which excess thiosulfate was present, and found all of them to have identical stoichiometry within narrow limits. It seems reasonable to assume that this stoichiometry is integral.

Regener (188) constructed an iodometric instrument which was claimed to be specific for ozone. Air was led into two substantially identical channels and was contacted with potassium iodide solution, and the liberated iodine was determined coulometrically. However, in one channel, the air was briefly heated to a temperature high enough to decompose the ozone. The difference in iodine liberated in the two channels was therefore proportional to the ozone concentration; the two electrical signals were therefore opposed, and a difference signal was directly recorded. However, there is no evidence that the instrument was ever tested for interference by some of the less stable organic peroxides and related compounds, which could well also have been pyrolyzed in the heated channel. Regener (189) subsequently developed a remarkably simple system based on an entirely different principle. Certain dyes, such as luminol (3-aminophthalhydrazide), when sorbed on silica gel were found to chemiluminesce in the presence of trace quantities of ozone, with the luminescent intensity being proportional to ozone flux, other things being equal. The silica gel was deposited on a small disk, and air was drawn past at a fixed rate. The disk was continuously viewed by a photomultiplier, and the resulting signal was suitably magnified and recorded. The method is in wide use for the determination of high altitude ozone concentrations; the data are telemetered to the ground from sounding balloons. The disadvantage is that each individual sensor must be calibrated immediately prior to release, since no particular stoichiometry is involved, and it appears difficult to produce identical disks in quantity. The response is also somewhat affected by both temperature and humidity. The data available seem to uphold the claim of chemical specificity. However, the system is quite awkward for measurements extending over a period of time, since the response of the disk steadily decreases with time. Watanabe and Nakadoi (253) have also reported a fluorometric determination based on a reaction of ozone to give fluorescent acridine.

Specific methods for other individual oxidants, other than nitrogen dioxide, have been studied considerably less. Peroxyacyl nitrates are normally determined by their characteristic infrared spectra (225) or gas chromatography with electron-capture detection (55). A few pure ozonides have been prepared and their infrared spectra studied (226), but the compounds have never been reported present in polluted air. It has been claimed that the oxidation of ferrous thiocyanate to the ferric state is unaffected by ozone, and it has been used as a test for peroxidic compounds in air (235). However, the data are sparse and insufficient to permit thorough evaluation. Sulfur dioxide would be expected to interfere.

### e. OXIDES OF CARBON

Carbon monoxide is normally determined by infrared techniques. Its stability makes it particularly suitable for determination by nondispersive methods (145,146,254). Compared with other pollutants, it is present at relatively high concentrations, with values as high as 500 ppm having been measured in particularly polluted locations (119). Even so, it is generally necessary to compress the sampled air to obtain enough sensitivity from a typical nondispersive instrument. Although this is not only possible, but quite widely done, it makes the resulting instrument both expensive and extremely bulky.

Most other techniques for carbon monoxide determination depend on the power of this gas to reduce palladium salts to metallic palladium. This is the chemical basis of the indicator tubes (218) which are widely used in industrial hygiene and occasionally used in air pollution studies as well, but which do not yield particularly precise results. If these are to be used, it is certainly necessary to purchase an adequate supply from a single lot and calibrate that lot against a standard carbon monoxide concentration (16,117). Feldstein and Levaggi (72,121) have recently published a related method in solution. However, equilibration between the solution and air appears very slow, and it is not obvious that it can be readily adapted to air monitoring; in justice to the authors, they make no claim that it can be so applied.

An instrument was developed which was based on the reduction of mercuric oxide to metallic mercury by carbon monoxide and the determination of the resulting mercury vapor, with the entire operation being carried out at elevated temperatures (148). Most organics interfere, but are usually present in substantially lower concentrations than carbon monoxide. Early forms of the instrument were beset by troubles, particularly caused by the slight spontaneous decomposition of the mercuric oxide. Robbins et al. (192a) appear to have solved this problem. Considering the enormous sensitivity with which mercury vapor can be detected by atomic absorption, this technique should be innately far more sensitive than the infrared method. It is possible that greater specificity can be achieved if the other problems of the instrument can also be solved by selective adsorption techniques. Other techniques are occasionally used (57). At present, the use of gas chromatography to determine carbon monoxide is being actively investigated (67,194).

Carbon dioxide is not a pollutant in the normal sense of the word, but since a significant portion of it in urban atmospheres is anthropogenic, it is frequently measured as an index of total human activity. It can be measured with high precision by nondispersive infrared techniques, and most modern data have been obtained by this method (43). Fonselius et al. (75) reported an ingenious titrimetric technique for carbon dioxide. Lodge and co-workers (141,142) gave two reports on a chemical equilibrium technique, but their instrument has still not fulfilled the hopes of the developers, and a fully usable instrument has not yet emerged.

### f. Organic Gases and Vapors

The most general technique for determining organic compounds in air is gas chromatography. The lighter organics are normally determined by absorption chromatography, and methane has been measured at a number of sites by Altshuller and co-workers (8) and Bainbridge and Heidt (17). It apparently exists naturally in concentrations of approximately 1.5 ppm and thus constitutes a background against which increases caused by pollution must be measured. Ortman (169) has described an ingenious continuous methane monitor based on chromatographic principles.

Rasmussen and Went (187) have demonstrated the utility of gas chromatography for the measurement of high molecular weight vapors at concentrations of the order of a few parts per billion. Long path infrared spectrophotometry (166), mass spectrometry following low temperature condensation (184), and a number of other generalized instrumental methods (18,155) have been used to determine a broad spectrum of organic substances in air. However, the gas chromatograph with a flame ionization detector probably remains the most versatile single instrument for this purpose (8). For specific substances, such as halogenated hydrocarbons, electron capture detectors are clearly more sensitive by several orders of magnitude (23).

It must be kept in mind that a sample of polluted air generally represents the ultimate in complexity. The gas chromatograph is a superb instrument for separating mixtures and detecting the presence of components. It can give only presumptive identifications, and it is extremely difficult in the general case to exclude the possibility of unknown substances being eluted along with known compounds. Identification may be made much more certainly if two different column materials are used to minimize the likelihood of this sort of coincidence. Chemical treatment can frequently be devised to remove certain types of compounds selectively (101); this type of "subtraction chromatography" has proven particularly useful in studies of automotive exhaust chemistry.

Another approach which is frequently used is the trapping of individual portions of eluate. (Since the sensitive detectors are destructive, this involves splitting the stream from the chromatographic column.) The individual fractions, presumably pure compounds, are then analyzed by independent instrumental methods or by specific chemical tests.

The above instrumental methods meet the usual tests for extreme elegance: they require substantial manipulative skill, they are of extreme sensitivity, they are quite slow, and they involve relatively expensive apparatus. They are the only satisfactory methods for determining the paraffinic hydrocarbons and are the most satisfactory techniques for most of the hydrocarbon gases and vapors encountered in polluted atmospheres. On the whole, they are less satisfactory for the oxygenated compounds and other more reactive species, and they are scarcely competitive in cost with a number of sensitive and selective or specific tests for individual compounds or functions which can be performed with simple air sampling equipment and a spectrophotometer or colorimeter. Needless to say, all these latter techniques may also be used to identify fractions from a gas chromatograph or other fractionating device.

Probably the most frequently measured organic, because of its role in photochemical pollution, is formaldehyde. A number of reactions have been used in the past for this species, but the technique most widely used now employs chromotropic acid in strong sulfuric acid as the reagent (203,259). Selection of the collecting medium and precise conditions for the final analysis depend on the concentration range and on other substances present. Altshuller et al. (10) have published a detailed evaluation of this group of methods which can be used as a guide to selecting the analytical details appropriate for the analysis at hand. Gas chromatography has also been used (120).

Olefins have been determined primarily along with other hydrocarbons by gas chromatography. They may be differentiated from the paraffins by a split column, subtractive technique since olefins are specifically removed by mercuric salts (101). Attempts to design a monitoring instrument for total unsaturation based on bromometric principles have been unsuccessful. Altshuller and Sleva (6a) published a colorimetric technique, but it has been little used. This lack of application probably derives from an intuitive feeling on the part of the profession that the olefins in the atmosphere are too diverse and variable for the resulting numbers (reported as equivalent 1-butene concentration) to be highly meaningful.

Acrolein has been determined less frequently, but is of considerable interest since it, together with formaldehyde and the peroxyacyl nitrates, is presumably responsible for most of the lachrimatory power of the typical photochemical pollution complex. A number of measurements have been published using the reaction with tryptophan as the basis for the analysis (180). However, Cohen and Altshuller (45) investigated the reaction with 4-hexylresorcinol, demonstrated its specificity and lack of serious interference, and showed that the tryptophan reaction is inhibited by the presence of nitrogen oxides.

Hauser and Cummins (85) have optimized the method originally developed by Sawicki and his co-workers (204) for the measurement of aliphatic aldehydes, using 3-methylbenzothiazolone hydrazone (MBTH), which discriminates very little among the aldehydes and which can be used together with the chromotropic acid technique to determine higher aldehydes and formaldehyde by difference. Some attempts have been made to use the Schiff reaction in aldehyde determination, but it seems generally too insensitive for this purpose (144).

PAN (peroxyacylnitrate), ozonides, and peroxidic compounds have been discussed above in paragraph section III-B-2-d.

Sawicki and his group have published numerous methods for the less common pollutants, such as glyoxal (205) and succinaldehyde (206). Researchers interested in compounds of this sort should consult Sawicki's published papers.

## IV. MONITORING INSTRUMENTS

A monitoring instrument has been frivolously defined as a black box which ingests air and excretes numbers. More formally, it may be described as any system for automatically conducting continuous or periodic analyses. The advantage of such instruments is in the production of continuous or closely spaced data 24 hours per day 7 days per week. The two principal disadvantages of most such instruments are: (1) there may be a tendency, or at least a temptation, to rely too uncritically on the data obtained and (2) their use may simply result in the replacement of a group of chemical technicians by an equal number of electronic maintenance engineers. It is certainly true that no instrument has been devised which will refrain from producing data of some sort, whether or not the analytical portion is functioning properly.

There is also a great temptation to regard continuous data as representing instantaneous values of the pollutant under study. Typical monitoring instruments actually report running mean values over periods ranging from a few seconds to some tens of minutes. In this connection, two points need to be kept in mind. First, there is every indication that truly instantaneous data are comparatively useless; the case of the nearly instantaneous ozone analyzer has already been discussed. Second, it is frequently possible to achieve better time resolution, where this is actually desirable, by sequential sampling with manual techniques.

Finally, it should be noted that, in those monitoring instruments in which chemical techniques are used for the actual analysis, the chemistry involved is frequently simplified by comparison with the corresponding manual method. While this is desirable from the standpoint of instrument design, it means that the instrumental methods are sometimes less specific than the corresponding manual measurement and, occasionally, less sensitive as well.

Careful study is necessary, both to determine the initial need for an automatic monitoring instrument and in the selection of the particular instrument for a given job. Only rarely should an automatic instrument be contemplated seriously before at least a few spot checks have been made with manual methods to assure that the substances sought are present and to delineate, at least crudely, the range of concentrations to be expected.

### A. GENERAL PRINCIPLES

A typical monitoring instrument may be considered to consist of three parts: an air mover, a transducer, and an output. A few instruments, such as long path infrared or ultraviolet analyzers, use the wind as their only air mover. Most others use an air pump to draw a sample into the system and to expel it after analysis. Since this air mover determines the flux of test substance through the instrument, in most cases the instrument response will be proportional to air flow rate, and all precautions must be taken to keep the sampling rate constant. A positive displacement pump of appropriate capacity is probably the best choice here, since nearly all techniques involving orifices, needle valves, and the like are prone to fluctuations caused by plugging of these small openings. If such flow constrictions are to be used, they must be protected from atmospheric particulate matter and/or from chemical reagents by an appropriate filter, and the filter must be changed before it becomes sufficiently plugged to affect the flow itself. Further, some filters will remove the pollutant being sampled (36a).

In most monitoring instruments, the transducer converts fluctuations in the composition of air into an electrical output signal. Transducers fall into several general categories. The first includes the purely physical devices, such as the long path spectrometers (see Sect. III-B-2-d). Nearly any physical property of the trace substance in air may be made the basis of continuous or continual measurement, at least in theory. The limitations of this approach are obvious. First, the physical signal must be large enough to measure in the environment (for example, present instrumentation is insufficiently sensitive to permit nuclear paramagnetic resonance to be used to determine unconcentrated species in air). Second, the property must be reasonably specific for the substance in question. (Thus, nitrogen oxides can scarcely be determined by their paramagnetism in the presence of oxygen. Relatively few wavelengths in the ultraviolet are truly specific for individual pollutants, unless either several wavelengths are used or other precautions are taken to exclude interfering substances.)

Chemical transducers fit preponderantly into four categories. The first of these, which has been little used, comprises detectors in which a reagent gas is added to the inlet air stream. Changes which occur in the gas phase, such as the formation of aerosols, are detected by changes in light transmission, in electrical conductivity, or in the ability of the air to nucleate fog formation at low supersaturations. The method is capable of enormous sensitivity, but gaseous reagents are insufficiently diverse to permit extreme sensitivity.

A second category might be called "exchange" devices. The test gas is brought into contact with the reagent, often solid, from which the test substance liberates another gas which is more readily detected, for example, a radioactive substance. Once again, the selection of reagents is limited, and instruments based on these principles have been quite sluggish in their response.

The third major category includes the electrochemical sensors. Here the test substance is dissolved in a suitable solvent, usually water, and causes a detectable change in some electrochemical property of the solution. Some of these instruments have already been described, particularly in the discussion of sulfur dioxide measurement. Systems have at least been attempted which make use of changes in conductivity, of electrode potential, and in electrode polarization; these may either be measured directly or used in a feedback system to control such processes as titration with electrolytically generated reagents.

The final class of transducer is the colorimetric type. These are, in the truest sense, "robot chemists." The air sample is brought into contact with a suitable sampling medium or with the reagent itself, and other reagents may be added. The solution is held long enough for a colored reaction product to form and is then passed through a flow colorimeter or spectrophotometer to measure the concentration of the final reaction product. These automatic colorimetric analyzers can probably achieve the greatest degree of specificity of any technique presently available. They are also generally the most complex and, therefore, the most prone to erroneous results, breakdown, and high maintenance cost, quite aside from the fact that they must be continuously supplied with reagents. In most, in addition to maintaining constancy of air flow, it is necessary also to maintain a constant flow of one or more liquid reagents over long periods of time. The design of the liquid flow system requires at least as much care as the selection of the prime air mover, as discussed above. It is also necessary either to design with extreme care to keep both the light source and the photoelectric detector constant or to design a "double beam" instrument which will compensate for such fluctuations as occur. Finally, provision must be made to store substantial volumes of both fresh and spent reagent. Obviously, this last consideration adds appreciably to the size of the instrument, and the stability of the reagent sets a final limit to its unattended operation, even if all other problems can be solved. By contrast, at least some of the electrochemical transducers continuously regenerate their own reagents in a comparatively small fixed volume.

In general, the purely physical transducers are directly coupled to their outputs. At least in theory, the other three classes, in addition to being attached directly, may be arranged in what has been called a "dosimetric" manner. In this technique, the reaction product accumulates in a fixed volume of the system to a preset level, at which time the entire system is flushed, and the entire process is then started over. The time required to reach a given accumulation level is then recorded and is presumably inversely proportional to concentration. If properly instrumented, this technique has the dual advantages of increasing the sensitivity of analytical methods and of providing data spaced in time according to how interesting the data are likely to be. Many continuous monitoring instruments may provide thousands of feet of analog record showing merely background concentrations for every foot which is of real importance from the air pollution standpoint.

Such dosimetric instruments can become quite complex from the mechanical standpoint, and there are few reagents which can be continuously aerated over long periods without some decomposition, which puts a lower limit on their sensitivity. Comparatively few such instruments have been built.

The typical continuous analyzer, then, has an output which is an electrical analog of the input concentration of the test substance, with deviations caused by interferences. In the very simplest case, this simply causes deflection in a meter. More commonly, a recording current meter or self-balancing potentiometer is used to provide a continuous trace of the output. Recently, these have been supplemented, or occasionally supplanted, by analog-to-digital converters which provide either a printed output or, more commonly, a punched tape compatible with a computer input. These periodic outputs should ideally be the time average of concentrations over the interval since the last printout; however, most such devices merely report the instantaneous value at the time the printout occurs, without any indication whether this is representative of the time period. As a result, such printouts must normally be manually compared with the analog record, and the first act in computer handling is usually the further smoothing of the data; for example, the computation of 3-hr averages. It seems legitimate to question whether the same data could not be obtained by automatic sequential sampling for 3 hr followed by manual analysis.

The period from 1950 to 1960 saw the production of a large number of prototype instruments, few of which were ever produced commercially. Since 1960, the number of commercially available monitoring instruments has increased, and a few of these are of good quality. There is every evidence of a more critical attitude on the part of potential users of these instruments, which should force better design practices on our manufacturers, a more critical evaluation of their output, and a more conservative evaluation of the benefits to be accrued by the use of automatic instruments. Finally, the general improvement in instrument reliability achievable through the newer solid-state circuits, together with the reduction in size, should make it possible, within the next decade, to produce monitoring instruments which are at least as reliable as a well-trained human chemist.

## B.  CRITIQUE OF INDIVIDUAL INSTRUMENTS

The above general principles are presently embodied in a variety of instruments, some of which have been only described in publications and some of which are commercially available (11). There has been a great increase in the number of available instruments in the period beginning about January 1965, and no one existing laboratory has the means to purchase one each of all the instruments and run them over a long enough period to permit a complete evaluation of the entire list. The need for something analogous to a "consumers union" is obvious, but the number of workers in the field is still too small to support such an activity. Furthermore, since the market is still small, the number of options for combining a particular air mover, a particular transducer, and a particular form of output is also quite limited.

The best protection for the individual purchaser lies in purchasing an instrument to a set of performance specifications. These should include instrumental response time, specificity, sensitivity, noise level, maintenance and down time, and overall accuracy. Ideally, each instrument should be checked in the laboratory against a known concentration of the pure substance and in the field against a well-authenticated manual method. It should again be emphasized that monitoring instruments inevitably require maintenance of a high order and thus do not constitute a complete substitute for manpower.

With the above preamble, it is instructive to examine some individual instruments. No attempt at complete coverage is contemplated. For example, monitoring instruments for carbon monoxide and carbon dioxide, already discussed in Section III-B-2-e, are largely physical in nature and appear to illustrate no unique points. Furthermore, there appears to be little difference among the commercially available models. The instruments are selected for discussion because of particular good or bad features, in many cases on the basis of fairly limited experience with a single instrument. With one or two exceptions, all the instruments mentioned have been used in the field with reasonable success, and any adverse criticism is intended to be constructive. There are a very few instruments intended for aerosol analysis (93), but they are both insufficient in number and insufficiently distinctive to permit a meaningful discussion.

## 1. Sulfur Dioxide Analyzers

Certainly the most venerable air monitoring instrument is the Thomas Autometer (234), produced commercially by the Leeds & Northrup Corporation. The instrument is available in several versions, all of which operate on the same principles, and all of which have the same advantages and disadvantages. Air is brought into contact with a dilute aqueous medium containing sulfuric acid and hydrogen peroxide. Sulfur dioxide dissolves to form sulfuric acid, thereby increasing the conductivity of the solution. A simple conductivity bridge responds to this change, and the unbalance signal is recorded on a self-balancing potentiometer. The arrangements for maintaining a constant air flow are somewhat primitive, but the air flow is large, and this is apparently a source of comparatively little difficulty. There are two versions, one of which measures conductivity changes in a fixed volume of the reagent for a given length of time, then discharges that volume and introduces a fresh one. The mean concentration during the sampling period may be read from the height to which the recorder trace rises during that fixed period. Shorter time resolution requires measurement of the slope of the output record, which is inconvenient. The continuous flow version requires maintenance of a constant liquid flow in addition to the air flow, which is a source of some difficulty, but many of these instruments have operated successfully for years.

The Autometer represents, on the whole, one of the simplest extant air monitoring instruments. It is comparatively trouble free and is very widely employed. Its greatest drawback is its almost total lack of specificity, which requires a substantial knowledge of the other contaminants in the environment before its output can be judged to be a true measure of sulfur dioxide concentration. Absolutely anything which is removed by the contacting system, which dissolves in water, and which affects the conductivity of the water will be an interference. Particulate matter, such as soluble salts, can be removed by a prefilter, which may in turn remove sulfur dioxide (36a). However, all other volatile acids will be reported as sulfuric acid, and ammonia and amines will cause negative interference by neutralizing some of the acid present. Thus, the instrument cannot be used in all possible environments. It does, however, well embody the concept that direct electrochemical transducers can be made far simpler than photometric ones.

Several other electrical conductivity devices are also available, both in the United States and abroad, and all more or less share the same advantages and disadvantages. One small novelty is provided by the version produced by Scientific Industries, Inc. This is a recording version of the Nash Analyzer (162) (see Sect. II-B-4), which gains specificity from the very minimal contact between sampled air and reagent. The lack of perfect collection efficiency can be corrected for in calibration. Many potential interferences do not dissolve on such brief contact and thus the interference problem is presumably minimized. Within its limitations, the instrument appears to have a number of attractive features. However, there are as yet no reports of field experience with the device, and it is not certain how fully the potentialities of the design have been realized. The extremely simple method of obtaining batch operation is also unique.

The Titrilog (see Sect. III-B-2-a) was an attempt to design a continuous coulometric titrator. A fixed volume of reagent (an acidic solution of potassium bromide) was placed in a cell containing four electrodes. One pair of these sensed the presence of a small amount of free bromine in the solution. The sampled air was bubbled through the solution, and when the presence of sulfur dioxide caused the removal of free bromine, the unbalance signal from the sensing electrode was amplified and was used to generate enough free bromine coulometrically to restore the balance. The generating current was continuously measured.

In all justice, the Titrilog was not intended as an air monitoring instrument, but rather for the measurement of far higher concentrations. Attempts were made to increase the sensitivity (151,161), but these were defeated by the huge solution volume of the system and the crudeness of the amplifier electronics. One inherent difficulty is the tendency of the aeration process to remove a small amount of bromine constantly; this is to some extent a function of temperature, making for a variable drift in the system. Finally, almost any reducing agent which is soluble in the electrolyte will be reported as sulfur dioxide, and any oxidant will constitute a negative interference. Thus, it is generally necessary to include some pretreatment of the sampled air to remove at least some of the interfering materials. However, there seems no a priori reason that a far more sensitive version could not be produced if it were desired. Here again, the simplicity of direct electrochemical transduction can in some measure compensate for the lack of specificity. Instead, the instrument is no longer produced commercially at all.

Beckman Instruments, Inc., Precision Scientific Company, Inc., and a few other manufacturers who have joined the field more recently produce flow colorimeters for sulfur dioxide monitoring. These all use a simplified version of the Schiff (or West-Gaeke) reaction. All require substantial precision in the preparation of reagents, all have substantial averaging times because the color development is slow in this reaction, and all have the inherent difficulty that both a liquid and an air flow must be maintained precisely. There is inadequate intercomparison of these instruments to permit a valid choice among them. In all these instruments, the necessary simplification of treatment has somewhat decreased the specificity of the Schiff reagent. However, they still remain more specific than the electrochemical sensors, which may weigh in their favor in spite of the probable greater need for maintenance.

## 2. Hydrogen Sulfide and Nitrogen Oxide Analyzers

In both of these cases, there is little choice among monitoring devices, since all available instruments use the same chemical means. The only available hydrogen sulfide instruments, so far as is known, draw air through a paper tape impregnated with a heavy metal salt and then measure the darkening caused by hydrogen sulfide, either by reflectance or transmittance measurement on the tape. Dust must obviously be removed by prefilter, and sulfur dioxide and ozone will almost certainly interfere, as will mercaptans to some degree.

All nitrogen oxide analyzers use a photometric transducer with some modification of the Saltzman reagent, which has been discussed previously. The discussion of techniques for oxidizing nitric oxide to nitrogen dioxide is also appropriate here. There are variations among instruments as to whether nitric oxide is measured separately in the air stream that has already passed the nitrogen dioxide column, or whether both oxides are measured together and nitric oxide determined by difference. Column efficiencies have been examined (179,195). All available instruments suffer the innate problems of flow colorimeters, together with those already discussed for the reagents. However, at the moment, no better instrument is available. There appears to have been comparatively little effort on the part of the manufacturers to optimize the systems within their own limitations.

## 3. Oxidant and Ozone Analyzers

These have been partially discussed under the same heading in Section III-B-2. Most of these instruments are flow colorimeters based on either iodide or dye oxidation, and they suffer the shortcomings which are obvious from this construction. The Brewer electrochemical transducer, mentioned previously, benefits from the greater simplicity of electro-chemical transduction. The author has had comparatively little difficulty with this instrument, but other users have reported difficulty in maintain-ing smooth liquid flow and maintenance problems with the pumps in the system. The instrument is commercially available from the Mast Development Co. Probably its outstanding advantage is its small size, compared with most other monitoring instruments (43,181).

Some of the inherent difficulties of the Brewer device are obviated by one devised by Komhyr (111a). This instrument uses a fixed volume of solution and therefore needs to be recharged every one to two days. However, since there are not liquid flows to maintain, it is extremely dependable and also very compact. The air pump is an unusually fine piece of design and will undoubtedly find its way into other instruments.

The Regener (189) chemiluminescent ozone sensor has also been dis-cussed above. Should it prove possible in the future to produce a more stable version, it could readily become an almost ideal field instrument. An instrument has also been described in which ozone attacks the hy-droquinone clathrate of krypton-85 (96), liberating the radioactive gas, which is then monitored. Ozone was also measured by passing the sampled air over two thermistors, one of which was coated with a decom-position catalyst (149). The heat of decomposition of the ozone warmed the coated thermistor, unbalancing the bridge circuit of which the two thermistors were legs. This instrument proved difficult to build and use because it called for such perfectly identical pairs of thermistors. A few other ozone or oxidant measuring devices have also been discussed previously. So far as it is possible to determine, none are presently in commercial production, and they do not enter into present consideration.

## 4. Conclusion

One monitoring system not previously mentioned is produced by Technicon Controls, Inc. It is a sort of "do-it-yourself" monitoring in-strument in that it is available piecemeal and may be adapted for any colorimetric determination, at least in theory. This system, together with a number of others, has been carefully evaluated, both in the laboratory and in the field (171a,193a). Unfortunately, all of the instruments tested had enough strengths and weaknesses to make a clear-cut recommenda-tion among them almost impossible. Nevertheless, the mere existence of comparative tests is new and certainly to be welcomed. The chief advantage of the Technicon instrument seems to lie in the peristaltic pump which enables a number of reagents to be pumped simultaneously in a fixed ratio to one another. This would theoretically permit the instrumentation of quite complex reaction sequences, so that the specificity of the laboratory methods would not have to be sacrificed. The system is still a flow colorimeter, and there are certain inherent difficulties which it is nearly impossible to avoid. It would appear risky for the totally uninitiated air pollution control agency to use this approach unless an adequate consultant were available to them, although the company maintains a substantial technical assistance activity. On the other hand, if there is already a good laboratory facility available, together with some knowledge of the problems and advantages of different analytical schemes, the ability to adapt the parts to the analysis of almost any trace substance could have great attraction. This type of instrumentation certainly should not be dismissed without study by anyone contemplating the purchase of monitoring instruments.

Monitoring instruments are a large investment, and one which should not be made without careful study. They are not a substitute for manpower or for knowledge of atmospheric chemistry. To date the market has been small, and there has been insufficient incentive for manufacturers to optimize their products.

Now, the market appears to be expanding, and the proliferation of new instruments has become a trifle overwhelming. Several years need to elapse before the present generation of instruments has been sufficiently studied to permit clearcut recommendations. Today, numerous compromises with the ideal are necessary. It can only be hoped that the future will bring the production of reliable instruments of known capabilities to permit the devotion of more attention to the evaluation of the environment and less to the evaluation of monitoring hardware.

## REFERENCES

1. Adams, D. F., R. K. Koppe, *Tappi*, **41**, 366 (1958).
2. Altshuller, A. P., T. A. Bellar, C. A. Clemons, and E. VanderZander, *Intern. J. Air Water Pollution*, **8**, 29 (1964).
3. Altshuller, A. P., A. F. Wartburg, I. R. Cohen, and S. F. Sleva, *Intern. J. Air Water Pollution*, **6**, 75 (1962).
4. Altshuller, A. P., T. A. Bellar, C. A. Clemons, *Amer. Ind. Hyg. Assoc. J.*, **23**, 164 (1962).
5. Altshuller, A. P., *J. Gas Chromatog.*, **1**, No. 7, 6 (1963).
6. Altshuller, A. P., *Tellus,* **10**, 479 (1958).
6a. Altshuller, A. P., and S. F. Sleva, *Anal. Chem.*, **33**, 1413 (1961).
7. Altshuller, A. P., C. M. Schwab, and M. Bare, *Anal. Chem.*, **31**, 1987 (1959).
8. Altshuller, A. P., G. C. Ortman, B. E. Saltzman, and R. E. Neligan, *J. Air Pollution Control Assoc.*, **16**, 87 (1966).

9. Altshuller, A. P., L. J. Leng, and A. F. Wartburg, *Intern. J. Air Water Pollution,* **6,** 381 (1962).

10. Altshuller, A. P., I. R. Cohen, M. E. Meyer, and A. F. Wartburg, *Anal. Chim. Acta,* **25,** 101 (1961).

11. American Conference of Governmental Industrial Hygienists, *Air Sampling Instruments,* 3rd ed., ACGIH, Cincinnati, Ohio, 1966.

12. American Conference of Governmental Industrial Hygienists, *Manual of Analytical Methods,* ACGIH, Cincinnati, Ohio, 1958.

13. American Society for Testing and Materials, ASTM Book of Standards, Part 23, Philadelphia, 1969.

14. Araki, S., and T. Kato, *Bunseki Kagaku,* **12,** 1027 (1963); through *Chem. Abstr.,* **58,** 10702 (1963).

15. Araki, S., and T. Kato, *Bunseki Kagaku,* **11,** 533 (1962); through *Chem. Abstr.,* **57,** 7562 (1962).

16. Ayer, H. E., and B. E. Saltzman, *Amer. Ind. Hyg. Assoc. J.,* **20,** 337 (1959).

16a. Axelrod, H. D., J. E. Bonelli, and J. P. Lodge, Jr., *Anal Chem.,* **42,** 512 (1970).

16b. Axelrod, H. D., J. H. Cary, J. E. Bonelli, and J. P. Lodge, Jr., *Anal. Chem.,* **41,** 1856 (1969).

16c. Axelrod, H. D., J. B. Pate, W. R. Barchet, and J. P. Lodge, Jr., *Atmos. Environment,* **4,** 209 (1970).

17. Bainbridge, A. E., and L. E. Heidl, *Tellus,* **18,** 221 (1966).

17a. Bamesberger, W. L., and D. F. Adams, *Environ. Sci. & Tech.,* **3,** 258 (1969).

18. Barlage, W. B., Jr., and F. C. Alley, *J. Air Pollution Control Assoc.,* **15,** 235 (1965).

19. Barnes, H., and A. R. Folkard, *Analyst,* **7,** 599 (1951).

20. Bell, F. A., Jr., *J. Air Pollution Control Assoc.,* **13,** 127 (1963).

21. Bellar, T., J. E. Sigsby, C. A. Clemons, and A. P. Altshuller, *Anal. Chem.,* **34,** 763 (1962).

22. Betz, C. E., J. H. Holden, and J. O. Handy, *Ind. Eng. Chem.,* **25,** 774 (1933).

22a. Bergshoeff, G, Pittsburgh Conference on Analytical Chemistry and Applied Spectroscopy, Cleveland, Ohio, March 1970.

23. Boettner, E. A., and F. C. Dallos, *Amer. Ind. Hyg. Assoc. J.,* **26,** 289 (1965).

24. Bostrom, C. E., *Intern. J. Air Water Pollution,* **10,** 435 (1966).

25. Boubel, R. W., *Amer. Ind. Hyg. Assoc. J.,* **26,** 318 (1965).

25a. Boulerice, M., and W. Brabant, *J. Air Pollution Control Assoc.,* **19,** 432 (1969).

26. Bovee, H. H., and R. J. Robinson, *Anal. Chem.,* **33,** 1115 (1961).

27. Bowden, S. R., *Intern. J. Air Water Pollution,* **8,** 101 (1964).

28. Bracewell, J. M., and A. E. M. Hodgson, *Intern. J. Air Water Pollution,* **9,** 431 (1965).

29. Bradley, C. E., and A. J. Haagen-Smit, *Rubber Chem. Technol.,* **24,** 750 (1951).

30. Bravo, H. A., and J. P. Lodge, *Anal. Chem.* **36,** 671 (1964).

31. Brenner, N., E. Cieplinski, L. S. Ettre, and V. J. Coates, *J. Chromatog.,* **3,** 230 (1960).

32. Brewer, A. W., and J. R. Milford, *Proc. Roy. Soc. (London),* **A256,** 470 (1960).

33. Brooman, D. L., and E. Edgerley, Jr., *J. Air Pollution Control Assoc.,* **16,** 25 (1966).

34. Bryan, R. J., and I. Cherniack, in *Proceedings, Summer Instruments Automation*

*Conference*, Instrument Society America, San Francisco, California, 1960, Preprint No. 22-SF60.

35. Buchwald, H., *Occupational Health Rev.*, **17**, 14 (1965).
36. Budd, M. S., and H. A. Bewick, *Anal. Chem.*, **4**, 1536 (1952).
36a. Byers, R. L., and J. W. Davis, *J. Air Pollution Control Assoc.*, **20**, 236 (1970).
37. Cadle, R. D., *Particle Size*, Reinhold, New York, 1965, p. 387.
38. Cadle, R. D., *Particles in the Atmosphere and Space*, Reinhold, New York, 1966.
39. Cadle, R. D., "Micrurgic Identification of Chloride and Sulfate," in *Atmospheric Chemistry of Chlorine and Sulfur Compounds*, J. P. Lodge, Ed., Geophysical Monograph No. 3, American Geophysical Union, Washington, D.C., 1959, pp. 18–21.
40. Calvert, S., and W. Workman, *Amer. Ind. Hyg. Assoc. J.*, **22**, 318 (1961).
41. Chamot, E. M., and C. W. Mason, *Handbook of Chemical Microscopy*, Wiley, New York, Vol. 1, 3rd ed., 1958; Vol. 2, 2nd ed., 1940.
42. Cherniack, I., and R. J. Bryan, *J. Air Pollution Control Assoc.*, **15**, 351 (1965).
43. Clark, J. F., and R. B. Faroro, *J. Air Pollution Control Assoc.*, **16**, 212 (1966).
44. Clemons, C. A., and A. P. Altshuller, *J. Air Pollution Control Assoc.*, **14**, 407 (1964).
45. Cohen, I. R., and A. P. Altshuller, *Anal. Chem.*, **33**, 726 (1961).
46. Cole, R., and H. I. Shulman, *Ind. Eng. Chem.*, **52**, 859 (1960).
47. Collinson, A. J. L., and A. K. M. M. Haque, *J. Sci. Instr.*, **40**, 521 (1963).
48. Conkle, J. P., J. W. Register, and G. L. Worth, *Aerospace Med.*, **36**, 869 (1965).
49. Conner, W. D., and J. S. Nader, *Amer. Ind. Hyg. Assoc. J.*, **25**, 291 (1964).
50. Crabtree, J., and A. R. Kemp, *Ind. Eng. Chem., Anal. Ed.*, **18**, 769 (1946).
51. Cropper, F. R., and S. Kaminsky, *Anal. Chem.*, **35**, 735 (1963).
52. Crossmon, G. C., *Occupational Health Rev.*, **16**, 3 (1964).
53. Crozier, W. D., and B. K. Seeley, "Some Techniques for Sampling and Identifying Particulate Matter in the Air," in *Proc. National Air Pollution Symp.*, 1950, 45.
54. Cummings, W. G., and M. W. Redfearn, *J. Inst. Fuel*, **30**, 628 (1957).
55. Darley, E. F., K. A. Kettner, and E. R. Stephens, *Anal. Chem.*, **35**, 589 (1963).
56. Demaio, L., and M. Corn, *Anal. Chem.*, **38**, 131 (1966).
57. DuBois, L., A. Zdrojewski, and J. L. Monkman, *J. Air Pollution Control Assoc.*, **16**, 135 (1966).
58. Eaves, A., and R. C. Macaulay, *Intern. J. Air Water Pollution*, **8**, 645 (1964).
59. Effenberger, E., *Z. Anal. Chem.*, **134**, 106 (1951).
59a. Eggertsen, F. T., and F. M. Nelsen, *Anal. Chem.*, **30**, 1040 (1958).
60. Ehmert, A., *Meteorol. Rundschau*, **4**, 64 (1951).
61. Ehmert, A., *J. Atmospheric Terrest. Phys.*, **2**, 189 (1952).
62. Elkins, H. B. *The Chemistry of Industrial Toxicology*, 2nd ed., Wiley, New York, 1959, pp. 284–287.
63. Ellis, C. F., *Intern. J. Air Water Pollution*, **8**, 297 (1964).
64. Ethrington, C. G., D. Warren, and F. C. Marsden, *Analyst*, **75**, 209 (1950).
65. Farlow, N. H., *Anal. Chem.*, **29**, 883 (1957).
66. Farlow, N. H., *Anal. Chem.*, **29**, 881 (1957).
67. Farre-Rius, F., and G. Guiochon, *J. Chromatog.*, **13**, 382 (1964).
68. Fedele, D., *Riv. Meteorol. Aeronaut.*, **16**, 31 (1956).

69. Feigl, F., *Chemistry of Specific, Selective and Sensitive Reactions,* Academic Press, New York, 1949, p. 75.

70. Feigl, F., *Spot Tests in Inorganic Analysis,* 5th ed., Elsevier, New York, 1958, pp. 303–306.

71. Feldstein, M., S. Balestrieri, and D. A. Levaggi, *J. Air Pollution Control Assoc.,* **15**, 215 (1965).

72. Feldstein, M., *J. Forensic Sci.,* **10**, 35 (1965).

73. Field, E., and C. S. Oldach, *Ind. Eng. Chem., Anal. Ed.,* **18**, 665 (1946).

74. Fieldner, A. C., G. G. Oberfell, M. C. Teague, and J. N. Lawrence, *Ind. Eng. Chem.,* **11**, 519 (1919).

75. Fonselius, S., F. Koroleff, and K. E. Warme, *Tellus,* **8**, 176 (1956).

76. Gage, J. C., *Analyst,* **84**, 519 (1959).

77. Gelman, C., *J. Air Pollution Control Assoc.,* **7**, 216 (1957).

78. Gilardi, E. F., and R. M. Manganelli, *J. Air Pollution Control Assoc.,* **13**, 305 (1963).

79. Gill, W. E., *Amer. Ind. Hyg. Assoc. J.,* **21**, 87, (1960).

80. Goetz, A., and O. Preining, "The Aerosol Spectrometer and Its Application to Nuclear Condensation Studies," in H. Weickmann, Ed., *Physics of Precipitation, Geophysical Monograph,* 5. Publ. No. 746, American Geophysical Union, Washington, D.C., 1960, pp. 164–183.

81. Greenberg, L., and G. W. Smith, *U.S. Bur. Mines, Rept. Invest.,* **2392**, 3 pp. (1922).

82. Greenburg, L., and M. B. Jacobs, *Ind. Eng. Chem.,* **48**, 1517 (1956).

83. Haagen-Smit, A. J., *J. Appl. Nutrition,* **6**, 298 (1953).

84. Haagen-Smit, A. J., and M. M. Fox, "Cumulative Test for Atmospheric Ozone," in *Proceedings of the Conference on Chemical Reactions in Urban Atmospheres,* L. H. Rogers, Ed., APF Report No. 15, Air Pollution Foundation, Los Angeles, California, 1956.

85. Hauser, T. R., and R. L. Cummins, *Anal. Chem.,* **36**, 679 (1964).

86. Hauser, T. R., and D. W. Bradley, *Anal. Chem.,* **38**, 1529 (1966); *ibid,* **39**, 1184 (1967).

87. Helwig, H. L., and C. L. Gordon, *Anal. Chem.,* **30**, 1810 (1958).

88. Hendricks, R. H., and L. B. Larsen, *Amer. Ind. Hyg. Assoc. J.,* **27**, 80 (1966).

89. Hickey, H. R., and E. R. Hendrickson, *J. Air Pollution Control Assoc.,* **15**, 409 (1965).

90. Hochheiser, S., Air Pollution Symposium, Division of Water and Waste Chemistry, 150th Meeting, American Chemical Society, Atlantic City, New Jersey, September 1965, Preprint, p. 124.

91. Hochheiser Y., *Methods of Measuring and Monitoring Atmospheric Sulfur Dioxide* Publ., No. 999-AP-6, U.S. Public Health Service, Cincinnati, Ohio, 1964.

92. Hochheiser, S., J. Santner, and W. F. Ludmann, *J. Air Pollution Control Assoc.,* **16**, 266 (1966).

93. Hodkinson, J. R., "Light-Scattering Instruments for Measuring Particulate Air Pollution," in *Air Sampling Instruments,* 3rd ed., American Conference Governmental Industrial Hygienists, Cincinnati, Ohio, 1966, Section B6.

94. Hodkinson, J. R., "Thermal Precipitators," in *Air Sampling Instruments,* 3rd ed., American Conference Governmental Industrial Hygienists, Cincinnati, Ohio, 1966, Section B3.

95. Holm-Jensen, I., *Anal. Chim. Acta,* **23**, 13 (1960).
96. Hommel, C. O., D. Chleck, and F. J. Brousaides, *Nucleonics,* **19**, No. 5, 94 (1961).
97. Hornstein, I., and W. N. Sullivan, *Anal. Chem.,* **25**, 496 (1953).
98. Hoschele, K., *Staub,* **24**, 140 (1964).
98a. Huey, N. A., *J. Air Pollution Control Assoc.,* **18**, 610 (1968).
99. Huitt, H. A., and J. P. Lodge, Jr., *Anal. Chem.,* **36**, 1305 (1964).
100. Huygen, C., *Anal. Chim. Acta,* **28**, 349 (1963).
100a. Huygen, C., *Anal. Chem.,* **42**, 407 (1970).
101. Innes, W. B., and W. E. Bambrick, *J. Gas Chromatog.,* **2**, 309 (1964).
102. Interbranch Chemical Advisory Committee, *Selected Methods for the Measurement of Air Pollutants,* Publ. No. 999-AP-11, U.S. Public Health Service, Cincinnati, Ohio, 1965.
103. Jacobs, M. B., M. M. Braverman, and S. Hochheiser, *Anal. Chem.,* **29**, 1349 (1957).
104. Jacobs, M. B., and S. Hochheiser, *Anal. Chem.,* **30**, 426 (1958).
105. Jacobs, M. B., *The Analytical Chemistry of Industrial Poisons, Hazards, and Solvents,* 2nd ed., Interscience, New York, 1949, pp. 21–53.
106. Jacobs, M. B., *The Chemical Analysis of Air Pollutants,* Interscience, New York, 1960.
107. Jacobs, M. B., M. M. Braverman, and S. Hochheiser, 12th Annual Meeting, Instrument Society of America, New York, September 1956, Paper No. 56-32-3.
108. Jones, E. E., L. B. Pierce, and P. K. Mueller, 7th Conference on Methods in Air Pollution Studies, California State Health Department, Los Angeles, California, January, 1965.
109. Kanno, S., *Intern. J. Air Water Pollution,* **1**, 231 (1959).
109a. King, H. G. C., and G. Pruden, *Analyst,* **94**, 43 (1969).
110. Kitano, Y., and H. Takakuwa, *Bunseki Kagaku,* **3**, 7 (1954); through *Chem. Abstr.,* **48**, 6913 (1954).
111. Kolthoff, I. M., and C. S. Miller, *J. Amer. Chem. Soc.,* **63**, 2818 (1941).
111a. Komhyr, W. D., *Ann. Géophys.,* **25**, 203 (1969).
112. Kothny, E. L., and P. K. Mueller, "Faster Analyses of Nitrogen Dioxide with Continuous Air Analyzers," in *Air Pollution Instrumentation,* D. F. Adams, Ed., Instrument Society of America, Pittsburgh, Pa., 1966, pp. 61–74.
113. Kozlyaeva, T. N., *Zh. Anal. Khim.,* **4**, 75 (1949).
114. Kumai, M., *J. Meteorol.,* **8**, 151 (1951).
115. Kumai, M., and K. E. Francis, *J. Atmospheric Sci.,* **19**, 474 (1962).
116. Kusnetz, H. L., "Internal Collectors," in *Air Sampling Instruments,* 3rd ed., American Conference Governmental Industrial Hygienists, Cincinnati, Ohio, 1966, Section B3.
117. Kusnetz, H. L., B. T. Saltzman, and M. E. Lanier, *Amer. Ind. Hyg. Assoc. J.,* **21**, 361 (1960).
117a. LaHue, M. D., J. B. Pate, and J. P. Lodge, Jr., *J. Geophys. Res.* **75**, 2922 (1970).
118. Lawrence, E. N., *Intern. J. Air Water Pollution,* **8**, 381 (1964).
119. Lawther, P. J., B. T. Commins, and M. Henderson, *Ann. Occupational Hyg.,* **5**, 241 (1962).
120. Leonard, R. E., and J. E. Kiefer, *J. Gas Chromatog.,* **4**, 142 (1966).
121. Levaggi, D. A. and M. Feldstein, *Amer. Ind. Hyg. Assoc. J.,* **25**, 64 (1964).

122. Liberti, A., G. P. Cartoni, and V. Cantuti, *J. Chromatog.*, **15**, 141 (1964).

123. Lidrell, H. F., *Analyst*, **80**, 901 (1955).

124. Lippmann, M., "Filter Holders and Filter Media," in *Air Sampling Instruments*, 3rd ed., American Conference Governmental Industrial Hygienists, Cincinnati, Ohio, 1966, Section B2.

125. Lippmann, M., "Electrostatic Precipitators," in *Air Sampling Instruments*, 3rd ed., American Conference Governmental Industrial Hygienists, Cincinnati, Ohio, 1966, Section B4.

126. Lippmann, M., and W. B. Harris, *Health Phys.*, **8**, 155 (1962).

126a. Liu, B. Y. H., K. T. Whitby, and H. H. S. Yu, *Rev. Sci. Instr.*, **38**, 100 (1966).

127. Lloyd, D. A., and M. Madden, *J. Sci. Instr.*, **41**, 622 (1964).

128. Lodge, J. P., Jr., "Identification of Aerosols," in *Advances in Geophysics*, Vol. 9, H. E. Landsberg and J. Van Mieghem, Eds., Academic Press, New York, 1962, pp. 97–130.

129. Lodge J. P., *Contamination Control*, **3**, No. 12, 18 (1964); **4**, No. 2, 10 (1965).

130. Lodge, J. P., Jr., J. B. Pate, P. E. Ammons, and G. A. Swanson, *J. Air Pollution Control Assoc.*, **16**, 197 (1966).

131. Lodge, J. P., Jr., and E. R. Frank, 6th International Conference on Condensation Nuclei, Albany, New York, May 11–14, 1966.

132. Lodge, J. P., Jr., *Nubila*, **2**, 58 (1959).

133. Lodge, J. P., Jr., and E. R. Frank, *Anal. Chim. Acta*, **35**, 270 (1966).

134. Lodge, J. P., Jr., *Anal. Chem.*, **26**, 1829 (1954).

135. Lodge, J. P., J. Ferguson, and B. R. Havlik, *Anal. Chem.*, **32**, 1206 (1960).

136. Lodge J. P., Jr., and K. J. Parbhakar, *Anal. Chim. Acta*, **29**, 372 (1963).

137. Lodge, J. P., Jr., and E. R. Frank, "The Detection and Estimation of Particulate Formaldehyde," in *Aerosols, Physical Chemistry and Application*, Czechoslovak Academy of Sciences, Prague, Czechosolovakia, 1965, p. 169.

138. Lodge, J. P., H. F. Ross, W. K. Sumida, and B. J. Tufts, *Anal. Chem.* **28**, 423 (1956).

139. Lodge, J. P., Jr., C. Xinteras, J. B. Pate, and A. P. Altshuller, *Intern. J. Air Water Pollution*, **7**, 79 (1963).

140. Lodge, J. P., Jr., "Production of Controlled Test Atmospheres," in *Air Pollution*, 2nd ed., A. C. Stern, Ed., Academic Press, New York, 1968, pp. 465–483.

141. Lodge, J. P., E. R. Frank, and J. Ferguson, *Anal. Chem.*, **34**, 702 (1962).

142. Lodge, J. P., Jr., E. R. Frank, and H. A. Huitt, 55th Annual Meeting, Air Pollution Control Association, Chicago, Ill., May 20–24, 1962, Paper No. 62-22.

143. Louw, C. W., and E. C. Halliday, *Intern. J. Air Water Pollution*, **7**, 1033 (1963).

144. Lyles, G. R., F. B. Dowling, and V. J. Blanchard, *J. Air Pollution Control Assoc.*, **15**, 106 (1965).

145. Lynn, D. A., and T. B. McMullen, *J. Air Pollution Control Assoc.*, **16**, 186 (1966).

146. McCormick, R. A., and C. Xinteras, *J. Appl. Meteorol.*, **1**, 237 (1962).

147. McCrone, W. C., R. G. Draftz and J. G. Delly, *The Particle Atlas*, Ann Arbor Science Publishers, Ann Arbor, Mich., (1967).

148. McCullough, J. D., R. A. Crane, and A. O. Beckman, *Anal. Chem.*, **19**, 999 (1947).

149. McCullly, C. R., J. F. Roesler, E. S. Gordon, J. N. Van Scoyoc, and R. A. Carrigan, *Trans. IRE,* **I-10,** 89 (1961).
150. McKay, R. J., and D. E. Ackerman, *Ind. Eng. Chem.,* **20,** 538 (1928).
151. McKee, H. C., and W. L. Rollwitz, *J. Air Pollution Control Assoc.,* **8,** 338 (1959).
152. Mast, G. M., and H. E. Saunders, *Instr. Soc. Amer. (Trans.),* **1,** 325 (1962).
153. May, K. R., *J. Sci. Instr.,* **22,** 187 (1945).
154. Mészáros, E., *J. Rech. Atmospheriques,* **1,** 151 (1963).
155. Morgan, D. J., and G. Duxbury, *Ann. Occupational Hyg.,* **8,** 253 (1965).
156. Morrow, J. I., A. Turk, and W. Baecht, Symposium on Air Pollution, Division of Water and Waste Chemistry, 144th Meeting, American Chemical Society, Los Angeles, March–April 1963, Preprint, p. 313.
157. Morrow, J. I., A. Turk, and S. Davis, Symposium on Air Pollution, Division of Water and Waste Chemistry, 144th Meeting, American Chemical Society, Los Angeles, March–April 1963, Preprint, p. 314.
158. Moses, H., H. F. Lucas, Jr., and G. A. Zerbe, *J. Air Pollution Control Assoc.,* **13,** 12 (1963).
159. Mueller, P. K., E. L. Kothny, N. O. Fansah, and Y. Tokiwa, 59th Annual Meeting, Air Pollution Control Assoc., San Francisco, June 1966, paper 66-112.
160. Nader, J. S., and W. L. Coffey, *Amer. Ind. Hyg. Assoc. J.,* **24,** 563 (1963).
161. Nader, J. S., and J. L. Dolphin, *J. Air Pollution Control Assoc.,* **8,** 336 (1959).
162. Nash, T., *J. Sci. Instr.,* **38,** 480 (1961).
163. Nash, T., *Intern. J. Air Water Pollution,* **8,** 121 (1964).
164. Naughton, J. J., E. F. Heald, and I. L. Parnes, Jr., *J. Geophys. Res.,* **68,** 539 (1963).
165. Nauman, R. V., P. W. West, F. Tron, and G. C. Gaeke, Jr., *Anal. Chem.,* **32,** 1307 (1960).
166. Nolan, P., *Ann. N.Y., Acad. Sci.,* **116,** 576 (1964).
167. Okita, T., and J. P. Lodge, Jr., Symposium on Air Pollution, Division of Water and Waste Chemistry, 148th Meeting, American Chemical Society, Chicago, August–September 1964, Preprint, p. 107.
168. Omichi, S., *Bunseki Kagaku,* **13,** 339 (1964); through *Chem. Abstr.,* **61,** 1273 (1964).
169. Ortman, G. C., Symposium on Air Pollution, Division of Water and Waste Chemistry, 148th Meeting, American Chemical Society, Chicago, August–September 1964, Preprint, p. 117.
170. Pack, M. R., and A. C. Hill, *J. Air Pollution Control Assoc.,* **15,** 166 (1965).
171. Palazzo, F. C., *Gazz. Chim. Ital.,* **92,** 1189 (1962).
171a. Palmer, H. F., C. E. Rodes, and C. J. Nelson, *J. Air Pollution Control Assoc.,* **19,** 778 (1969).
172. Pare, J. P., *J. Air Pollution Control Assoc.,* **16,** 325 (1966).
173. Pate, J. B., and E. C. Tabor, *Amer. Ind. Hyg. Assoc. J.,* **23,** 145 (1962).
174. Pate, J. B., J. P. Lodge, Jr., and M. P. Neary, *Anal. Chim. Acta,* **28,** 34, (1963).
175. Pate, J. B., J. P. Lodge, Jr., and A. F. Wartburg, *Anal. Chem.,* **34,** 1660 (1962).
176. Pate, J. B., B. E. Ammons, G. A. Swanson, and J. P. Lodge, *Anal. Chem.,* **37,** 942 (1965).

177. Paulus, H. J., E. P. Floyd, and D. H. Byers, *Amer. Ind. Hyg. Assoc. Quart.,* **15,** 277 (1954).

178. Pearce, S. J., and H. H. Schrenk, "Determination of Sulfur Dioxide in Air by Means of the Midget Impinger," *U.S. Bur. Mines, Rept. Invest,* **4282** (1948).

179 Pierce, L., Y. Tokiwa, and K. Nishikawa, *J. Air Pollution Control Assoc.,* **15,** 204 (1965).

180. Platnikova, M. M., *Gigiena Sanit.,* **22,** 10 (1957).

181. Potter, L., and S. Duckworth, *J. Air Pollution Control Assoc.,* **15,** 207 (1965).

182. Preining. O., *Staub,* **39,** 45 (1955).

183. Preining, O., M. Sedlacek, F. Ernst, W. Resch, and J. A. Schedling, *Staub,* **23,** 407 (1963).

184. Quiram, E. R., and W. F. Biller, *Anal. Chem.,* **30,** 1166 (1958).

185. Rabson, S. R., *Ind. Chem.,* **37,** 219 (1961).

186. Rajewsky, M. F., *Nature,* **199,** 162 (1963).

187. Rasmussen, R. A., and F. W. Went, *Proc. Natl. Acad. Sci.* (U.S.), **53,** 215 (1965).

188. Regener, V. H., "Automatic Chemical Determination of Atmospheric Ozone," in *Ozone Chemistry and Technology, Advan. Chem. Series,* **21,** 124 (1959).

189. Regener, V. H., *J. Geophys. Res.,* **69,** 3795 (1964).

190. Renzetti, N. A., *J. Chem. Phys.,* **24,** 909 (1956).

191. Renzetti, N. A., and J. C. Romanovsky, *J. Air Pollution Control Assoc.,* **6,** 154 (1956).

192. Ripley, D. L., J. M. Clingenpeel, and R. W. Hurn, *Intern. J. Air Water Pollution,* **8,** 455 (1964).

192a. Robbins, R. C., K. M. Borg, and E. Robinson, *J. Air Pollution Control Assoc.,* **18,** 106 (1968).

193. Roberts, L. R., and H. C. McKee, *J. Air Pollution Control Assoc.,* **9,** 51 (1959).

193a. Rodes, C. E., H. F. Palmer, L. A. Elfers, and C. H. Norris, *J. Air Pollution Control Assoc.,* **19,** 575 (1969).

194. Russell, S., *Amer. Ind. Hyg. Assoc., J.,* **25,** 359 (1964).

195. Saltzman, B. E., and A. L. Mendenhall, Jr., *Anal. Chem.,* **36,** 1300 (1964).

196. Saltzman, B. E., *Anal. Chem.,* **33,** 1100 (1961).

197. Saltzman, B. E., *Anal. Chem.,* **26,** 1949 (1954).

198. Saltzman, B. E., and N. Gilbert, *Amer. Ind. Hyg. Assoc. J.,* **20,** 379 (1959).

199. Saltzman, B. E., and N. Gilbert, *Anal. Chem.,* **31,** 1914 (1959).

200. Sanderson, H. P., A. F. W. Cole, M. Katz, and S. Baburek, *Amer. Ind. Hyg. Assoc. J.,* **24,** 404 (1963).

201. Sanderson, H. P., R. Thomas, and M. Katz, *J. Air Pollution Control Assoc.,* **16,** 328 (1966).

202. Sawicki, E., T. Stanley, and T. Hauser, *Chemist Analyst,* **47,** 31 (1958).

203. Sawicki, E., T. R. Hauser, and S. McPherson, *Anal. Chem.,* **34,** 1460 (1962).

204. Sawicki, E., T. R. Hauser, and F. T. Fox, *Anal. Chim. Acta,* **26,** 229 (1962).

205. Sawicki, E., T. R. Hauser, and R. Wilson, *Anal. Chem.,* **34,** 505 (1962).

206. Sawicki, E., and J. D. Pfaff, *Chemist-Analyst,* **55,** 6 (1966).

207. Sawicki, E., *Talanta,* **16,** 1231 (1969).

208. Scaringelli, F. P., B. E. Saltzman, and S. A. Frey, *Anal. Chem.,* **39,** 1709 (1967).

209. Schadt, C., and R. D. Cadle, *Anal. Chem.,* **29,** 864 (1957).

210. Schleien, B., *Amer. Ind. Hyg. Assoc. J.*, **24**, 180 (1963).
211. Schmitt, K. H., *Staub*, **21**, 173 (1961).
212. Seely, B. K., *Anal. Chem.*, **27**, 93 (1955).
213. Seely, B. K., *Anal. Chem.*, **24**, 576 (1952).
214. Sensenbaugh, J. D., and W. C. L. Hemeon, *Air Repair*, **4**, 5 (1954).
215. Shaffer, P. A., Jr., A. Briglio, Jr., and J. A. Brockman, Jr., *Anal. Chem.*, **20**, 1008 (1948).
216. Shoji, H., T. Yamamoto, and K. Nishida, *Trans. Japan Soc. Civil Engr.*, **91**, 25 (1963); through *Air Pollution Control Assoc. Abstr.* No. 5316.
217. Silverman, L., *Air Cond. Heat. Vent.*, **52**, No. 8, 87 (1955).
218. Silverman, L., and G. R. Gardner, *Amer. Ind. Hyg. Assoc. J.*, **26**, 97 (1965).
219. Skare, I., *Intern. J. Air Water Pollution*, **9**, 601 (1965).
220. Slobod, R. L., and M. E. Krogh, *J. Amer. Chem. Soc.*, **72**, 1175 (1950).
221. Smith, R. B., and B. S. T. Freis, *J. Ind. Hyg.*, **13**, 338 (1931).
222. Smith, S. B., and R. J. Grant, "A Nonselective Collector for Sampling Gaseous Air Pollutant," Tech. Report A59-3, U.S. Public Health Service, Cincinnati, Ohio, 1959.
222a. Spurný, K. R., J. P. Lodge, Jr., E. R. Frank, and D. C. Sheesley, *Environmental Sci. Tech.*, **3**, 453 (1969).
223. Steigmann, A., *J. Soc. Chem. Ind.*, **61**, 18 (1942).
224. Stephens, B. G., and F. Lindstrom, *Anal. Chem.*, **36**, 1308 (1964).
225. Stephens, E. R., F. R. Burleson, and E. A. Cardiff, *J. Air Pollution Control Assoc.*, **15**, 87 (1965).
226. Stephens, E. R., *Anal. Chem.*, **36**, 928 (1964).
227. Stratmann, H., and M. Buck, *Intern. J. Air Water Pollution*, **10**, 313 (1966).
228. Suzuki, S., K. Ishimaru, and I. Hikawa, *Bunseki Kagaku*, **12**, 1065 (1963); through *Air Pollution Control Assoc. Abstr.*, No. 6381 (1965).
229. Tada, O., and K. Nakaaki, *Rodo Kagaku*, **39**, 595 (1963); through *Air Pollution Control Assoc. Abstr.*, No. 6018 (1964).
230. Terraglio, F. P., and R. M. Manganelli, *Anal. Chem.*, **34**, 675 (1962).
231. Thomas, M. D., and J. N. Abersold, *Ind. Eng. Chem., Anal. Ed.*, **1**, 14 (1929).
232. Thomas, M. D., J. A. MacLeod, R. C. Robbins, R. C. Goettelman, R. W. Eldridge, and L. H. Rogers, *Anal. Chem.*, **28**, 1810 (1956).
233. Thomas, M. D., and R. J. Cross, *Ind. Eng. Chem.*, **20**, 645 (1928).
234. Thomas, M. D., J. O. Ivie, and T. C. Fitt, *Ind. Eng. Chem., Anal. Ed.*, **18**, 383 (1946).
235. Todd, G. W., *Anal. Chem.*, **27**, 1490 (1955).
236. Tufts, B. J., *Anal. Chem.*, **31**, 238 (1959).
237. Tufts, B. J., *Anal. Chem.*, **31**, 242 (1959).
238. Tufts, B. J., and J. P. Lodge, *Anal. Chem.*, **30**, 300 (1958).
239. Tufts, B. J., *Anal. Chim. Acta*, **23**, 209 (1960).
240. Tufts, B. J., *Anal. Chim. Acta*, **25**, 322 (1961).
241. Turk, A., J. Morrow, P. F. Levy, and P. Weissman, *Intern. J. Air Water Pollution*, **5**, 14 (1961).
242. Turner, B. M., *Mikrochim. Acta*, **1958**, 305.
243. Turner, B. M., *Nature*, **179**, 964 (1957).
244. Twomey, S., *J. Meteorol.*, **11**, 334 (1954).
245. Twomey, S., and G. T. Severynse, *J. Atmos. Sci.*, **20**, 392 (1963).
246. Urone, P., J. B. Evans, and C. M. Noyes, *Anal. Chem.*, **37**, 1104 (1965).

247. Urone, P. F., and W. E. Boggs, *Anal. Chem.*, **23**, 1517 (1951).
248. Vance, B. H., "Air Movers," in *Air Sampling Instruments,* 3rd ed., American Conference Governmental Industrial Hygienist, Cincinnati, Ohio, 1966, Section B3.
249. Vittori, A. O., *Arch. Meteorol. Geophys. Biokl.*, **A8**, 204 (1955).
250. Wadelin, C. W., *Anal. Chem.*, **29**, 441 (1957).
251. Waller, R. E., *Intern. J. Air Water Pollution*, **7**, 773 (1963).
252. Wartburg, A. F., A. W. Brewer, and J. P. Lodge, Jr., *Intern. J. Air Water Pollution*, **8**, 21 (1964).
252a. Wartburg, A. F., J. B. Pate, and J. P. Lodge, Jr., *Environmental Sci. Tech.*, **3**, 767 (1969).
253. Watanabe, H., and T. Nakadoi, 59th Annual Meeting, Air Pollution Control Assoc., San Francisco, June, 1966, Paper 66-113.
254. Waters, J. L., and N. W. Hartz, Annual Meeting, Instrument Society of America, Houston, September 1951.
255. West, P. W., B. Sen, and N. A. Gibson, *Anal. Chem.*, **30**, 1390 (1958).
256. West, P. W., "Chemical Analysis of Inorganic Particulate Pollutants," in *Air Pollution,* 2nd ed., A. C. Stern, Ed., Academic Press, New York, 1968, pp. 147–185.
257. West, P. W., and G. C. Gaeke, *Anal. Chem.*, **28**, 1816 (1956).
258. West, P. W., and F. Ordoveza, *Anal. Chem.*, **34**, 1324 (1962).
259. West, P. W., and B. Sen, *Z. Anal. Chem.*, **153**, 177 (1956).
260. White, H. J., *Industrial Electrostatic Precipitation,* Addison-Wesley, Reading, Mass., 1963.
261. Whitman, N. E., and A. E. Johnston, *Amer. Ind. Hyg. Assoc. J.*, **25**, 464 (1964).
262. Williams, I. H., *Anal. Chem.*, **37**, 1723 (1965).
263. Woodcock, A. H., *J. Meteorol.*, **9**, 200 (1952).
264. Zurlo, N., and A. M. Griffini, *Med. Lavoro,* **53**, 330 (1962).

# ANALYTICAL CHEMISTRY IN THE CONTROL OF WATER TREATMENT PLANTS

By Floyd B. Taylor, *Carlisle, Massachusetts*

## Contents

**Contents** (*continued*)

# I. INTRODUCTION

The control of water treatment began early in history when man sought a better quality drinking water. The analytical tools by which he then judged water quality were simple. They consisted of his nose, eyes, and mouth, and possibly his observations that people became ill from drinking poor quality water. Likewise, his control of water quality was elemental and was often no more complex than the selection of a better, more attractive source of supply. For example, in what is the earliest known reference to improvement of a public water supply, it is recorded (1,2) that about 710 B.C. King Hezekiah, for reasons which could possibly have been defense, improved the water supply of Jerusalem by building dams in the mountains outside the city walls and leading the water into the city by means of a conduit.

In the sixth century B.C., as noted by Herodotus (3), Cyrus the Great, monarch of the Persians, took boiled water in silver flagons on his military expeditions. This lends support to the theory that the ancients were aware of the health significance of pure water and it is of interest that modern day research has demonstrated the bactericidal and bacteriostatic properties of silver.

Improving water quality on a large scale was practiced by the Romans who, according to Sextus Julius Frontinus, superintendent of the Rome water department in 97 A.D., built a large settling basin at the head of one of the aquaducts and provided pebble catchers in many of their water conduits (4). The Romans also went to the mountains for their sources of domestic water supply, having noted that the waters of the low lands were apparently responsible for sickness among the people. There is no record, however, of quality control by analytical procedures.

During the millenium which followed the collapse of the Roman Empire, and particularly in the 17th and 18th centuries, the concept developed (5) of water purification by filtration through sand, charcoal, stone, and other porous materials*, sometimes preceded by plain sedimentation. Some kinds of chemical treatment were also advocated.

It is of particular interest to this paper that one of the earliest, modern references to chemical water treatment was in 1724 when the Dutch

---

* The practice of filtration through porous material goes back as far as ancient Hindu cultures. This was usually on an individual use basis rather than for a public water supply. For example, Sanskrit literature, probably dating from around 2000 B.C. describes a process for filtering water through charcoal and then keeping it in copper vessels (8).

chemist Boerhaave prescribed certain measures in his *Elements of Chemistry* (6). He recommended that putrid water be purified by boiling and the addition of acid and that further putrifaction be prevented by adding spirit of vitriol. However, the first sustained practice of chemical treatment of public water supplies did not occur until the early part of the 19th century. This chemical treatment consisted of the use of alum to coagulate water for better settling and clarification prior to filtration.

In 1851 a Chemical Commission made a report (7,8) to the London General Board of Health on purifying the water of the Thames, a river noted for high turbidity during floods. In this report there was recorded testimony of one London Water Company official of a water company serving London who stated that seven grains of alum per imperial gallon was sufficient to precipitate the clay and decolor the Thames River water. Further chemical treatment involved adding sulfuric acid to convert lime into sulfate, but this, it was observed, also increased hardness. This report also described the chemical and physical reactions involved in coagulation.

Chemical analyses as a tool in understanding water treatment had also been developed by the middle of the 19th century. It is documented (9) that in 1856, Henry Witt, a chemist in the Government School of applied science, made chemical analysis of the Thames River water before and after filtration in order to determine the effect of filtration upon the chemical content of the water.

In concluding this introduction and short review of the history of water treatment and its chemistry, it must be stated that by the late 19th and early 20th centuries the practice of water coagulation by chemical means was established as a necessary step prior to rapid sand filtration. Also, by this time it was understood that the water filtration process, particularly coagulation and sedimentation, was more than straining to remove particles of dirt; that it was also a chemical and biological method for improving water quality and controlling waterborne disease.

It is noted above that the first analytical "tools" for evaluating water quality were sight, taste, and smell. By the use of these, coupled with observations that impure water caused illness, man selected and conditioned his water supplies. As far as chemical quality is concerned, he probably did quite well, for a water which is clear, tasteless, and odorless frequently possesses acceptable chemical characteristics. It cannot be assumed, however, in the present era that such a water is free from disease organisms nor from the dissolved, toxic chemicals being discharged to the environment in industrial, commercial, and domestic wastes. The presence, or potential presence of such toxic elements and radicals has lead to an increasing number of chemical limits in modern drinking water standards. The determination of the chemical constituents of drinking water has become a highly complex and expensive operation, requiring properly trained and experienced analytical chemists. Without the skills of these chemists to control water quality, modern water supply treatment and conditioning would be most difficult. The remainder of this chapter will be devoted to describing how water supply and chemistry are closely related, so that the analytical chemist may find some assistance in making his contributions to the enormous task of producing and distributing high quality water to the people. First will be a discussion of terminology, basic water chemistry, and kinds of modern water treatment systems.

## II. TERMINOLOGY

Although the profession of public water supply production and distribution embraces several disciplines, it nevertheless has a language all its own, and this language has developed principally in hydraulic and engineering terms. The analytical chemist therefore should become acquainted with the terminology used, but it is quite beyond the scope of this chapter to define many of the words which are commonly employed. This has been done in a glossary containing definitions of over 3000 terms (10). However, definitions of a few terms are needed for a better understanding of the text. These are as follows and are quoted from the glossary except as noted.

*Agglomeration.* The coalescence of dispersed suspended matter into larger flocs or particles which settle rapidly.

*Ammoniator.* Apparatus used for applying ammonia or ammonium compounds to water.

*Aquifer.* A porous, water bearing geologic formation. Generally restricted to materials capable of yielding an appreciable supply of water.

*Backwashing.* The operation of cleaning a filter by reversing the flow of liquid through it and washing out matter previously captured in it. Filters would include true filters such as sand and diatomaceous-earth types but not other treatment units such as trickling filters.

*Chlorine-Ammonia Treatment.* The application of chlorine to water, before or after the application of ammonia, to provide a persistent combined chlorine residual or to control the production of chlorinous tastes.

*Chlorination, Combined Residual.* The application of chlorine to water or wastewater to produce, with the natural or added ammonia, or with certain organic nitrogen compounds, a combined chlorine residual.

*Chlorination, Free Residual.* The application of chlorine or chlorine compounds to water or wastewater to produce a free available chlorine residual directly or through the destruction of ammonia, or certain organic nitrogenous compounds.

*Chlorine, Combined Available Residual.* That portion of the total residual chlorine remaining in water or wastewater at the end of a specified contact period, which will react chemically and biologically as chloramines or organic chloramines.

*Chlorine, Free Available Residual.* That portion of the total residual chlorine remaining in water or wastewater at the end of a specified contact period, which will react chemically and biologically as hypochlorous acid or hypochlorite ion.

*Chlorine Demand.* The difference between the amount of chlorine added to water or wastewater and the amount of residual chlorine remaining at the end of a specified contact period. The demand for any given water varies with the amount of chlorine applied, time of contact, and temperature.

*Coagulation.* In water and wastewater treatment, the destabilization and initial aggregation of colloidal and finely divided suspended matter by the addition of a floc-forming chemical or by biological processes.

*Coagulation, Chemical.* The process of forming flocculent particles in a liquid by the addition of a chemical coagulant; also the removal of colloidal or finely divided suspended matter from the liquid by the floc, and the agglomeration of the flocculated matter.

* *Concentration.* A measure of the amount of dissolved substances contained per unit volume of solution. May be expressed as parts per million, grains per gallon, pounds per million gallons.

*Contamination.* Any introduction into water of microorganisms, chemicals, wastes, or wastewater in a concentration that makes the water unfit for its intended use.

*Cross Connection.* (*1*) A physical connection through which a supply of potable water could be contaminated or polluted. (*2*) A connection between a supervised potable water supply and an unsupervised supply of unknown potability.

* *Detention Time.* The theoretical length of time for water to pass through a basin or tank, if all the water moves through with the same uniform velocity; mathematically equal to the volume of basin divided by the rate of flow. Also called retention time, detention period, period of retention, etc.

*Effluent.* (*1*) A liquid that flows out of a containing space. (*2*) Wastewater or other liquid, partially or completely treated, or in its natural state, flowing out of a reservoir, basin, treatment plant, or industrial treatment plant, or part thereof. (*3*) An outflowing branch of a main stream or lake.

*Filter, Slow Sand.* A filter for the purification of water where water without previous treatment is passed downward through a filtering medium consisting of a layer of sand or other suitable material, usually finer than for a rapid sand filter, and from 24 in. to 40 in. thick. The filtrate is removed by an underdrainage system and the filter is cleaned by scraping off and replacing the clogged layer. It is characterized by a slow rate of filtration, commonly from 3 mgd to 6 mgd per acre of filter area.

*Filter, Rapid Sand.* A filter for the purification of water, in which water that has been previously treated, usually by coagulation and sedimentation, is passed downward through a filtering medium. The medium consists of a layer of sand, prepared anthracite coal, or other suitable material, usually 24–30 in. thick, resting on a supporting bed of gravel or a porous medium such as carborundum. The filtrate is removed by an underdrainage system which also distributes the wash water. The filter is cleaned periodically by reversing the flow of the water upward through the filtering medium, sometimes supplemented by mechanical or air agitation during washing, to remove mud and other impurities which have lodged in the sand. It is characterized by a rapid rate of filtration, commonly from 2 gal. to 3 gal. per min per sq ft of filter area.

*Filtration.* The process of passing a liquid through a filtering medium (which may consist of granular material such as sand, magnetite, or diatomaceous earth, finely woven cloth, unglazed porcelain, or specially prepared paper) for the removal of suspended or colloidal matter usually of a type that cannot be removed by sedimentation.

*Hardness.* A characteristic of water, imparted by salts of calcium, magnesium, and iron such as bicarbonates, carbonates, sulfates, chlorides and nitrates, that causes curdling of soap and increased consumption of soap, deposition of scale in boilers, damage in some industrial processes, and sometimes objectionable taste.

*Influent.* Water, wastewater, or other liquid flowing into a reservoir, basin, or treatment plant, or any unit thereof.

*Mudballs.* (*1*) Accretions of siliceous incrustations on the exterior surface of sand grains from which incrustations grow numerous filamentous organisms and over which there is a gelatinous coating. They are approximately spherical in shape and vary in size from that of a pea up to

1 or 2 in. or more in diameter, and are formed principally by the retention and gradual building up of growths that are not completely removed by the washing process. (2) Balls of sediment sometimes found in debris-laden flow and channel deposits.

*Pollution.* A condition created by the presence of harmful or objectionable material in water. See also contamination.

*Postchlorination.* The application of chlorine to water or wastewater subsequent to any treatment, including prechlorination.

*Prechlorination.* The application of chlorine to water or wastewater prior to any treatment.

*Recarbonation.* (1) The process of introducing carbon dioxide as a final stage in the lime-soda ash softening process in order to convert carbonates to bicarbonates and thereby stabilize the solution against precipitation of carbonates. (2) The diffusion of carbon dioxide gas through liquid to replace the carbon dioxide removed by the addition of lime. (3) The diffusion of carbon dioxide gas through a liquid to render the liquid stable with respect to precipitation or dissolution of alkaline constituents.

*Residual Chlorine.* Chlorine remaining in water or wastewater at the end of a specified contact period as combined or free chlorine.

* *Slurry.* A suspension of small undissolved particles in a very high concentration.

*Superchlorination.* Chlorination wherein the doses are deliberately selected to produce free or combined residuals so large as to require dechlorination.

*Tuberculation.* The formation of tubercules in pipes, with a concomitant increase in frictional coefficient.

*Water, Potable.* Water which does not contain objectionable pollution, contamination, minerals, or infection, and is considered satisfactory for domestic consumption.

*Well, Artesian.* A well tapping a confined or artesian aquifer in which the static water level stands above the bottom of the confining bed. The term is used to include all wells tapping such basins or aquifers. Those in which the head is insufficient to raise the water to or above the land surface are called Subartesian Wells.

*Well, Drilled.* A well that is excavated wholly or in part by means of a drill (either percussion or rotary) which operates by cutting or by abrasion; the materials are brought to the surface by means of a bailer, sand pump, hollow drill tool, or by a hydraulic or self-cleaning method.

*Well, Driven.* A well that is constructed by driving a casing, at the end of which there is a drive point, without the use of any drilling, boring, or jetting device.

*Well, Dug.* A well that is excavated by means of picks, shovels, or other hand tools, or by means of a power shovel or other dredging or trenching machinery, as distinguished from one put down by a drill or auger.

† *Zeta Potential.* A term which refers to the electrical charge on ions surrounding suspended particulate matter, especially particles of 1 $\mu$ or less. As encountered in water coagulation the charges are usually negative and their value, expressed in millivolts, is zeta potential.

## III. THE BASIC CHEMISTRY OF WATER TREATMENT

The increase of knowledge in water supply treatment has continually revealed the chemical nature of the process. For example, when coagulation with the use of alum was first introduced, the process was viewed as the very interesting and useful agglomeration of particles. Nearly 100 years later basic research into the causes of coagulation began and today an understanding of the electrokinetic nature (11–14b) of this phenomenon is beginning to emerge. Water treatment may be divided into the following distinct processes or phases.

1. Coagulation-flocculation
2. Disinfection
3. Filtration
4. Iron and manganese removal
5. Prophylaxis (fluoridation)
6. Scale and corrosion control
7. Softening
8. Taste and odor control
9. Sedimentation
10. Special processing for commercial and industrial uses

In all these, with the possible exception of sedimentation, one or more chemical processes are involved and the number of chemicals which are employed is extensive. Table I lists the more commonly used chemicals and Table II is included to illustrate the growing number of coagulant

* Taken from Appendix A of *Manual of Instruction for Water Treatment Plant Operators,* New York State Department of Health, Albany, New York, First Edition.

† After E. L. Bean: *"Zeta Potential Measurements in the Control of Coagulation Chemical Doses,"* J. Amer. Water Works Assoc. **56**, 214 (1964).

TABLE I

Chemicals Used in Water Treatment Processes

| Process | Chemical Name | Formula | Common Name | AWWA[a] Standard |
|---|---|---|---|---|
| Coagulation | Aluminum sulfate | $Al_2(SO)_3 \cdot 14H_2O$ | Alum | B403-64 |
| | Bauxite | Complex | Bauxite | B401-53 |
| | Calcium hydroxide | $Ca(OH)_2$ | Lime | B202-54 |
| | Ferric chloride | $Fe(Cl)_3$ or $Fe(Cl)_3 \cdot 6H_2O$ | Ferrichlor | None |
| | Ferric sulfate | $Fe_2(SO_4)_3 \cdot 9H_2O$ | Ferrifloc | B406-61T |
| | Ferrous sulfate | $FeSO_4 \cdot 7H_2O$ | Copperas | B402-53 |
| | Sodium aluminate | $Na_2O \cdot Al_2O_3$ | Soda alum | B405-60 |
| | Sodium silicate | $Na_2O \cdot SiO_2$ | Water glass or activated silicate | B404-58 |
| | Coagulant aids (See Table II) | | | |
| Disinfection | Anhydrous ammonia | NH | Ammonia | None |
| | Ammonium sulfate | $(NH_3)_2SO_4$ | Sulfate of ammonia | B302-64 |
| | Calcium hypochlorite | $Ca(OCl)_2$ | High test hypochlorite | B300-64 |
| | Chlorine | $Cl_2$ | Chlorine | B301-59 |
| | Chlorine dioxide | $ClO_2$ | Chlorine dioxide | None |
| | Ozone[b] | $O_3$ | Ozone | None |
| | Sodium chlorite | $NaClO_2$ | Technical sodium chlorite | B303-65T |
| | Sodium hypochlorite | $NaOCl$ | Sodium hypochlorite | B300-64 |
| Filtration | Coagulant aids | (See Table II) | | |
| Iron and manganese removal | Calcium hydroxide | $Ca(OH)_2$ | Lime | B202-54 |
| | Chlorine | $Cl_2$ | Chlorine | B301-59 |
| | Oxygen | $O_2$ | Oxygen | None[c] |
| | Sodium permanganate | $NaMnO_4$ | Sodium permanganate | None |
| Prophylaxis (fluoridation) | Fluosilicic acid | $H_2SiF_6$ | Fluosilicic acid | B703-60 |
| | Sodium fluoride | $NaF$ | Fluoride | B701-60 |
| | Sodium silicofluoride | $Na_2SiF_6$ | Sodium silicofluoride | B702-60 |
| Scale and corrosion control | Sodium hexametaphosphate | $Na_2HPO_4 \cdot 12H_2O$ | Glassy phosphate | None |
| | Sodium hydroxide | $NaOH$ | Caustic soda | B501-64 |
| | Sodium silicate | $Na_2O \cdot SiO_2$ | Water glass | B404-58 |
| | Trisodium phosphate | $Na_3PO_4 \cdot 12H_2O$ | Normal sodium phosphate | B500-53 |
| Softening | Calcium hydroxide | $Ca(OH)_2$ | Slaked lime | B202-54 |
| | Calcium oxide | $CaO$ | Quick-lime | B202-54 |
| | Sodium carbonate | $Na_2CO_3$ | Soda ash | B201-59 |
| | Sodium chloride | $NaCl$ | Common salt | B200-64 |
| Taste and odor control | Carbon (activated) | C | Activated carbon | B600-53 |
| | Chlorine | $Cl_2$ | Chlorine | B301-59 |
| | Chlorine dioxide | $ClO_2$ | Chlorine dioxide | None[d] |
| | Copper sulfate | $CuSO_4 \cdot 5H_2O$ | Blue stone | B602-59 |
| | Ozone | $O_3$ | Ozone | None[d] |
| | Sodium chlorite | $NaClO_2$ | Technical sodium chlorite | B303-65T |
| | Sodium pyrosulfite | $Na_2S_2O_5$ | Sodium bisulfite | B601-64 |
| | Sulfur dioxide | $SO_2$ | Sulfur dioxide | None |

[a] These *American Water Works Association Standards* contain details on chemical methods for determining the acceptability of the chemical.

[b] Little used in the United States, but fairly common in Europe.

[c] Usually provided by air applied through cascade aerators or pumps.

[d] Generated as used.

## TABLE II
Coagulant Aids Accepted by the United States Public Health Service[a]
for Use in the Treatment of Potable Water
(To April 1969)

| Product | Manufacturer | Maximum concentration recommended by manufacturer, parts per million (mg/liter) |
|---|---|---|
| All-Flok-Ade | Allstate Chemical Co. | 3.0 |
| All-Flok-Ade No. 6 | Box 3040 | 1.0 |
| | Euclid, Ohio | |
| Aquafloc 408 (liquid) | Dearborn Chemical Div. | 50.0 |
| Aquafloc #409 | W. R. Grace & Co. | 1.0 |
| Aquafloc 411 | Merchandise Mart Plaza | 2.0 |
| Aquafloc 422 | Chicago, Illinois | 1.0 |
| Bondfloc No. 1–101 | Bond Chemicals, Inc. | 5.0 |
| | 1500 Brookpark Road | |
| | Cleveland, Ohio | |
| Burtonite #78 | The Burtonite Co. | 5.0 |
| | Nutley, New Jersey | |
| Carboxymethylcellulose | Hercules Powder Co. | 1.0 |
| | 910 Market Street | |
| | Wilmington, Delaware | |
| CAT-FLOC | Calgon Corporation | 7.0 |
| | P.O. Box 1346 | |
| | Pittsburgh, Pennsylvania | |
| Coagulant Aid #2 | Calgon Corporation | 1.0 |
| Coagulant Aid #18 | P.O. Box 1346 | 15.0 |
| Coagulant Aid #961 | Pittsburgh, Pennsylvania | 5.0 |
| Coagulant Aid #233 | | 1.0 |
| Coagulant Aid #243 | | 1.0 |
| Coagulant Aid #253 | | 1.0 |
| Claron | Allyn Chemical Co. | 1.5 |
| Claron #207 | 2224 Fairhill Road | 2.0 |
| | Cleveland, Ohio | |
| Coagulant Aid 70 | Garrett-Callahan | 2.0 |
| Coagulant Aid 72 | 111 Rollins Road | 2.0 |
| Coagulant Aid 74B | Millbrae, California | 30.0 |
| Coagulant Aid 76 | | 40.0 |
| Coagulant Aid 76A | | 50.0 |
| Coagulant Aid 78B | | 50.0 |
| Coagulant Aid 72A | | 50.0 |
| Coagulant Aid Speedifloc #1 | Commercial Chemical Products, Inc. | 10.0 |
| | 11 Patterson Avenue | |
| | Midland Park, New Jersey | |
| Drewfloc No. 3 | Drew Chemical Corp. | 3.0 |
| Drewfloc 21 | 522 Fifth Avenue | 5.0 |

(continued)

TABLE II (continued)

| Product | Manufacturer | Maximum concentration recommended by manufacturer, parts per million (mg/liter) |
|---|---|---|
| Drewfloc 1 | New York, New York | 1:8 Alum; 0.5:10 lime[b] |
| Drewfloc 225 | | 1.0 |
| Drewfloc 922 | | 10.0 |
| Ecco Suspension Catalyzer #146 | Electric Chemical Co. 8001 Franklin Boulevard Cleveland, Ohio | 3.5 |
| Floc-Aid-1038 | National Starch & Chemical | 5.0 |
| Floc-Aid 1063 | Corp. 1700 West Front Street Plainfield, New Jersey | 5.0 |
| Gamlen CS-25 | Ionac Chemical Co. Birmingham, New Jersey | 5.0 |
| Genfloc LT-24 | General Mills, Inc. | 5.0 |
| Genfloc LT-25 | 9200 Wayzata Boulevard Minneapolis, Minnesota | 5.0 |
| Guartec F | General Mills, Inc. | 10.0 |
| Guartec SJ | 9200 Wayzata Boulevard Minneapolis, Minnesota | 10.0 |
| Hallmark 81 | Stein, Hall & Co., Inc. | 1.0 |
| Hallmark 82 | 605 Third Avenue New York, New York | 1.0 |
| HAMACO 196 | A. E. Staley Manufacturing Co. P.O. Box 151 Decatur, Illinois | 5.0 |
| Hercofloc 816 | Hercules Powder Co. | 1.0 |
| Hercofloc 822 | 910 Market Street Wilmington, Delaware | 1.0 |
| Illco IFA 313 | Illinois Water Treatment Co. 840 Cedar Street Rockford, Illinois | 10.0 |
| Ionac Wisprofloc 20 | Ionac Chemical Co. | 5.0 |
| Ionac Wisprofloc 75 | Birmingham, New Jersey | 5.0 |
| Ionac 700-12 | | 1.0 |
| Ionac NI-702 | | 4.0 |
| Jaguar | Stein, Hall & Co., Inc. 605 Third Avenue New York, New York | 0.5 |
| Kelcosol | Kelco Company 8225 Aero Drive San Diego, California | 2.0 |

(continued)

Table II (continued)

| Product | Manufacturer | Maximum concentration recommended by manufacturer, parts per million (mg/liter) |
|---|---|---|
| Kelgin W | | 2.0 |
| Key-Floc-W | Key Chemicals | 25.0 |
| | 4346 Tacony | |
| | Philadelphia, Pennsylvania | |
| Magnifloc 845-A | American Cyanimid Co. | 1.0 |
| Magnifloc 846-A | Berdan Avenue | 1.0 |
| Magnifloc 847-A | Wayne, New Jersey | 1.0 |
| Magnifloc 860-A | | 1.0 |
| Magnifloc 971-N | | 1.0 |
| Magnifloc 972-N | | 1.0 |
| Magnifloc 985-N | | 1.0 |
| Magnifloc 990 | | 1.0 |
| Metalene Coagulant P-6 | Metalene Chemical Co. | 5.0 |
| | Bedford, Ohio | |
| MOGUL CO-982 | The Mogul Corporation | 1.5 |
| MOGUL CO-980 | 20600 Chagrin Boulevard | 2.0 |
| MOGUL CO-983 | Cleveland, Ohio | 1.0 |
| MOGUL CO-986 | | 5.0 |
| MRL-19 | Stein, Hall & Co., Inc. | 1.0 |
| MRL-13 | 605 Third Avenue | 1.0 |
| MRL-14 | New York, New York | 1.0 |
| MRL-22A | | 1.0 |
| Nalcolyte #110A | Nalco Chemical Co. | 5.0 |
| Nalcolyte #671 | 6216 West 66th Place | 1.0 |
| | Chicago, Illinois | |
| No. 102 | Henry W. Fink & Co. | 1.0 |
| No. 109 Kleer Floc | 6900 Silverton Avenue | 1.0 |
| | Cincinnati, Ohio | |
| NALFLOC A-370 (name change from Alfloc #370) | Imperial Chemical Industries, Ltd. | 0.5 |
| | P.O. Box 7 | |
| | Winnington, Northwich | |
| | Cheshire, England | |
| O'B-Floc | O'Brien Industries, Inc. | 10.0 |
| | 95 Dorsa Avenue | |
| | Livingston, New Jersey | |
| Perfectamyl A5114/2 | Frank Herzel Corp. | 10.0 |
| | 299 Madison Ave. | |
| | New York, New York | |
| Poly-Floc 4D | Betz Laboratories, Inc. | 25.0 |
| | Gillingham & Worth Streets | |
| | Philadelphia, Pennsylvania | |

(continued)

TABLE II (continued)

| Product | Manufacturer | Maximu mconcentration recommended by manufacturer, parts per million (mg/liter) |
|---|---|---|
| Polyhall M-295 | Stein, Hall & Co., Inc. 605 Third Avenue New York, New York | 1.0 |
| Purifloc N 17 | The Dow Chemical Co. | 1.0 |
| Purifloc A 22 | Abbott Road Center | 1.0 |
| Separan NP 10 Potable Water Grade | Midland, Michigan | 1.0 |
| Separan AP 30 | | 1.0 |
| Sink-Floc Z3 and AZ-3 | Narvon Mines, Ltd. | 10.0 |
| Sink-Floc Z4 and AZ-4 | Affiliate of Irl Daffin Assoc., | 10.0 |
| Sink-Floc Z5 and AZ-5 | Inc. Keller Avenue & Fruitville Pike Lancaster, Pennsylvania | 10.0 |
| Super Col Guar Gum | General Mills, Inc. 9200 Wayzata Boulevard Minneapolis, Minnesota | 10.0 |
| Superfloc 16 | American Cyanamid Co. | 1.0 |
| Superfloc 20 | Berdan Avenue | 1.0 |
| Superfloc 84 | Wayne, New Jersey | 1.0 |
| Superfloc 127 | | 1.0 |
| Wisprofloc P | W. A. Scholten's Chemische Fabrieken M.V. Foxhol, Postbus 1 The Netherlands | 5.0 |
| Zeta-Floc O | Narvon Mines, Ltd. | 20.0 |
| Zeta-Floc C | Affiliate of Irl Daffin Assoc., Inc. | 20.0 |
| Zeta-Floc K | Keller Avenue & Fruitville Pike Lancaster, Pennsylvania | 20.0 |
| Zimmite | W. E. Zimmie, Inc. 810 Sharon Drive Westlake, Ohio | 1.0 |

[a] The acceptance by the Public Health Service pertains only to the effects upon health and does not imply that these products are necessarily superior, equivalent, or inferior in performance to other products intended for similar use, nor does it constitute endorsement or recommendation by the Public Health Service of these products.

[b] One part of Drewfloc to 8 parts of alum when used simply as an aid in alum coagulation, and 0.5 ppm (mg/liter) of Drewfloc to 10 ppm of lime when used in connection with lime softening.

aids, an increasingly important class of chemicals in coagulation and filtration operations.

A recent addition to the chemicals available to water works operators is that group of polymers known as coagulant aids or polyelectrolytes. These are polymers with electrical properties which have been found useful in the coagulation process. The polyelectrolytes which have been advanced thus far for use in water treatment are principally anionic. In Table II there are listed those which have been cleared by the U.S. Public Health Service. Periodically updated lists appear in the *Journal of the American Water Works Association* (15).

Any exhaustive treatment of the chemistry involved in the water treatment processes is not possible within the space of a single chapter. However, in order that the analytical chemist may have some background and a point from which to project further study in the subject, there follow brief descriptions of the basic chemistry involved in the different processes and references to late work.

First, however, a word about one quality or aspect of water chemistry which, in terms of the water treatment process itself, sets it apart from the chemistry of many industrial processes and even from the chemistry of industrial waste treatment. This quality is that of minutia. For example, the doses of chemicals which are added to produce the chemical reactions needed for water purification are in the order of parts per million and frequently in the range of 1–10 ppm (mg/liter). Secondly, chemical analyses of a representative sample of the finished drinking waters of the United States show average values (16) below 1.0 ppm (mg/liter) in 12 of 22 chemicals covered by the *Public Health Service Drinking Water Standards* (17). One of the basic reasons for the purification of water is to make it safe for human consumption, and in recent years a concept of using a public water supply for the improvment of the public health has developed. This is fluoridation, and in the fluoridation process the addition of, on the average, only 1 ppm fluoride ion has been found effective in the reduction of dental caries. Still more recently, with the advent of knowledge (18) on carcinogenic effects of organic chemicals in drinking water and the appearance of pesticides in water supplies, the sensitivity levels of detection, measurement and expression of results have dropped to parts per billion ($\mu$g/liter) and parts per trillion ($\mu\mu$g/liter) (19). In the field of radiochemistry, as applied to water supply, the concentrations involved are even smaller. For example, the limit (20) for radium permitted by the *Public Health Service Drinking Water Standards* is 3 pico curies/liter. It is this significance of tiny amounts of chemicals in a water supply that adds a certain intriguing quality to the work of the analytical chemist who devotes his life to this field.

In the material discussed in this chapter the terms parts per million and milligrams per liter are used frequently. The first is the traditional term of the water works professional and the second the term of the analytical chemist. They are, of course, synonymous. The first is frequently applied to the dosages of the various chemicals used in water treatment and the second appears on laboratory reports.

## A. COAGULATION

As cited above, coagulation was among the first of the chemical processes which developed in the art or science of water purification. For nearly 75 years after its advent the chemical reactions involved were generally understood simply in terms of reactions between a salt of a heavy metal and either the natural alkalinity of the water being treated or alkalinity induced by the addition of a base, often lime or sodium carbonate, thereby producing the insoluble hydroxide of the heavy metal. This precipitate, or floc as the water professional calls it, absorbed dirt and color as it settled through the water to the bottom of the sedimentation basin. The chemical reactions are:

a. Aluminum Sulfate

$$2Al^{3+} + 3SO_4^{2-} + 3Ca^{2+} + 6HCO_3^- \rightarrow 2Al(OH)_3\downarrow + 6CO_2 + 3Ca^{2+} + 3SO_4^{2-} \quad (1)$$
$$2Al^{3+} + 3SO_4^{2-} + 3Ca^{2+} + 6OH^- \rightarrow 2Al(OH)_3\downarrow + 3Ca^{2+} + 3SO_4^{2-} \quad (2)$$
$$2Al^{3+} + 3SO_4^{2-} + 6Na^+ + 3CO_3^- \rightarrow 2Al(OH)_3\downarrow + 3CO_2 + 6Na^+ + 3SO_4^{2-} \quad (3)$$

b. Salts of iron. Ferric chloride.

$$2Fe^{3+} + 6Cl^- + 3Ca^{2+} + 6HCO_3^- \rightarrow 2Fe(OH)_3\downarrow + 6CO_2 + 3Ca^{2+} + 6Cl^- \quad (4)$$
$$2Fe^{3+} + 6Cl^- + 3Ca^{2+} + 6OH^- \rightarrow 2Fe(OH)_3\downarrow + 3Ca^{2+} + 6Cl^- \quad (5)$$

c. Salts of iron. Ferrous sulfate

This reaction takes place often with the addition of lime according to the following reactions.

$$Fe^{2+} + SO_4^{2-} + Ca^{2+} + 2OH^- \rightarrow Fe^{2+} + 2OH^{--} + Ca^{2+} + SO_4^{2-} \quad (6)$$
$$4Fe^{2+} + 8OH^- + O_2 + 2H_2O \rightarrow 4Fe(OH)_3\downarrow \quad (7)$$

The second of this series of reactions occurs in the presence of dissolved oxygen naturally present in the water.

Whether or not the coagulation process was effective was determined largely by visual observations of the floc in the sedimentation basin, and the chief guide to coagulation control was the jar test. Then coagulation became the subject of research by water, soil, and colloid chemists.

L. B. Miller (21) investigated the nature of the precipitates formed by trivalent aluminum and iron in solutions of varying alkalinity Mattson (22), a soil chemist, demonstrated the importance of pH adjustment in obtaining efficient flocculation of electronegative material by aluminum salts. He also described the hydrolysis of aluminum and iron salts and suggested that it was hydrolysis products of these metals which accounted for the electrical neutralization and flocculation of electronegative colloids.

Black and his co-workers at the University of Florida in recent years have shed much light upon the coagulation process as it is applied in water treatment. They have investigated the removal of color and have demonstrated the value of zeta potential as an advance over the jar test control procedure (23). Zeta potential has also been studied extensively by Riddick (24,25), one of its early users and chief proponents, and by Bean and co-workers (26).

An excellent summary of some modern views of the chemistry of coagulation by salts of aluminum and iron is found in an article by Stumm and Morgan (27). These authors describe the older chemical theory and the newer physical theory of coagulation and suggest that these are by no means mutually exclusive, but rather interdependent. The older chemical theory illustrated by the above equations indicated a rather simple precipitate as the chief mechanism in floc formation. These authors cite no less than 23 insoluble products of aluminum and iron which may be formed by hydrolysis of or the interaction of $Al(III)$ and $Fe(III)$ with various anions. It is also suggested by their work, that the agglomeration of floc particles may be the result of polymerization. For example ferric hydroxo complexes form polymers, the simplest of which is a dimeric species according to reaction (8).

$$2[Fe(H_2O)_5(OH)]^{2+} \rightarrow [Fe_2(H_2O)_8(OH)_2]^{4+} + 2H_2O \qquad (8)$$

The importance of polymerization is further emphasized by the advances in coagulation brought about through use of the synthetic coagulant aids or polyelectrolytes.

The polyelectrolytes used in water purification fall under three classifications. One, carrying a positive charge is the cationic polyelectrolyte. Another, known as anionic, carries a negative charge, and a third type, sometimes called a polyampholyte, has both positive and negative charges. The latter is also frequently called a nonionic polyelectrolyte.

The polyelectrolytes are either of natural origin, such as starch, or are synthetically prepared under a number of trade names, some of which are listed in Table II.

Some concept of the size and other properties of these substances is gained by noting that they are colloids with particle sizes ranging from 1 to 100 $\mu$.

These polymers are important to the water works profession because some of them are effective aids in the coagulation of water. When used in conjunction with ordinary coagulants, a large and rapidly settling floc is often formed. Some polyelectrolytes have been noted to be good coagulants when used alone.

A clue to the effectiveness of the polyelectrolytes in water coagulation is found in the experimental work of Fuoss and Sadek (28), who write as follows: "Polyelectrolytes, even in the most dilute solution, give regions of high charge density in the neighborhood of each polyion, as a simple consequence of structure. We might, therefore, expect a strong electrostatic interaction between the fields of polycations and polyanions which would lead to mutual precipitation." Data were then shown to verify this observation.

Another investigator, Michaels (29), suggested that the mechanism whereby the polyelectrolytes exert their action is that of adsorption accompanied by what he called "bridging." According to this explanation, the polyelectrolytes, which are pictured as tiny chains of molecules, are attracted at one end of a chain to an adsorptive face on the surface of one floc or dirt particle and in a like manner at the other end of the chain to another particle, thus tying the two together into a larger settlable clump. Michaels also attributed the ineffectiveness of larger doses of the substances to the attachment of many single chain ends to all adsorptive faces of the particles present, with no bridging, thus isolating the particles and preventing them from clumping.

An example of the importance of electrical charge was shown by Black (30), who investigated the effectiveness of four coagulant aids in removing organic color from surface water. One cationic material was effective, two anionic substances only slightly improved color removal, and a nonionic polyelectrolyte was of little benefit.

Knowledge about the effectiveness of these agents in water purification has resulted from experimental application. Early research by Fuoss has already been cited. Johnson (31) conducted extensive "jar" tests using suspensions of solid, highly hydrated, clay particles ranging in size from 0.01 to 3 $\mu$. He, also, found differences in the effectiveness of different polymers. He pointed out too that, although high in cost per pound, the small amounts of the polyelectrolytes required to benefit the coagulation process justify the additional expense. Costs range from 15¢ to over $1.00 per pound (1968).

Cohen (32) and his co-workers at the Robert A. Taft Sanitary Engineering Center, USPHS, conducted extensive experiments with both natural and synthetic polymers and certain natural waters, also utilizing the jar test method. In these tests, natural waters were employed, including Ohio River water with a turbidity of 98 units, a pond water containing 300 units of turbidity, and a highly turbid and mineralized river water from Nevada. With the first two waters, a nonionic, natural polyelectrolyte was found to be ineffective, but the same polymer, applied to the Nevada water, notably increased the settling rate of alum floc. Among the values of their work was the clear demonstration that a polyelectrolyte for use with a given water must be selected carefully. What is effective with one water may not be effective with another. Cohen also found that certain cationic polyelectrolytes increased the benefits of alum coagulation in removing from solution alkylbenzenesulfonate, a synthetic detergent.

Black (33) and others studied some of the polymers used by Cohen and then evaluated the efficiency of 14 additional anionic types. Using the jar test method, they employed demineralized water containing suspensions of added clays. Again the conclusion was reached that some polyelectrolytes are effective and some are not. It was also found that the order in which the coagulant and coagulant aid were added had an effect upon the process. Addition of the coagulant aid 1 min after the coagulant was found suitable. Still another variant is dosage. For example, flocculation of a certain turbid water was greatly enhanced when 0.5 mg/liter of an anionic polyelectrolyte was used with 10 mg/liter alum. Increasing the coagulant aid dosage four times with the same amount of alum actually dispersed the floc.

This rather extensive, discussion of the coagulation process (in comparison to the ones which follow), has been included for several reasons. First, the coagulation process is the most important one in the water conditioning sequence; if a water is not properly preconditioned by proper coagulation and sedimentation the filtration phase which follows cannot function effectively. Second, research into the chemistry of water treatment has been more extensive in the area of coagulation. Third, the possibilities for advances in coagulation and water quality control through electrophoretic means and the use of coagulant aids is an exciting area for future research.

Water coagulation is accomplished by adding the coagulant and rapidly mixing it with the water, which then enters a chamber for much slower mixing and formation of the precipitate. This is followed by sedimentation or settling, which is brought about in large basins where a period of hours is provided for the completion of the coagulation process and considerable clarification of the water before it reaches the filters.

## B. SEDIMENTATION

It was stated above that there were chemical processes involved in all phases of water treatment, with the possible exception of sedimentation. This is true in the sense that sedimentation (settling) itself has been considered a mechanical or physical process wherein particles settle to the floor of the settling basin, frequently resulting in much clarification of the water being treated. In a larger sense, however, the sedimentation process is an important part of the chemical treatment of water for it is here that that essential element of all chemical reactions, time, is provided. After the coagulant and, if used, coagulant aid are added to the water at the start of its passage through the treatment plant, the next step is a short, 15 min to 1 hr, gentle mixing in a tank or basin. Mixing is usually accomplished by baffles or mechanical means. The purpose of the flocculator, suggested by the term itself, is to cause the agglomeration of floc particles into larger particles. Water leaving the flocculator enters the sedimentation basin for the intent and with results described above.

Much of the chemistry which has been discussed above takes place in the flocculation and sedimentation phases of the process. An example is the removal of color. As one observes color removal in a water treatment plant one notices the lessening of color as the water passes through the sedimentation basin. Cohen and Hannah (14a) regard color removal as a process of chemical precipitation and believe it to be explained as a chemical reaction between partially hydrolyzed coagulant and an acidic group or the color molecule forming an insoluble basic salt. It is possible that there are other chemical reactions, as Stumn and Morgan (27) have suggested, namely, the removal of phosphates, phenolates, and some aliphatic and aromatic carboxylic acids existing in noncolloidal, true solutions. Cohen, as cited above, noted removal of a detergent. It may be said of the sedimentation process that less is known about what goes on in it than in any of the other phases of water clarification.

## C. FILTRATION

Attempts to explain what happens in a water filter have, until very recently been in terms of physical phenomena. These include (1) Brownian movement (34), (2) diffusion (35), (3) inertial impingement (36),

(4) probability (37), (5) sedimentation (38), and (6) straining (39); none of these, however, have satisfactorily explained the observed differences in filtering various kinds of water, nor have they answered the question of why some flocs penetrate farther into the sand beds than others. Again the answers are being sought in the realm of chemistry. It has been noted that high dissolved solids, especially chlorides and sulfates of sodium and magnesium, appear to increase bed penetration by floc. Workers with rapid sand filters have long observed or believed that the work of the filter was done in the top few inches, even though sand beds up to 36 in. have been commonly employed. A recent, significant improvement of rapid sand filtration has been the so-called microfloc filter, in which, by the use of coagulant aids, much or all of the depth of the filter bed is penetrated by floc, thus greatly increasing the capacity of the filter to remove suspended and colloidal solids and possibly some dissolved chemicals. As polyelectrolytes are essential to this kind of filter, it is possible that the action may be explained on the basis of the electrical charges on the polymers. Zeta potential has been employed as a tool in understanding filtration (40), and van der Waals forces have also been investigated (41).

## D. DISINFECTION

The chemistry of water disinfection is largely the chemistry of the second member of the halogen family. Two reasons for this are that chlorine was the first water disinfectant used on a large scale and its cost is the lowest of the disinfectants used for public water supply disinfection. The third and fourth halogens have also been advocated for water disinfection, but so far have not been popularly received. Only in recent years has iodine been seriously considered, chiefly for swimming pools, and considerable basic research into its properties has been conducted by Professor Black (42–44) of the University of Florida. Chlorine, bromine, and iodine are all known to be active germicides, but the exact biochemical reason for their germicidal properties is still obscure. Different organisms react to chlorine and iodine in different manners, i.e., it requires more of the agents to kill some bacteria, protozoa, and viruses than others. The analytical chemist is not ordinarily concerned with the determination of lethal doses of chlorine in a water treatment plant for the destruction of various organisms, but he is very much concerned with the chemical reactions involved in the various ways chlorine combines with water and substances in it. He is concerned also with the chemistry of determining the amount of chlorine and its compounds which may be present in a water sample and with the determination of dissolved chemical substances which may interfere with the disinfection process. These interfering substances include: *alkalinity,* ammonia and some of its compounds; and *oxidizable,* inorganic, metallic, and organic chemicals.

Chlorine as used for water disinfection is applied either as the gas or as hypochlorites of calcium and sodium. When the gas is dissolved in water reaction (9) occurs and the bactericidal properties of the result-

$$Cl_2 + H_2O \rightleftharpoons HCl + HOCl \tag{9}$$

ing compounds are attributed principally to the hypochlorous acid which ionizes into a proton and a hypochlorite ion as shown in eq. (10). The hydrolysis of $Cl_2$ may be expressed as

$$HOCl \rightleftharpoons H^+ + OCl^- \tag{10}$$

or

$$\frac{(H^+)(OCl^-)}{(HOCl)} = k_d \tag{11}$$

$$\frac{(HOCl)(H^+)(OCl^-)}{Cl_2} = k_h \tag{12}$$

with $k_h$ being the hydrolysis constant. The concentrations of the reaction products are dependent upon the pH of the water with HOCl predominating in the lower pH values and $OCl^-$ ions above pH 7.5. One of the modern theories about the effectiveness of chlorine as a bactericidal agent holds that the hypochlorous acid can effectively penetrate organism cell walls and oxidize the matter within the cell, whereas the $OCl^-$ is not as effective.

Equations (9) and (10) are oversimplifications of what actually takes place when chlorine is added to a water, for they would apply only if the water were free from interfering substances, an occurrence which rarely happens. The classes of interfering substances are cited above. Some of their constituents are: iron, manganese, nitrites, calcium and magnesium carbonates and bicarbonates, ammonia, and certain amines. Among these, ammonia is of special interest because of the reaction products formed when it unites with hypochlorous acid. These reaction products, or chloramines, are also germicidal, but at much slower rates than the hypochlorous acid alone. Typical reactions are given by eqs.

| | | |
|---|---|---|
| $NH_3 + HOCl \rightarrow NH_2Cl + H_2O$ | at pH 8.5 and above (monochloramine) | (13) |
| $NH_3 + HOCl \rightarrow NHCl_2 + 2H_2O$ | at pH 4.3 to 5.0 (dichloramine) | (14) |
| $NH_3 + HOCl \rightarrow NCl_3 + 3H_2O$ | at pH 4.3 and below (trichloramine) | (15) |

(13–15). Between pH values of about 5.0 and 8.5 a mixture of monochloramine and dichloramine is found.

In addition to the chloramine series formed by chlorine in combination with ammonia, there are many and complex reactions of this element with other substances when it is introduced into a water containing a broad spectrum of organics. Ferrous and manganous oxides are oxidized by chlorine in the presence of alkalinity to form the hydroxides of those metals. A pH of 7.0 or more is optimum for iron removal, while pH 10.0 is optimum for the removal of manganese.

As bromine has not found much place in water disinfection, its chemistry will not be discussed here.

Iodine, also, hydrolyzes according to eq. (16):

$$I_2 + H_2O \rightleftharpoons HIO + H^+ + I^- \tag{16}$$

or

$$\frac{(HIO)(H^+)(I^-)}{I_2} = k_h \tag{17}$$

The hydrolysis constant, $k_h$ may be calculated for various temperatures, and for 25°C it has a value of $3 \times 10^{-13}$. Also hypoiodous acid reacts according to eq. (18).

$$HIO \rightleftharpoons H^+ + IO^- \tag{18}$$

or

$$\frac{(H^+)(IO^-)}{(HIO)} = k_d \tag{19}$$

As in the case of chlorine the equilibrium products are dependent upon pH values. For example, when $I_2$ residual is present in the amount of 0.5 mg/liter, at pH 5.0, 99% exists as $I_2$, 1% as HIO, and 0.0% as $IO^-$. At pH 8.0 the corresponding values are 12%, 88%, and 0.005% (44). It is of interest that the germicidal action of iodine is more effective than that of chlorine over a broader pH range, thus indicating that both the elemental iodine, $I_2$, and hypoiodous acid, HIO, are active germicidal agents. Iodine does not combine with ammonia compounds like chlorine does and therefore the counterparts of the chloramines are not commonly found.

Other major germicidal agents which have been tried for treatment of public water supplies are ozone, ultraviolet light, and silver. The first has not been accepted in the United States, but has found considerable favor in Europe. It is, of course, a powerful oxidizing agent, and chemical reactions typical of oxidation are encountered. The bactericidal action of silver is a function of the silver ion, $Ag^+$, which may be introduced into a water as one of the salts of silver or by oligodynamic processes. Ultraviolet light cannot be said to display many chemical reactions with water constituents, some of which, such as turbidity and color, are interferences, but from the standpoint of physically preventing penetration of the uv rays. The ability of uv to disinfect a water is a function of its energy, and recent work (45) has shown that a wavelength of 2537 A° at an intensity and time of 11,000 $\mu$W sec/cm$^2$ is required for effective germicidal activity. In order to be effective, the uv ray must reach all bacteria in the water being treated before they have the range of penetration since there is no residual action as with chlorine and iodine.

Coagulation, sedimentation, filtration, and disinfection form the chief building blocks of the water purification process. When these have been properly performed, a water which is safe and potable results, but it may not be palatable and it may still contain substances which are objectionable for aesthetic or economic reasons. These are iron, manganese, hardness, taste and odors, and high mineral content. Therefore certain supplemental water conditioning procedures are sometimes required, the principle ones being iron and manganese removal, softening, scale and corrosion control, and taste and odor control. Finally, as mentioned previously, there appeared in the mid 20th century, the new* concept of using public water supply as a means of preventing tooth decay. This procedure has been classified as prophylaxis. All these auxiliary or supplemental water conditioning measures are accomplished by the use of chemicals in the manner now described.

## E. IRON AND MANGANESE REMOVAL

Iron and manganese are troublesome water constituents because they cause stains of laundry, plumbing fixtures, cooking utensils, and other water containers. Manganese can be a major nuisance in a water treatment plant by coating walls and equipment with a hard, black film which is hard to remove. Because of these objectionable characteristics, the low limits of 0.3 and 0.05 mg/liter for iron and manganese, respectively, are recommended in the *Public Health Service Drinking Water Standards*.

Iron and manganese exist in water in either the soluble reduced state or the insoluble oxidized forms. The chief method of control is to oxidize the ferrous and manganous forms to the ferric and manganic states and remove the precipitates by filtration. Oxidation is afforded by aeration or by the use of oxidants such as chlorine, chlorine dioxide, and

---

* The concept might better be said to have been revived, for during the 1920's the application of iodine in water supplies for goiter prevention had been advocated. It was tried in a few instances, but fell into disfavor with the advent of iodized salt.

potassium permanganate. Other iron and manganese removal processes include ion exchange and lime treatment.

## F. SOFTENING

A water high in hardness is objectionable because it interferes with laundering processes using soap, or detergents not designed for hard water, and because from hard water, scale can be deposited on the inside of pipes, boiler tubes, cooking utensils, and other water containers or conduits. Softening has therefore been widely adopted both on a municipal scale and for individual water supplies. Softening of public water supplies may be accomplished by use of the following: cold lime, cold lime–soda, cold lime plus calcium chloride, hot lime–soda, and ion exchange. For the elimination of hardness in boiler feedwaters some compound of phosphate is commonly employed.

Hardness is caused by the presence of the bicarbonates and sulfates of calcium and magnesium and chlorides and nitrates of these two elements, but the bicarbonates and sulfates are the chief offenders. Sulfates, chlorides, and nitrates of calcium and magnesium are called noncarbonate hardness, whereas the bicarbonates are called carbonate hardness. Typical chemical reactions involved in some of the above named methods for removing these objectionable water constituents are as follows:

a. Reactions with lime

$$2Ca^{2+} + 2HCO_3^- + 2OH^- \rightarrow 2CaCO_3\downarrow + 2H_2O \tag{20}$$
$$Mg^{2+} + CO_3^{2-} + Ca^{2+} + 2OH^- \rightarrow Mg(OH)_2\downarrow + Ca^{2+} + CO_3^{2-} \tag{21}$$
$$Mg^{2+} + SO_4^{2-} + Ca^{2+} + 2OH^- \rightarrow Mg(OH)_2\downarrow + Ca^{2+} + SO_4^{2-} \tag{22}$$
$$Mg^{2+} + 2NO_3^- + Ca^{2+} + 2OH^- \rightarrow Mg(OH)_2\downarrow + Ca^2 + 2NO_3^- \tag{23}$$
$$CO_2 + Ca^{2+} + 2OH^- \rightarrow CaCO_3\downarrow + H_2O \tag{24}$$

b. Reactions with sodium carbonate

$$Ca^{2+} + SO_4^{2-} + 2Na^+ + CO_3^{2-} \rightarrow CaCO_3\downarrow + 2Na^+ + SO_4^{2-} \tag{25}$$
$$Ca^{2+} + 2Cl^- + 2Na^+ + CO_3^{2-} \rightarrow CaCO_3\downarrow + 2Na^+ + 2NO_3^- \tag{26}$$
$$Ca^{2+} + 2NO_3^- + 2Na^+ + CO_3^{2-} \rightarrow CaCO_3\downarrow + 2Na^+ + 2NO_3 \tag{27}$$
$$Ca^{2+} + 2HCO_3^- + 2Na^+ + CO_3^{2-} \rightarrow CaCO_3\downarrow + 2Na^+ + 2HCO_3^- \tag{28}$$

c. Reactions with phosphate

$$Mg^{2+} + SO_4^{2-} + 2Na^+ + 2H_2PO_4^- \rightarrow Mg(H_2PO_4)_2\downarrow + 2Na^+ + SO_4^{2-} \tag{29}$$
$$3Ca^2 + 3SO_4^{2-} + 6Na^+ + 2PO_4^{3-} \rightarrow Ca_3(PO_4)_2\downarrow + 6Na^+ + 3SO_4^{2-} \tag{30}$$
$$3Ca^{2+} + 3HCO_3^{2-} + 6Na^+ + 2PO_4^{3-} \rightarrow Ca_3(PO_4)_2\downarrow + 6Na^+ + 3HCO_3^{2-} \tag{31}$$

d. Ion exchange reactions (sodium zeolite)

$$\left.\begin{array}{c} Ca^{2+} + 2HCO_3^- \\ Ca^{2+} + SO_4^{2-} \\ Mg^{2+} + 2NO_3^{2-} \end{array}\right\} + 2Na^+ + Z^{2-} \rightarrow \left.\begin{array}{c} 2Na^+ + HCO_3^- \\ 2Na^+ + SO_4^{2-} \\ 2Na^+ + 2Cl^- \end{array}\right\} + \begin{array}{c} CaZ \\ MgZ \end{array} \tag{32}$$

The zeolite, when exhausted, is regenerated by the use of sodium chloride, thus converting CaZ and MgZ back to Na$_2$Z. A similar series of reactions is obtained when water containing these constituents is softened by the use of hydrogen zeolite (cation exchanger), but the regenerating agent is sulfuric acid.

For additional information on softening processes reference is made to a treatise by Hoover (46) and an article on ion exchange by Alsentzer (47). Hoover (1884–1950), a chemist with the Columbus, Ohio, Water Department was known internationally as the Dean of Water Works Chemists.

## G. SCALE AND CORROSION CONTROL

Scale and corrosion must be controlled in a water supply in order to protect the metallic parts of the distribution system from being eaten away or from being coated with insoluble material to a point where the carrying capacity is greatly reduced. It is, of course, necessary to prevent the formation of scale in boiler tubes for efficient operation. Scale control is closely related to hardness removal and the processes cited above are used. However, a softened water is frequently a corrosive water and it is necessary therefore to adjust pH to values which are indicative of a balanced or stabilized water, i.e., one which will neither cause corrosion nor deposit scale; pH values from 8.0 to 9.0 are commonly used. Actually, before attempting to maintain a balanced water, it is desirable to form a thin protective coating of calcium carbonate on the interior of metallic pipe surfaces, thereby providing a barrier against corrosion. This is accomplished by distributing a water which is or which becomes slightly supersaturated with calcium carbonate. It may therefore be necessary to add to softened water, or to naturally soft water, chemicals which will produce these conditions. In municipal softening plants a commonly used method is recarbonation, the last sequential step in the softening process, which is accomplished by the addition of carbon dioxide. This reacts with excess lime or caustic alkalinity to form carbonates. An excess of carbon dioxide will convert the carbonates to bicarbonates and reactions are as given by eqs (33–35).

$$Ca^{2+} + 2OH^- + CO_2 \rightarrow CaCO_3 + H_2O \tag{33}$$
$$Ca^{2+} + CO_3^{2-} + CO_2 + H_2O \rightarrow Ca(HCO_3)_2 \tag{34}$$
$$2Na^+ + 2OH + CO_2 \rightarrow Na_2CO_3 + H_2O \tag{35}$$

It must be stated that not all waters need recarbonation and also that another function of recarbonation of lime-softened water is to prevent the deposition of normal carbonates on sand grains of filters which follow the softening process. The sand grains sometimes become enlarged and the condition can become so serious that they, and even the gravel pieces, become cemented together, thus destroying the effectiveness of the filter.

It is not uncommon to practice corrosion control at water treatment plants where softening is not employed. Methods for so doing include the addition of lime or sodium hexametaphosphate. When lime is added to water leaving a treatment plant it reacts with natural alkalinity to form calcium carbonate according to eq. (20). Sodium hexametaphosphate acts to prevent the deposition of calcium compounds when applied in concentrations of 0.5–1.0 ppm, and if used in higher concentrations, up to 5 ppm, it may form a protective coating of iron phosphate on pipe interiors. Protective coatings are also formed by use of sodium silicate.

## H. TASTE AND ODOR CONTROL

Tastes and odors objectionable to the water consumer are caused by dissolved organic substances, such as phenols, various industrial wastes, hydrogen sulfide, chloramines, and other chlorine organic compounds. They may also be caused by algae and the decomposition products of algal decay. Although certain inorganic chemicals can also cause tastes and odors, the chief offenders come from the organics. When phenols react with chlorine they form some of the most obnoxious products known to the water industry. The water works operator deals with the problem through the use of one or more of the following processes: aeration, coagulation, break point process, and the application of certain chemicals. These include activated carbon, chlorine dioxide, ozone, potassium permanganate and copper sulfate, the last frequently being applied as an algicide in reservoirs. This is a preventive rather than a corrective measure. A glance at these procedures shows that the predominant principles involved are oxidation and adsorption. The chemistry of taste and odor control is complex and not well defined, and the test for tastes and odors in a water sample is empirical and involves organoleptic procedures. There is much room for research and discovery in the chemistry of this phase of water treatment.

The last remaining process to be discussed is prophylaxis which, at the time of this writing, is confined to fluoridation.

## I. PROPHYLAXIS

The major fluoridation chemicals employed during the mid-1960's are listed in Table I. Hydrofluoric acid was tried in the early days, but it has not gained wide acceptance, due in part to handling difficulties. Calcium fluoride, $CaF_2$, as found in commercial fluorspar has also been advocated, as it is the least expensive source of commercial fluoride. The difficulties lie in dissolving it, but Maier and Bellack (48) discovered a practical method for doing so by mixing it with alum solution, and in this way the fluoridation and coagulation chemicals can be applied together. Much of the chemistry involved in fluoridation takes place in the human body, which transforms $F^-$ from the fluoride chemicals applied to water into an essential part of the tooth structure. The water works chemist is, therefore, not directly concerned with this set of fluoride reactions. He is, however, concerned with determining that the proper concentration of $F^-$, on the average about 1 mg/liter, is present in fluoridated water. He may also be concerned with defluoridation procedures in areas where fluoride ion concentrations exceed the limits (49) of the *Public Health Service Drinking Water Standards*. Methods of defluoridation include: use of apatites, activated alumina, ion exchange, and lime softening. Franz J. Maier, internationally known authority on fluoridation, has written extensively on defluoridation (50–52), and a wealth of information on all phases of fluoridation—dental, medical, chemical, and engineering—is found in *Fluoride Drinking Waters* (53), a compilation of published papers.

The discussion of Section III has described principles of basic water treatment processes and the chemistry involved in them. We now proceed to a description of the ways in which units and combinations of these processes are found in public water supply treatment works. The following discussion, together with that above, provides the key to the analytical control determinations in which the water works chemist is directly involved.

## IV. KINDS OF WATER TREATMENT PLANTS

Public water supply installations range in complexity from the simple well or spring used without treatment to huge plants providing complete conditioning by coagulation, sedimentation, filtration, disinfection, softening, and the other components of water processing. However these represent the two ends of the spectrum, and the average plant is more likely to afford conventional treatment, including disinfection. The kind of treatment which is required depends upon the quality of the raw water. Some concept of the variations is provided in Table III, which gives chemical data on surface waters. Ground water chemical quality tends to remain rather constant for any one geographical area, but varies

TABLE III

Chemical Analyses of[a] Various Surface Waters (Results in mg/liter)

| Constituent | 1[b] | 2[c] | 3[d] | 4[e] | 5[f] | 6[g] | 7[h] |
|---|---|---|---|---|---|---|---|
| Ammonia nitrogen (N) | 0.2 | 6.4 | 0.4 | 1.3 | 0 | — | 0.1 |
| Alkalinity as $CaCO_3$ | 127 | 63 | 220 | 180 | 64 | 120 | 37 |
| Chlorides (Cl) | 9 | 49 | 25 | 158 | 16 | 7 | 8 |
| Dissolved oxygen ($O_2$) | 8.8 | 0 | 10.5 | 6.8 | 7.1 | 7.3 | 5.3 |
| Hardness (total) | 128 | 112 | 256 | 624 | 146 | 132 | 97 |
| Phosphates ($PO_4$) | — | — | 1.2 | 0.2 | 0.6 | 0.1 | 0 |
| Sulfates ($SO_4$) | 32 | — | 40 | 648 | 94 | 28 | 66 |
| Total dissolved solids | 157 | — | 345 | 1411 | 258 | 163 | 161 |
| Color[i] | 5 | 10 | 5 | 10 | 46 | 10 | 4 |
| pH | 8.0 | 7.2 | 8.2 | 8.4 | 7.7 | 8.4 | 7.1 |
| Turbidity[i] | 5 | 13 | 25 | 76 | 18 | 25 | 7 |

[a] Adopted from National Quality Network, Annual Compilation of Data October 1, 1961 to September 30, 1962, PHS 663, 1962 Ed.

[b] Lake Michigan at Gary, Indiana, July 3, 1962.

[c] Kanawha River at Winfield Dam, W. Va., August 16, 1962.

[d] Little Miami River at Cincinnati, Ohio, September 26, 1962.

[e] Colorado River at Loma, Colorado, September 4, 1962.

[f] Schuylkill River at Philadelphia, Pa., June 18, 1962.

[g] Shenandoah River at Berryville, Va., June 6, 1962.

[h] Susquehanna River at Conowingo, Md., May 29, 1962.

[i] Results in standard units.

Note: One attribute of stream water is turbidity variation. On some days it may be low and on other days it may exceed several hundred standard units.

from one part of a country to another as shown in Table IV. It must be kept in mind that the reason for disinfection is to eliminate from a water supply the pathogenic organisms which are responsible for disease outbreaks. The Public Health Service requires* that all surface water supplies be disinfected and recommends that ground water installations be like-wise protected against the chance introduction of contamination. It is required* also that ground water sources subject to contamination be disinfected.

## A. WELL OR SPRING

The well or spring water supply consists of one or more sources connected to a distribution system either directly or through intermediate storage. Many such supplies are encountered with which no chemical

* This requirement pertains to interstate carrier water supplies which are under the jurisdiction of the Public Health Service.

TABLE IV

Selected Chemical Analyses[a] of Various Well Waters

| Constituent | 1[b] | 2[c] | 3[d] | 4[e] | 5[f] | 6[g] | 7[h] |
|---|---|---|---|---|---|---|---|
| Bicarbonate (HCO₃) | 63 | 12 | 351 | 216 | 422 | 315 | 147 |
| Calcium (Ca) | 24 | 5.0 | 89 | 72 | 1.7 | 17 | 43 |
| Carbonate (CO₃) | 0 | 0 | 0 | — | 0 | 10 | 0 |
| Chloride (Cl) | 36 | 13 | 23 | 75 | 186 | 11 | 4.9 |
| Fluoride (F) | 0.2 | 0.2 | 1.2 | 0.4 | 0.6 | 1.0 | 0 |
| Hardness as CaCO₃ | | | | | | | |
|   Total | 99 | 17 | 399 | 287 | 6 | 116 | 141 |
|   Noncarbonate | 47 | 8 | 112 | 110 | 0 | 0 | 21 |
| Iron (Fe) | 1.2 | 0.01 | 0.58 | 0.03 | 0.03 | 0 | 0 |
| Magnesium (Mg) | 9.4 | 1.2 | 43 | 26 | 0.4 | 18 | 8.3 |
| Manganese (Mn) | 0.28 | 0.02 | 0 | 0 | — | — | 0 |
| Nitrate (NO₃) | 1.0 | 1.0 | 5.6 | 7.1 | 0.5 | 5.3 | 1.4 |
| Potassium (K) | 3.6 | 0.6 | 16 | 1.9 | 1.2 | 3.6 | 1.0 |
| Silica (Si) | 13 | 12 | 12 | 15 | 11 | 16 | 7.0 |
| Sodium (Na) | 18 | 7.4 | 126 | 54 | 281 | 118 | 4.7 |
| Sulfate (SO₄) | 37 | 4.8 | 345 | 121 | 1.9 | 84 | 24 |
| Total dissolved solids | 181 | 61 | 834 | 479 | 697 | 433 | 170 |
| pH | 6.0 | 6.1 | 7.5 | 7.7 | 8.0 | 8.0 | 7.8 |
| Color | 3 | 1 | 2 | — | 35 | 0 | 2 |
| Turbidity | — | 0.9 | 1 | <1 | — | — | 9.5 |

[a] Adopted from U.S.G.S. Water Supply Papers 1299 and 1300 (1952) (figures in mg/liter except pH, color and turbidity).
[b] Well No. 1, Camden, N.J.
[c] Well No. 26, North Kingston, R.I.
[d] Well No. 5, Grinnell, Iowa.
[e] Well No. 7, Huntington Park, California.
[f] Well No. Mo-65, Bastrop, La.
[g] Well 1, Tucumcari, N.D.
[h] Well No. 2, Schenectady, N.Y.

treatment is used. This represents the simplest kind of supply and it is illustrated by Fig. 1. Even this type, however, requires the services of the analytical chemist to determine whether its quality meets drinking water standards.

## B. WELL OR SPRING WITH DISINFECTION AND CHEMICAL TREATMENT

The next variation is the well or spring supply with which one or more treatment processes are used to render the water satisfactory. These may include disinfection, fluoridation, iron and manganese removal, hardness removal, and corrosion control. It may also be required to provide means for the removal of hydrogen sulfide or carbon dioxide. Figure 2 shows the arrangements which may be encountered and, by letter code (which corresponds with Tables V and VI), the kinds of analyses which are needed to check and control the effectiveness of the treatment processes and the points at which they are needed.

One variation of the well kind of water supply deserves special mention. Many well waters contain fluoride ion in solution and this is called naturally occurring fluoride. It is just as effective in preventing dental decay as the fluoride which is added mechanically, in fact, the benefits of fluoridation were discovered through observations of the teeth of people who used naturally fluoridated water (54,55). Unfortunately, all naturally fluoridated waters do not contain the optimum amount of fluoride and it may be necessary to either supplement or reduce the concentrations present.

## C. SURFACE WATER SUPPLIES

### 1. With Disinfection

Surface water supplies serve about two-thirds of the United States population which consumes water from public supplies. No surface water should be used without disinfection, but there are some areas, such as in the Pacific Northwest, where they can still be used with disinfection alone. This kind of supply is shown by Fig. 3. In the figures which are used to illustrate this section of the chapter a fluoridator is usually shown, and wherever one appears it is accompanied by the indicated requirement of fluoride determinations before and after the fluoride application.

### 2. With Conventional Treatment

Where the term "conventional treatment" is used in this chapter it pertains to coagulation, sedimentation, filtration, and disinfection. Many public water supplies are processed with just these methods and, possibly, stabilization of the plant effluent. Figure 4 illustrates a typical arrangement.

### 3. With Conventional and Auxiliary Treatment

Some communities are so situated that they must use the nearest source of water supply regardless of its quality. For example, there are many older riverside cities which, when young, found the quality of the stream sufficiently high that it could be used directly or with disinfection alone. Gradually, however, with the increase in population and growing industrial complexes, the water became loaded with waste products. This sort of condition may occur in a stream which emanates from a limestone area and which therefore contains objectionable hardness. With this combination of conditions a water plant employing all known methods of water purification could be required, including the application of activated carbon for the control of tastes and odors. At Philadelphia several years ago ozone was applied for this purpose. An idea of how such a plant could be laid out is given by Fig. 5.

## D. DESALTING PLANTS

Increasing water shortages have lead to research and development in the use of salt and brackish water sources by converting them to potable water through various means. Although the plants in service today are of capacities not exceeding 9 million gallons per day, there are plans for building installations which will produce up to 50,000,000 gallons per day. One of the processes, flash distillation, employs chemical conditioning as a first step by adding sulfuric acid to convert sea water carbonates and bicarbonates into carbon dioxide, which is later removed together with dissolved oxygen in a deaerator. The conditioned water is then converted to steam by the flash method (56) (see Fig. 6). A major chemical control problem in flash distillation is the prevention of scale. Methods for preventing scale include (57): use of polyphosphate, pH adjustment, use of calcium carbonate seed crystals as nuclei for formation, and ion exchange.

Other methods for desalting water are conventional distillation, reverse osmosis, solar distillation, and electrodialysis. The principle of conventional distillation and solar distillation is simply condensation of evaporated salt water by heat obtained from various fuels in the first instance and from solar energy in the second. Scale formation is also a problem with conventional distillation, but, with solar evaporation, a method has been found which involves the use of plastic sheeting and concrete basins for holding the salt water so that condensation is obtained with little or no formation of scale.

Reverse osmosis is what the name implies. In naturally occurring osmosis a fluid passes through a membrane from a less saturated solution to a more saturated solution. It has been found possible to desalt sea water by forcing the flow in a reverse direction, i.e., from dense sea water to fresh water, by exerting pressure of some 600 psi on the sea water side of the specially prepared membranes (58). In electrodialysis salt water is converted to fresh water by passage between electrically charged, parallel plates in such a way that the charged salt ions migrate to respective, oppositely charged plates and are removed, leaving behind the purified water which forms the effluent of the process.

Regardless of the desalting method chosen for the task it is necessary to make certain chemical adjustments before admitting the final effluent to a public water supply distribution system. As in the case of softening plants where there is a removal of alkaline substances, the effluent of a desalting operation is an aggressive water. It is therefore necessary to adjust the pH. It has also been found advantageous to maintain a certain level of total dissolved solids, which is accomplished by split treatment i.e., mixing the desalted water with some salt or brackish water.

## E. WATER TREATMENT FOR SPECIAL APPLICATIONS

There are many special cases which require a quality water which must be prepared either from an individual source of supply or from the public water supply with which the industrial, commercial, or other kind of establishment is served. Most of these special requirements are for a high quality water from the standpoint of either total chemical content or some categorical chemical content, such as hardness. However, a few, such as cooling water for heavy industry, may require only the application of some chemical for the control of slime or other biological growth, and the removal of dissolved solids is not needed.

Probably the most widespread need for a specially treated water is that for boiler feed and hot water heaters. This is nearly universal wherever heat is a necessity for human life or where it is used for generating steam for industrial purposes. The main difficulties encountered using improperly conditioned boiler feed water are: scale formation with resultant heat loss and carrying capacity in the boiler tubes, corrosion and foaming, the last being caused by caustic or bicarbonate alkalinity of the element sodium. To minimize these conditions a boiler feed water should be free from turbidity, noncarbonate hardness, oil, oxygen, and silica. Total hardness should not exceed 35 ppm for moderate pressure boilers (58). Feed water for boilers in large installations is prepared by anion–cation exchange and lime or lime–soda softening. The removal of silica, a troublesome scale former, can be done by use of ion exchange or hot or cold lime softening utilizing dolomitic lime which contains magnesium hydroxide. Oxygen, a cause of corrosion, can be removed through deaeration or by chemical means, which include the addition of sulfites or tannin. Monosodium, disodium, and trisodium phosphates are employed for the further reduction of hardness remaining after conventional softening. A complex boiler feed water treatment plant is sketched in Fig. 7.

There are many industries that require a high quality water and, in general, their requirements are for a water which is of higher quality than can be derived from a nearby stream and sometimes higher than that normally delivered to them from a public supply. Some stipulations are: complete freedom from tastes and ordors, zero or near zero turbidity, low or no hardness, no iron or manganese, no residual chlorine, and low or no color. Industries which depend upon high quality water include: paper mills, textile and rayon mills, food and beverage producers, dairies, milk reconstituting plants, cheese manufacturers, soft drink bottlers, and pharmaceutical houses. Reference is made to *Water Quality Criteria* (59) in which will be found recommended water quality standards and references to recommended water quality criteria for the following industrial applications:

| | |
|---|---|
| Aluminum manufacture | Food processing, general |
| Baking | Ice manufacturing |
| Boiler feed water | Laundering |
| Brewing | Oil well flooding |
| Carbonated beverages | Paper manufacture |
| Carbon black manufacture | Photographic processing |
| Chemical processes (general) | Plastics manufacturer |
| Concrete mixing | Pulp and paper industry |
| Confectionary production | Rayon and acetate fiber production |
| Cooling water | Steel manufacture |
| Copper industry | Sugar manufacture |
| Dairy industry | Synthetic rubber |
| Electroplating and metal finishing | Tanning |
| Food canning and freezing | Television picture tube making |
| Food equipment washing | Textile manufacture |

Many industrial water treatment plants are similar to those used for the production of public water supplies. However there has been more application made of pressure vessels for the containment of filtration media, and so-called "package" or compact water treatment devices are more frequently found. An example is the up-flow, single structure device which provides softening, clarification, or stabilization of ground or surface water. Pressure tanks containing ion exchange media are common and two high efficiency processes have been developed. These are diatomaceous earth filters to produce a low or zero turbidity water and pressure filters containing activated carbon for the complete removal of tastes and odors and residual chlorine.

## F. SWIMMING POOLS

The next kind of water treatment to be discussed in this chapter is swimming pool water purification. It is in a class by itself because, unlike other treatment sequences which produce an end product which is then consumed by persons or processes, the swimming pool system conditions water in an endless succession of repetitive passes called "recirculation." In other words the swimming pool application of water treatment is a cycle in which the water goes round and round and is used over and over again. In a very strict sense this is not true because in every swimming pool recirculation system there is need for adding fresh make-up water daily and occasionally the entire pool contents must be emptied to waste and the system filled with all fresh water. Figure 8 shows a typical swimming pool arrangement. The techniques of analytical chemistry are required for proper swimming pool operation because the standards which pool water must meet are high and there is need for routinely making several tests, the most frequent of which are those for pH and residual chlorine.

## G. BOTTLED WATER PLANTS

The next kind of water treatment to be discussed is a variation of the first in that extensive treatment is not usually provided. The bottled water industry in the United States has developed into a multi-million dollar enterprise, chiefly in areas where the quality of the water otherwise available was not palatable or attractive enough to satisfy the consumers. Consequently, sources of water near to these areas were developed and plants were constructed to bottle the product, usually at the site of the spring or well, and distribute it to the public by truck delivery or through commercial outlets. Three sources of bottled water have been utilized: wells, springs, and the public supply, the latter being distilled through one or more stages. Some springs or wells are used without treatment and others are chlorinated for disinfection purposes and then dechlorinated for taste and odor removal. Ultraviolet light disinfection has been employed by operators of bottled water plants because it does not cause taste and odor problems, the reason being that no odor-causing compounds are formed. Another device used by bottled water producers is the polishing filter of the layered felt or paper mat variety, which removes traces of turbidity. Two types of establishments are shown on Fig. 9. These are the simple spring and the more complex distillation kinds. In addition to frequent checks on turbidity, taste and odor, and color, analyses required in the production of bottled water are those listed in the *Public Health Service Drinking Water Standards* and those to determine mineral content. Several companies, for example, bottle spring or well water which is advertised for its mineral content, chiefly sulfates, chlorides, and various combinations of carbonates and citrates. It is not customary for the average bottled water plant to employ its own analytical chemist, and analyses are often performed by a consulting chemist and, for regulatory purposes, in health department laboratories.

On the sketches illustrating the kinds of water treatment plants, use has been made of a code system for designating chemical analysis. This system is explained by Table V. The analyses shown at the various points on the flow diagrams are those which are used for quality and operation control of the various water treatment processes. In addition to the points and tests designated there may be additional points and analyses which would be required or used at a specific installation to meet its peculiar conditions. There are few water treatment plants and raw waters which are exactly alike, and it is therefore necessary to modify control systems to meet specific needs. However the material presented herein is intended to furnish the analytical chemist with the basic patterns of chemical quality control of basic water treatment systems. There now follows a discussion of analytical procedures, instrumentation, and interpretation of results. Detailed instructions on how to perform the analyses will not be given as these appear in standard texts. Table VI lists analyses used in plant control, keyed to Fig. 1–9 and Table V, and designates where they are found in three published texts used extensively in the water works field and cites a fourth text which contains useful information not found in the others. The first of these is *Standard Methods for the Examination of Water and Waste Water* (60), which contains legally recognized procedures for conducting water analyses. When court cases involving water quality are tried, the analytical methods, results from which are admitted as evidence, are usually those in *Standard Methods*. *Standard Methods* is, however, much more than legal, analytical procedures, for it is the work of over 70 years of experimentation, trial, and development of water tests which, before being published in *Standard Methods*, are approved by a committee of water experts of international reputation and are endorsed by the American Water Works Association, American Public Health Association, and the Water Pollution Control Federation. The second document, *Simplified Procedures for Water Examination* (61), was published in 1964 by the American Water Works Association to make available to the water supply technician a readily understood and much condensed compendium of the water tests routinely used for plant control. Both these documents cover biological examinations as well as chemical analyses. The third brochure, *Water Chemistry Laboratory Manual* (62), also contains simplified versions of the routine determinations and, in addition, an excellent discussion of some bases for interpretation. The *Water Chemistry Laboratory Manual* has been translated into Portuguese for use by Brazilian water works operators. The fourth manual is a publication (63) of the U.S. Geological Survey, which does extensive work in analytical water chemistry.

It will be noted that the analyses required for routine plant control

TABLE V
Chemical Analyses Code Used on Figs. 1–9

| Code letter or number | Chemical Analysis | Symbol |
|---|---|---|
| | *Analyses commonly needed* | |
| A | Acidity | As $CaCO_3$ |
| B | Alkalinity | As $CaCO_3$ |
| C | Carbon dioxide | $CO_2$ |
| D | Chloride | Cl |
| E | Chlorine demand | Cl |
| F | Chlorine residual | Cl |
| G | Coagulation | — |
| H | Color | — |
| I | Fluoride | F |
| J | Hardness | As $CaCO_3$ |
| K | Hydrogen ion | pH |
| L | Iron | Fe |
| M | Manganese | Mn |
| N | Odor | — |
| O | Residue | — |
| P | Turbidity | — |
| | *Other analyses often used* | |
| 1 | Aluminum | Al |
| 2 | Ammonia | As N |
| 3 | Dissolved oxygen | O |
| 4 | Calcium | Ca |
| 5 | Phosphates | As $PO_4$ |
| 6 | Sodium | Na |
| 7 | Silica | Si |
| D.W.S. | *Examinations required by public health service drinking water standards* | |

TABLE VI

Analyses for Control of Water Treatment Plants and Water Supply Systems

| Identification of analysis | | | Page(s) of reference in which procedure is found | | | |
|---|---|---|---|---|---|---|
| Code letter or no.[a] | Name | Chemical symbol of result | 1[b] | 2[c] | 3[d] | 4[e] |
| *Analyses commonly needed* | | | | | | |
| A | Acidity | As CaCO$_3$ | 46 | — | 19, 20 | 87–91 |
| B | Alkalinity | As CaCO$_3$ | 48 | 13 | 22, 23 | 93 |
| C | Carbon dioxide | CO$_2$ | 77–85 | 22 | 24, 25 | 137 |
| D | Chloride | Cl | 85–87 | 24 | 26–27 | 141 |
| E | Chlorine demand | Cl | 112–115 | 31 | 28 | — |
| F | Chlorine residual | Cl | 90–108 | 25–29 | 29 | 147 |
| G | Coagulation | — | — | 42 | 44 | — |
| H | Color | — | 127 | 33 | 33, 34 | 155 |
| I | Fluoride | F | 135–144 | 36 | 36 | 163 |
| J | Hardness | As CaCO$_3$ | 146 | 37 | 39–40 | 173 |
| K | Hydrogen ion | pH | 225–226 | 52 | 41 | 237 |
| L | Iron | Fe | 154–161 | 39 | 42, 43 | 183 |
| M | Manganese | Mn | 172–176 | 49 | 45 | 205 |
| N | Odor | — | 304 | 59 | 46–50 | — |
| O | Residue | — | 242–2400 | 56 | — | 269 |
| P | Turbidity | — | 312 | 62 | 53 | 289 |
| *Other analyses used* | | | | | | |
| 1 | Aluminum | Al | 53 | 15 | — | 97 |
| 2 | Ammonia | As N | 186–193 | 16 | — | 211 |
| 3 | Dissolved oxygen | O | 218 | 50 | — | 233 |
| 4 | Calcium | Ca | 70–74 | 19 | — | 127 |
| 5 | Phosphates | As PO$_4$ | 230–236 | 54 | — | 245 |
| 6 | Sodium | Na | 273–277 | — | — | 265 |
| 7 | Silica | Si | 258–264 | 57 | — | 259 |
| D.W.S. | *Examinations required by Public Health Service Drinking Water Standards* | | | | | |
| | Alkyl benzene sulfonate | ABS | 296–298 | — | — | — |
| | Arsenic | As | 56–58 | — | — | 101 |
| | Barium | Ba | — | — | — | 107 |
| | Cadmium | Cd | 67 | — | — | — |
| | Chloride | Cl | 85–87 | 24 | 26–27 | 141 |
| | Chromium | Cr$^{6+}$ | 122–126 | — | — | 151 |
| | Copper | Cu | 129–133 | — | — | 157 |
| | Carbon chloroform extract | CCE | 214 | — | — | — |
| | Cyanide | CN | 134 | — | — | — |
| | Fluoride | F | 135–144 | 36 | 36 | 163 |
| | Iron | Fe | 154–161 | 39 | 42–43 | 183 |
| | Lead | Pb | 163 | — | — | — |
| | Manganese | Mn | 172–176 | 49 | 45 | 205 |
| | Nitrate | NO$_3$ | 195–202 | — | — | 216 |
| | Phenols | — | 229 | — | — | 239 |
| | Selenium | Se | 250–255 | — | — | 253 |
| | Silver | Ag | 266–270 | — | — | — |
| | Sulfate | SO$_4$ | 287–291 | — | — | 279 |
| | Total dissolved solids | — | 242–247 | 56 | — | 268 |
| | Zinc | Zn | 316–322 | — | — | 293 |

[a] Corresponds to code letters and numbers on Figs. 1–9.
[b] *Standard Methods for the examination of water and Waste Water*, 12th Ed.
[c] *Simplified Procedures for Water Examination*, AWWA M12, Simplified Laboratory Manual.
[d] *Water Chemistry Laboratory Manual*.
[e] *Methods for Collection and Analysis of Water Samples*.

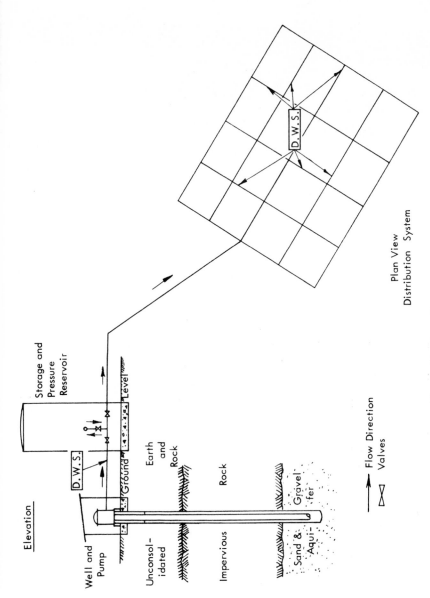

Elevation

Storage and
Pressure
Reservoir

D.W.S.

Ground Level

Well and
Pump

Unconsol-
idated

Earth
and
Rock

Impervious

Rock

Sand & Gravel Aqui-fer

→ Flow Direction
⋈ Valves

D.W.S.

Plan View
Distribution System

Fig. 1. Simple well water supply system.

291

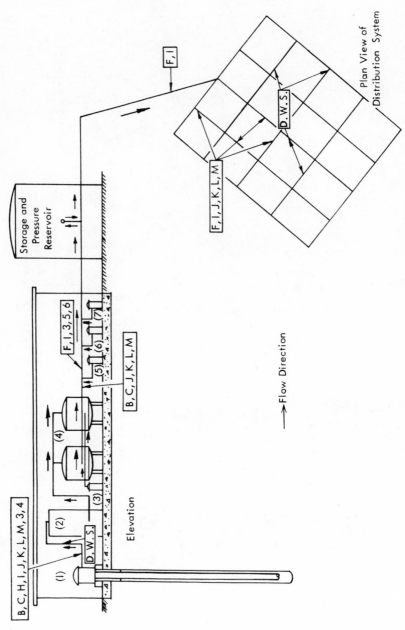

Fig. 2. Well water supply with iron and manganese removal, softening, fluoridation, and corrosion control: (*1*) well and pump; (*2*) aerator; (*3*) salt feeder; (*4*) zeolite softeners; (*5*) chlorinator; (*6*) fluoridator; (*7*) phosphate feeder. Letters and numbers in boxes (Figs. 2–8) are identified in Tables V and VI.

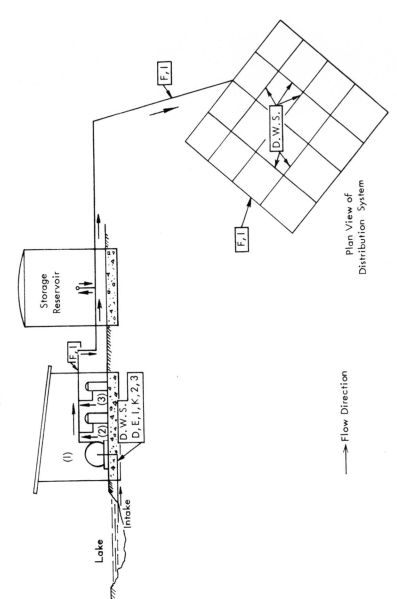

Fig. 3. Surface water supply with disinfection and fluoridation: (1) pump; (2) chlorinator; (3) fluoridator.

293

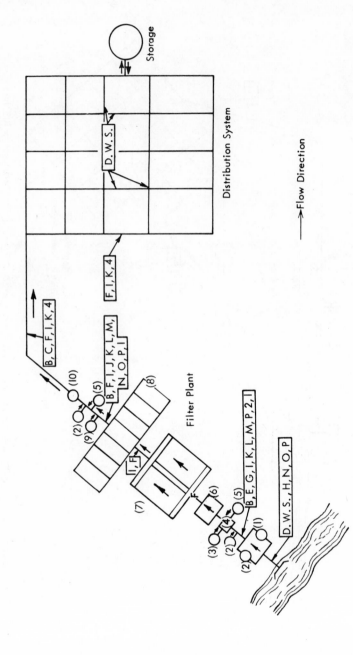

Fig. 4. Surface water supply with conventional treatment: (1) low lift pumps; (2) chlorinator; (3) alum feeder; (4) mixing tank; (5) lime feeder; (6) flocculator; (7) settling basins; (8) filters and clear well; (9) fluoridator; (10) high lift pump.

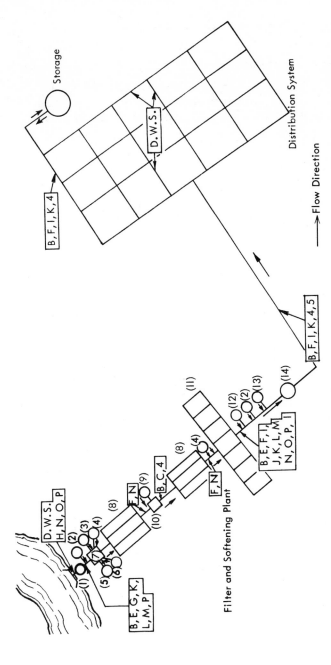

Fig. 4. Surface water supply with conventional treatment plus softening, taste and odor control, and stabilization:
(1) Low lift pumps; (2) chlorinator; (3) alum feeder; (4) carbon feeder; (5) lime feeder; (6) soda ash feeders; (7) mixing basin; (8) settling basins; (9) CO₂ generator; (10) recarbonator; (11) filters; (12) fluoridator; (13) lime or phosphate feeder; (14) high lift pumps.

Storage

Distribution System

B, F, I, K, 4

D.W.S.

→ Flow Direction

B, F, I, K, 4, 5

Filter and Softening Plant

(11)

(12)

(2)

(13)

(14)

B, E, F, I,
J, K, L, M,
N, O, P, 1

F, N

(8)

(4)

B, C, 4

(10)

(8)

F, N

(8)

D.W.S.
H, N, O, P

(2)

(3)

(4)

(9)

(1)

(7)

(5)

(6)

B, E, G, K,
L, M, P

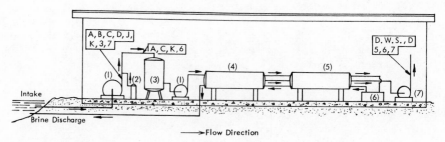

Fig. 6. Simplified sketch of sea water flash distillation plant: (1) salt water pump; (2) sulfuric acid feeder; (3) deaerator; (4) heat rejection-condenser; (5) heat recovery-condenser; (6) brine heater; (7) fresh water pump.

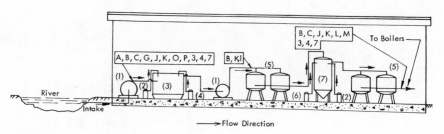

Fig. 7. Treatment system for boiler feed water from river source: (1) pump; (2) lime feeder; (3) upflow clarifier; (4) alum feeder; (5) sand filters; (6) soda ash feeder; (7) lime soda softener.

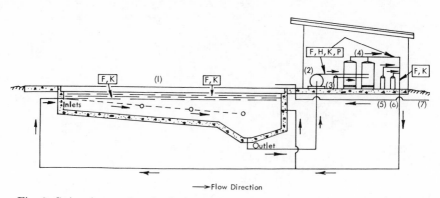

Fig. 8. Swimming pool recirculation and filtration system: (1) pool; (2) pump; (3) body feeder; (4) diatomaceous earth filters; (5) chlorinator; (6) soda ash feeder; (7) fresh water line.

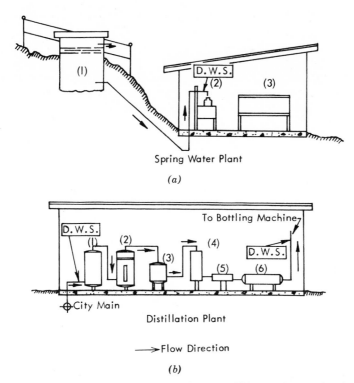

Spring Water Plant

(a)

Distillation Plant

⟶Flow Direction

(b)

Fig. 9. Bottled water plants (a): (1) spring; (2) filling table; (3) bottle washer, (b): (1) softeners; (2) stills; (3) charcoal filter; (4) aerator; (5) felt filter; (6) ultraviolet sterilizer.

are in some instances the same as some in the *Drinking Water Standards*. When reports are made on the overall operation of the system, for example, for certification under the *Drinking Water Standards*, the constituents for which limits are prescribed therein should be listed as a group on the official or record reports. The other routine tests should be recorded in daily plant operation records.

## V. CHEMICAL ANALYSES COMMONLY USED FOR WATER TREATMENT PRODUCTION CONTROL

The first step in making a chemical determination is the collection of a sample. Many water treatment plants have a centrally located sink where small diameter lines continuously discharge water from different points on the system. The analytical chemist can collect at this sink either the amount required for a specific test or a sample large enough for several determinations. When samples for an extensive series of tests are required, say from a distribution system, glass or inert plastic bottles of about 1-gallon capacity are used. Special analyses require special sampling techniques. The sample collected for the carbon chloroform extract (CCE) determination, for example, is obtained by allowing about 5000 gallons of water to flow through a glass or plastic cylinder containing granular carbon at a rate of 0.25 gallons per minute. Also ollection of samples for the new or organic chemical examinations is done by means of a liquid-to-liquid procedure, wherein water from the selected sample point is run into and out of the sample bottle, which contains an immiscible solvent, at a very low rate of flow until about 1000 gallons have been sampled. In any event, regardless of the method of collecting the sample, the objective is to obtain for the required test the amount of water needed for it in such a manner that it will not be contaminated by the sampling procedure. In each of the chemical analyses described in the above-cited texts, or hereinafter, the amount required is specified. The reader is referred to the work of Rainwater and Thatcher (63) for further information on methods for sample collection.

Some idea of the magnitude of the analytical chemist's task is indicated by a recent report on utilities in Saginaw, Michigan. Over 80,000 chemical determinations are performed annually in providing water supply for some 175,000 inhabitants of that metropolitan area.

The frequency of individual determinations varies with the needs of the plants and the variable chemical content of raw waters, and there is no set pattern. Some randomly selected frequencies from the writers experience for specific tests are as follow:

| | |
|---|---|
| Alkalinity | 12 per day |
| Chloride | 2 per day |
| Fluoride | 1 per day |
| Hardness | 2 per day |
| Iron | 1 per month |
| Manganese | 1 per day |
| pH | 12 per day |
| Sodium | 1 per month |
| Sulfates | 2 per week |
| Taste and odor | 1 per day |
| Total solids | 2 per week |
| Trace elements (arsenic, copper, lead, selenium) zinc | 1 per quarter |
| Turbidity | 12 per day |

The frequency of sampling also may vary with the sampling points, but it is often alike for raw and finished water at the treatment plant. Distribution system samples, with the possible exception of those for residual chlorine and pH, are less frequent than at the plant.

The analyses required for comparison with drinking water standards are recommended at 6-month intervals until the chemical pattern of the supply is well known. Thereafter the frequency may be reduced, but it should be no less than once in 3 years. Also if any change in chemical quality is suspected due to changing environmental conditions, a complete analysis should be performed at such times.

The analytical chemist should avoid complete rigidity of a sampling schedule, remembering that water treatment can be a highly variable process. He should also be prepared at any time to perform common or exotic analyses which may be required in emergency situations.

## A. ACIDITY

The determination for acidity is not universally used in water treatment plants, but it is often employed with water which contain free mineral acids, carbon dioxide, or salts of strong acids and weak bases. It is performed by titrating a suitable aliquot of sample, usually 100 ml, with 0.02 $N$ sodium hydroxide, which, in the presence of free mineral acid, reacts as shown by eq. (35).

$$2H^+ + SO_4{}^{2-} + 2Na^+ + 2OH^- \rightarrow 2H_2O + 2Na^+ + SO_4{}^{2-} \tag{35}$$

The titration is conducted with the use of phenolphthalein and methyl orange indicators. Results are expressed in parts per million of calcium carbonate and, in some instances, in terms of hydrogen.

### 1. Interpretation of Results

The presence of any acidity in finished drinking water is conducive to the corrosion of metallic pipes and containers and is therefore regarded as undesirable. This is particularly important in distribution systems. In some parts of a water treatment process, as for example with softening or flash distillation, it may be desirable to have acidity at a given point

## B. ALKALINITY

This is one of the most commonly used of all water chemistry analyses. The principle is to neutralize carbonate, bicarbonate, and hydroxide alkalinity by 0.02 $N$ sulfuric acid in the presence of phenolphthalein and methyl orange indicators used in succession. The elemental reactions are given by eqs. (36)–(38).

$$Ca^{2+} + 2HCO_3^{2-} + 2H^+ + SO_4^{2-} \rightarrow CaSO_4 + 2CO_2 + 2H_2O \tag{36}$$

$$Ca^{2+} + CO_3^{2-} + 2H^+ + SO_4^{2-} \rightarrow CaSO_4 + CO_2 + H_2O \tag{37}$$

$$Ca^{2+} + 2OH^- + 2H^+ + SO_4^{2-} \rightarrow CaSO_4 + 2H_2O \tag{38}$$

The principle substances interfering with this determination are those which affect color formation. Free available chlorine will bleach the color, and suspended calcium carbonate and magnesium hydroxide may cause it to fade (64).

### 1. Interpretation of Results

The results of the alkalinity determination are important for at least three reasons in water treatment plant control. One is in the lime–soda water softening process, the second in coagulation, and the third in the calcium carbonate stability test (65,66). A method for calculating the approximate quantities of lime and soda ash required for softening purposes utilized the sum of $CO_2$ and a halfbound $CO_2$ (44% of the total alkalinity) times 0.0106 to compute the pounds of calcium oxide, CaO, needed to react with the $CO_2$ and the half-bound $CO_2$ in 1000 gallons of water.

Alkalinity is important in coagulation as shown by equations. (1)–(5). However, precise calculations of alum dosage, based on the amount of alkalinity present, have not been found practical due to turbidity and other substances which interfere with or promote floc formation. Until recently the method for computing coagulant dosage was confined to the empirical jar test which is described below.

Another useful application of the results of the alkalinity test is in the desalting of sea water. As cited previously the flash distillation method employs as a first step the reacting of sulfuric acid with the alkalinity of the sea or brackish water to produce carbon dioxide. It is therefore necessary to determine the alkalinity in order to compute sulfuric acid doses.

These three cases have been more related to application than to interpretation; however, the latter is also implied.

In 1946 the Public Health Service recommended that the alkalinity of drinking and culinary water subject to the Public Health Service Drinking Water Standards be limited to the following: phenolphthalein alkalinity as $CaCO_3$ should not exceed 15 mg/liter plus four-tenths of the total alkalinity; the normal carbonate alkalinity should not exceed 120 mg/liter; and if excess alkalinity was produced by treatment, the total alkalinity, as $CaCO_3$ should not exceed the hardness by more than 35 mg/liter (67). This recommendation was not continued in the 1962 *Standards,* but it is still useful as a guide to suitable water alkalinity content.

## C. CARBON DIOXIDE

*Standard Methods* describes the determination of $CO_2$ by either of two methods as an estimation (68), the reason being that the carbon dioxide content of a water sample is constantly changing. A sample collected in the field and transported to the laboratory usually has a much different $CO_2$ content than that of the water from which it was taken. Also a sample drawn directly from a well will have at least slightly different concentrations than the ground water strata. It is therefore important that a direct titration for $CO_2$ be done as close as possible to the site of the sample collection.

A nomographic method (69), based on ionization equilibria equations of carbonates and water, permits a close approximation of total free carbon dioxide when the pH, alkalinity and temperature values have been accurately measured at the time of sampling. The titration procedure, the endpoint of which is found colorometrically or potentiometrically, utilizes either 0.0454 $N$ sodium carbonate or 0.0227 $N$ sodium hydroxide, which reacts as follows with free carbon dioxide in two steps.

$$CO_2 + 2NaOH \rightleftharpoons Na_2CO_3 + H_2O \tag{39}$$

$$Na_2CO_3 + CO_2 + H_2O \rightleftharpoons 2NaHCO_3 \tag{40}$$

## 1. Interpretation of Results

The presence of carbon dioxide in a ground water is indicative of organic matter in the aquifer which has decomposed by aerobic or anaerobic means. The importance of the gas when dissolved in water arises from the corrosive properties it imparts. It is therefore essential that the carbon dioxide content of water turned into a metallic distribution system be low or zero. As noted above it is important to know the carbon dioxide content of waters being softened in order to determine needed quantities of lime. Carbon dioxide in large concentrations has been known to be damaging to concrete structures, and if such containers are to contain water in which the $CO_2$ content exceeds 20 mg/liter, they should be protected by an inert coating. Knowledge of free carbon dioxide values is also required when computations are being made of total carbon dioxide content (70). Carbon dioxide in water solution has no known adverse affects upon human health or animals.

## D. CHLORIDE

The determination of the chloride ion, $Cl^-$, is important in determining the degree to which a water source has been subjected to salt water intrusion or contamination by sewage or other pollutions. The attention of the reader is called to the chloride values which appear in Tables III and IV and which give some idea of the range encountered in ground and surface waters.

The classical Mohr method for chloride determination depends upon the formation of red silver chromate according to reactions (41) and (42). The later mercuric nitrate procedure, invented by F. E. Clarke

$$Ag^+ + NO_3^- + Na^+ + Cl^- \rightarrow AgCl \tag{41}$$

$$2Ag^+ + CrO_4^- \rightarrow Ag_2CrO_4 \tag{42}$$

and covered by U.S. Patent 2,783,064, utilizes diphenylcarbazone as an indicator, and the chemical reaction between $Hg^{2+}$ and $2Cl^-$ produces slightly dissociated mercuric chloride ions. Excess $Hg^{2+}$ ions combine with the indicator to form a purple complex.

### 1. Interpretation of Results

Interpretation of the results of the chloride determination is approached from two points of view. The first is from the standpoint of sewage pollution of a ground or surface water. Sewage may contain from 20 to 100 mg/liter of chloride. If a ground water which has been found routinely to contain 7 mg/liter chloride ion suddenly, or over a longer time period, shows an increase to 16 or more mg/liter chloride, a water plant operator would be suspicious that the ground water strata had become contaminated. These figures are cited as examples only; the variations of change are many. The second criterion for interpreting chloride results is concerned with the fact that sea and brackish waters are high in chlorides, and an increase in chloride content of a water supply source may indicate that it has been invaded by salt water. The chloride content of sea water varies from 12,000 to 23,000 mg/liter, with an average value of about 19,000 mg/liter. Consider now the case of the fifth surface water described in Table III. A chloride value of 16 mg/liter was found in the Schuylkill River on June 18, 1962. Philadelphia is situated at the confluence of the Schuylkill and Delaware Rivers at a point which is subject to tidal action. Should the chloride value at this point begin to climb and approach values of several hundred milligrams per liter chloride, it would be evidence of the presence of sea water. This condition actually occurred in the fall of 1965 to the extent that emergency plans were adopted to bring fresh water to the Torresdale Filter Plant intake from a point higher up on the Delaware River.

The reader may have recognized by now one of the principles used in the interpretation of the results of water analyses. This is a comparison of the results with the normal water content of some element or chemical group. When changes suddenly occur or gradually persist it is evidence that some basic change has taken place in the quality of the water supply. As this change may be harmful, a precaution, such as the inexpensive chemical analysis, may result in the saving of lives or a considerable amount of money.

Two other chloride values which may be useful in interpretation of analyses are those for rainwater and naturally occurring salt brine. The chloride content of the former averages about 3 mg/liter (71), and there is record of 200,100 mg/liter $Cl^-$ (72) found in a sample collected on March 26, 1952 from a well at Midland, Michigan.

## E. CHLORINE DEMAND

An important reason for the application of chlorine to a water supply is for disinfection. However, it is necessary to add more chlorine than the amount which is required for destroying the microorganisms, as it reacts with many other kinds of material before, or in addition to, killing the bacteria which may be present. This may frequently be beneficial when the chlorine oxidizes substances which are sources of troublesome tastes and odors, and chlorine is used for this purpose. As cited above chlorine also reacts with iron and manganese. The sum total of all the reactions constitutes the chlorine demand of the water. To determine this demand is therefore useful in estimating the amounts of chlorine which will be required for the operation of the water treatment system. Some water works operators utilize the chlorine demand test for routine plant control and some do not, for, at best, it is an approximation.

Chlorine demand is obtained by noting the difference between an amount of chlorine applied and the amount which remains as a residual after a suitable contact period. The results vary with contact time, pH, temperature, and the applied chlorine dosage, and it must not be conducted in direct sunlight. The test itself is empirical and there are no easily identified chemical reactions.

### 1. Interpretation of Results

The analytical chemist, having the results of a chlorine demand determination, is in a position to advise the operator of the plant on the regulation of the chlorine dosage. Under emergency conditions the results of the chlorine demand test become very important, as this analysis is useful as a screening procedure in the detection of chemical warfare agents. Arsenicals, free cyanide from hydrogen cyanide, some nerve agents, and sulfur mustard and its hydrolytic product exert a chlorine demand; nitrogen mustard and its hydrolysis products do not at low pH (73). When overt or covert action has been suspected in the contamination of a water supply with a chemical warfare agent, a considerable number of chlorine demand tests should be made on the raw water, in the treatment works, and on the distribution system. Any results above the normal experience for the system should be noted and a search made for the reason.

### F. CHLORINE RESIDUAL

The determination of chlorine residual is considered the most important analysis in the operation of any water supply system in which chlorine is used for disinfecting purposes. There are two forms of it: one is free available chlorine residual and the other is combined available residual chlorine. Free available chlorine residual may exist in the form of the chlorine molecule, $Cl^2$, below pH 5.0; hypochlorous acid, $HOCl$, between pH 5.0 and 6.0 or hypochlorite ion, $OCl^-$, in the pH region above 7.5. The products of which combined available chlorine residual consists are formed by the reaction of chlorine with ammonia as shown in eqs. (13)–(15). Dependent upon pH, they are: monochloramine ($NH_2Cl$), dichloramine ($NHCl_2$), and trichloramine ($NCl_3$).

Both free and combined residual chlorine are commonly determined with the use of *ortho*-toludine dihydrochloride, and sodium arsenite is employed to differentiate between the two forms. Amperometric titration affords a precise laboratory tool, but it requires delicate apparatus, dependent upon the availability of electric current, and is, therefore, not suitable for rough field use. Several manufactures produce sturdy, quite accurate field kits for determining chlorine residual by either the *ortho*-toludine dihydrochloride or *ortho*-toludine sodium arsenite (OTA) methods.

## 1. Interpretation of Results

As the most important action of chlorine is to disinfect a water supply, the interpretation of results of the chlorine residual analysis must be made in the light of requirements for the destruction of microbial life. There are four variables: time, temperature, pH, and the amount of chlorine applied. An oversimplification of the interpretation process is as follows. A certain amount of chlorine is required to destroy bacteria; the water works operator, based on experience and possibly the use of the chlorine demand test, applies a certain chlorine dosage. The analytical chemist, utilizing certain criteria, can estimate the amount required under given conditions of pH, time, and temperature and, by use of the chlorine residual test, can evaluate the effectiveness of the results. The plant bacteriologist confirms the interpretation process by examining the water for microorganisms. Chlorine is also viricidal (74).

Figure 10 will be found useful in interpreting the results of free and combined available chlorine determinations. The area between the dashed lines of pH 6.5 and 10.5 emphasizes the point that it requires more time and higher combined chlorine residuals to effect bacteria kill than

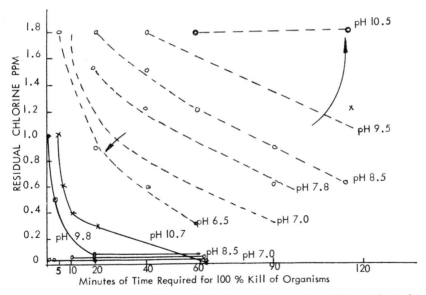

Fig. 10. Effect of time and kind of chlorine residual on the killing of bacteria: (From Public Health Service Publication) (solid rule) free available chlorine; (dashed rule) combined available chlorine.

it does for free available chlorine residual. Note the ascending order of chlorine residuals required to produce a 100% kill of organisms in 20 min. Note also the effect of pH.

Figure 11 further illustrates the effect of pH. Consider the curve for free available chlorine at 22°C, which is the plot of chlorine residual concentrations required to effect 100% bacterial kill in 60 min. At a pH of 6.5 only 0.3 mg/liter are needed, 1.2 mg/liter at pH 8.5, but 1.8 mg/liter when the pH reaches 10.5. This figure further demonstrates the marked differences between the bacteria-destroying power of free available chlorine over combined available chlorine.

An intriguing and important phenomenon associated with the chlorination of water is the breakpoint process. Under theoretical conditions of a water completely free from inorganic and organic chlorine-combining

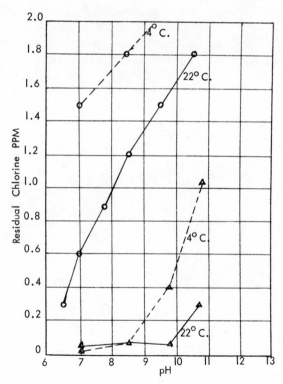

Fig. 11. Effect of pH and chlorine residual in producing 100% kill of bacteria: (From Public Health Service Publication) (○) combined available chlorine at 60 min.; (△) free available chlorine at 20 min.

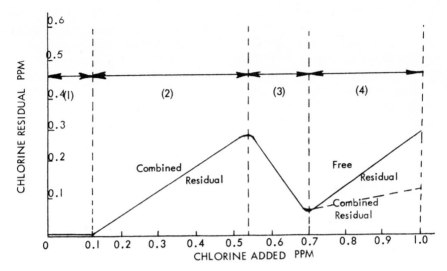

Fig. 12. The breakpoint process. *Zones:* (*1*) destruction of chlorine by reducing compounds; (*2,3*) formation of chloroorganic compounds and chloramines; (*3*) destruction of chloroorganic compounds and chloramines; (*4*) formation of free chlorine with or without combined chlorine.

substances other than bacteria, the amount of free chlorine residual would be in proportion to the amount of chlorine added. However, under operating conditions, this does not often occur. What can occur is shown by the curve on Fig. 12. The initial chlorine application produces little or no residual. As the dose is increased a combined residual is noted due to the formation of chloroorganic and chloramine compounds, up to a certain point where there is a drop in the residual even though the dose is increasing. It is in this area that the destruction of taste and odor-producing chloro-organic compounds occurs, and when reactions have advanced to a point there is the appearance of free chlorine residual with or without the simultaneous presence of a combined chlorine residual. This is the breakpoint. It is important because, once reached, the free chlorine residual is the most effective bactericide and there is often freedom from tastes and odors. The breakpoint curve of Fig. 12 is a classical example. There are many variations and sometimes it is nearly impossible to detect a breakpoint.

There is still another important factor in interpreting the results of residual chlorine determinations. The operators of some water treatment plants employ an ammoniator for introducing ammonia gas into the system for the deliberate purpose of producing a combined chlorine residual. With such a residual it is possible to carry a disinfecting agent to remote parts of the distribution system because, once formed, the chloramine is a long lasting, although much slower, bactericide. Recent American water works practice has seen a decrease in the use of ammonia and an increase in carrying free chlorine residuals into the distribution system as far as they will go.

## G. COAGULATION TESTS

The laboratory control of the coagulation process is accomplished in filter plants by the jar test. The theory is to simulate on the laboratory benchtop, with a stirrer and a series of jars or beakers, the coagulant addition, rapid mix, flocculation, and settling conditions which exist in a given plant. This is an empirical rather than a precise determination. A sample of the plant influent is measured in equal amounts into a number of beakers, and to each is added an increasing increment of a solution of the coagulant used in the plant. The stirrers which are all attached to a common rotating shaft are speeded up to simulate the flash mix and then operated at a slower rate similar to the action in the flocculation basin. After a period of 15 min, or a time comparable to the detention time in the flocculator, the analyst notes which jar contains the best appearing floc. The coagulant dose, pH, and temperature are determined. The jar test is performed soon after the collection of the sample to avoid a raise in temperature over that of the plant influent. The test should be repeated as aften as necessary to compensate coagulant dosage for changes in the turbidity or chemical content of the raw water.

### 1. Interpretation of Results

After noting which of the jars contains the best floc, the analyst advises the plant operator of the coagulant dose which was used. In addition to routine coagulation control the jar test is useful in evaluating the relative merits of various coagulants and coagulant aids. It is also helpful when designing a new filter installation to determine the kind of coagulant best suited to the characteristics of the raw water.

A valuable tool to the interpretation of coagulation tests is zeta potential measurement, a development of the early 1960's, which helps to understand and control the coagulation process. According to Riddick (25) and Bean and co-workers (26) zeta potential, a measure of electrokinetic charge that surrounds suspended particulate material, is usually negative on raw water turbidity. Its value is expressed in millivolts, and it is strong enough to result in substantial mutual repulsion of particles. Floc from coagulation by aluminum salts is also usually electronegative.

By means of an electrophoresis cell the zeta potential of both floc and suspended (colloidal) material can be measured. Assume that the zeta potential of a fine aluminum floc is $-16$ mV and the colloidal material present has a similar zeta potential. The result would be repulsion of colloids by floc rather than the desired attraction. But suppose that the zeta potential of the floc could be raised to $-7$ or, maybe better near 0 mV. There would then be an attraction of floc for the still negatively charged suspended material, and heavier, more easily settled clumps would result. This raising of zeta potential can be accomplished by increasing the alum dosage, but by so doing it may also deplete alkalinity to an undesirable level. It is at this point where the polyelectrolytes are useful. They may be added to increase the zeta potential of the floc with little change in pH or alkalinity.

Present practice suggests the use of zeta potential as an adjunct to the jar test. The limitations of the coagulant aids must also be kept in mind.

This discussion illustrates the second principle of interpreting the results of analytical chemistry in the control of a segment of the water treatment process. The result of the determination is applied in governing some facet of treatment which in itself is designed to cope with variable conditions.

## H. COLOR

Color in a water supply is caused by iron and manganese, peat bogs, decaying vegetable material, and certain industrial wastes. An example is a stream which receives the liquid wastes of a tannery and a sulfite paper pulp mill; the reaction between the two produces compounds which are high in color. Color is objectionable in the manufacture of textiles and paper and to the water consumer, but in some areas natural water of high color is used without treatment. The test for color consists of visually comparing a water sample with a set of color standards. Color may also be determined by a spectrophotometric procedure (75).

### 1. Interpretation of Results

At this point the third principle of interpreting analytical results is introduced. It consists of a comparison of the results of an analysis with some standard limit, which in many cases is established as an upper limit of concentration. In this principle it is axiomatic that the concentration of the element or chemical group or other constituent should not exceed the given limit and that values progressively lower than the limit are better, with zero content being best. Color is a good example. The writer knows of no instance where color is desirable in a water supply and the converse is equally true, namely, that a water perfectly free from color is most desirable. In public bathing places color is a safety hazard and a water that may appear colorless in a glass sometimes exhibits a deep shade when observed through the depth of a swimming pool against a light tile floor. The color test for swimming pools consists of placing a black, 6-in. disk on the floor of the pool at the deepest part and being able to see it from the pool sides.

## I. FLUORIDE

Several methods are available by which to determine drinking water fluoride content, but the colorimetric procedures are considered to be the most reliable at the time of this writing (76). Several depend upon the reaction between the fluoride ion and a mixture of zirconyl chloride octahydrate and alizarin red S after the latter reagents have formed a reddish-violet lake. The fluoride ion decolorizes the lake by forming a colorless anion according to reaction (43).

$$6F^- + Zr^{4+} \rightarrow ZrF_6^- \tag{43}$$

The reaction occurs in an acid solution and decolorization is in proportion to the fluoride ion concentration. As there are several substances which at various concentrations may interfere with the fluoride test it is sometimes necessary to distil the sample before adding the reagents. The fluoride ion minus the objectable substances passes over into the distillate. The analysis procedures are applicable to both naturally occurring fluoride ion and that which is added mechanically to a water supply; mention is made of this for it is sometimes charged that there is some difference between the two.

## 1. Interpretation of Results

Interest in the fluoride analysis stems from its public health importance. The approach to the interpretation of results is therefore by comparison with standards in which limits are placed for optimum, as well as maximum, values. This is a variation of the principle of interpretation discussed under Section H-1 as, in addition to controlling fluoride ion so that it does not exceed an upper concentration, an attempt is made to adjust it to a value which is useful in the control of dental decay Additional material on interpretation is included with the discussion of fluoride in this chapter under the *Drinking Water Standards*.

## J. HARDNESS

For many years the test for hardness was based upon its soap combining capacity and it was commonly called the soap test. It depended upon adding increments of a standard soap solution to a sample until, after repeated shaking, a lasting suds appeared on the surface of the water. This obviously left something to be desired as an analytical procedure, but it was quite in keeping with the reason for doing the test in the first place, namely, that hardness has a soap-neutralizing effect. During this period, of course, hardness could be calculated by first determining the cations which caused it ($Ca^{2+}$, $Mg^{2+}$, $Al^{3+}$, etc.) and multiplying each by a factor (77) which would express their hardness contribution in terms of calcium carbonate. Obviously it was much easier to do the soap test and this was the one the water works operator depended upon. Then the EDTA method was developed by Schwarzenbach, who holds U.S. patents No. 2,583,890 and 2,583,891 covering the procedure. It functions because certain metallic ions, among them $Ca^{2+}$, and $Mg^{2+}$, the two principal causes of hardness, form a soluble chelated complex with ethylenediaminetetraacetic acid and its sodium salts. A dye, Eriochrome Black T, is the indicator used to detect the endpoint of the titration.

### 1. Interpretation of Results

There is considerable latitude in interpreting the results of a hardness determination because of the variety of special conditions and tastes which must be considered. First, there is the need to determine just what is a hard water and about this there is a difference of opinion. People used to the hard water of the north central states often find the soft water of the eastern seaboard distasteful and vice versa. However there are certain ranges which can be delineated and these are as follows:

| Hardness, mg/liter | Description |
|---|---|
| 0–40 | Soft |
| 40–100 | Moderately hard |
| 100–300 | Hard |
| 300–500 | Very hard |
| 500–up | Extremely hard |

These are the writer's opinions and it must be kept in mind that others may have a different scale of values. One thing, however, is observable, which is that an industry of manufacturing home-water softeners is flourishing and they are being sold throughout the country because the housewife, and often her husband, has become convinced of the desirability of the soft water. Municipal softening plants are used widely.

There is no mention of hardness among the limits of the *Public Health Service Drinking Water Standards* and so there is no guiding figure there. Recently, it has been suggested by some investigators (78–80), that hardwater may actually be beneficial to health, but it is not clear whether the relationships are due to the hardness itself or to some element associated with hardness.

It has already been cited that a water free from hardness is necessary for certain industrial processes, notably the production of steam and hot water.

### K. HYDROGEN ION (pH)

If there is any water supply test and theory about which the analytical chemist should need no further instruction, it would probably be hydrogen ion concentration. The principles which govern its behavior in chemistry generally are equally applicable to the water supply field, and the methods for measuring it are similar. It is difficult, however, to overemphasize the importance which pH has come to play in the many water conditioning and distribution practices. Part of this is perhaps due to the simplicity of making the test, but it is more due to the fact that so many of the chemical reactions employed in water treatment are dependent upon pH and that it is the simplest indicator of whether a basic change has occurred in water quality. It is therefore not strange to find that the pH determination is advocated as a screening measure in the detection of chemical warfare agents (81). Hydrogen ion concentration in water is measured by the glass electrode method and by use of a variety of dyes that change colors in proportion to hydrogen ion concentration. Some of these are as follows:

| Name of dye | pH range | Color change |
| --- | --- | --- |
| Methyl red | 4.4–6.0 | Red to yellow |
| Chlorphenol red | 5.2–6.8 | Yellow to red |
| Brom thymol blue | 6.0–7.6 | Yellow to blue |
| Phenol red | 6.8–8.4 | Yellow to red |
| Cresol red | 7.2–8.8 | Light brown to red |
| Thymol blue | 8.0–9.6 | Yellow to blue |
| Thymol phthalein | 9.2–10.6 | Colorless to blue |

## 1. Interpretation of Results

The results of pH tests must be evaluated in the light of the requirements of the process or other chemical analysis in which pH plays a part. The importance of pH in chlorination has already been discussed. Coagulation occurs best in the acid range of pH values and corrosion control best in the decidedly alkaline portion of the pH scale. Marked changes in hydrogen ion concentration over the norm for any given point in a treatment or water distribution system are indicative of chemical changes, some of which could be harmful and all of which should be investigated.

## L. IRON

Iron is determined by first reducing $Fe^{3+}$ to $Fe^{2+}$ by heating with hydrochloric acid and hydroxylamine ($NH_2OH \cdot HCl$). Two chelating agents are utilized to produce color changes which are in proportion to the iron concentration and which may be observed visually in Nessler tubes or by use of a spectrophotometer. The first reagent, used for total iron determination, is phenanthroline ($C_{12}H_8N_2 \cdot H_2O$) three molecules of which chelate each atom of Fe and form a red–orange complex. The second is 2,2′,2″-tripyridine, of which two molecules chelate an Fe atom and produce a reddish-purple color.

## 1. Interpretation of Results

Iron occurs in ground waters in either or both the ferrous and ferric states, but upon being exposed to the atmosphere the ferrous iron is oxidized and hydrolyzes to form ferric hydroxide precipitate. As such it is most objectionable as a stain on laundry and plumbing fixtures. Iron oxide from corroded iron distribution systems gives rise to the condition called "red water," which does the same thing. The results of the iron test are compared to some standard below which these objectionable conditions are not noticeable. The Public Health Service recommends an upper limit for iron of 0.3 mg/liter and the Quality Water Committee of the American Water Works Association sets an even lower standard of 0.1 mg/liter. These limits are not health related, but have been established for aesthetic reasons.

## M. MANGANESE

This element is the trouble-twin of iron when it comes to the formation of stains, but manganese, fortunately, is not as widespread in its occurrence. It is determined colorimetrically after the manganous forms have been oxidized to the permanganate.

## 1. Interpretation of Results

Hem states that the amount of manganese in most natural waters is less than 0.20 mg/liter (82), which is quite in contrast to iron which may reach concentrations of several milligrams per liter. However, because of its more serious staining characteristics and impairment of the taste of tea and coffee (83), a much lower limit has been prescribed for it, namely, 0.05 mg/liter (84).

## N. ODOR

Odor is usually linked with taste, and many people find it hard to differentiate between the taste and odor of a water supply. As there are four true taste sensations (85), bitter, sour, salty and sweet, it is most likely that the reaction would be caused by odor. *Standard Methods* lists 8 major groups and 14 subgroups of odors by which this quality of water is judged. Odor is measured according to a scale of numerical values called "threshold odor numbers." These are calculated as the ratio by which the sample is diluted with odor-free water so that the odor of the sample is barely detectable.

## 1. Interpretation of Results

Although there may be some odors which would be pleasant in drinking water, the author is not aware of them. Odor, together with color and turbidity constitute the sources of complaints most often received in a water company office. The odor test is subjective and the results vary from observer to observer; for this reason a panel of testers is desirable in critical cases as individual variations of observation are thus compensated. As a standard reference is made to the maximum threshold odor number of 3 prescribed by the *Public Health Service Drinking Water Standards*.

## O. RESIDUE (TOTAL DISSOLVED SOLIDS)

Residue is classified in three ways: total, filtrable or dissolved, and nonfiltrable or suspended. Total residue is obtained by evaporating a suitably sized sample in a weighed dish and noting the gain in weight of the dish after it has heated in a drying oven. Dissolved solids are measured by first filtering the sample through a membrane or a paper filter and proceeding in the same manner, and the nonfiltrable residue may be calculated by subtracting the filtrable from the total.

## 1. Interpretation of Results

A rule of thumb which may be applied to interpreting the results of the residue determinations is: the lower, the better. Waters which are high in total dissolved mineral substances are objectionable both to water consumers and the manufacturers of many commodities. For this reason a limit of 500 mg/liter has been established for drinking water.

## P. TURBIDITY

The test for turbidity is another of those water analyses, or rather estimations, in which the results are expressed not in the precise milligrams per liter terminology, but rather in a standard unit (su) which is related to the length of a path of light. The officially prescribed method for measurement (86) is the standard candle turbidimeter, and an error of measurement is permitted. Individual variations occur between observers due to the visual nature of the test.

## 1. Interpretation of Results

Turbidity of water is caused by suspended material of both inorganic and organic nature. The turbidity of a single stream may vary from less than 1 su during periods of low flow to several hundred and even thousands of units when there are flood conditions. For this reason, and because surface waters are subject to bacterial contamination, they should receive filtration. A properly operated filter plant can produce water in which turbidity is consistently below 1 su, and this should be the goal of the water plant operator. However, because all waters are not filtered and because even a filtered water may acquire turbidity in the distribution system a limit of 5 su has been recommended by the Public Health Service for interstate carrier water supplies.

This section brings to a close the discussion of those analyses which are more commonly performed in the operation of a water supply system or plant. There are several others which are useful in plant quality control under certain conditions and among these are aluminum, ammonia, dissolved oxygen, calcium, phosphate, sodium, and silica. These are the subject of the following section.

# VI. OTHER ANALYSES OFTEN USED

## A. ALUMINUM

The analysis for aluminum utilizes the ability of that element to unite with an ammonium salt of aurin tricarboxylic acid and form a red to pink color. A series of aluminum standards are prepared and standards and sample are subjected to the same reagents. The color of the sample can be compared to the color of the standards by use of Nessler tubes. A more accurate method is to use a photometric device to determine the light transmittance of the sample, which is then compared with a curve of light transmittance values versus milligrams of aluminum prepared from the standard solutions.

### 1. Interpretation of Results

Aluminum is found in nearly all natural waters because this element is the third in abundance among the elements making up the earth's crust. However, the concentrations are not usually very striking. The usefulness of the aluminum test occurs in a filter plant which utilizes aluminum coagulants. It is a measure of the carryover of flocculating agents onto the filters or beyond into the clear well and distribution system.

## B. AMMONIA

Ammonia and its oxidized forms, nitrite and nitrate, have, along with chlorides, long formed the backbone of the sanitary chemical analysis of water. Each represents a stage in the so-called ammonia cycle which can indicate a progression in sewage contamination, with ammonia being the sign of fresh pollution, nitrite rather recent contamination, and nitrate the indicator of pollution in the past. For this reason analytical chemists have developed several methods for the determination of these substances. The procedure for ammonia in low concentrations involves the distillation of the water sample whereupon the $NH_3$ passes over into the distillate, and this is then processed with the final addition of Nessler reagent. This mixture of $HgI_2$ and $KI$, in the presence of ammonia, produces a characteristic yellow to brown color. A series of standard ammonia solutions is also Nesslerized, and the color of the sample test is compared with that of the standards utilizing a spectro- or filter photometer or by direct observation in Nessler tubes.

## 1. Interpretation of Results

Ammonia in a water supply can be indicative of things other than sewage contamination. It can result from the reduction of higher nitrogen compounds, from industrial wastes, and from anhydrous ammonia fertilizer. It is therefore unwise to assume that an ammonia content is positive evidence of human waste products, but when it is found in naturally occurring ground water the cause of it should be ascertained. This is one of the reasons for the sanitary survey of water supplies conducted by sanitary engineers. As cited above, ammonia is added to some water supplies deliberately in order to produce, with chlorine, long lasting chloramine disinfectants. A natural water, high in ammonia, will have a high chlorine demand and it will be necessary to add substantial amounts of chlorine before a free chlorine residual can be produced. The interpretation of the results of the ammonia determination is therefore based upon a large number of considerations. The discussion on chlorination should be reviewed.

## C. DISSOLVED OXYGEN

Dissolved oxygen may be determined by the azide-modified Winkler method, which is suitable for most conditions of naturally occurring water or in plant control, or by the permanganate procedure when the water is high in iron, as in the case of acid mine drainage. Other tests are also described in *Standard Methods*. Samples for the dissolved oxygen analysis must be collected carefully with a sampling device so arranged that there will be a minimum of mixture of oxygen in the sample bottle with the water being sampled. See Fig. 29 on p. 405 of the 12th edition of *Standard Methods for the Examination of Water and Waste Water*.

## 1. Interpretation of Results

The presence of oxygen in solution is largely beneficial. It is essential for fish life and aquatic plants and without it a water containing organic matter often becomes foul with the products of anaerobic decomposition.

Oxygen is also necessary, or at least helpful, in making water palatable. It is important to know the dissolved oxygen content of the water in the control of certain treatment processes where aeration is utilized because oxygen is important in getting rid of carbon dioxide and hydrogen sulfide. One exception to the good role which oxygen plays in water treatment and supply is its corrosive qualities. For this reason it is sometimes completely removed, particularly in the case of boiler feed waters. The results of the dissolved oxygen determination are calculated in the customary milligram per liter form, and the dissolved oxygen content of a water is often expressed as per cent saturation. Saturation is a function of water temperature and chloride content and the reader is referred to Table 25 on p. 409 of *Standard Methods* for solubility ratios in relation to these constituents.

## D. CALCIUM

It is important to determine calcium because it is one of the chief causes of water hardness and it is used in lime softening processes. Its concentration may be measured by the gravimetric procedure or by titration utilizing potassium permanganate or ethylenediaminetetraacetic acid.

### 1. Interpretation of Results

The results of the test may be used for direct calculation of the calcium contribution to total hardness. A high calcium content in naturally occurring waters is indication that they have passed through limestone. Waters which come from limestone formations are suspect for bacterial contamination because such pollution can flow for long distances through limestone crevices and caverns into a source of water supply. When the calcium carbonate saturation method is used for the control of scale and corrosion, the calcium analysis is useful in determining the amount of calcium carbonate which may be in solution. However, a better test is the calcium carbonate stability which depends upon the measurement of the water's alkalinity content (87).

## E. PHOSPHATES

Wherever phosphates are employed for the control of corrosion it is important to test for phosphate. There are analyses for both the ortho- and polyphosphate forms which sometimes occur together.

## 1. Interpretation of Results

Phosphate is an essential fertilizer, but when it appears in a water supply reservoir it can be a real nuisance, for it promotes the growth of algae and aquatic plants. Phosphate content is, although not necessarily, an indicator of water contamination by drainage from fertilized fields, certain industrial establishments, or a sewer. As in the case of evaluating the results of the ammonia test, it is necessary to employ the techniques of the sanitary survey to determine the source of high phosphate concentrations.

### F. SODIUM

The method of choice in making the analysis for sodium is the flame photometric test, as it has both speed and good sensitivity, but it is also necessary to observe certain precautions. Among these are the need to maintain constant temperature in the room housing the flame photometer and to limit the length of runs on the instrument. During a massive survey by the Public Health Service in 1964–1965 of the sodium content of some 2100 public water supplies, which produced that number of samples each quarter for a period of 2 years, it was found important to limit the length of a run to 33 standards and samples which could be done before the room temperature changed significantly (88). It is essential to avoid contamination of glassware.

## 1. Interpretation of Results

The sodium analysis may be used to check the end of a recharge cycle for ion exchange filters which are regenerated by sodium chloride. A much more important reason for doing so is because of the health significance of sodium. A sodium content of 20 mg/liter is significant to a person who is on a strict sodium restricted diet of 500 mg/day, as by drinking water at the average rate of 2.3 liters/day he would obtain 46 mg from his drinking water alone. In the above cited survey over 40% of the community water supplies sampled have a sodium content in excess of 20 mg/liter and the range of values was from 0.4 to 1900 mg/liter. An important interpretive reference point for the sodium content of any water is the medical implications of the results. Not only heart disease patients are placed on sodium restricted diets, but also some who are suffering from renal and metabolic disorders and hypertension. Sodium restriction is also important in some pregnancy cases. The medical profession of any community should be apprized of the sodium content of the public water supply in order that they may properly advise their patients.

## G. SILICA

Several procedures are prescribed (89) for silica, among which are gravimetric and colorimetric tests, one of which is dependent upon the reaction of silica with ammonium molybdate, thereby producing yellow molybdosilicic acid.

### 1. Interpretation of Results

Silica is a most undesirable constituent of water which will be used in the production of steam, and such water, at the time of introduction into the boiler, should be free from this element. Sometimes silica in the form of sodium silicate is used for corrosion control because it can, under the right circumstances, form a dense, hard coating on the interior of metal pipes. Silica may be encountered in most ground and surface waters and it may be added in water treatment as "activated silica," which is prepared at the treatment plant by the neutralization of sodium silicate solution with sulfuric acid, alum, or chlorine. Activated silica is used to enhance the coagulation process, but it should be so applied, and it can be so applied, that there is no increase in the silica content of the water passing through the plant. The silica test, therefore, is a useful control in the use of activated silica.

This concludes the discussion of those chemical analyses which are frequently used in the control of water treatment plants. There are others which may be required at some plants or under special conditions, and methods for performing them will be found in the standard texts.

In the routine operation of a water supply, many of the constituents of water which are harmful to health may be removed, although they are not necessarily removed, and it is also possible that some may be introduced. It is necessary at periodic intervals to make a complete chemical evaluation of drinking water to determine whether it meets health quality standards. Also there is now a set of water quality criteria (90) which has been recommended by a committee of the American Water Works Association and which, if met, constitutes evidence that the water can be called a quality water. Still a third set of widely used (outside of the U.S.) water quality criteria is the *International Standards for Drinking Water* (91) promulgated by the World Health Organization. All three sets of standards cover similar water constituents, and the limits prescribed by each are found in Table VII. Before proceed-

TABLE VII
Comparison of Limits from Three Sets of Drinking Water Quality Limits

| Class and kind of water quality criteria | PHS drinking water standards. | International standards for drinking water 1963[a]. | AWWA task group 2225M ideals. |
|---|---|---|---|
| Biological | | | |
| Coliform organisms | 1.0/100 ml | 10/100[b] ml | 0.1/100 ml |
| Total count | —[c] | cited, but no limit | — |
| Macroscopic organisms | — | — | 0 |
| Viruses | — | — | — |
| Physical | | | |
| Color (units) | 15 | 5 | 3 |
| Odor (T.O. No.) | 3[d] | e | — |
| Taste | d | e | None |
| Turbidity (units) | 5 | 5 | 0.1 |
| Chemical[f] | | | |
| Alkyl benzene sulfonate (ABS) | 0.05[g] | 0.5 | 0.2 |
| Aluminum (Al) | — | — | 0.05 |
| Arsenic (As) | 0.01[g]–0.05[h] | 0.05[i] | 0.01 |
| Barium (Ba) | 1.0[h] | 1.0[i] | 0.5 |
| Cadmium (Cd) | 0.01[h] | 0.01[i] | 0.01 |
| Calcium (Ca) | — | 75 | — |
| Carbon alcohol extract (CAE) | — | — | 0.1 |
| Carbon chloroform extract (CCE) | 0.2[g] | 0.2 | 0.04 |
| Chloride (Cl$^-$) | 250[g] | 200 | — |
| Chromium hexavalent (Cr$^6$) | 0.05[h] | 0.05[i] | 0.01 |
| Copper (Cu) | 1.0[g] | 1.0 | 0.2 |
| Cyanide (CN) | 0.01[g] 0.2[h] | 0.2[i] | 0.01 |
| Fluoride (F) | 0.8 to 1.7[g] 1.4 to 2.4[h] | 1.0 to 1.5 | 0.7 to 1.2 |
| Hardness (as CaCO$_3$) | — | — | 80 |
| Hydrogen ion (pH) | — | 7.0 to 8.5 | — |
| Iron (Fe) | 0.3[g] | 0.3 | 0.05 |
| Lead (Pb) | 0.05[h] | 0.05[i] | 0.05 |
| Magnesium (Mg) | — | 50 | — |
| Magnesium Sodium sulfate | — | 500 | — |
| Manganese (Mn) | 0.05[g] | 0.1 | 0.01 |
| Nitrate (NO$_3$) | 45 | 45 | 23 |
| Phenol | 0.001[g] | 0.001 | 0.0005 |
| Selenium (Se) | 0.01[h] | 0.01[i] | 0.01 |
| Silver (Ag) | 0.05[h] | — | 0.02 |
| Sulfate (SO$_4$) | 250[g] | 200 | — |
| Total dissolved solids | 500 | 500 | — |
| Zinc | 5.0 | 5.0 | 1.0 |
| Radiochemical[j] | | | |
| Strontium-90 (Sr-90) | 10[k] | 30 | 5 |
| Radium-226 (Ra-226) | 3[k] | 10 | 3 |
| Gross beta | 1000[k] | 1000 | 100 |

[a] Unless otherwise indicated, this is the recommended limit; much higher acceptable limits are frequently stated.

[b] In untreated water in 90% of the samples examined in any one year. In treated water 1.0/100 ml is recommended.

[c] Indicates no requirement.

[d] Inoffensive.

[e] Unobjectionable.

[f] All figures except pH are in parts per million (mg/l).

[g] Recommended.

[h] Mandatory.

[i] Tolerance limits; this is comparable to the mandatory limit of the PHS Standards.

[j] Values are in picocuries per liter.

[k] For full interpretation refer to 1962, *Public Health Service Drinking Water Standards*.

ing to a discussion of the *Public Health Service Standards* a brief background will be given of the reasons for them and of the increasing prominence of chemical limits in them.

## H. BASES FOR QUALITY STANDARDS

The *Public Health Service Drinking Water Standards* have a history beginning in 1914. In that year a commission of public health leaders appointed by the Surgeon General made its report to the Secretary of the Treasury, Mr. W. G. McAdoo, who promulgated it as the standards which must be met by common carriers furnishing water for passengers in interstate traffic. These first, official drinking water standards of the United States prescribed only limits of bacteriological quality, but reference was made to the subject of physical quality. The Commission saw its problem as that of recommending the following requirements (92):

*1.* "That water supplies conforming to the prescribed requirements shall be free from injurious effects upon the human body and free from offensiveness to the sense of sight, taste, or smell."

*2.* "That supplies of the quality required shall be obtainable by common carriers without prohibitive expense."

*3.* "That the examinations necessary to determine whether a given water supply meets the requirements shall be as few and as simple as consistent with the end in view."

The *Standards* were first revised in 1925 and then in 1942, 1946, and 1962.

A section on source and protection was added in 1925 (93), and limits for copper, iron, lead, magnesium, sulfates, chlorides, total dissolved solids, and carbonates were incorporated. In the 1942–1946 (94) revisions, the chemical list was extended to 15 elements and chemical groups. By 1962 the number of chemicals cited in the *Standards* had grown to 23 and included for the first time were barium (Ba), cadmium (Cd), radium (Ra-226), silver (Ag), strontium (Sr-90), cyanide (CN), nitrates ($NO_3$), alkyl benzene sulfonate (ABS), carbon chloroform extract (CCE), and gross beta. Thus from 1914 to 1962 the major emphasis of the *Drinking Water Standards* was shifting from biological to chemical water quality criteria.

A chemical limit in drinking water is determined mostly on the basis of its toxicity or its adverse physiological effect. This is an interesting concept because it is essentially a negative approach. For example, a limit of 0.05 ppm is prescribed for lead. This means that toxicological and physiological data have shown that there could not be harmful effects upon an individual's health if he drank water over a lifetime at 4.5 pints/day with that much lead in it. On the basis of this reasoning, it is also evident that water containing less than 0.05 ppm lead must be considered a higher quality water with respect to lead, and the highest quality water with respect to lead would be one with no lead in it at all. This reasoning lies behind most of the trace element and chemical group limits in the *Standards* and also the limits for color, taste and odor, and turbidity.

Of growing significance is the positive concept of establishing a chemical limit at which an element will be beneficial to health. The outstanding example to date has been the discovery and application of the fact that about one part per million of the element fluorine, as fluoride ion ($F^-$), in drinking water is effective in reducing dental caries. The 1962 *Drinking Water Standards* have, for the first time, included a range of recommended fluoride concentrations which are optimum under the stated conditions of air temperatures.

## VII. EXAMINATIONS REQUIRED BY PUBLIC HEALTH SERVICE DRINKING WATER STANDARDS

### A. GENERAL

Several of the analyses required for comparison with the *Standards* are the same as those discussed in Section III. These are chloride, color, fluoride, iron, manganese, odor, total dissolved solids (residue), and turbidity, and the principles for determining them and all the chemicals listed in Sections III and IV were also considered. As the tests for drinking water standards are not performed as often as routine control determinations, consideration of their principles will be left to the reader to follow in the standard texts. All will be found in *Standard Methods for the Examination of Water and Waste Water*, except for barium, and that is described in the monograph by Rainwater and Thatcher as cited in Table VI.

There are a set of metallic elements in the *Drinking Water Standards* which lend themselves to rapid and accurate measurement by spectrographic means. These are arsenic, barium, cadmium, chromium,* copper, iron, lead, manganese, silver, and zinc. Developments in emission spectrography have lead to the development of direct reading, dial-the-element

---

* Total chromium. The standard is for hexavalent chromium ($Cr^{6+}$).

equipment, with which these elements and 11 other trace elements can be determined simultaneously. A photographic plate is also produced with each run so that a permanent record of the results can be preserved. The sensitivity of the emission spectrograph permits measurement of elements in the parts per billion range ($\mu$g/liter), but it has one important disadvantage. Because of the interference caused by elements which cause bright spectral lines, there are many occasions when it is possible to report a result only in terms of "less than." Although this usually satisfies the accuracy needed to compare results with limits in drinking water standards, it leaves much to be desired when attempting to apply the data in research. The atomic absorption method overcomes much of this uncertainty.

Atomic absorption adapts flame emission spectrography by taking advantage of the large number of neutral or ground-state atoms in the flame as contrasted to the atoms which are so excited that they emit light. The ground-state atoms absorb light of wavelength equal to that which they would emit if ignited. This light is furnished by cathode lamps which are specific for the element being determined, and the amount of light absorbed is proportional to the number of metal atoms present and it is measured by a photomultiplier tube. Early atomic absorption devices were limited to determining one element at a time, but once the desired tube was in place a large number of tests for that element could be conducted within a short time period. Later improvements have made it possible to mount several tubes on a holder so that as many as 10 elements can be identified simultaneously. When utilizing the single tube technique it is possible to determine an element precisely with a sensitivity of 1 ppb by direct aspiration and beyond this by concentration of the sample.

Another new method for determining the elements is neutron activation, but this has so far been used little in water supply work.


## B. INTERPRETATION OF RESULTS

The interpretation of the results of the water supply analyses performed to determine if water conforms to the limits of drinking water standards related to health must be done in the light of the health considerations upon which the standards were selected and of the limits themselves. The public, and individual, health reasons for the *Public Health Service Drinking Water Standards* will now be considered. A glance at Table VII will show the reader that all three sets of drinking water standards cover essentially the same elements. The two later ones

(*International Standards* and AWWA criteria) used the *Public Health Service Standards* as a base and modified them.

It is also helpful in interpreting the results of analyses to know what average values and range of values are encountered elsewhere. With the three parameters of (*1*) limiting value, (*2*) reason for limiting value, and (*3*) experience with other water supplies, the analytical chemist can form an opinion as to the significance of his work. Table VIII contains the elements and chemical groups of the *Public Health Service Drinking Water Standards,* their chemical symbol, a brief digest of information on their effects upon health, limiting values, and their occurrence in a group of over 130 United States public, finished, drinking water supplies.

Examples of how this table may be used are as follows: (*1*) Assume that a test for arsenic gives a result of 0.3 mg/liter. Arsenic is noted to be a serious systemic poison and there is a mandatory limit set for it of 0.05 mg/liter. The analyst should determine if the results were a chance occurrence by immediately obtaining another sample and if the high arsenic content was found again he should advise against further use of the supply. He would note also that the average for several other water supplies was less than 0.01 mg/liter. (*2*) A sample for zinc is run and the concentration of that element is found to be 7.3 mg/liter. It is noted in Table VIII that zinc is, in small amounts, an element which is essential to health and that the limit of 5.0 mg/liter allows some latitude for judgment because it is a limit not to be exceeded where other more suitable supplies are or can be made available. Also the range for several other supplies is 0.06–7.0 mg/liter. There would not be any cause for alarm, but still an investigation should be made to determine the source of this rather high amount of zinc, for the average of several supplies is only 1.33 mg/liter. (*3*) Sulfates in a well water supply are determined to be 130 mg/liter. This is less than half the recommended limit and well within the range of 0–320 ppm. The supply shows evidence of dissolved minerals, but is not harmful to drink. Further guidance in the interpretation of results is afforded by Table IX, which provides information on the frequency distribution of the results of over 100 analyses for the chemicals which are listed in Table VIII. The samples were collected during 1960–1961 from public water supplies randomly distributed across the United States. Comparison of an analytical result with the data in the intervals will allow the chemist to determine how his result compares with the frequency distribution of a larger number of analytical results.

Reference should be made to the Appendix of the *Public Health Ser-*

TABLE VIII

Public Health Significance of Certain Chemicals and Their Occurrences
in Interstate Carrier Water Supplies

| Chemical element or group | Symbol | Effect upon health | 1962 PHS drinking water standards limit, mg/liter | Occurrence in interstate carrier water supplies, mg/liter[a] | |
|---|---|---|---|---|---|
| | | | | Average | Range |
| Alkyl benzine sulfonate | ABS | PHS limit gives a safety factor of 15,000; not highly toxic | 0.5[b] | 0.054 | 0–0.640 |
| Arsenic | As | Serious systemic poison; 100 mg usually causes severe poisoning; is cumulative and causes chronic effects | 0.01[b] 0.05[c] | 0.01[d] | 0–0.10 |
| Chloride | Cl | Limit set for taste reasons | 250[b] | 41 | 1.0–490 |
| Copper | Cu | Body needs copper at level of about 1 mg/day for adults; not a health hazard except when large amounts are ingested | 1[b] | 0.03 | 0–0.600 |
| Carbon chloroform extract | CCE | At limit stated, organics in water are not considered a health hazard | 0.2[b] | 65 | 7–267 |
| Cyanide | CN | Rapid fatal poison, but limit set provides safety factor of about 100 | 0.01[b] 0.2[c] | [e] | [e] |
| Fluoride | F⁻ | Beneficial in small amounts; above 2250 mg dose can cause death | 0.8–1.7[bg] 1.4–2.4[cg] | 0.69 | 0–10.0 |
| Nitrate | NO₃ | Excess amounts can cause methemoglobinemia in infants | 45[b] | 1.6 | 0.0–19.0 |
| Sulfate | SO₄ | Above 750 mg/liter usually has laxative effects | 250[b] | 57.9 | 0.0–279 |
| Zinc | Zn | Zinc is beneficial in that a child needs 0.3 mg/kg/day; 675–2280 mg/liter may be an emetic | 5[b] | 1.33[d] | 0.06[f]–7.0[f] |
| *Trace elements* Barium | Ba | Fatal dose is 550–600 mg as the chloride; is a muscle, including heart, stimulant | 1.0[c] | 0.049 | 0.0007–0.9 |
| Cadmium | Cd | 13–15 ppm in food has caused illness | 0.01[c] | 0.008[d] | 0.0004[f]–0.06[f] |
| Chromium | Cr⁶⁺ | Limit provides a safety factor; carcinogenic when inhaled | 0.05[c] | 0.003[d] | 0.0003[f]–0.040 |
| Lead | Pb | Serious, cumulative, body poison | 0.05[c] | 0.017[d] | 0.001–0.400 |
| Selenium | Se | Toxic to both humans and animals | 0.01[c] | 0.008[d] | 0–0.01 |
| Silver | Ag | Can produce irreversible, adverse cosmetic changes | 0.05[c] | 0.13[d] | 0–2 |
| Radium-226 | Ra-225 | A bone-seeking, internal alpha emitter which can destroy bone marrow | 3 pc/liter[g] | 1.21 pc/liter[d] | 0.5[f]–28.8 pc/liter |
| Strontium-90 | Sr-90 | A bone-seeking, internal beta emitter | 10 pc/liter[g] | 1.0 pc/liter | 0.1–3.3 pc/liter |

[a] Analyses made by Water Quality Section Laboratory, Basic Data Branch, Division of Water Supply and Pollution Control.
[b] Not to be exceeded where other more suitable supplies are or can be made available.
[c] Exceeding constitutes grounds for rejection of the supply.
[d] True average significantly less than shown due to significant numbers of "less than" values in the results.
[e] Nationwide data not available.
[f] Less than.
[g] Consult 1962 *Public Health Service Drinking Water Standards* for interpretation.

TABLE VIIIA

Public Health Significance of Certain Trace Elements in Finished Drinking Water[c]

| Chemical element | Symbol | Effect upon health | Occurrence in interstate carrier water supplies, mg/liter | |
|---|---|---|---|---|
| | | | Average | Range |
| Antimony | Sb | Similar to arsenic, but less acute; recommended limit not to exceed 0.1 mg/liter; routinely below 0.05 mg/liter; over long time periods below 0.01 mg/liter | $0.025^a$ | $0.001^a–0.1^a$ |
| Beryllium | Be | Poisonous in some of its salts in occupational exposure | $0.00013^a$ | $0.00001–0.0007^a$ |
| Bismuth | Bi | A heavy metal in the arsenic family; avoid in water supplies | $0.013^a$ | $0.00007^a–0.07^a$ |
| Boron | B | Little known about toxic properties | 0.1 | 0–1.0 |
| Cobalt | Co | Beneficial in small amounts; about 7 mug/day | $0.0056^a$ | $0.0003^a–0.03^b$ |
| Molybdenum | Mo | Necessary for plants and ruminants; excessive intakes may be toxic to higher animals; acute or chronic effects not well known | $0.0096^a$ | $0.0004^a–0.2$ |
| Nickel | Ni | May cause dermatitis in sensitive people; doses of 30–73 mg $NiSO_4\cdot6H_2O$ have produced toxic effects | $0.0117^a$ | $0.0004^a–0.04$ |
| Tin | Sn | Long used in food containers without known harmful effects | $0.006^a$ | $0.0003^a–0.03$ |
| Vanadium | V | Some evidence that vanadium may be beneficial with respect to heart disease | $0.006^a$ | $0.0004^a–0.07$ |

[a] Less than.

[b] Not an interstate carrier water supply.

[c] Elements not in PHS Drinking Water Standards.

vice *Drinking Water Standards* for detailed discussions of the reasons for the selection of the limiting values.

The reader is encouraged to make up his own tables of interpretation for the limits of the *International Standards for Drinking Water* and the *Quality Water Criteria* of the American Water Works Association by utilizing the limits which are given in Table VII. He will then be in a position to evaluate results of overseas water sample analyses or to determine whether a given water meets quality water standards.

There are a series of trace elements which appear in water supply and for which analyses may sometimes be made. As yet they do not appear in any published drinking water standards, but they are the object of considerable research on water quality and its effect upon health. These elements, a digest of current knowledge about their health effects, and their occurrence in over 100 United States public water supplies are shown in Table VIIIA, which may be used as a guide for chemists doing research in this area.

TABLE IX[a]

Chemical and Physical Data on U.S. Water Supplies—1961.[b]

| Upper limit for interval | No. of supplies | Upper limit for interval | No. of supplies | Upper limit for interval | No. of supplies | Upper limit for interval | No. of supplies |
|---|---|---|---|---|---|---|---|
| ABS | | Barium | | Carbon chloroform extracts | | Chromium (hexavalent 6+) | |
| Range: 0.000–0.640 | | Range: 0.0007–0.9000 | | Range: 7–267 ppb | | Range: 0.0003–0.0400 | |
| USPHS limit: 0.5 | | USPHS limit: 1.0+ | | USPHS limit: 200 ppb | | USPHS limit: 0.05+ | |
| Mean = 0.054 | | Mean = 0.0497 | | Mean = 65 ppb | | Mean = 0.0033 | |
| No. of "less than" | | No. of "less than" | | | | No. of "less than" | |
| values = 12 | | values = 18 | | | | values = 141 | |
| 0.024 | 67 | 0.0099 | 31 | 019 ppb | 16 | 0.0009 | 27 |
| 0.049 | 43 | 0.0199 | 24 | 039 ppb | 33 | 0.0019 | 23 |
| 0.074 | 26 | 0.0299 | 33 | 059 ppb | 45 | 0.0029 | 45 |
| 0.099 | 10 | 0.0399 | 12 | 079 ppb | 20 | 0.0039 | 20 |
| 0.124 | 3 | 0.0499 | 13 | 099 ppb | 29 | 0.0049 | 17 |
| 0.149 | 2 | 0.0599 | 14 | 119 ppb | 14 | 0.0059 | 9 |
| 0.174 | 3 | 0.0699 | 7 | 139 ppb | 7 | 0.0069 | 7 |
| 0.199 | 2 | 0.0799 | 4 | 159 ppb | 4 | 0.0079 | 2 |
| 0.224 | 4 | 0.0899 | 5 | 179 ppb | 1 | 0.0089 | 1 |
| 0.249 | 2 | 0.0999 | 4 | 199 ppb | 1 | 0.0099 | 3 |
| 0.274 | 1 | 0.1099 | 10 | Over | 2 | 0.0109 | 7 |
| 0.299 | 0 | Over | 6 | | | Over | 2 |
| Over | 2 | | | Total: | 172 | | |
| | | Total: | 163 | | | Total: | 163 |
| Total: | 165 | | | | | | |
| Arsenic | | Cadmium | | Chloride | | Copper | |
| Range: 0.0000–0.1010 | | Range: 0.0004–0.0600 | | Range: 1.0–490.0 | | Range: 0.00000–0.60000 | |
| USPHS limit 0.01 | | USPHS limit: 0.01+ | | USPHS limit: 250 | | USPHS limit: 1.0 | |
| 0.05+ | | Mean = 0.0082 | | Mean = 41.2 | | Mean = 0.02973 | |
| Mean = 0.0099 | | No. of "less than" | | No. of "less than" | | No. of "less than" | |
| No. of "less than" | | values = 160 | | values = 1 | | values = 23 | |
| values = 131 | | | | | | | |
| 0.0009 | 10 | 0.0024 | 29 | 29.9 | 88 | 0.00499 | 69 |
| 0.0019 | 0 | 0.0049 | 29 | 59.9 | 20 | 0.00999 | 30 |
| 0.0029 | 0 | 0.0074 | 45 | 89.9 | 5 | 0.01499 | 15 |
| 0.0039 | 0 | 0.0099 | 12 | 119.9 | 3 | 0.01999 | 0 |
| 0.0049 | 0 | 0.0124 | 28 | 149.9 | 2 | 0.02499 | 8 |
| 0.0059 | 0 | 0.0149 | 0 | 179.9 | 3 | 0.02999 | 0 |
| 0.0069 | 5 | 0.0174 | 0 | 209.9 | 0 | 0.03499 | 7 |
| 0.0079 | 1 | 0.0199 | 0 | 239.9 | 3 | 0.03999 | 0 |
| 0.0089 | 0 | 0.0224 | 11 | 269.9 | 1 | 0.04499 | 5 |
| 0.0099 | 0 | 0.0249 | 0 | 299.9 | 1 | 0.04999 | 0 |
| 0.0109 | 145 | 0.0274 | 0 | Over | 2 | 0.05499 | 7 |
| 0.0119 | 2 | 0.0299 | 0 | | | 0.05999 | 0 |
| Over | 2 | 0.0324 | 6 | Total: | 128 | 0.06499 | 4 |
| | | Over | 3 | | | Over | 18 |
| Total: | 165 | | | | | | |
| | | Total: | 163 | | | Total: | 163 |

(continued)

## TABLE IX (continued)

| Upper limit for interval | No. of supplies | Upper limit for interval | No. of supplies | Upper limit for interval | No. of supplies | Upper limit for interval | No. of supplies |
|---|---|---|---|---|---|---|---|
| Flouride | | Lead | | Nitrate | | Sulfate | |
| Range: 0.00–10.00 USPHS limit: 1.4–2.4[d] Mean = 0.69 | | Range: 0.0010–0.4000 USPHS limit: 0.05+ Mean = 0.0172 No. of "less than" values = 148 | | Range: 0.0–19.0 USPHS limit: 45 Mean = 1.6 No. of "less than" values = 9 | | Range: 0.0–279.0 USPHS limit: 250 Mean = 57.9 No. of "less than" values = 2 | |
| 0.09 | 3 | 0.0049 | 28 | 00.9 | 88 | 29.9 | 54 |
| 0.19 | 29 | 0.0099 | 43 | 01.9 | 19 | 59.9 | 29 |
| 0.29 | 17 | 0.0149 | 38 | 02.9 | 9 | 89.9 | 16 |
| 0.39 | 10 | 0.0199 | 0 | 03.9 | 2 | 119.9 | 9 |
| 0.49 | 16 | 0.0249 | 30 | 04.9 | 1 | 149.9 | 8 |
| 0.59 | 6 | 0.0299 | 0 | 05.9 | 1 | 179.9 | 3 |
| 0.69 | 11 | 0.0349 | 13 | 06.9 | 0 | 209.9 | 3 |
| 0.79 | 1 | 0.0399 | 0 | 07.9 | 2 | 239.9 | 1 |
| 0.89 | 2 | 0.0449 | 3 | 08.9 | 0 | 269.9 | 2 |
| 0.99 | 11 | 0.0499 | 0 | 09.9 | 1 | 299.9 | 1 |
| 1.09 | 19 | 0.0549 | 4 | Over | 6 | Over | 0 |
| 1.19 | 19 | Over | 4 | | | Total: | 126 |
| 1.29 | 15 | | | Total: | 129 | | |
| Over | 6 | Total: | 163 | | | | |
| Total: | 165 | | | | | | |
| Iron | | Manganese | | Selenium | | Total dissolved solids | |
| Range: 0.0030–1.0000 USPHS limit: 0.3 Mean = 0.0754 No. of "less than" values = 2 | | Range: 0.0020–1.0000 USPHS limit: 0.05 Mean = 0.0424 No. of "less than" values = 88 | | Range: 0.0000–0.0100 USPHS limit: 0.01+ Mean = 0.0079 No. of "less than" values = 150 | | Range: 4.0–1362.0 USPHS limit: 500 Mean = 286.0 | |
| 0.0099 | 16 | 0.0099 | 57 | 0.0009 | 8 | 99.9 | 16 |
| 0.0199 | 24 | 0.0199 | 30 | 0.0019 | 7 | 199.9 | 38 |
| 0.0299 | 37 | 0.0299 | 29 | 0.0029 | 1 | 299.9 | 37 |
| 0.0399 | 18 | 0.0399 | 8 | 0.0039 | 1 | 399.9 | 12 |
| 0.0499 | 11 | 0.0499 | 6 | 0.0049 | 4 | 499.9 | 8 |
| 0.0599 | 6 | 0.0599 | 4 | 0.0059 | 33 | 599.9 | 5 |
| 0.0699 | 7 | 0.0699 | 0 | 0.0069 | 0 | 699.9 | 3 |
| 0.0799 | 7 | 0.0799 | 1 | 0.0079 | 0 | 799.9 | 3 |
| 0.0899 | 3 | 0.0899 | 2 | 0.0089 | 0 | 899.9 | 1 |
| 0.0999 | 3 | 0.0999 | 3 | 0.0099 | 0 | 999.9 | 3 |
| 0.1099 | 14 | 0.1099 | 13 | Over | 111 | Over | 2 |
| Over | 16 | Over | 10 | | | Total: | 128 |
| | | | | Total: | 165 | | |
| Total: | 162 | Total: | 163 | | | | |

(continued)

## TABLE IX (continued)

| Upper limit for interval | No. of supplies | Upper limit for interval | No. of supplies | Upper limit for interval | No. of supplies |
|---|---|---|---|---|---|
| Zinc | | Color | | Strontium–90 | |
| Range: 0.06–7.00 | | Range: 0.0–40 units | | Range: 0.1–3.3 μμc/liter | |
| USPHS limit: 5 | | USPHS limit: 15 units | | USPHS limit: 10 μμc/liter | |
| Mean = 1.31 | | Mean = 3.9 units | | Mean = 1.0 μμc/liter | |
| No. of "less than" values = 157 | | No. of "less than" values = 7 | | No. of "less than" values = 8 | |
| 0.49 | 30 | Units | | 00.2 μμc/liter | 4 |
| 0.99 | 43 | 00.9 | 39 | 00.5 μμc/liter | 4 |
| 1.49 | 40 | 01.9 | 13 | 00.8 μμc/liter | 4 |
| 1.99 | 0 | 02.9 | 4 | 01.1 μμc/liter | 10 |
| 2.49 | 31 | 03.9 | 3 | 01.4 μμc/liter | 1 |
| 2.99 | 0 | 04.9 | 1 | 01.7 μμc/liter | 0 |
| 3.49 | 10 | 05.9 | 23 | 02.0 μμc/liter | 2 |
| 3.99 | 0 | 06.9 | 0 | 02.3 μμc/liter | 0 |
| 4.49 | 3 | 07.9 | 1 | 02.6 μμc/liter | 0 |
| 4.99 | 0 | 08.9 | 1 | 02.9 μμc/liter | 0 |
| 5.49 | 4 | 09.9 | 0 | Over | 2 |
| 5.99 | 0 | 10.9 | 12 | | |
| 6.49 | 1 | Over | 5 | Total | 27 |
| 6.99 | 0 | | | | |
| Over | 1 | Total: | 102 | | |
| Total: | 163 | | | | |
| Turbidity | | Odor number | | Gross beta | |
| Range: 0.00–45 units | | Range: 0.0–3.0 | | Range: 0.6–300 μμc/liter | |
| USPHS limit: 5 units | | USPHS limit: 3 | | USPHS limit: 1000 μμc/liter | |
| Mean = 2.01 units | | Mean = 0.2 | | Mean = 7.2 μμc/liter | |
| No. of "less than" values = 1 | | No. of "less than" values = 2 | | No. of "less than" values = 55 | |
| | | | | 01.9 μμc/liter | 3 |
| | | | | 02.9 μμc/liter | 15 |
| Units | | | | 03.9 μμc/liter | 67 |
| 0.99 | 61 | 00.9 | 73 | 04.9 μμc/liter | 12 |
| 1.99 | 21 | 01.9 | 8 | 05.9 μμc/liter | 10 |
| 2.99 | 8 | 02.9 | 3 | 06.9 μμc/liter | 10 |
| 3.99 | 9 | Over | 1 | | |
| 4.99 | 2 | | | 07.9 μμc/liter | 4 |
| 5.99 | 1 | Total: | 85 | 08.9 μμc/liter | 1 |
| 6.99 | 0 | | | 09.9 μμc/liter | 1 |
| 7.99 | 0 | | | 10.9 μμc/liter | 3 |
| 8.99 | 0 | | | 11.9 μμc/liter | 2 |
| 9.99 | 0 | | | 12.9 μμc/liter | 2 |
| Over | 7 | | | 13.9 μμc/liter | 0 |
| | | | | 14.9 μμc/liter | 1 |
| Total: | 109 | | | 15.9 μμc/liter | 1 |
| | | | | Over | 4 |
| | | | | Total: | 136 |

[a] Taken by permission of the American Water Works Association from "Effectiveness of Water Utility Quality Control Practices," *J. Amer. Water Works Assoc.* **54**, 1257 (October 1962).

[b] Unless otherwise designated, all values are in parts per million.

[c] Constitutes "grounds for rejection of supply" on interstate carrier water supplies.

[d] Range of twice the set of optimum values for the temperature averages stated in the Standards.

## VIII. ORGANIC CHEMICALS IN DRINKING WATER

One increasingly important category of chemicals in water supply is the organics. Only three limits in the *Drinking Water Standards* apply to them and these are for alkyl benzene sulfonate, carbon chloroform extracts (CCE), and phenols. Two are specific entities and the third is a catchall. The Advisory Committee which drew up the 1962 *Drinking Water Standards* adopted a CCE limit of 200 μg/liter and prescribed for determining CCE a method "which will afford a large measure of protection against the presence of undetected toxic materials in finished drinking water" (95). They also, however, stated that "the most desirable condition is one in which the water supply delivered to the consumer contains no organic residues" (95). Carbon chloroform extracts may contain a broad spectrum of organics, including water solubles, straight chain hydrocarbons, the simpler cyclic hydrocarbons, and some of the branched structure. Infrared spectroscopy is used for precise indentification but it is usually necessary to separate components by thin layer or gas chromatography.

Pesticides form a distinct class of organic chemicals which have become of great concern to the water works profession. The reason is their toxicity, which is the ability of a chemical to cause harm to the human body. Pesticides enter water supplies in drainage from watersheds on which there have been pest control operations, and they have also been introduced into distribution systems through cross connections. It is not known that they are reduced substantially in passing through slow sand filters, but not many communities use this kind of water treatment. Pesticides can be removed from water by conventional treatment (rapid sand filters preceded by coagulation and sedimentation), augmented when necessary by the use of activated carbon. Robeck and his co-workers at the Robert A. Taft Sanitary Engineering Center conducted extensive studies (96) on a pilot plant scale and discovered that not all pesticides respond to treatment in the same manner. Conventional treatment was effective in removing DDT, but not lindane and parathion. Chlorine and potassium permanganate were not effective with the chlorinated hydrocarbon pesticides and actually converted parathion into a more toxic compound. However, activated carbon was demonstrated to be effective with a broad spectrum of pesticides and the highest removal (greater than 99% for DDT, lindane, parathion, dieldrin, 2,4,5-T Ester and endrin) was obtained by use of a granulated, activated carbon bed at a filter rate of 0.5 gpm/ft$^3$. These results were obtained with applied pesticide doses of 10 ppb.

As of this writing a limited amount of data from conventional water treatment plants has shown that they can reduce low concentrations of certain pesticides to still lower amounts. The reduction was of the order of from 0.2 ppb to less than 0.1 ppb.

Answers to the problems of detection and measurement of pesticides are found in the field of analytical, organic chemistry, where recent improvements have been made in both measurement and sampling procedures. The techniques of chromatography make possible the identification and measurement of many members of the chlorinated hydrocarbon family of pesticides and several of the organic phosphorous group. The gas chromatograph (see chapter on gas chromatography, Part I) has been found most useful in dealing with the minute amounts of pesticides which are encountered in finished drinking water.

In examining a water sample for the presence of pesticides, it is necessary to have information on which pesticides are being sought. In other words, it is necessary that the person collecting the sample provide data on which pesticides have been used on the watershed or which are suspected in the water. Without this information a chromatograph curve may be obtained as shown in Fig. 13, where it was possible to identify only DDE, dieldrin, and endrin. Seven peaks were unidentified. A prerequisite to identifying peaks on a chromatograph curve is the preparation of a standard curve, illustrated by Fig. 14, which then places a given pesticide at a given point on the graph. The identity of a pesticide is determined by where it appears on the curve, which is a function of time, and the amount of the pesticide is calculated from the height of the peaks, which is a function of electric current.

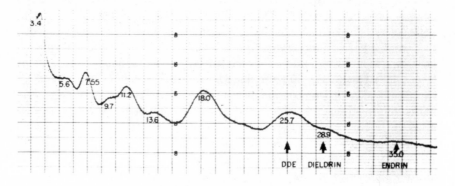

Fig. 13. Chromatograph curves showing pesticides and other organic chemicals in finished drinking water.

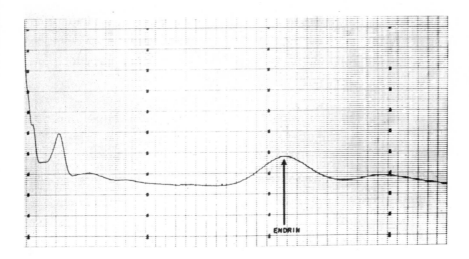

Fig. 14. Standard chromatograph curve for the pesticide endrin.

Pesticide samples can be obtained by the use of carbon filters (97), which has been the method most used up to the time of this writing. However, the recovery characteristics of this method leave something to be desired, and there has been considerable experimentation with liquid-to-liquid extraction procedures. Dr. J. E. Campbell of the Robert A. Taft Sanitary Engineering Center (PHS) has developed a liquid-to-liquid extraction technique, the prototype of which is shown by Fig. 15 and a later version by Fig. 16. The principle is to constantly feed a small stream of water from the point being sampled into and out of the device, and the organics, including pesticides, are continuously extracted by purified hexane. Aliquots of the hexane are then processed through the chromatograph.

## A. INTERPRETATION OF RESULTS

As pesticides are toxic agents dangerous to health, the interpretation of results of analyses for them is based on the principle of limits. Limits for pesticides appear in no current drinking water standards. The advisory committee which helped produce the 1962 *Public Health Service Drinking Water Standards* considered limits for both major pesticide groups, but concluded that information on them and the state of instrumentation were such that standards could not be established. However, it is recognized that conditions have changed and there was appointed

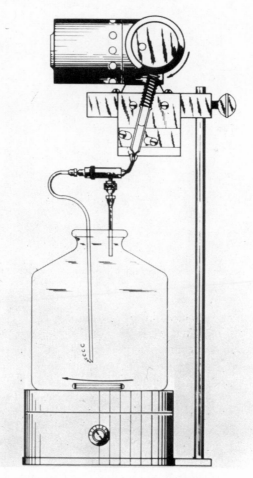

Fig. 15. Prototype of liquid-to-liquid, organics, continuous water sampler.

two years ago a new Advisory Committee on Use of the Public Health
Service Drinking Water Standards, which has devoted its meeting thus
far to the subject of pesticides in drinking water. This group appointed
a toxicological task group which has reconsidered the limits for certain
pesticides which had been considered by the 1962 committee.

These limits have been used for guidance on an interim basis in assessing the health hazards along the Mississippi River and in other areas
of the country. They are summed up below.

For the organic phosphorous group, a limit of 1.0 mg/liter of total

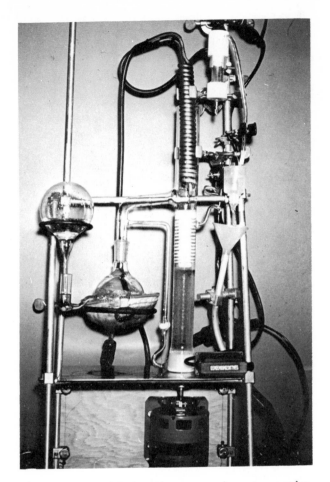

Fig. 16. Later model of continuous organics water sampler.

cholinergic organic phosphates (parent compounds and toxic degradation products) should not be exceeded. In actual practice the absence of the organic phosphorous group in any amount is considered best. A list of some of the more common organic phosphorous pesticides is as follows:

| | |
|---|---|
| Delnav | Methyl parathion |
| Demeton | Parathion |
| Diazinon | Phosdrin |
| EPN | Schradan |
| Guthion | Trithion |
| Malathion | |

Recommended limits for the chlorinated hydrocarbon group range from 0.0013 mg/liter for endrin to 0.069 mg/liter for chlordane. Some of the more common chlorinated hydrocarbon pesticides are named below:

| | |
|---|---|
| Aldrin | Endrin |
| BHC (benzene hexachloride) | Heptachlor |
| Chlordane | Methoxychlor |
| Dieldrin | Toxaphene |
| DDT | |

It is expected that the current *Public Health Service Drinking Water Standards* will be amended to incorporate specific mandatory and recommended limits for specific pesticides.

## IX. CONCLUSION

Analytical chemistry is the heart of water quality control. The writer in this discussion has attempted to show that the techniques of water treatment and analysis have progressed and are becoming ever more sophisticated. It has also been mentioned that there is a tremendous area for research. As of this writing there are signs that someday we may be able to identify and quantitate all the chemical constituents in a water sample by virtue of their molecular weight and arrangement.

Water treatment processes have changed little for some 100 years, but the future will witness new methods and new problems, which will require new analytical tools and procedures. Regardless of the analyses which will be developed and performed, it will always be necessary to interpret the results. The author would, therefore, restate the three principles of interpretation:

*1.* Results are used to determine whether there has been change in water quality from the norm for a given water supply or portion thereof.

*2.* Results are used to determine whether water quality meets stated, standard limits.

*3.* Results are used to control some treatment process, or part thereof, in which there are, or may be, changing variables.

Where examples have been used in this discussion it must be remembered that they are only guides to the experiences of practice. The practice of analytical chemistry in the field of water supply does and will present an infinite variety of combinations which will challenge and excite those chemists who enter this area of science.

REFERENCES

1. II Kings 20:20.
2. II Chronicles 32:30.
3. Herodotus, *History,* Vol. I, transl. and edited by G. Rawlinson, Appleton, New York, 1859; p. 252.
4. Frontinus, Sextus Julius, *The Two Books on the Water Supply of the City of Rome,* transl. by C. Herschel, Dana Estes & Co., Boston, 1899.
5. Baker, M. N., *The Quest for Pure Water,* American Water Works Association, New York, 1949, Chapters I–III.
6. Baker, M. N., *The Quest for Pure Water,* American Water Works Association, 1949, p. 20.
7. Graham, T., "Chemical Report On the Supply of Water to the Metropolis," *J. Chem. Soc.,* **4,** 375 (1852).
8. Baker, M. N., *The Quest for Pure Water,* American Water Works Association, New York, 1949.
9. Witt, H. M., *On A Peculiar Power Possessed by Porous Media of Removing Matter from Solution in Water, Phil. Mag. J. Sci., 4th Ser.,* **12,** 23 (1846).
10. "Glossary, Water and Wastewater Control Engineering," (APHA, ASCE, AWWA, WPCF) Report, American Water Works Association, New York, 1969.
11. Philipovich, J. B., A. P. Black, F. A. Eidsness, and T. W. Steams, "Electrophoretic Studies of Water Coagulation," *J. Amer. Water Works Assoc.,* **50,** 1467 (1958).
12. Black, A. P., and S. A. Hannah, "Electrophoretic Studies of Turbidity Removal by Coagulation with Aluminum Sulfate," *J. Amer. Water Works Assoc.,* **53,** 438 (1961).
13. Black, A. P., and D. G. Willems, "Electrophoretic Studies of Coagulation for Removal of Organic Color," *J. Amer. Water Works Assoc.,* **53,** 589 (1961).
14. Black, A. P., and Ching-lin Chen, "Electrophoretic Studies of Coagulation and Flocculation of River Sediment Suspensions with Aluminum Sulfate," *J. Amer. Water Works Assoc.,* **57,** 354 (1965).
14a. "Theory and Control of Coagulation-Flocculation," Education Committee of the American Water Works Association and the U.S. Public Health Service (June 1969). (*Note:* This contains a bibliography of 237 items on coagulation and flocculation.)
14b. Camp, T. R., "Floc Volume Concentration," *J. Amer. Water Works Assoc.,* **60,** 656 (1968).
15. "Coagulant Aids for Potable Water Treatment," *J. Amer. Water Works Assoc.,* **57,** 800 (1965).
16. Taylor, F. B., "Effectiveness of Water Utility Quality Control Practices," *J. Amer. Water Works Assoc.,* **54,** 1257 (1962).
17. *Public Health Service Drinking Water Standards—1962;* Public Health Service Publication No. 956, Superintendent of Documents, U.S. Government Printing Office, Washington, D.C., 40¢.
18. Heuper, W. C., and W. W. Payne, "Carcinogenic Effects of Adsorbates of Raw and Finished Water Supplies," *Amer. J. Clin. Pathol.,* **39,** 475 (1963).
19. Taylor, F. B., "Current Status of the Pesticide and Insecticide Problem," *J. New Engl. Water Works Assoc.,* **79,** 256 (1965).
20. *Public Health Service Drinking Water Standards— 1962,* Public Health Service

Publication No. 956, Superintendent of Documents, U.S. Government Printing Office, Washington, D.C. 40¢, p. 9.

21. Miller, L. G., "On the Composition of the Precipitate from Partly Alkalinized Solutions," *Publ. Health Rept.*, **38**, 1995 (1923).

22. Mattson, S., "Cataphoresis and the Electrical Neutralization of Colloid Materials," *J. Phys. Chem.*, **32**, 1532 (1928).

23. Black, A. P., J. E. Singley, G. P. Whittle, and J. S. Maudling, "Stoichiometry of the Coagulation of Color Causing Organic Compounds with Ferric Sulfate," *J. Amer. Water Works Assoc.* **55**, 1347 (1963).

24. Riddick, T. M., "Zeta Potential: New Tool for Water Treatment, Parts I and II," *Chem. Eng.*, **68**, 13:121 and **68**, 14:141 (1961).

25. Riddick, T. M., "Zeta Potential and Its Application to Difficult Waters," *J. Amer. Water Works Assoc.*, **53**, 1007 (1961).

26. Bean, E. L., S. J. Campbell, and F. R. Anspach, "Zeta Potential Measurements in the Control of Coagulation Chemical Doses," *J. Amer. Water Works Assoc.*, **56**, 214 (1964).

27. Stumm, W., and J. J. Morgan, "Chemical Aspects of Coagulation," *J. Amer. Water Works Assoc.*, **54**, 971 (1962).

28. Fuoss, R. M., and H. Sadek, "Mutual Interaction of Polyelectrolytes," *Science*, **110**, 552 (1949).

29. Michaels, A. S., "Aggregation of Suspensions by Polyelectrolytes," *Ind. Eng. Chem.*, **46**, 1485 (1954).

30. Black, A. P., "Current Research On Coagulation," *J. Amer. Water Works Assoc.*, **51**, 1545 (1959).

31. Johnson, C. E., "Polyelectrolytes As Coagulants and Coagulant Aids," *Ind. Eng. Chem.*, **48**, 1080 (1956).

32. Cohen, J. M., G. A. Rourke, and R. L. Woodward, "Natural and Synthetic Polyelectrolytes as Coagulant Aids," *J. Amer. Water Works Assoc.*, **50**, 463 (1958).

33. Black, A. P., A. I. Bon, A. L. Black, R. A. Boudet, and T. N. Campbell, "Effectiveness of Polyelectrolyte Coagulant Aids in Turbidity Removal," *J. Amer. Water Works Assoc.*, **51**, 247 (1959).

34. Ives, K. J., "New Concepts in Filtration. Part III: Surface Force Concepts, Experimental Concepts and Conclusions," *Water and Waste Water Eng.*, **65**, 385 (1961).

35. Hunter, R. J., and A. E. Alexander, "Surface Properties and Flow Behavior of Kaolinite, Part III: Flow of Kaolinite Sols Through a Silica Column," *J. Colloid Sci.*, **18**, 846 (1963).

36. O'Melio, C. R., and D. K. Crapps, "Some Chemical Aspects of Rapid Sand Filtration," *J. Amer. Water Works Assoc.*, **56**, 1326 (1964).

37. Grace, H. P., "Structure and Performance of Filter Media, II Performance of Filter Media in Liquid Services," *Amer. Inst. Chem. Eng. J.*, **2**, 316 (1956).

38. Hazen, A., "On Sedimentation," *Trans. Amer. Soc. Civil Eng.*, **53**, 45 (1904).

39. Baylis, J. R., "Experiences in Filtration," *J. Amer. Water Works Assoc.*, **29**, 1010 (1937).

40. Jordan, R. M., "Electrophoretic Studies of Filtration," *J. Amer. Water Works Assoc.*, **55**, 771 (1963).

41. Mackrle, V., and S. Mackrle, "Adhension in Filters," *Proc. Amer. Soc. Chem. Eng.*, **87**, SA5 (1961), p. 17.

42. Black, A. P., Swimming Pool Disinfection with Iodine, *Water Sewage Works,* **108,** 286 (July 1961).
43. Black, A. P., J. B. Lackey, and T. W. Lackey, "Effectiveness of Iodine for the Disinfection of Swimming Pool Water," *J. Amer. Public Health Assoc.,* **49,** 1060 (1959).
44. Black, A. P., R. H. Kinman, W. C. Thomas, G. Fruend, and E. D. Bird, "The Chemistry, Technology and Physiology of Iodine in Water Disinfection," paper presented at 29th Annual Educational Conference, National Association of Sanitarians, Miami Beach, June 1965.
45. Huff, C. B., H. F. Smith, W. D. Boring, and H. A. Clarke, "Study of Ultraviolet Disinfection of Water and Factors in Treatment Efficiency," *Public Health Rept.,* **80,** 695 (1965).
46. Hoover, C. P., *Water Supply and Treatment,* National Lime Association, Washington, D.C.
47. Alsentzer, H. A., "Ion Exchange in Water Treatment," *J. Amer. Water Works Assoc.,* **55,** 742 (1963).
48. Maier, F. J., and E. Bellack, "Fluorspar for Fluoridation," *J. Amer. Water Works Assoc.,* **48,** 199 (1957).
49. *Public Health Service Drinking Water Standards—1962,* Public Health Service Publication No. 956, Superintendent of Documents, U.S. Government Printing Office, Washington 25, D.C., p. 8, 30¢.
50. Maier, F. J., "Methods of Removing Fluorides from Water," *Amer. J. Publ. Health,* **37,** 1559 (1947).
51. Maier, F. J., "Defluoridation of Municipal Water Supplies," *J. Amer. Water Works. Assoc.,* **45,** 879 (1953).
52. Maier, F. J., "Partial Defluoridation of Water," *Publ. Works,* **91,** 11 (1960), p. 90.
53. "Fluoride Drinking Waters," Public Health Service Publication No. 825, Superintendent of Documents, U.S. Government Printing Office, Washington 25, D.C., 1962 $3.50.
54. Eager, J. M., "Denti di Chiaie (Chiaie Teeth)" *Publ. Health Rept.,* **16,** 2 (1901), p. 2576.
55. Kempf, G. A., and F. S. McKay, "Mottled Enamel in a Segregated Population," *Publ. Health Rept.,* **45,** 2923 (1930).
56. "Desalination Via Flash Distillation," brochure by Foster Wheeler, 1967.
57. Tidball, R. A., and R. E. Woodbury, "Methods for Scale Control in Flash Systems," paper presented before the First International Symposium on Water Desalination, Washington, D.C., 1965.
58. Hoover, C. P., *Water Supply & Treatment,* National Lime Association, Washington 5, D.C. 1962, p. 147.
59. McKee, J. E., and T. T. Wolf, *Water Quality Criteria,* The Resources Agency of California, State Water Quality Control Board, Publication No. 3-A, Sacramento, California, 1963, prepared with the assistance of the Division of Water Supply and Pollution Control/Public Health Service.
60. *Standard Methods for the Examination of Water and Waste Water,* 12th ed. APHA, AWWA, and WPCF, published by American Public Health Association, Inc. New York, 1965.
61. *Simplified Procedures for Water Examination,* AWWA M12 Simplified Laboratory Manual, American Water Works Association, New York, 1964.

62. Rosencrance, J. E., *Water Chemistry Laboratory Manual,* Division of Sanitary Engineering, West Virginia State Health Department, Charleston, W. Va., 1964.

63. Rainwater, F. H., and L. L. Thatcher, "Methods for Collection and Analysis of Water Samples," Geological Survey Water-Supply Paper 1454, Superintendent of Documents, U.S. Government Printing Office, Washington, D.C., 1960.

64. *Standard Methods for the Examination of Water and Waste Water,* 12 ed. American Public Health Association, 1965, p. 49.

65. *Simplified Procedures for Water Examination,* AWWA Manual M12, American Water Works Association, New York, 1964, p. 21.

66. Reihl, M. L., *Water Supply and Treatment (Hoover),* National Lime Association, Washington, D.C., p. 98.

67. *Public Health Service Drinking Water Standards (1946),* Public Health Service, Washington, D.C.

68. *Standard Methods for the Examination of Water and Waste Water,* 12th ed., American Public Health Association, 1965, p. 77.

69. *Standard Methods for the Examination of Water and Waste,* 12th ed., American Public Health Association, 1965, p. 78.

70. *Standard Methods for the Examination of Water and Waste,* 12th ed., American Public Health Association, 1965, p. 85.

71. Hem, J. D., "Study and Interpretation of the Chemical Characteristics of Natural Water," Geological Survey Water-Supply Paper 1473, Superintendent of Documents, U.S. Government Printing Office, Washington, D.C., 1959, p. 104.

72. *Manual for Protection of Public Water Supplies from Chemical Agents,* Health Mobilization Series, J-1, Public Health Service Publication No. 1071 J-1, Superintendent of Documents, U.S. Government Printing Office, Washington, D.C. 1965, p. 9, 15¢.

73. *Manual for Protection of Public Water Supplies from Chemical Agents,* Health Mobilization Series, J-1, Public Health Service Publication No. 1071 J-1, Superintendent of Documents, U.S. Government Printing Office, Washington, D.C. 1965, p. 77, 15¢.

74. Keilly, S., and W. W. Sanderson, "The Effect of Chlorine in Water on Enteric Viruses," *J. Amer. Publ. Health Assoc.,* 48, 1323 (1958).

75. Rainwater, F. H., and L. L. Thatcher, "Methods for Collection and Analysis of Water Samples," Geological Survey Water-Supply Paper 1454, p. 47; Superintendent of Documents, U.S. Government Printing Office, Washington D.C., 1960, $1.50.

76. *Standard Methods for the Examination of Water and Waste Water,* American Public Health Assoc., 1965, p. 135.

77. *Standard Methods for the Examination of Water and Waste Water,* American Public Health Assoc., 1965, p. 147.

78. Schroeder, H. A., "Relation between Mortality from Cardiovascular Disease and Treated Water Supplies," *J. Amer. Med. Assoc.,* 172, 1902 (1960).

79. Morris, J. H., M. D. Crawford, and J. S. Heady, "Preliminary Communication; Hardness of Local Water Supplies and Mortality from Cardiovascular Diseases in the County Boroughs of England and Wales, *Lancet,* 7182, 860 (1961).

80. Schroeder, H. A., "Relation Between Hardness of Water and Death Rates from Certain Chronic and Degenerative Diseases in the United States," *J. Chronic Diseases,* 12, 586 (1960).

81. Reference 72.

82. Hem, J. D., "Study and Interpretation of the Chemical Characteristics of Natural Water," Geological Survey Water-Supply Paper 1473, 1959, p. 68.
83. Griffin, A. E., *Manganese Removal With Chlorine and Chlorine Dioxide; J. New Engl. Water Works Assoc.,* **72,** 321 (1958).
84. *Public Health Service Drinking Water Standards—1962,* Public Health Service Publication No. 956, Superintendent of Documents, U.S. Government Printing Office, Washington, D.C., 1962, p. 7.
85. English, H. B., and A. C. English, *Comprehensive Dictionary of Psychological and Psychoanalytical Terms,* Longmans' Green and Co., New York, 1958, p. 543.
86. *Standard Methods for the Examination of Water and Wastewater;* 12th Ed. American Public Health Association, 1965, p. 312.
87. *Simplified Procedures for Water Examination,* AWWA M12 Simplified Laboratory Manual, American Water Works Association, New York, 1964, p. 21.
88. White, J. M., J. G. Wingo, L. M. Alligood, G. R. Cooper, J. Gutridge, W. Hydaker, R. T. Benack, J. W. Dening, and F. B. Taylor, "Sodium Ion in Drinking Water," *J. Amer. Dietetic Assoc.,* **50,** 1 (1967), pp. 32–36.
89. *Standard Methods for the Examination of Water and Waste Water,* 12th ed., American Public Health Association, 1965, pp. 258–266.
90. Bean, E. L., "Progress Report on Water Quality Criteria," *J. Amer. Water Works Assoc.,* **54,** 1313 (1962).
91. *International Standards for Drinking Water,* 2nd ed. World Health Organization, Columbia University Press, International Documents Service, New York, $5.25.
92. *U.S. Treasury Drinking Water Standards, 1914,* Library of Congress, Washington D.C.
93. "Report of Advisory Committee on Official Water Standards," *Publ. Health Rept.* **40,** 693 (1925).
94. "Public Health Service Drinking Water Standards, *Publ. Health Rept.* **61,** 371 (1946).
95. *Public Health Service Drinking Water Standards—1962,* Public Health Service Publication No. 956, Superintendent of Documents, U.S. Government Printing Office, Washington, D.C., Appendix p. 32.
96. Robeck, G. G., K. A. Dostal, J. M. Cohen, and J. F. Kreissl, "Effectiveness of Water Treatment Processes in Petsicide Removal, *J. Amer. Water Works Assoc.,* **57,** 181 (1965).
97. Taylor, F. B., "The Application of Carbon Chloroform Extraction Technic to Several Water Supplies," *Health Lab. Sci.,* **1,** 33 (1964).

# POTABLE AND SANITARY WATER

BY ROBERT C. KRONER AND DWIGHT G. BALLINGER,
*Physics and Chemistry Section, Federal Water
Quality Administration, Analytical Quality Control
Cincinnati, Ohio*

Contents

**Contents** (*continued*)

**Contents** (*continued*)

# I. SOURCE AND VARIETY OF DISSOLVED MATERIALS IN WATER

The composition and appearance of natural water is determined by solubilization and fragmentation of the terrain through which it flows. Soils, rocks, and vegetable matter each contribute a share to the mass of suspended and dissolved constituents which influence its properties. Soluble organic materials, however, originating from vegetable growth, do not greatly influence the chemical properties of water except in special cases, such as bog and swamp drainage. Suspended matter in the form of silt, clay, and sand is generally considered a physical property of water, which is easily removed. The dissolved minerals in water, therefore, are the determinants that shape its chemical properties.

The quantity of dissolved mineral matter in a natural water depends upon a number of factors, among which are: (*1*) the solubility of the geological deposits through which the water passes; (*2*) the length of time during which the water is in contact with the geological substrate; (*3*) special contributions from mines, oil fields, subsurface brines, agricultural activities, and municipal and industrial wastes. Snow melt, originating in mountainous areas, flowing rapidly over granite substrate may be low in dissolved minerals until it reaches an alluvial plain, after which the dissolved and suspended matter may rapidly increase. Ground water is usually higher in dissolved minerals because it remains in contact with subsurface soils and rocks for much longer periods.

The dissolved mineral materials are present in water as ions of elements such as $Na^+$, $K^+$, $Ca^{2+}$, and $Cl^-$ or radicals such as $SO_4^{2-}$, $PO_4^{3-}$, and $NH_3^+$. Some of the chemical entities produce certain effects which are measured as properties of water. For instance, Ca and Mg and certain other trace elements are responsible for the soap-consuming property called "hardness." Some radicals, including $CO_3$, $HCO_3$, and $PO_4$, influence the alkalinity of the water. The presence and behavior of organic matter can be characterized by such tests as chemical or biological oxygen demand or chlorine demand. A complete list of elements, radicals, and other analytical parameters used to describe the chemical composition of water would be lengthy. A simple tabulation of detectable constituents in sea water, for example, includes about 35 elements and radicals, of which 11 are present in concentrations above 1 mg/liter. Many of the constituents which might be listed, however, would be below the detection limits of conventional chemical procedures and would require special instrumentation for their measurement.

An estimate of the number of parameters used in characterization of water is given by a system now employed in the Federal Water Pollution Control Administration. To meet the demand for systematic storage and retrieval of data pertaining to natural waters, the Basic Data Branch of the FWPCA has designed a system called STORET. This elaborate computerized system provides for coding of more than 350 parameters, not including biological identifications. Of the total, however, approximately 20 tests may be used to adequately describe the chemical and physical properties of treated and untreated water. The measurements most frequently used for pollutional characteristics and the trace elements may include another 40 parameters. A list of the commonly used measurements is given in Table I. It should be noted that certain analyses, such as those of dissolved gases or radioactive materials, are omitted. Likewise, under the heading "Biological" only the commonest identifications are listed. Tables II and III list the source, significance, properties, and range of concentrations for the most important constituents. When referring to the range and mean of various constituents, it should also be noted that exceptional waters do not fall within these limits.

## A. SIGNIFICANCE OF SOLUBLE CONSTITUENTS IN WATER

### 1. Major Constituents

#### a. CALCIUM (Ca)

Calcium is one of the most important major constituents of natural water. It is dissolved from rocks and soils, principally limestone and

## TABLE I

### Tests Used for Characterization of Water

| Mineral constituents | Properties (various) | Trace elements | Pollutional characteristics | Biological |
|---|---|---|---|---|
| *Major constituents* | *Physical* | Antimony | Dissolved oxygen | *Bacteriological* |
| Calcium | pH (hydrogen ion) | Aluminum | Biochemical oxygen demand | Total coliform |
| Magnesium | Conductivity | Arsenic | Chemical oxygen demand | Fecal coliform |
| Sodium | Temperature | Barium | Chlorine demand | Fecal streptocci |
| Potassium | | Beryllium | Total carbon | Crenothrix (iron bacteria) |
| | *Chemical* | Bismuth | | Sphaerotilus |
| Carbonate | | Boron | Nitrogen | |
| Bicarbonate | Hardness | Cadmium | Ammonia | *Planktonic* |
| Sulfate | Alkalinity | Chromium | Nitrate | |
| Chloride | Acidity | Cobalt | Nitrite | Alga |
| | | Copper | Nitrogen (organic) | Dinobryon |
| Total dissolved solids | | Iron | | Synura |
| | | Lead | Phosphorus: | |
| *Minor constituents* | | Lithium | Phosphate (ortho) | Diatoms |
| | *Esthetic* | Manganese | Phosphate (poly) | Synedra |
| Iron | | Molybdenum | Phosphorus (organic) | Aphanizomenon |
| Manganese | Taste | Nickel | | |
| Silica | Odor | Selenium | Sulfur | |
| Aluminum | Suspended matter | Silver | Sulfide | |
| Phosphate | Color | Strontium | Sulfite | |
| Fluoride | | Tin | | |
| Nitrate | | Vanadium | Grease and oils | |
| | | Zinc | | |
| | | Bromide | Residues | |
| | | Iodide | Fixed | |
| | | | Volatile | |
| | | | Detergents | |
| | | | Phenols | |
| | | | Cyanide | |
| | | | Heavy metals | |

347

## TABLE II
### Major Chemical Constituents in Water—Source, Concentration, and Effects

| Constituent | Major sources | Concentrations — Range and mean, mg/liter | Effects |
|---|---|---|---|
| Calcium (Ca) | Rocks, minerals, soils, gypsum, and calcite | 0–250<br>50 | Scaling in pipes, boilers, etc. "Hardness" constituent. |
| Carbonate ($CO_3$) | Rocks, minerals, and soils, limestone | 0–10<br><5 | Combines with calcium and magnesium in scale formation. |
| Bicarbonate ($HCO_3$) | Rocks, minerals, soils, limestone | 0–300<br>100 | With heat reverts to carbonate; scale formation |
| Chloride (Cl) | Rocks, minerals, soils, sea water, natural brines, and industrial brines | 0–500<br>50 | Little effect at normal concentrations; taste at levels in excess of 250 ppm. |
| Dissolved solids | Sum total of mineral constituents in water | 2.0–750<br>300 | Depending on constituents, causes scaling and foaming in boilers, scaling in plumbing, tastes in drinking water, laxative effects, some physiological effects. |
| Fluoride (F) | Rocks, minerals, soils, fluorite, and mica | 0–2<br>0.5 | No effect below 0.5 ppm, beneficial effect to children's teeth at 0.6–1.2 ppm; above 1.2 ppm causes mottling of teeth. |
| Iron (Fe) | Rocks, minerals, soils, pyrites, iron piping, and pickling liquors | 0–0.5 in aerated surface waters<br>0–25 in ground waters | Objectionable tastes and color in drinking water, staining of plumbing fixtures and laundry. |
| Magnesium (Mg) | Rocks, minerals, soils, clays, and magnesite | 0–100<br>15 | Same as calcium. Laxative at higher concentrations. |
| Manganese (Mn) | Rocks, minerals, and soils | 0–0.2 in aerated surface waters<br>0–25 in ground waters | Same as iron. |

| Constituent | Source | Concentration | Effects |
|---|---|---|---|
| Nitrates ($NO_3$) | Rocks, minerals, soils (esp. salt-peter), leguminous plants, and agricultural chemicals | 0–5<br>1 | No effects at normal concentrations; at high concentrations toxic effects in infants. |
| Potassium (K) | Rocks, minerals, soils | 0–25<br>15 | Same as sodium. |
| Silica ($SiO_2$) | Rocks, minerals, soils, clays, and feldspars | 0–100<br>25 | Scaling in pipes, boilers, etc. |
| Sulfate ($SO_4$) | Rocks, minerals, soils, gypsum, and natural oxidation of sulfides | 0–500<br>100 | Combines with calcium and magnesium in scale formation at higher concentrations; with magnesium has laxative effect. |

TABLE III

Properties of Water—Source, Concentration, and Effects[a]

| Property | Description and cause | Concentration | | Effects |
|---|---|---|---|---|
| | | Range and mean | | |
| Acidity (mg/liter as CaCO₃ [H⁺]) | Counterpart of alkalinity; ability of water to neutralize basic materials; caused by mineral acids, dissolved gases, organic acids, etc. | Insufficient data | | Highly acid water can be very corrosive. |
| Alkalinity (mg/liter as CaCO₃, CO₃ HCO₃ or OH) | The ability of water to neutralize acid; stemming from carbonates and bicarbonates; sometimes hydroxides, phosphates, nitrates, etc. | 10–500 | 100 | Waters very low or very high in alkalinity may be corrosive; high alkalinity produces tastes. |
| Color (color units) | Usually yellow-brown color resulting from leaching of decaying vegetable matter; industrial wastes may contribute colors. | 0–50 | 10 | Esthetically objectionable in drinking water and some industrial processes. |
| Hardness (mg/liter as CaCO₃) | "Soap-consuming" property of water caused principally by calcium and magnesium; other heavy metals and acids contribute. | 5–1000 | 150 | Low hardness contributes to corrosive property of water. Excessive hardness contributes to scaling, plumbing, and laundry problems. |
| pH or hydrogen ion concentration (pH units) | A function of the concentration and amount of dissolved solids in natural waters influenced chiefly by alkaline earths, carbonates, and bicarbonates. Defined as the negative logarithm (to the base 10) of the hydrogen ion concentration. | 6.0–9.0 | 7.5 | Waters below pH 6.0 are acid and corrosive; 7.0–9.5 normal for drinking water; 8.5 and higher retards corrosion. |

(Note: $CaCO_3$, $H^+$, $CO_3$, $HCO_3$, OH)

| | | | |
|---|---|---|---|
| Specific conductance (micromhos) | Measure of the electrical conductance of water; a function of the amount and kind of dissolved solids in water; used to approximate the dissolved solids concentration in water. | 30–1000 400 | |
| Temperature (°F or °C) | Surface waters approximate mean monthly temperatures. Industrial cooling waters raise stream temperatures. | 0–30°C 20°C | Warm drinking water is generally less desirable. Low temperature is desirable for industrial cooling purposes; elevated temperatures promote some biological growth. |
| Turbidity (ppm $SiO_2$ or Jackson units) | Finely divided, suspended matter usually resulting from soil erosion, silts, and clays. Streams and lakes may become turbid after rainstorms or thermal turnovers. | 0–1000 JU 100 | Esthetically objectionable in drinking water, harmful in many industrial processes. Removal of suspended or settled matter may be problem in water treatment. |

[a] Adapted from *Public Water Supplies of the 100 Largest Cities in the United States*, U.S. Dept. of Interior, Geological Survey, Water Supply Paper #1812, U.S. Government Printing Office, Washington, D.C., 1962.

gypsum, and is the predominant material causing hardness of water. It is also a major factor in formation of boiler and pipe scale. Waters flowing through limestone areas may contain as much as 100 mg/liter and this value may be several times higher when the water is in contact with gypsum deposits. Calcium is not known to cause any adverse physiological defects in man. There is, however, statistical evidence which indicates a lowering of heart ailments in hard-water areas.

### b. MAGNESIUM (Mg)

Magnesium usually occurs along with calcium and derives from the same sources but at lesser concentrations. Its effect in water is similar to that of calcium.

### c. SODIUM (Na)

In many waters, sodium is a major cation since it is dissolved from most rocks and soils. Concentrations may range from a few milligrams per liter in soft waters to several hundred milligrams per liter in natural brines. Concentrations of sodium in the range of 100 mg/liter and higher cause difficulties in boiler operation. In recent years, information on sodium content of drinking water has attained medical significance for overall control of low-sodium diets.

### d. POTASSIUM (K)

Potassium occurs in natural waters along with sodium and has the same significance. Potassium concentrations seldom, if ever, reach the concentrations observed for sodium, the ratio of sodium to potassium normally being about 10 or 20 to 1.

### e. CHLORIDE (Cl)

Chloride is present in all natural waters covering a range from about one to several hundred milligrams per liter. Natural brines and sea water may contain up to 15 or 20 thousand mg/liter chlorides. In arid areas of the United States, chlorides are leached from soils and rocks and may raise stream concentrations up to several hundred milligrams per liter. Irrigation-return waters may have the same effect.

Chloride has no physiological effects, but can cause taste in concentrations above several hundred milligrams per liter. Corrosiveness of water increases with increasing concentrations of chlorides.

## f. Sulfate ($SO_4$)

Sulfate is usually one of the major anions present in natural waters since it is dissolved from most rocks and soils. Sulfate also originates from the natural oxidation of sulfur-containing materials, both mineral and vegetable. The biological conversion of sulfides to sulfuric acid (acid mine drainage) is a common phenomena in coal mining regions.

At average concentrations, sulfate has no physiological effects; at higher concentrations, combined with magnesium (as Epsom salts), it has a laxative effect. Sulfates also combine with calcium in deposition of boiler and pipe scale.

## g. Bicarbonate ($HCO_3$) and Carbonate ($CO_3$)

Carbonate and bicarbonate ions in natural waters originate from a variety of sources: solution from carbonate rocks, solution of carbon dioxide from air, and production of carbon dioxide by aquatic organisms. Carbonate and bicarbonate exist together in water, and the proportion of the two anions is a function of pH. If the pH is lowered, carbonate is converted to bicarbonate; conversely, an increase in pH results in a decrease in bicarbonate.

Carbonate and bicarbonate, either singly or together, are usually the predominant constituents affecting alkalinity. Concentrations range from about 50 to 400 mg/liter of the two ions measured together. Moderate amounts have no adverse effects on consumers, but as major constituents in water carbonates and bicarbonates contribute to formation of pipe scale.

## h. Dissolved Solids

Dissolved solids represent the sum total of the soluble constituents in water, including mineral and organic matter. Dissolved solids may range from 10 to 20 mg/liter in soft water areas to several hundred milligrams per liter in hard water areas; waters containing more than a 1000 mg/liter are not uncommon.

Waters very high in dissolved solids may possess a salty taste and cause diarrhea to the infrequent consumer. High solids are also undesirable because of scaling in plumbing and boilers. The USPHS recommended limit on dissolved solids in drinking water is 500 mg/liter.

## 2. Commonly Occurring Minor Constitutents

### a. ALUMINUM (Al)

Aluminum originates in water from various types of clays and shales, especially bauxite. It is seldom present in natural waters in excess of 1 mg/liter and has no physiological significance. It may be troublesome in power plant operations where it tends to deposit scale on boiler tubes.

### b. BARIUM (Ba)

Barium is a minor element in water and is seldom measured except by emission methods. Its concentration is minimized by natural precipitation with sulfates.

Waters containing more than 1.0 mg/liter of barium are considered unfit for domestic use because of toxic effects on nerves, heart, and blood vessels (*U.S. Public Health Service Drinking Water Standards*, Rev. 1962).

### c. BORON (B)

Boron is a secondary constituent of natural waters and, while usually present in natural waters, seldom occurs in excess of 1 mg/liter. Measurement of boron is desirable in farming areas where irrigation is practiced, since concentrations greater than 1 mg/liter can be detrimental to certain sensitive crops, particularly citrus types. Boron has no physiological importance at normal concentrations.

### d. FLUORIDE (F)

Fluoride is dissolved in small amounts from many rocks and minerals. Except in unusual cases, it rarely exceeds 3 mg/liter in natural waters; the average content in surface waters is about 0.5 mg/liter.

Within the last 30 years, fluoride has been shown to have a beneficial effect on teeth at concentrations between about 0.8 to 1.2 mg/liter. Optimum concentrations, whether naturally occurring or artificially created, are reported to reduce the DMF rate (decayed, missing, and filled) by almost 70%. At higher concentrations (1.5 mg/liter and up), teeth became mottled and discolored.

The PHS limit on fluoride in drinking waters is set at 0.8–1.2 mg/liter, depending upon average annual temperature.

### e. BROMIDE (Br) AND IODIDE (I)

Bromide and iodide occur as trace anions and are seldom measured. Their presence in concentrations above 0.1 mg/liter may indicate intrusion of natural brines. Neither anion at normal concentrations has any significance.

## f. Nitrate ($NO_3$) and Nitrite ($NO_2$)

Nitrate in water may originate occasionally from solution of localized deposits of nitrate compounds. More often, however, traces of nitrate are the result of oxidation of nitrogenous vegetable materials from land runoff. Sudden increases in nitrate in water may indicate sewage pollution. Concentrations in surface waters rarely exceed 3 mg/liter.

Extremely high concentrations of nitrate—50 mg/liter or more—sometimes found in ground waters, may cause methemoglobinemia in infants. Although this ailment does not affect adults or children, the USPHS has set 45 mg/liter as the limit because of the hazard associated with infant feeding.

Nitrate in low concentrations, at about 2 mg/liter, has also been reported to retard embrittlement of boiler plate. More important, nitrate is a source of nitrogen, a necessary nutrient in the growth of aquatic organisms.

Nitrite occurs as a result of natural oxidation of nitrogenous organic matter, such as proteins and amino acids. It is an intermediate between reduced forms of nitrogen and nitrate. When detected it is usually at concentrations below 0.1 mg/liter and its presence is temporary.

## g. Phosphate ($PO_4$) and Polyphosphate

Phosphorus usually occurs as the anion $PO_4$ in natural waters. While phosphate may derive from rocks and soils, other and commoner sources are decomposition of vegetable matter, agricultural chemicals, and household washing compounds. Average concentrations in natural waters may be from about 0.01 to 0.5 mg/liter, but in streams receiving domestic wastes, levels may be several times higher.

Phosphate has no adverse physiological effects and is an essential nutrient for all forms of life. Waters containing little or no phosphorus are sparsely populated with aquatic forms. Conversely, waters with high concentrations of phosphate may, under proper conditions of temperature and sunlight, be overpopulated, even to nuisance conditions, with many forms of aquatic life, especially planktonic forms.

Polyphates are man-made condensation products of several inorganic phosphorus compounds used in synthetic detergent formulations. They hydrolyze by effect of temperature, light, and pH to the ortho form, $PO_4$.

### h. Iron (Fe)

Iron is dissolved by natural weathering process from many kinds of rocks, soils, and geological deposits. In fully aerated streams, iron exists in the ferric form, but seldom in amounts above 0.5 mg/liter. In ground waters it is often present in the reduced ferrous state at concentrations up to 50 and even 100 mg/liter. Upon aeration, the ferrous iron is oxidized to the ferric state and precipitates as the hydroxide. Abnormal amounts of iron are found in streams in coal mining areas resulting from acid mine drainage.

The chief objection to iron in water supplies relates to laundering problems and staining of plumbing fixtures. The PHS recommended limit of iron is 0.3 mg/liter.

### i. Manganese (Mn)

The source and behavior of manganese in water is similar to iron. In aerated waters it is seldom found above 0.05 mg/liter, the recommended PHS limit for drinking water.

### j. Trace Elements

A complete list of trace elements found in natural waters would be difficult to compile because the elements which might be included resist rigid classification. A convenient method of grouping could list all minor elements detectable by the emission spectrograph, which would number about 60 metals. Certain of these metals, however, occur so infrequently at such low concentrations that their inclusion would be superfluous. Other elements, such as iron and manganese which are frequently found in raw and finished waters and easily measured by other methods, might reasonably be excluded. A few nonmetallic elements, such as arsenic and selenium, are not easily detected using ordinary spectrographic procedures, but do possess significant toxic properties and therefore require listing in any tabulation of important trace elements. An arbitrary compilation of trace elements could include elements with at least two of the following characteristics:

*a.* Can be measured spectrographically.

*b.* Occurs in natural waters with some frequency.

*c.* Is known to possess some physiological significance, either adverse or beneficial.

Trace elements which conform to this classification are shown in Table IV. Some of these elements, particularly aluminum, barium, boron, iron, and manganese, have been discussed above.

## TABLE IV
### Significant Trace Elements in Natural and Finished Waters

| Element | Effect | Permissible limits, mg/liter | |
| --- | --- | --- | --- |
| | | PHS | WHO |
| Antimony (Sb) | Rarely found; similar to arsenic. | None | None |
| Aluminum (Al) | None. | None | None |
| Arsenic (As) | | 0.05 | 0.2 |
| Barium (Ba) | Muscle stimulant, nerve blocking agent. | 1.0 | None |
| Beryllium (Be) | Rarely found; causes bone damage at high concentrations. | None | None |
| Bismuth (Bi) | Rarely found; causes diarrhea, skin reactions stomatitis at high doses. | None | None |
| Cadmium (Cd) | Renal poison; accumulates in hard and soft tissues above 0.1 mg/liter. | 0.01 | None |
| Boron (B) | Toxic to some plants, especially citrus growths. | — | — |
| Chromium (Cr) | Skin sensitizer, potentially cancerigenic in the lungs. | 0.05 | 0.05 |
| Cobalt (Co) | Rarely found; essential nutrient. | None | None |
| Copper (Cu) | Essential at low concentrations; above limit may produce emesis and liver damage; astringent. | 1.0 | 1.5 |
| Iron (Fe) | Esthetic nuisance; taste producer. | 0.03 | 1.0 |
| Lead (Pb) | Cumulates in tissues, causes lead poisoning. | 0.05 | 0.1 |
| Lithium (Li) | None. | None | None |
| Manganese (Mn) | Esthetic nuisance. | 0.05 | 0.5 |
| Molybdenum (Mo) | Essential nutrient. | None | None |
| Nickel (Ni) | Rarely found; skin sensitizer, affects cardiac and respiratory nerves. | None | None |
| Selenium (Se) | Rarely found; cumulative poison in all body tissues. | 0.05 | 0.05 |
| Silver (Ag) | Rarely found; skin discoloration after prolonged intake. | 0.05 | None |
| Strontium (Sr) | Similar to calcium, no physiological effect. | None | None |
| Tin (Sn) | Rarely found; imparts taste and turbidity to water. | None | None |
| Vanadium (V) | Rarely found; anticholinesterogenic agent at low levels. | None | None |
| Zinc (Zn) | Essential element; imparts taste and turbidity to water at low concentrations. | 5.0 | 15 |

## B. PROPERTIES OF WAR

### 1. Specific Conductance

Specific conductance is a measure of the electrical conductivity of water and is a direct function of the concentration of mineral constituents. The measurement is used as a quick means of estimating the dissolved solids in water. For most waters, the dissolved solids in milligrams per liter, are about 60–70% of the specific conductance measured as micromhos per centimeter.

### 2. Color

In natural waters, color is usually the result of organic matter leached from leaves, bark, roots, and decaying organic matter. Natural color varies from yellow through brown; sewage and industrial water may contribute other colors. It has no particular significance, but causes a lack of consumer acceptance when noticeably present. The recommended limit for color is 15 chloroplatinate units.

### 3. Turbidity

Turbidity is caused by insoluble, suspended matter in water, originating chiefly from rock and soil runoff. It may consist of silt, sand, clay, and various particles ranging in size from colloidal to macroscopic.

Turbid water is objectionable for many industrial uses because of its clogging and abrasive properties. Small amounts of visible turbidity in drinking water has no adverse effects, but is esthetically objectionable.

### 4. Hardness

Hardness in water is caused principally by the presence of calcium and magnesium and to a lesser degree by iron, manganese, aluminum, barium, and other trace metals. Hardness is indicated by an increased soap consumption, visible soap scum, and formation of pipe scale in plumbing, boilers, radiators, etc. Hardness, with attendant scale formation is undesirable because of reduced flow in pipes and loss of heat transfer. Modern household detergents are unaffected by hardness so that this property has become less of a problem to the housewife.

Hardness, measured in terms of calcium carbonate, ranges from about 25 mg/liter in soft waters to about 500 mg/liter in very hard waters.

## 5. Alkalinity

Alkalinity is the measure of the capacity of a water to neutralize hydrogen ions and is expressed in terms of equivalent amounts of calcium carbonate. It is not a specific substance, but rather a combined effect of several substances and conditions. Alkalinity is caused by the presence of carbonates, bicarbonates, hydroxides, and, to a lesser extent, by borates, silicates, and phosphates. In natural waters, however, the major contribution to alkalinity is from the carbonate and bicarbonate content; hydroxide alkalinity is rare and, if observed, is probably due to man-made contribution.

Alkalinity is both desirable and detrimental to various industrial operations. It is desirable in many industrial operations because it inhibits corrosion, but is detrimental to many food and beverage processing operations. In itself, alkalinity is not considered detrimental to humans, but it is usually associated with high pH values, hardness, and high dissolved solids, all of which may be deleterious.

Alkalinity in natural waters reported as calcium carbonate may range from a few milligrams per liter up to about 400 or 500 mg/liter for highly alkaline waters.

## II. SAMPLING AND SAMPLE HANDLING

### A. IMPORTANCE OF REPRESENTATIVE SAMPLES

When a water sample is collected for analysis it usually represents a minute fraction of the total volume of water under study. Yet, in the interpretation of the results of the testing, the body of water or flow will be judged to have the identical chemical and bacteriological characteristics of the sample. While this is true of all industrial quality control, the relative volumes involved are far more disproportionate than normal. It is very important, therefore, that the homogeniety of the water source be established or that measures be taken to determine the degree of variation in water quality as a function of vertical and horizontal distribution and time (115).

It is axiomatic that the results of analysis are no better than the reliability of the sample. It is equally true that the sample represents a total investment in analytical costs far beyond the intrinsic value of the material, in addition to the value placed upon the quality of the water itself.

In many situations, the results of the water analysis may be entered as legal evidence. In these cases, it is imperative that the exact circumstances of location, time, method of sampling, and details of sample handling before analysis be permanently recorded and that the individual responsible for the collection of the sample be prepared to testify to these facts. In short, the integrity of the sample must be established and maintained throughout.

## B. SAMPLE COMPOSITING

When a single water sample is collected, it is often referred to as a "grab" sample. The results derived represent the quality of the water source at the point of sampling and at the moment the sample was taken. If the water is homogenous and does not vary with time, the grab sample is representative of the whole water mass. In many cases, however, it is necessary to collect several samples in the stream or lake, because of variations within the water body, either shore to shore or from top to bottom. Further, if the characteristics change during the day or from day to day, the sampling schedule must be adjusted to compensate for these variations as well (41).

Whenever possible, it is advisable to lighten the analytical load by mixing the grab samples to get a representative composite of all the samples collected (88). Samples may be composited in a number of ways, depending upon the circumstances of the examination. When sampling a fixed body of water, such as a small reservoir, it is usually satisfactory to mix equal amounts of the individual samples to obtain a volume sufficient for analysis. If the flow is apt to vary with time, as in a stream or pipe, the added sample volumes must be weighted proportional to the flow at the time of collection. Intelligent compositing of samples requires prior knowledge of the distribution of components in the system and the time rate of change in the volume of the water mass being examined. It is therefore advisable to examine a sufficient number of descrete samples and to measure the flow characteristics of the system before arranging a compositing schedule. The analyst should recognize that the composite represents a compromise between the ideal continuous measurement of water quality and the practical considerations of economics.

One further restriction should be noted: water samples for bacteriological examination should not be composited, because of the probability of changes in the biological systems during the interval between sample collection and final completion of the composite. Bacteriological examination should be made as quickly as possible after the sample is collected.

A general rule applied to sampling frequency is that samples be collected at least daily, and at more frequent intervals if discharge or chemical characteristics change by more than 25% within the 24-hr period. Specific conductance is often used to determine the degree of change in the principal mineral components of the samples.

## C. SELECTION OF SAMPLING SITES

### 1. Raw Waters

Unfortunately, sampling sites are often selected on the basis of the location of a convenient structure, such as a bridge or intake, rather than on logical determination of the optimum site. As indicated above, the primary consideration should be the distribution of the measured constituents. Because of temperature, topography, and tributary flow, the water body may not be homogeneous at the time of sample collection. When this is true, samples must be collected from each area showing significant variation from the "average." When necessary, the site for a single sample can then be chosen in the area having characteristics closest to the overall average of the water. In most cases, this will be within the largest "mass" of the body of water. Collection should normally be at mid-depth to avoid influences from floating material or bottom sediments.

### 2. Process Waters

Normally, process water will be sampled from the piping system conveying the water to the point of treatment. It is often convenient to install a small diversion pipe to permit the continuous flow of a small part of the flowing water. Even though samples will be collected only at intervals, the sample tap should flow constantly to avoid buildup of sediment or changes due to stagnation. It is important that the sample flow be large enough to be truly representative of the water passing that point (66). Polyethylene piping is often used in sample systems.

### 3. Finished Waters

Potable water is generally collected from a faucet, often in the analytical laboratory. The tap selected should be one in relatively constant use, yet protected from contamination by laboratory reagents or handling. The water should be turned on at full volume for 5 min to flush out any residual materials in the piping.

## D. SAMPLE CONTAINERS

Polyethylene bottles have been found to be best for chemical water samples. The advantages of initial cost, absence of adsorption, weight, and freedom from breakage are readily apparent. It is advisable to fill the new bottles with water and store them for several days to permit possible leaching of materials from the plastic. Attention should be given to the closures. When possible, polyethylene screw caps should be used. If other plastic materials are used in the cap, the analyst should determine that the cap does not contaminate the sample.

In some instances, glass containers may be preferred, especially if it is known that a plastic container is not resistant to attack by the sample. Pyrex-type glass may be preferred since some kinds of soft glass are liable to attack by highly alkaline solutions.

Except in the special cases cited below, about ½ gal should be collected for chemical examination to permit a variety of determinations, as well as reruns where necessary. Approximately 200 ml is usually sufficient for bacteriological examination. A small air space should be left to provide for vigorous mixing of the sample.

Because of the need for sterilization of bacteriological sample containers, plastic bottles are unsatisfactory. The most popular type is a wide-mouth, glass-stoppered bottle having a capacity of 300 ml. The stopper must be protected from contamination during and after sterilization by means of metal foil or paper hood which extends well below the lip of the bottle and is secured by a string. Sample containers are sterilized by autoclaving for 20 min at 120°C or by dry heat at 180°C for 3 hr.

## E. SPECIAL SAMPLING PROBLEMS

Certain substances present in water are difficult to sample correctly because of their physical properties. These include suspended solids, dissolved gases, and oily matter. Special techniques are necessary to secure representative samples when these materials are present.

### 1. Suspended Solids

Solid matter in water may be floating freely, suspended somewhat uniformly throughout the water mass, or settling near the bottom. Since the purpose of the analysis is to determine the concentration of suspended matter in the water itself, the sample will normally be collected from the center of the water mass to avoid the floating material on the surface and the bottom sediments. The type of sampling gear is important, since constrictions in the sampler may prevent inclusion of large particles or the samples may become clogged during collection of the sample. An ideal sampling device for suspended solids in water is the Kemmerer sampler described later.

The sample should be sufficiently large to permit a representative collection of all the suspended particles and care must be exerted in the laboratory in removing an aliquot for testing. Constant agitation is recommended.

Many materials will adhere to the inside of the sample container during transport and storage, and these must be resuspended in the sample before analysis. Since polyethylene bottles are not transparent and interference from soft glass is not a problem, quart mason jars are often used for solids sampling.

## 2. Dissolved Gases

Ordinarily, the only dissolved gases of interests in sanitary water analysis are oxygen and carbon dioxide. Special sampling devices must be used to insure that the sample container is completely filled to avoid air contamination. These samplers are designed to flush the sample bottle two or three times with sample before filling. In this manner, the air originally in the bottle does not contact the sample. The sample bottle must remain sealed until analysis begins. Since increase in temperature would lower the solubility of the gas and produce bubbles, the sample must be held at or below the temperature of collection until analyzed.

## 3. Oils and Greases

The sampling of oily matter is particularly difficult. Oil may be floating as an extremely thin surface layer, emulsified in the water, or exist as sludge on the bottom. It is virtually impossible to collect a representative sample of oil film. A subsurface sample is best, although analysis may indicate absence of oil even when surface slicks are visible. The sample collector should not be influenced by the appearance of the water, but should collect the sample objectively.

In the laboratory, a representative aliquot cannot be withdrawn unless the oil is uniformly distributed. To prevent error, a separate sample

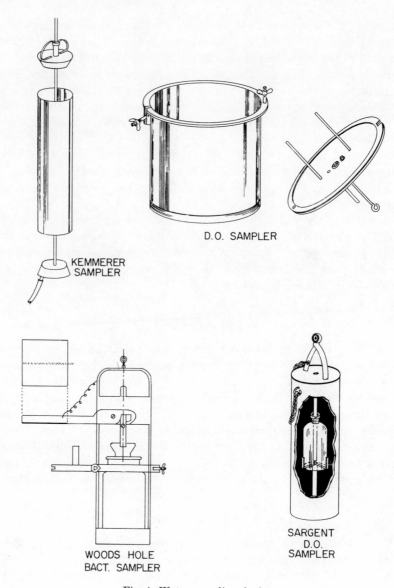

Fig. 1. Water sampling devices.

should be collected for oil and grease, and the whole sample, usually 1 liter, should be analyzed.

## F. SAMPLING EQUIPMENT

Figure 1 illustrates typical water sampling devices. In general, the simplest device should be used, providing it accomplishes the purpose of collecting a representative sample of sufficient volume without contamination.

## G. PRESERVATION AND STORAGE OF WATER SAMPLES

A general recommendation for water samples is that the analyses be completed as soon as possible after the sample is collected. For most chemical and bacteriological constituents, the shorter the time interval between collection and analysis, the more reliable will be the results. In many situations, however, the location of the laboratory with respect to the sample site and the work load in the laboratory may require that part of the analyses be deferred. In such cases, the analyst must be guided by the possible changes in the characteristics of the sample and the availability of suitable preservation methods.

### TABLE V

*Analyze as soon as possible*
Bacteria
Dissolved oxygen
Biochemical oxygen demand
Residual chlorine
pH
Odor

*Preserve*

| | |
|---|---|
| Ammonia nitrogen | 0.8 ml $H_2SO_4$ per liter |
| Nitrate nitrogen | 0.8 ml $H_2SO_4$ per liter |
| Phosphorus | 5 ml chloroform per liter |
| Suspended matter | 20 ml formalin per liter |
| Heavy metals | 10 ml $HNO_3$ per liter |

*No preservative required*

| | | |
|---|---|---|
| Hardness | Color | Alkalinity |
| Calcium | Turbidity | Fluoride |
| Magnesium | Specific conductance | Dissolved solids |
| Chloride | Sodium | |
| Sulfate | Potassium | |

Commonly measured constituents in water suggest that the analyses may be divided into three categories:

  *a.* Those which must be performed as soon as possible,
  *b.* Tests which may be conducted on preserved samples,
  *c.* Determination of relatively stable constituents requiring no preservation of the sample.

Table V shows representative analytical determinations and the recommended handling procedure.

## III. ANALYTICAL PROCEDURES FOR CHARACTERIZATION OF POTABLE WATER

### A. INTRODUCTION

The composition of natural water varies across a broad spectrum, from the nearly pure condition of rain water to the highly mineralized condition of the oceans. Between the limits of this spectrum, natural waters exist in a continuum of infinite compositions.

Lakes formed by melting snow, rivers burdened with soluble top-soil elements, agricultural chemicals, industrial and domestic wastes, and aged ground waters containing dissolved solids of all descriptions are only a few of the kinds of water that require examination by the sanitary chemist. The range of concentrations and number of constituents complicates the job of the analyst. Frequently, an analytical procedure which is reliable for a certain determination in one kind of water will not apply to another sample because of the presence of a certain interference. In this respect, water differs from other fluids, such as blood, in which the same constituent materials are always present and only vary within a narrow range.

### B. SOURCES OF LITERATURE AND REFERENCES

Methods for the analysis of water, to a large extent, have been standardized by various professional groups with special interests and objectives. There are analytical procedures which are used to evaluate the suitability of water for domestic use, other procedures for industrial and agricultural suitability, and still others which define the source and mineral quality. Consequently, the literature devoted to water analysis tends to be diverse, voluminous, and sometimes contradictory. In the discussion of analytical procedures that appears in this text, the authors have therefore tried to confine themselves to the most commonly used texts in the field. These are:

*Manual on Industrial Water and Industrial Waste Water,* 2nd ed. ASTM Special Technical Publication, No. 148-G, 1964.
*Methods for Collection and Analysis of Water Samples,* U.S. Dept. of Interior, Geological Survey, Water Supply Paper 1454, U.S. Government Printing Office, Washington, D.C.
*Study and Interpretation of the Chemical Characteristics of Natural Water,* U.S. Dept. of Interior, Geological Survey, Water Supply Paper 1473, U.S. Government Printing Office, Washington, D.C.
*Standard Methods for the Examination of Water and Wastewater,* 11th ed., American Public Health Assoc., 1960.

In later discussions where reference is made to "approved procedures," such procedures are outlined in these texts referred to above.

## C. METHODS FOR MAJOR CONSTITUENTS IN WATER

### 1. Calcium

Calcium may be measured in several ways, depending upon the requirements of accuracy or personal preference of the analyst. In the conventional gravimetric method, calcium is precipitated as the oxalate and weighed either as the oxalate or as calcium oxide, depending upon the final ignition temperature (58,117). This procedure is time consuming and not adaptable to large numbers of samples, but it is extremely accurate. A volumetric procedure is also used in which the calcium oxalate is filtered from the precipitating solution, redissolved in acid, and titrated with potassium permanganate (48). This method is faster than the gravimetric procedure and more adaptable to analyses of multiple samples.

The most commonly used method for measurement of calcium is the EDTA titrimetric procedure (32). This method is not as accurate as the gravimetric or permanganate methods, but it is completely suitable for routine calcium measurement and is designed for rapid analyses. Ethylenediaminetetraacetic acid, or its sodium salt, forms a stable, soluble, colorless chelate with calcium. A suitable indicator (ammonium purpurate, calcein, calcon) added to the sample will indicate the stoichemetric point between calcium and EDTA (102). The titration is usually performed at a pH of 10 or above to eliminate interference from magnesium. Other cations frequently present in surface or finished waters, such as iron, manganese, barium, strontium and other trace metals, may interfere by reacting either with the EDTA or with the indicator. In most cases, however, the interference from other trace metals negligible and may be overcome by addition of sodium sulfide or sodium cyanide as complexing agents for the interferences.

*Indicators.* The success of the titration is influenced to a certain extent by the choice of indicator for the endpoint detection.

*Calculation.* Standard EDTA titrant, 0.0100 $M$, is prepared to be equivalent to 1.000 mg of $CaCO_3$ or 0.4008 mg of Ca using the indicator of choice. If this is done

$$\text{mg/liter Ca} = \frac{\text{ml EDTA} \times 400.8}{\text{ml of sample}}$$

or

$$\text{mg/liter CaCO}_3 = \frac{\text{ml EDTA} \times 1000}{\text{ml of sample}}$$

## 2. Magnesium

Magnesium may be determined in several ways, depending upon the requirements of the analyst. It can be measured gravimetrically after removal of calcium salts and, in fact, is usually measured on the filtrate and washings from the calcium determination (22). It may also be measured volumetrially with EDTA reagent and Eriochrome Black T (104) or colorimetrically using Brilliant Yellow solution (119).

Diammonium hydrogen phosphate precipitates magnesium in ammoniacal solution. Since the precipitate, magnesium ammonium phosphate, is very soluble, a large excess of ammonium hydroxide is required. Interferences from calcium, strontium, and manganese can be minimized if the precipitation is performed on the filtrate from the calcium determination. If extreme accuracy is required, a double precipitation should be performed, in which case quantitative removal of the magnesium along with some interferences from salts of ammonium, phosphates, chlorides, and oxalates is obtained in the first precipitation. The precipitate is then redissolved with a minimum of acid and the magnesium is reprecipitated under conditions more favorable to isolation of magnesium ammonium phosphate uncontaminated with coprecipitants. After removal of the precipitate, ignition time and temperature are important; 1000–1100°C at 30 min brings the optimum condition for conversion to magnesium pyrophosphate ($M_{g2}P_2O_7$).

The volumetric procedure is the most commonly used at some sacrifice in accuracy. A hardness measurement, using EDTA titrant and Erio-chrome Black T indicator, is performed followed by a calcium determination using the same titrant, but with a different indicator. Since the usual hardness determination includes both calcium and magnesium ions and the calcium measurement includes only calcium, magnesium may be calculated by difference.

The standard photometric procedure as described in *Standard Methods* uses a dye called Brilliant Yellow. In principle, magnesium hydroxide precipitate adsorbs the dye, which changes in color from orange to red. Calcium and aluminum interfere, but this interference is avoided by addition of these ions to a concentration level where their influence is predictable. A stabilizing solution is also used to maintain the magnesium hydroxide in colloidal suspension.

### 3. Sodium and Potassium

Methods for measurement of sodium and potassium by means other than flame photometry are tedious, time consuming, and generally unreliable unless the analyst has acquired skill and experience in the particular operation.

A gravimetric method for measurement of sodium is based on the reaction of sodium with a solution of zinc uranyl acetate to form a salt complex, sodium uranyl zinc acetate hexahydrate. While the reagent is fairly specific for sodium, the major requirement for accurate results is good technique. The method is outlined in detail in both *Standard Methods for the Examination of Water and Wastewater*, (12th ed.), and *Methods for the Collection and Analysis of Water*, but it is rarely used in laboratories performing routine water analysis.

Potassium may be run colorimetrically by precipitation with sodium cobaltinitrite and oxidation of the precipitate with standard potassium dichromate in the presence of sulfuric acid. The excess dichromate is then measured colorimetrically. Because the time of precipitation and temperature have a marked effect on the results, a set of standards must be run with each set of samples. This procedure is also outlined in *Standard Methods*, but like the gravimetric procedure for sodium, is rarely used.

Both sodium and potassium are easily measured by flame photometry (9,19,27,124). In fact, several manufacturers offer low cost instruments which are designed to measure only these two elements with sensitivities in the milligram per liter range. Since manufacturers' specifications for various instruments differ with regard to types of fuel, pressure setting, preparation of standards, etc., no detailed instructions are given here. It is sufficient to say that flame measurement is the only convenient method for sodium and potassium. A laboratory requiring an occasional measurement of either of these elements and which does not possess a flame photometer may do well to seek analytical assistance from a consultant group.

### 4. Chloride

Since it is a major constituent of water the measurement of chloride ion is one of the most commonly used tests in sanitary chemistry. A variety of procedures have been developed, but only two remain in popular use—the silver nitrate (Mohr procedure) (43,59) and the mercuric nitrate procedures.

In the former method the sample is titrated with a standard solution of silver nitrate in the presence of a small amount of potassium chromate. At the endpoint of the titration the silver nitrate combines with the chromate ion to form the highly colored silver chromate. In practice, the silver chloride precipitate which forms in the titrating flask may obscure the endpoint, especially in high chloride samples. For experienced operators the test is reliably performed at concentrations of 1 mg/liter.

A method of more recent development, the mercuric nitrate procedure (21,35) is based on the formation of soluble mercuric chloride and reaction of excess mercuric nitrate titrant with the dye, diphenylcarbazone. To perform the test, the pH of the sample is adjusted to about 2.5, at which point the color change at endpoint is most pronounced. The indicator diphenylcarbazone is added and the sample is titrated with standard mercuric nitrate. The reaction of excess mercuric nitrate with the indicator produces a quick color change from green to purple.

The method is as sensitive and reproducible as the silver nitrate method and does not produce a precipitate. Interferences are sulfite, chromate, and ferric ions at concentrations of about 10 mg/liter, but those present no difficulty in average surface waters of drinking water.

### 5. Sulfate

Sulfates in combination with the common metallic elements sodium, potassium, calcium, and magnesium are soluble in water and very stable except in unusual circumstances. Because of the wide distribution of sulfate in natural waters, the range of concentration, and ease of measurement, this determination is one of the most common parameters of water quality. Methods of measurement cover the range of gravimetric, volumetric, and photometric.

The gravimetric procedure is still the most widely used and most accurate, although it is much more time consuming. Conditions for performing the analysis are thoroughly described by Kolthoff and Sandell (57), Hillebrand et al., (47) and many others. In practice a suitable filtered aliquot, containing not more than 100 mg of $SO_4$, is adjusted to a convenient volume of about 250–400 mg, either by evaporation or dilution. The sample is then acidified with HCl and brought to boiling and a solution of $BaCl_2$ added in excess. The $BaSO_4$ precipitate is allowed to digest for 2–3 hr or, preferably, overnight at about 60–70°C. The precipitate is then filtered off, either in a Gooch crucible or on an ashless paper, washed to remove chlorides, dried and ignited at approximately 800°C for 1 hr, and weighed.

In this procedure, there may be some coprecipitation of other ions by occlusion or adsorption on the $BaSO_4$, but these do not significantly affect the accuracy of the method. The analyst should be aware, however, of possible interference from sulfides, sulfites, foreign suspended matter, iron, and, especially, silica. If a complete analysis of a sample is performed, the filtrate from the silica determination may be used for the sulfate determination; otherwise, this interference may be removed by a preliminary precipitation or a perchloric acid volitilization after the final weighing of the $BaSO_4$. Where the sulfate determination is performed routinely, some analysts use a single Gooch crucible for successive determinations.

Sulfate can be measured turbidimetrically using a photometric device in situations where less accuracy is required. Barium chloride, in crystal form, is added directly to a 25-ml volume of filtered sample previously acidified with HCl. The fine cloudy precipitate of $BaSO_4$ is held in suspension with a stabilizing solution of glycerol, isopropyl alcohol, and sodium chloride or a solution of sodium carboxymethyl cellulose (34,122). Factors which cause inaccurate results are failure to maintain a uniform suspension of $BaSO_4$ crystals and growth of the $BaSO_4$ crystals. Partial compensation for these defects may be obtained by uniform stirring of samples and standards and readings at equal time intervals. The selection of a wavelength for the transmittance of the samples is somewhat arbitrary; a range between 400 and 450 m$\mu$ is satisfactory.

A proprietary mixture in the form of a dry powder consisting of $BaCl_2$, NaCl, and a water soluble organic material for suspension and suppression of crystal growth is available.*

Another excellent procedure for sulfate is the visual thorin method, a volumetric technique approved and used routinely by the USGS.

---

* Sulfa-Ver, distributed by Hach Chemical Company, Ames, Iowa

Thorin (1-[0-arsenophenylazo-2-naphthol-3,6- disulfonic] acid sodium salt) reacts with barium to give a red color. To perform the titration the sample is first passed through an ion-exchange column to remove cation interferences, especially calcium. The sample is then titrated with a standard solution of barium chloride to the red endpoint. The color is more intense in organic media than in aqueous solutions; dioxane, ethyl alcohol, or methyl alcohol may be used. The optimum pH for the reaction is about 2.5, which also serves to intensify the endpoint change.

## 6. Residue

Residue is the term applied to the material remaining either on a filter after filtration of a water sample or in a vessel after evaporation. Residue is classified as filterable or nonfilterable, fixed or volatile, according to the method of determination. All residue measurements are operationally defined according to the method of filtration, drying temperature, or ignition temperature.

In the approved procedures, filtration is carried out by several methods, including Gooch crucible with asbestos mats, hard finish filter paper capable of retaining fine particles, membrane, glass fiber filters, or fritted glass crucibles. In general, any filtering device with a 5-$\mu$ pore size or less is permissible. Drying is accomplished in ovens at 103–105°C or at 180°C. Ignition or muffling is usually performed at 600°C. Dishes for containing the sample during evaporation may be platinum, porcelain, silica, or Pyrex and should contain a volume of at least 100 ml.

### a. TOTAL RESIDUE

A sample of sufficient volume to contain a residue of at least 25 mg is evaporated to dryness in a tared dish or a steam bath, dried at 103–105°C, and weighed. The increase in weight is reported as total residue or total solids in milligrams per liter.

### b. FILTERABLE RESIDUE

An accurately measured volume of sample sufficient to contain a residue of at least 25 mg is filtered through the filter of choice. The filtrate is placed in a suitable dish, evaporated to dryness, and weighed. The increase in weight is reported as filterable residue. For all except unusual samples this result is the "total dissolved solids." The material remaining on the filter may be weighed and reported as nonfilterable, or suspended, residue.

### c. Nonfilterable Residue

An accurately measured volume of sample is put through a suitable tared filter which is then dried and weighed. The increase in weight is reported as nonfilterable residue or suspended matter. The entire sample must be well mixed while the portion for analysis is being removed. If the sample is sufficiently high in dissolved solids, the filtrate may be used for the filterable residue or TDS measurement.

In each of these determinations the residues may be ignited at 600°C for 1 hr. The loss in weight is reported as volatile material, and the weight of the residue remaining after ignition is reported as fixed residue. All results are customarily reported in milligrams per liter.

The residue tests are simple to perform, but errors related to sampling, filtering, and drying are common. In samples containing amounts of suspended matter complete mixing must be attained while the sample aliquot is being removed. Residues dried at 103–105°C may retain water of hydration and occluded water. Drying at 180°C converts carbonates and bicarbonates to carbon dioxide and may also volatilize other compounds. Some dried residues may be especially hygroscopic requiring special cooling and dessication before and during weighing.

## 7. Acidity and Alkalinity

The acidity of water may be defined as the equivalents of strong base required to raise the pH to a selected endpoint. Similarly, alkalinity (basicity) is the equivalents of strong acid required to lower the pH to a selected endpoint. In practice, pH 8.3 and pH 4.5, respectively, are chosen as endpoints. The choice of endpoints for the titration is based on the following rationale:

In natural waters, the predominant species controlling pH are carbonic acid, bicarbonate ion, and carbonate ion. As shown in a typical titration curve (Fig. 2), equivalence points occur at pH 8.3 and pH 4.5, corresponding to the equilibrium conditions:

$$\text{pH 8.3} \quad [H^+] + [H_2CO_3] = [CO_3^{2-}] + [OH^-]$$
$$\text{pH 4.5} \quad [H^+] + [HCO_3^-] + 2\,[CO_3^{2-}] + [OH^-]$$

Thus, in the determination of acidity the quantity of strong base required is a measure of the acidic components $[H^+]$ and $[H_2CO_3]$, while in the alkalinity measurements $[HCO_3^-]$, $[CO_3^{2-}]$, and $[OH^-]$ are reacted. In Figure 2, the volume of acid required for the first endpoint ($P$ alkalinity) is due to the OH⁻ neutralization and conversion of the $CO_3^{2-}$ to

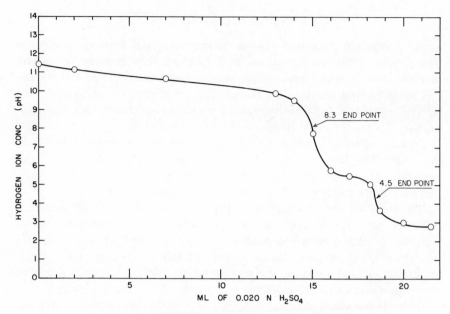

Fig. 2. Alkanity measurement using titration with electrometric endpoint.

$HCO_3^-$. The second endpoint represents the complete conversion of $HCO_3$ to $H_2CO_3$.

The principal cationic constituents in natural waters are calcium and magnesium. Therefore, the buffer capacity of the water is assumed to be due to calcium and magnesium carbonates and bicarbonates, and acidity and alkalinity are customarily reported as milligrams per liter of equivalent calcium carbonate. This method of expression should be recognized as convenient, but not precisely accurate, since a variety of chemical and biochemical systems may affect the pH.

The acidity determination is usually carried out by titrating a 50-ml aliquot of the sample with 0.02 $N$ sodium hydroxide to pH 8.3, using a standard electrometric pH instrument as described in *Standard Methods for the Examination of Water and Wastewater*.

*Calculation.*

$$\text{Acidity as mg/liter } CaCO_3 = \frac{\text{ml standard NaOH} \times N \times 50,000}{\text{ml sample}}$$

In the alkalinity measurement, samples above pH 8.3 are titrated to that pH with 0.02 $N$ sulfuric acid, the acid equivalents are recorded, and the titration is then continued to pH 4.5. In the past, phenolphthalein and methyl orange were used as indicators and the respective equivalents were reported as "phenolphthalein" and "total" alkalinity. In modern laboratories, the electrometric endpoints are used and the values reported as alkalinity to pH 8.3 and pH 4.5, in equivalent calcium carbonate. Calculations are:

Alkalinity to pH 8.3, as mg/liter $CaCO_3$

$$= \frac{\text{ml standard acid} \times N \times 50{,}000}{\text{ml sample}}$$

Total alkalinity to pH 4.5, as mg/liter $CaCO_3$

$$= \frac{\text{ml standard acid} \times N \times 50{,}000}{\text{ml sample}}$$

Occasionally, it is desirable to determine the concentrations of the separate alkaline species present in the sample. A good approximation may be obtained by use of Table VI. In the table, titration to pH 8.3 is designated as "$P$," while the complete acid equivalents to pH 4.5 are termed "$T$" for total alkalinity.

Alternative procedures for determining acidity and alkalinity are those prescribed by the American Society for Testing and Materials and the United States Geological Survey. In the ASTM method, 0.02 $N$ hydrochloric acid may be substituted for sulfuric acid and a complete titration curve may be developed by plotting pH versus milliliters of standard acid or alkali. Inflection points are determined from the curve and the results calculated as follows:

$$\text{acidity (or alkalinity), in equivalents per million} = \frac{1000}{AN \times \text{ml sample}}$$

### TABLE VI
#### Alkalinity Relationships[a]

| Result of titration | Hydroxide alkalinity | Carbonate alkalinity | Bicarbonate alkalinity |
|---|---|---|---|
| $P = 0$ | 0 | 0 | $T$ |
| $P < 1/2T$ | 0 | $2P$ | $T - 2P$ |
| $P = 1/2T$ | 0 | $2P$ | 0 |
| $P > 1/2T$ | $2P - T$ | $2(T - P)$ | 0 |
| $P = T$ | $T$ | 0 | 0 |

[a] $P$ = phenolphthalein alkalinity; $T$ = total alkalinity.

where $A$ = milliliters of standard acid or alkali required for the titration, and $N$ = normality of the standard solution.

The USGS procedure determines acidity to pH 7.0 by the use of 0.0248 $N$ sodium hydroxide, and the results are reported as ppm $H^+$. Alkalinity, reported as parts per million calcium carbonate, is measured by titration to pH 8.2 and pH 4.5. The values of the individual alkaline constituents are obtained by formula, using the titrant volumes to the respective pH endpoints.

An excellent discussion of the equilibrium relationships in acidity and alkalinity determinations has been published by Weber and Stumm (123). Application of the test to water treatment practice is presented in a classic paper by Langelier (63).

## D. METHODS FOR MINOR CONSTITUENTS IN WATER

### 1. Iron

Preservation of samples and sample handling have already been discussed in Section II. The behavior of iron in natural waters and waste waters is such, however, that the measurement may be missed completely if the sample is mishandled.

Iron in water may be in solution in either the ferrous or ferric state. Under reducing conditions iron is in the ferrous state and very soluble. With exposure to air, iron is oxidized to the ferric state and precipitates as ferric hydroxide. Iron may also occur as an oxide. in a complexed state with various minerals, or in a peptized state with organic matter. It is therefore important that the analytical requirements be clearly understood before sampling is started.

The determination of iron in water is most commonly achieved by use of the reagent 1–10 phenanthroline (26,40). Other organic reagents which are structurally similar, such as bipyridyl and tripyridyl, are sometimes used (72,75,76), but, for all practical purposes, the reagents and reaction conditions are similar. The colored complex formed by 1–10 phenanthroline and the ferrous iron has been postulated to be composed of three molecules of the reagent and one of ferrous iron. Ferric iron does not react.

Iron is brought into solution, usually by boiling hydrochloric acid, and reduced to the ferrous state with hydroxylamine. The sample is then buffered at a pH of 3.2–3.4 with a solution of ammonium acetate. If significant volume loss is experienced during the boiling step, the sample is diluted to the original volume followed by addition of the

1–10 phenanthroline reagent. Color development is immediate and stable for a period of months.

The reaction is sensitive to as little as 1 mg/liter so that all reagents should be low in iron. Since phosphates and polyphosphates complex iron causing a slow color reaction with 1–10 phenanthroline, it is advisable to acid rinse all detergent-washed glassware before use.

Interferences may be caused by other metals, especially cobalt, chromium, copper, and zinc, but these elements are rarely encountered in surface or finished waters at troublesome levels.

## 2. Manganese

The behavior of manganese in water is similar (but not identical) to that of iron, and special precautions should be taken to insure that the sample is valid. Like iron, manganese in water may oxidize to the manganic state upon aging and precipitate from solution. Manganese frequently adsorbs onto container walls, and even vigorous shaking of the container will not insure a true aliquot of sample. If the sample is not to be analyzed within a few hours after collection, it should be acidified immediately.

Manganese is measured in the permanganate state because of the highly tinctorial property of the $Mn^{7+}$ ion. Either potassium persulfate (80) or potassium periodate (71) may be used to achieve the required oxidation. The periodate procedure is preferred for samples containing more than 0.01 mg manganese and in which chlorides and organic matter are low. The persulfate method is preferred for low manganese concentrations and because it is less subject to chloride interference. The persulfate reaction, however, requires more control of reaction variables, such as reagent excess, heating time, and sample cooling.

In the periodate reaction, the sample is pretreated by boiling several times with sulfuric and nitric acids to $SO_3$ fumes to obtain chloride removal. If iron is present, phosphoric acid is used for complexing. After the sample is cooled and diluted to the original volume, 0.3–0.5 g of potassium persulfate is added and boiling is continued for color development. For very small amounts of manganese, about 0.05 mg, heating to just below the boiling point for about 1 hr may be necessary.

The persulfate method requires the use of a special solution containing mercuric sulfate and phosphoric acid to complex chlorides and iron, nitric acid to insure complete solution of the manganese, and silver nitrate to catalyze the manganese oxidation to permanganate ion. After the sample containing the special solution has been brought to a boil, about

1 g of persulfate is added, heating is continued for about 1 min, and the solution is then cooled rapidly under running water. Heat destroys the persulfate, and an excess of persulfate must be kept to prevent loss of permanganate color. Too long a boiling time or too slow cooling result in loss of persulfate and, consequently, color.

Materials which reduce permanganate—chiefly natural occurring organic materials in surface water—interfere. These may be removed by the sample pretreatment required in the periodate method or by prolonged boiling and additional reagent in the persulfate method. Colored ions may also interfere, but in surface or finished waters such interferences are seldom encountered.

### 3. Silica

Silicon is the most abundant element in the earth's crust, occurring in a wide variety of forms in rocks and minerals. Crystalline silica ($SiO_2$) as quartz is a major constituent of igneous rocks and also of the resistates and hydrolyzates of sedimentary rocks. It is probable that most of the silicon in water comes from the breakdown of silicates ($SiO_4$) in the process of weathering. Although it is an ubiquitous element in natural waters, its significance has not been well understood because of the uncertainty of the form silicon takes in solution, although it has been customary to report silicon in terms of the oxide $SiO_2$. Discussions on the forms of silicon in natural waters have been presented by Mason (67), Roy (95), Iler (50), and Hem (45).

A gravimetric procedure and two colorimetric procedures for measurement of silicon as silica are given in *Standard Methods*. The gravimetric method is recommended for samples containing more than 20 mg/liter of silica and for samples containing severe interferences. A filtered sample containing at least 10 mg silica is placed in a 200-ml platinum dish to which is added 5 ml of 1:1 HCl. The mixture is evaporated to dryness on a water bath, but during the process, an additional 15 ml of 1:1 HCl is added in small aliquots. The dish is then dried at 110°C for about $\frac{1}{2}$ hr. The residue is then taken up in 5 ml of 1:1 HCl and about 50 ml of distilled water, warmed, and filtered through an ashless paper. The filtrate and chloride-free washings are again evaporated as before and refiltered through a second paper. The two filter papers containing the dehydrated silicic acid residue are dried and then ignited at 100°C to constant weight. This weight represents the weight of silicic acid plus insoluble nonsilicon material in the sample. The residue in the dish is then treated with a few drops of 1:1 $H_2SO_4$ and

10 ml of hydrofluoric acid and evaporated slowly to dryness on a hot plate in a hood. The dish is again dried and ignited at 1200°C to constant weight. The loss in weight represents the weight of $SiO_2$ in the original sample. Perchloric acid may be used instead of hydrochloric acid to shorten the digestion time and to yield a more filterable residue. In many cases, the silicic acid residue is sufficiently pure so that the hydrofluoric acid volatilization may be omitted and the weighing made directly. For this determination, platinum ware is required during the evaporation and a blank using all reagents should be run.

The two colorimetric procedures are very similar and employ the same reagents, with the exception that one of the procedures uses an additional reagent for more intense color development. A clear filtered sample is placed in either a Nessler tube or an Erlenmeyer flask, depending on whether the sample is to be read visually or photometrically, followed by 1:1 HCl and ammonium molybdate solution. The sample is allowed to stand for 1 hr and oxalic acid solution is added to eliminate interference by phosphates and tannins. After 5–15 min, the yellow color is read and compared to standards prepared in a similar manner.

The second colorimetric method is identical to the procedure just described; however, following the addition of oxalic acid, a reducing solution of 1-amino-2-naphthol-4-sulfonic acid, sodium sulfite, and sodium bisulfite is added to the sample. With this addition, the yellow molybdic acid is reduced to "heteropoly blue," which is much more intense and provides increased sensitivity.

In at least one of its forms, silica does not react with molybdate even though it appears to be completely soluble. In order to include this "colloidal" or "ionic" silica in the colorimetric method, an optional step is provided in which sodium bicarbonate and sulfuric acid is added to the sample and digested on a steam bath for 1 hr after which either colorimetric procedure may be used.

Silica is a common impurity in many reagent grade chemicals. Glassware used in performing the analysis may also contribute silica to the reaction. It is strongly recommended, therefore, that suitable blanks be run on all measurements.

### 4. Nitrate

The measurement of nitrate ion in water remains one of the classical problems in sanitary chemistry. At the time of this writing, no single procedure has been accepted as superior for all types of samples, although a number of procedures are available. These are: (1) reduction of the nitrate to nitrite or ammonia and the use of the colorimetric procedures for those ions; (*2*) production of color by reaction (nitration) with an organic material such as phenoldisulfonic acid or brucine; (*3*) ultraviolet absorption; (*4*) polarographic technique. Of these procedures, the first mentioned has not found wide usage because of the difficulty of controlling the reduction step. The ultraviolet procedure lacks dependability because of the possible presence of other ultraviolet absorbing materials, especially tannins and lignins. The polarographic procedure has been shown to be accurate and reproducible, but has not been widely used because of the special equipment required.

In the phenoldisulfonic acid method (13,118), the neutral or mildly alkaline sample is evaporated to dryness and treated with a small volume (usually about 2 ml) of reagent prepared from phenoldisulfonic acid and concentrated sulfuric acid. The acidified sample is then made alkaline with ammonium hydroxide and the resulting yellow color read photometrically.

Several interferences are commonly encountered. Chlorides, which are found in practically all water samples, must be removed by precipitation with silver sulfate. An excess of silver, however, may peptize following neutralization, resulting in a difficult-to-read color. If color is initially present in the sample, it should be removed by treatment with aluminum hydroxide or a similar decolorizing reagent. Other colorless organic materials may char upon addition of the reagent to the dried sample which results in an off color in the final alkalinized sample.

In the brucine procedure (36,79), the reagent is prepared by mixing 1 g of brucine sulfate with 0.1 g of sulfanilic acid in hot distilled water containing a small volume of hydrochloric acid. A 2-ml sample is then treated with 1 ml of the reagent, the whole of which is then poured into 10 ml of concentrated sulfuric acid. The resulting solution is then poured back and forth between the two containers four to six times to insure complete mixing and then allowed to stand in the dark for about 10 min. The solution is then diluted slightly with distilled water and allowed to stand for another 30 min before photometric reading.

Chloride does not interfere and the sulfanilic acid eliminates the possible interference from nitrite ion. Oxidizing and reducing agents must be absent and there is some positive interference from iron and quadrivalent manganese.

The descriptions of the foregoing procedures as well as the methods for measurement by ultraviolet and polarograph are outlined in *Standard Methods for the Examination of Water and Wastewater*. The brucine method is identical to the ASTM method designated D992-52.

## 5. Nitrite

It is perhaps ironic that of the various forms of nitrogen, the nitrite ion is least significant and most easily measured. The reaction used is a classic diazotization of alpha-naphthalamine and sulfanilic acid by the nitrite ion to form an intensely colored red dye (4,92). The colored end product is sensitive to 1 mg/liter when read in a 50-cm Nessler tube and is relatively free of interferences.

The sample is first filtered to remove suspended matter and decolorized with aluminum sulfate if necessary. A small volume, usually 1 ml, of a solution of sulfanilic acid is added to a 50-ml volume of sample and allowed to stand for about 5 min. A 1-ml volume of alpha-naphthalamine hydrochloride is then added and the entire solution buffered at a pH of 2.0–2.5. The reddish-purple color develops in about 10–20 min and is stable for several hours. This same reaction may be used for measurement of nitrate ion, following reduction to the nitrite form.

The procedure is commonly used whenever it is necessary to measure nitrite ion and is completely outlined in all reliable texts on sanitary analysis.

## 6. Phosphorus

Phosphorus is present in all natural waters in trace amounts. In waters receiving domestic sewage, agricultural chemicals and certain industrial wastes phosphates may reach levels of 5–10 mg/liter. Synthetic polyphosphates (molecularly dehydrated phosphates) commonly used in household washing compounds and discharged in raw or treated sewage into receiving streams hydrolyze to orthophosphate under certain conditions of temperature, pH, and sunlight.

To measure total phosphate (ortho plus poly), the sample is first digested with sulfuric acid to hydrolyze all polyphosphate to the ortho form. For separate measurements, two samples are required, one of which is analyzed without hydrolysis. A reagent of ammonium molybdate and sulfuric acid is added to the sample to form a slightly yellow compound, molybdophosphoric acid, which is then reduced to the molybdenum blue by addition of stannous chloride (25,128).

The measurement is sensitive to about 0.02 mg/liter and is simple to perform, but a number of precautions must be vigorously observed for accurate results. Frequently, laboratory glassware is washed with detergent materials containing phosphate compounds which are not removed by simple rinsing. All glassware used for the phosphate measurement should therefore be conditioned by carrying out the molybdenum blue reaction preliminarily using distilled water as a substitute sample.

The concentration of sulfuric acid affects the color production of molybdenum blue. It is necessary, therefore, to make compensatory addition of sulfuric acid to unhydrolyzed samples and to all standard solutions to insure proper color development in all samples. All samples and standards solutions must be cooled to room temperature before reagent addition, and the time allowed for color development must be controlled.

A stable solution of stannous chloride may be prepared by dissolving the reagent in glycerine (106). Amino naphthol sulfonic acid is frequently used as a substitute for stannous chloride, but is said to be less sensitive (55). At concentrations of phosphate below 1 mg/liter, arsenic, tannins, and lignin are possible interferences.

A more recent method that has gained quick acceptance in the sanitary chemistry field is the method of Murphy and Riley (77), which incorporates sulfuric acid, ammonium molybdate, potassium antimonyl tartrate, and ascorbic acid into a single sensitive reagent. Gales, Julian, and Kroner (30) have shown that to measure all forms of phosphorus present in a sample, including organically bound phosphorus, it may be necessary to employ a more rigorous digestion by use of ammonium persulfate.

### 7. Fluoride

The methods of measurement for fluoride are largely based on a single reaction. A dye, Alizarin red S, is complexed with a zirconium salt in an acid solution. The addition of a sample containing fluoride results in the displacement of the zirconium from the dye complex. The net result is a bleaching of the colored solution by the fluoride. As the concentration of fluoride increases, the color produced becomes lighter or different in hue. In practice, the concentration of the dye or the zirconium may be altered to meet certain analytical demands.

In the Scott-Sanchis procedure (99,105), designed for visual use in Nessler tubes, a single reagent consisting of Alizarin red S, zirconium oxychloride, and hydrochloric and sulfuric acids is added directly to the samples. After 1 hr, the samples are compared visually with fluoride standards similarly prepared. The procedure is sensitive to about 0.05 mg/liter fluoride and has good tolerance to usual interferences.

The Megregian-Maier procedure (70) is designed for photometric use and employs the same reagents. In this method, the alizarin dye is prepared separately in aqueous solution and sulfuric acid; hydrochloric acid and zirconium oxychloride are combined in a second solution. These two solutions are then added separately to the sample, and the resulting color is read in a photometer after a closely timed interval. Another photometric procedure developed by Megregian (69) uses a modified dye, Eriochrome Cyanine R, and the usual zirconium reagent. This method is used by the U.S. Geological Survey, but has been altered by the addition of barium chloride to the zirconium reagent to overcome the method's sensitivity to sulfate. Removal of the barium sulfate precipitate requires an extra step.

The most popular method published in recent years is the so-called SPADNS method developed by Bellack and Schouboe (8). A zirconium-acid solution is still used, but the alizarin is replaced by the dye sodium 2-(parasulfophenylazo)-1,8-dihydroxy-3,6-naphthalene sulfonate.* This method has found acceptance by water analysts because of its improved tolerance to the usual interferences.

The most recent development in fluoride analysis utilizes a specific ion electrode (29). This device is similar in construction to a hydrogen ion electrode, except that the tip of the probe consists of a crystalline membrane composed of lanthanum fluoride doped with minute amounts of a divalent cation, such as europium. The membrane is selectively permeable to fluoride ions. In use, the fluoride probe and a reference electrode are placed in an aqueous sample which has been treated with a citric acid buffer. The response of the electrometer, as in a pH measurement, is proportional to the concentration of fluoride in the sample. Reaction time of the probe is about 3 min at 0.5 mg/liter fluoride. The fluoride probe has been quickly adopted for routine fluoride analysis because it eliminates, in most cases, the troublesome distillation.

### a. INTERFERENCES IN THE FLUORIDE MEASUREMENT

Most finished water samples contain amounts of aluminum, phosphate, sulfate, and a degree of alkalinity, each of which is a potential interference in the fluoride determination. Table VII shows the effect of these constituents on the various methods.

For fluoride measurement in samples containing gross amounts of interfering materials, distillation is recommended. A procedure devised by Bellack (7) employs a simple distillation from a sulfuric acid solution with close control of temperature. A solution of sulfuric acid and water is prepared and distilled until a boiling temperature of 200°C is reached. The distilling solution is cooled and a volume of sample containing less

---

* Eastman Organic Chemicals, No. 7309.

TABLE VII
Concentration of Interfering Substances Causing
0.1 mg/liter Error at 1.0 mg/liter Fluoride[a]

| Interference | Type of error | Scott-Sanchis Conc. mg/liter | Megregian-Maier Conc. mg/liter | Eriochrome Cyanine R Conc. mg/liter | SPADNS Conc. mg/liter |
|---|---|---|---|---|---|
| Alkalinity (as CaCO₃) | Negative | 400 | 325 | Unknown | 5000 |
| Aluminum | Negative | 0.25 | 0.20 | | 0.1 |
| Chloride | Negative | 2000 | 1800 | | 7000[b] |
| Phosphate | Positive | 5 | 5 | | 16 |
| Hexameta-phosphate | Positive | 1 | 1 | | 1 |
| Sulfate | Positive | 300 | 400 | | 200 |

[a] Residual chlorine must be completely removed with arsenite reagent. Color and turbidity must be removed or compensated for. Aluminum is self-correcting with time; after 2 hrs 3.0 mg/liter can be tolerated.
[b] Positive error.

than 3 mg of fluoride is added. The distillation is then continued until the temperature of the solution again reaches 200°C. The distillate, containing all the fluoride, is then analyzed by the method of choice. A series of samples may be distilled from the same solution if they are not too highly mineralized.

This procedure is simple and straightforward, but caution must be observed to avoid excessive carryover of sulfate and chlorides. Brine solutions and sea waters may result in excessive chlorides in the distillate, in which case the chlorides may be removed by silver nitrate precipitation.

## E. PHYSICAL PROPERTIES OF WATER

### 1. pH

Measurement of the pH of water samples should be made by means of a potentiometric meter. Since changes may occur as the result of precipitation of salts or the release of dissolved gases, pH should be determined at the time the sample is collected. Although kits are available for colorimetric measurement of pH, the results may be unreliable because of color or turbidity of the sample. Portable, battery-operated meters are available and are sufficiently accurate for most uses. Readings are reported to the nearest tenth of a unit.

## 2. Hardness

Hardness is a property of water caused by a number of dissolved materials: calcium, magnesium, heavy metals, alkaline earths, and free acid. Visual evidence of hardness is exhibited by the reaction with soap to form a scummy precipitate. The "scum" is formed when calcium and magnesium (and other cations) react with the dissolved soap to form insoluble calcium and magnesium salts of the fatty acids. Modern synthetic detergents (nonsoap cleaners) do not form insoluble salts with calcium and magnesium so that hardness has become less of a problem in the modern household. Hardness is also observed as incrustations on plumbing fixtures and scale formation in pipes, boilers, etc. Calcium and magnesium, as major constituents of water, are generally considered the principal ions contributing to hardness. Other metals, such as iron, manganese, aluminum, strontium, and barium, also contribute to hardness, but negligibly so.

Until about 1950, hardness was measured by titration with a standard solution prepared from an alcohol solution of castile soap. More recently, the chelating properties of the sodium salt of ethylenediaminetetra acetic acid (EDTA) have been used. In this procedure, a solution of EDTA is prepared and standardized by titration into a solution of known calcium concentration.

The indicator used in the titration is Eriochrome Black T, which displays a deep purple-red color in the presence of calcium, magnesium, and other heavy metals and is a flat blue in their absences. The titration with EDTA chelates the "hardness" cations, removing them from the dye complex, which results in the color change from purple-red to blue at the endpoint (103). The optimum pH of the titration is 10.

Interference from heavy metals can be minimized by complexing with cyanide or sodium sulfide (33). In routine practice, the cyanide may be added to the ammonia buffer which is used for pH control. Results are accurate and reproducible to less than 1 mg/liter.

Total hardness, calcium hardness, or magnesium hardness may also be run by determining the individual cations and calculating as $CaCO_3$. The U.S. Geological Survey measures both calcium and magnesium by atomic absorption and reports the results, after calculation, as total hardness.

## 3. Temperature

The temperature of a water may be important as a guide to treatment requirements or in detecting the presence of abnormalities, such as cooling water. Measurement should always be made at the time of collection of a water sample, but may also be continuously monitored with recording devices when necessary. For discrete samples, a good grade of mercury thermometer or a metal dial thermometer may be used. Occasional checking against a National Bureau of Standards reference thermometer is recommended.

Thermistor devices are available for measurement of temperature at subsurface depths or for the continuous monitoring of water temperature at plant intakes. Such systems are often quite accurate.

Water temperature is reported to the nearest whole degree centigrade.

## 4. Specific Conductance

Specific conductance is defined as the reciprocal of the resistance measured between two electrodes 1 cm apart and 1 cm² in cross section. The conductance of a water sample is a measure of the total concentration of ionized substances and is affected by:

*1.* The magnitude of the applied emf.
*2.* Electrode area.
*3.* Distance between electrodes.
*4.* Temperature.
*5.* Ion mobility.
*6.* Concentration of ions in solution.

The first three of these variables are controlled by designing the instrument to meet rigid specifications. A constant voltage source is used and the cell is designed with electrode surface area and distance chosen to yield resistance equivalent to the theoretical cell in the definition, or stated multiples of those resistances. Temperature is measured at 25°C. With these variables held constant, the specific conductance is directly proportional to the concentration of electrolytes in the sample (42).

The measurement is made by adjusting the temperature of the sample to 25°C, dipping the cell into the sample, while reading the resistance from the galvanometer. By suitable circuitry, the meter may be made to read directly in reciprocal ohms or "micromhos."

Since specific conductance is directly related to the concentration of dissolved solids in the sample, the value may be used as a rapid, convenient index of the total ionic concentration. Because of differing ion mobility, no universal relationship can be established, but on a particular water the relationship of dissolved substance to specific conductance can be readily established (111,126).

## TABLE VIII
### Equivalent Conductance of Common Ions

| Ion | Equivalent conductance, $\mu$mhos per mg/liter (25°C) |
|---|---|
| Cl | 2.14 |
| SO$_4$ | 1.54 |
| CO$_3$ | 2.82 |
| HCO$_3$ | 0.71 |
| NO$_3$ | 1.15 |
| Ca | 2.60 |
| Mg | 3.82 |
| Na | 2.16 |

The measurement of conductance may be useful in checking the reliability of mineral analyses. Rossum (94) found that a satisfactory correlation could be obtained in 92% of the water samples investigated. In practice, the concentration of each ion, determined by appropriate test, is multiplied by the equivalent conductance (see Table VIII), and the sum of the individual conductances is calculated. This value should agree with the specific conductance of the sample within ±2%.

The procedure is not valid for waters of high or low pH, since the specific conductances of H$^+$ and OH$^-$ are very high.

Specific conductance may be used to check the quality of distilled water in the laboratory. For satisfactory quality, specific conductance should be less than 2 $\mu$ohms.

### 5. Turbidity

#### a. DEFINITION AND SOURCES

Turbidity is generally considered to be a measure of the light-absorbing properties of the water sample. Light scattering and absorption are due to the presence of suspended particles of clay, silt, organic matter, or microorganisms (110).

#### b. TURBIDITY TEST PROCEDURES

The most common procedure for the measurement of turbidity is the Jackson candle method. The Jackson turbidimeter (125) is a long glass cylinder, calibrated according to an arbitrary scale of units, mounted above a standard beeswax candle. The test is performed by pouring the well-mixed sample slowly into the tube while observing the image of the candle longitudinally through the tube. When the image of the flame is no longer visible, the turbidity of the sample, in Jackson units, is read from the calibrations on the side of the tube corresponding to the depth of the sample.

The turbidimeter is limited to the measurement of turbidities between 25 and 1000 units. For values below 25 units, the sample is compared with standards prepared by diluting standard suspensions of fullers earth in french square bottles and viewing samples and standards through the sides of the bottles. Samples having turbidity greater than 1000 units must be diluted with distilled water to reach the range of the turbidimeter.

Alternatively, turbidity may be measured photometrically using a commercial photometer or nephelometer (5,82). When such instruments are used, however, they must be calibrated with standard suspension prepared by means of the Jackson turbidimeter. Photometric measurements are influenced by the color of the sample, although the effect of color may be minimized by selecting a wavelength where the interference is minor. Results are reported in terms of Jackson units.

The turbidity test is useful as a measure of the amount of suspended matter in the sample, although it cannot be directly correlated with the weight per unit volume of suspended material. It is routinely used as a control test in water treatment. It should be emphasized that the test is based on light extinction. Obviously, the particle size and the refractive index of the suspended material will have an effect on the values obtained, since small amounts of finely dispersed solids will exhibit higher readings than equal amounts of larger particles. In addition, a highly colored sample will yield high turbidity values due to light absorption by the color. The chief sources of error in the Jackson candle method are:

*1.* Failure to adequately disperse the solids immediately before and during testing.

*2.* Settling of the particles in the turbidimeter tube.

*3.* Color in the sample.

*4.* Failure to properly clean the glass tube and adjust the candle.

Precision of the test is approximately ±30 units.

A recent improvement in turbidity measurements has been achieved by development of a stable turbidity standard. A suspension of formazine is embedded in a transparent lucite cylinder and standardized in Jackson candle units. Turbidity readings of samples contained in glass vials of the same size as the lucite standard are obtained photometrically. The instrument is commercially available (37).

## 6. Color

The color of most natural waters is due to minute amounts of humus materials derived from decaying vegetable matter. Occasionally, however, industrial wastes may cause color. In color measurements, it is necessary to distinguish between true color and apparent color. The "color" that one observes when viewing a body of water is created by reflections from the sky and shoreline, from particulate matter suspended in the water, and from the solution color itself. In the laboratory only the true color, i.e., materials in the solution or in extremely fine colloids, are measured. Therefore, all suspended matter must be removed from the sample before color determination.

The color test is performed by centrifuging the sample to remove particulates, comparing the color visually against standards, and reporting the results as standard color units (109). Standards are prepared from a dilute mixture of potassium chloroplatinate and cobaltous chloride which has a yellow color visually similar to the hue of natural waters (44). Some analysts prefer to measure the color of the sample photometrically (56), but often the colored material in the sample has an absorption wavelength significantly different from the salt standards. In the author's laboratory, water samples collected from a variety of rivers and lakes in the United States showed absorption maximum varying from 450 to 600 $\mu$.

In the opinion of many water chemists, the color determination is considered to be the least precise of all quantitative tests (89), primarily because the test depends upon the judgement of the analyst in matching "colors" of materials derived from natural organic substances with standards prepared from inorganic reagents. Attempts have been made to develop a more reproducible test for color and to characterize the color as to hue, brightness, and purity (98). The procedures, however, are cumbersome, requiring measurement of three separate wavelengths and the use of a diagram for calculating the results.

While color is an important consideration in the public acceptance of a water supply, the laboratory determination has a number of serious weaknesses. These are:

*1.* The arbitrarily selected color standards often fail to match the hue of the sample, resulting in considerable guesswork on the part of the analyst.

*2.* The true or solution color of the sample is often not a valid measure of the appearance of the water due to removal of colored particulate matter.

*3.* The test measures a physical property of the water, but yields no information concerning the identity of the substances producing that property.

## 7. Odor

The term "taste and odor," often referred to in water quality analysis, is a misnomer, since water is rarely tasted in the analytical laboratory. Instead, the odor of the water is quantitatively measured.

Odor determination is not a precise test, since it depends upon a highly variable human sense. Careful control of test conditions, however, can greatly reduce the subjective nature of the determination. The variables which must be considered and controlled are:

*1.* Sampling and sample container
*2.* Test procedure
*3.* Test panel
*4.* Glassware and dilution water

Since many compounds producing odor are volatile or unstable, the odor determination should be made as quickly as possible after sample collection. The sample should be collected in a very clean 500-ml glass-stoppered bottle, filled to the top. If storage is necessary, the sample should be refrigerated.

A variety of test procedures have been suggested, but the most useful is a dilution technique employing a test panel of several individuals. The use of a number of participants reduces error due to individual differences in odor detection. The panel should be experienced in odor testing, since greater sensitivity is acquired through regular practice. Smoking and eating immediately before participating in an odor panel seriously reduces sensitivity. Complete objectivity is desired, though seldom obtainable.

The test procedure is designed to determine the dilution of the sample at which odor is just perceptible. The dilution is expressed as the "threshold odor number." Thus a threshold number of 4 indicates that odor is detectable in a 1:4 dilution, but not at higher dilutions.

Special precautions are required to insure that all glassware is odor-free and that the atmospheric environment does not contribute odors. Odor-free water, prepared by slow filtration through activated carbon, is required for dilution.

Because of the wide range of abilities in detecting odors, the threshold odor number reflects only the opinion of the panel at the time of testing. If the same panel is used regularly, the results of a single test will be significant with respect to other samples examined by the same group, but probably will not agree with values reported by a different panel.

Since the type of odor present may lead to an identification of the source of contamination, qualitative descriptions are often useful. Odors described as "medicinal," "fishy," "earthy," or "chemical" often indicate the presence of phenols, algae, decaying vegetation, or chlorine (16,73,93).

An excellent discussion of the threshold odor test is found in various issues of the *Taste and Odor Control Journal,* published by The West Virginia Pulp and Paper Company (100,107).

## 8. Dissolved Oxygen

The basic analytical procedure for the determination of dissolved oxygen, first published by Winkler (127) in 1888, is the quantitative oxidation of manganous hydroxide to a higher form of hydroxide at high pH by the dissolved oxygen in the water. This complex hydroxide in turn liberates free iodine from potassium iodide when the solution is acidified. The liberated iodine is titrated with thiosulfate, using a starch endpoint. The following reactions are thought to take place:

$$MnSO_4 + 2KOH \rightarrow Mn(OH)_2 + K_2SO_4$$
$$2Mn(OH)_2 + O_2 \rightarrow 2MnO(OH)_2$$
$$MnO(OH)_2 + 2H_2SO_4 \rightarrow Mn(SO_4)_2 + 3H_2O$$
$$Mn(SO_4)_2 + 2KI \rightarrow MnSO_4 + K_2SO_4 + I_2$$
$$I_2 + 2Na_2S_2O_3 \rightarrow 2NaI + Na_2S_4O_6$$

Since the procedure is based upon a series of oxidation and reduction reactions, it is apparent that other oxidizing agents present in the water may act to produce a positive error, while reducing agents may consume iodine and result in a low value.

In order to make the method applicable to natural waters, the original procedure was modified extensively. The most important changes were suggested by Alsterberg (2) and Rideal and Stewart (91).

Nitrite ion, present in many polluted waters, produces iodine upon acidification, resulting in a large error. The Alsterberg procedure, as later modified by Ruchoft et al. (97) incorporates sodium azide in the alkaline-iodide reagent to convert the nitrite to molecular nitrogen. In order to prevent interference from ferrous iron, the Rideal-Stewart modification utilizes a preliminary oxidation of the iron with acid potassium permanganate and removal of excess permanganate with oxalate, followed by the regular Winkler reagents.

Because large amounts of organic matter may hydrolyze under the rigorous alkaline conditions, or exert an iodine demand upon acidification, Theriault (121) proposed an extremely short contact period for the alkaline reaction, with immediate acidification and titration. Rennerfelt (90) suggested the use of a control bottle titrated with iodine to determine the effect of reducing substances.

Although the presence of interfering materials may often require one or more of the above modifications, the method in widest use is the following (112).

Two milliliters of the manganous sulfate reagent and 2 ml of the combined alkaline iodide–azide solution are added to a full 300-ml bottle of the sample. After mixing and settling to permit completion of the oxidation of the manganese, 2 ml of concentrated sulfuric acid is added. After mixing, 203 ml of the sample is transferred to a flask and titrated with 0.025 $N$ thiosulfate solution to a blue starch endpoint. Each milliliter of the thiosulfate used is equivalent to 1 mg./liter dissolved oxygen in the sample. A recent innovation, which increases the speed of the test, involves transfer of the entire contents of the bottle and titration with 0.038 $N$ thiosulfate.

When performed by an experienced analyst, the dissolved oxygen test is accurate to ±0.05 mg/liter. By utilizing special techniques for sampling and a potentiometric endpoint, a precision of ±0.001 mg/liter can be obtained (1).

The increasing use of instrumentation in the laboratory has influenced the determination of dissolved oxygen. In some laboratories, the dropping mercury polarograph is used (3,10). The polarograph offers equal precision and accuracy, increased speed, and less manipulation. An electrolyte, containing KCl and a maxima suppressor, is the only reagent required. An applied voltage of 0.4 vs. saturated calomel electrode is recommended, since a complete polarogram is not required.

In many cases it is desirable to determine dissolved oxygen in the field, either on freshly collected sample or, more often, directly in the stream. For measurements *in situ*, the dissolved oxygen probe (12) is the only satisfactory instrument. This electrode system is a modification of the polarographic determination, using a noble metal cathode and lead or zinc anode. The cell is surrounded by a gas-permeable membrane, such as polyethylene or Teflon, which retains a thin film of electrolyte. Oxygen diffusion through the membrane is reduced at the cathode, producing a current which is measured on a micrometer. The current is directly proportional to the partial pressure of oxygen in the water. A similar instrument, developed by Mancy and Westgarth (64) is in reality a galvanic cell, since the electrode reaction develops a potential across the electrodes.

These instruments are commercially available (85) and have been used extensively for both reconnaissance surveys of stream conditions and continuous recording of dissolved oxygen levels (15).

## 9. Biochemical Oxygen Demand

Biochemical oxygen demand (BOD) is defined as "the quantity of dissolved oxygen, in milligrams per liter, required during stabilization of the decomposable organic matter by aerobic biochemical action" (108). In the simplest form, the test is conducted as follows (113): Two identical 300-ml bottles of special design are filled with the sample to be examined. The dissolved oxygen concentration of one of the bottles is determined by any of the acceptable laboratory methods. The second bottle is incubated under standard conditions (20°C, in the dark, with air excluded from the bottle by a water seal) for 5 days. At the end of the incubation period, the dissolved oxygen concentration of the incubated bottle is determined. The reduction in oxygen content (difference between the initial and final DO) is due to the demand exerted by the microbiological population and is a measure of the oxidizable organic material in the sample. The value is reported as "5 day BOD" of the sample.

Since the sample is incubated at 20°C, the initial DO of the sample should be near saturation (9.2 mg/liter) at that temperature.

The final DO concentration, however, should not be below 1.0 mg/liter, since DO determinations below this concentration are not sufficiently accurate for precise work. Therefore, if the oxygen demand of the sample is greater than approximately 8.0 mg/liter, a suitable dilution of the sample must be made, using dilution water (96) containing essential mineral nutrients, but having a very low oxygen demand.

In Table IX, the ranges of BOD usually encountered are shown, along with the appropriate dilutions to be used.

A number of substances found in polluted waters interfere in the BOD test. Heavy metals and toxic organic compounds inhibit or eliminate biological action essential to satisfactory completion of the test (83). Acids and alkalies in sufficient concentration present unfavorable pH conditions during incubation. Further, some synthetic organic compounds

TABLE IX

Range of Biochemical Oxygen Demand for Various Waters
and Appropriate Dilutions

| Type of sample | BOD, mg/liter | Dilutions (% sample) |
|---|---|---|
| Unpolluted rivers | 1.0–3.0 | 100 |
| | | 100–20 |
| Polluted rivers | 5.0–20.0 | |
| Treated sewage | 50–100 | 10–5 |
| Raw sewage | 100–400 | 5–1 |
| Industrial wastes | 100–10,000 | 5–0.05 |

are sufficiently resistant to biological attack to preclude oxidation (74). Where possible, the interfering substances must be removed from the sample prior to the start of the test.

When carefully carried out on samples containing biologically decomposable materials, the BOD test is a reliable measure of the concentration of these materials, but in many cases, conditions of the sample are such that other analytical procedures must be used to characterize the organic content.

## F. BACTERIOLOGICAL EXAMINATION OF WATER

### 1. Importance

In any evaluation of the acceptable nature of a water supply for domestic consumption, the examination of the supply for the presence of microorganisms is essential. Evidence of human contamination can be established by rather simple bacteriological tests, permitting a judgement of the relative health hazard of the water. Where significant levels of contamination are found, alternative sources must be used or the supply treated extensively in a modern treatment plant to remove disease-producing organisms.

### 2. Indicator Organisms

Because of the difficulty in estimating the numbers of pathogenic bacteria in water samples, it is customary to resort to an enumeration of certain nonpathogens which always occur in waters contaminated with sewage. The most commonly used indicator organisms are those of the coliform group. Human excreta contains vast numbers of these bacteria, and their presence in a water supply in significant numbers is prima facie evidence of sewage contamination. Experience over many years has established a correlation between numbers of coliforms and domestic sewage pollution.

Since coliform organisms may occur without direct contamination from human sources, increasing attention has been focused on the specific subgroup which occurs only in warm-blooded animals, the "fecal coliforms" (52). By special tests, these bacteria can be enumerated and the relative proportion to the total coliform numbers determined. Thus, the evidence for human contamination may be strengthened. In addition to the coliform determination, another group of pollution indicators, the fecal streptococci, may be isolated (54). The presence of this organism suggests recent pollution of human origin.

### 3. Methods

Coliform organisms may be determined by either of two methods (51,116). In the older method, portions of the sample are inoculated into liquid medium and incubated at 35°C. Fermentation of sugars, producing gas, is presumptive evidence of coliforms, which may be confirmed by subculturing in a more selective medium. For the detection of fecal coliform, an elevated temperature (44.5°C) is employed (31). Since the bacteria are not actually counted in the test, the results are termed a "most probable number" (MPN), which serves as an index of coliform numbers.

The newer and more precise test is carried out by filtering the bacteria from the sample onto a cellulose membrane, where the organisms are cultured to produce visible colonies. Since it may be assumed that each colony represents a single bacterium in the original sample, the actual numbers of organisms may be determined by counting the colonies produced from a given aliquot of sample. Total coliform, fecal, coliform, and fecal streptococci may be enumerated by appropriate modifications of this method.

It is sometimes of value to estimate the total bacteria which will multiply at 35°C. By preparation of agar plates inoculated with sample, the "standard plate count" can be determined. This value is useful in judging the water for industrial uses and to measure the efficiency of treatment processes.

### 4. Interpretation of Results

Standards for acceptance quality of drinking water have been published by the U.S. Public Health Service (86). The standards recommend that the average coliform density of all samples examined per month should not exceed one per 100 ml. Surveys of modern water treatment plants indicate that this standard can be routinely achieved.

A commonly applied criteria for raw water to be treated for domestic consumption is that the coliform density should not exceed 5000 per 100 ml.

## IV. ADVANCED INSTRUMENTAL METHODS FOR WATER ANALYSIS

### A. INTRODUCTION

In the general area of water analysis there is a very broad trend of analytical requirements. In many small city water treatment plants the frequently used parameters, such as turbidity, color, hardness, and chlorides, may be determined two or three times daily. In special situations it may be necessary to measure iron and manganese or to perform a chlorine demand test, but the number of samples and variety of tests performed are limited. On the other hand, in control laboratories of large city treatment plants, consulting companies, and state and Federal laboratories, a very large number of samples and a wide variety of tests may be performed daily.

To meet the requirements of massive sampling programs and specialized measurements, a number of special instruments are available.

These instruments may be relatively inexpensive, such as special purpose flame photometers, or they may be very costly, such as the direct reading emission spectrograph. Nevertheless, the instruments described below provide special capabilities to laboratories engaged in extensive water analysis. The list does not include the very simple specialized instruments or the instruments normally found in analytical laboratories, such as pH meters and spectrophotometers.

### B. FLAME PHOTOMETERY

#### 1. Emission Technique

Flame photometry is an extremely simple method of analysis for certain metallic elements which can be spectrally excited at relatively low temperatures. Sodium and potassium are among the elements which can be easily measured using a flame technique.

The water sample to be analyzed is sprayed or aspirated into a gas flame and spectral excitation takes place under carefully controlled conditions. The rate of sample introduction into the flame and the flame temperature must be constant and reproducible in order to obtain a reliable analysis. The procedure is extremely rapid and is the best method available for measurement of both sodium and potassium. Much work has been published on determination of many of the metallic elements (20,68), but in addition to the two already named, only calcium, magnesium, strontium, and lithium are measured to any extent using the flame method.

Sodium is probably the most easily excited element and has a very strong emission line at 589 mμ. In normal river waters and drinking water, sodium may be accurately determined without special techniques. Potassium has a strong emission line at 768 mμ, but is not as interference-free as sodium. To avoid using special techniques for the potassium measurement, many analysts simply replace the usual blue-sensitive phototube with a red-sensitive phototube for elimination of adjacent spectral interferences.

Although all flame photometers operate on the same basic principles, the details of operation for various instruments differ.

Inexpensive instruments, designed for the specific measurement of only sodium and potassium, are available. Sophisticated spectrophotometric instruments, such as the Unicam 500 which permits measurement of more elements throughout the range of the visible spectrum, are also available. The analyst should, of course, acquaint himself with the operation manual for his particular instrument and should also be familiar with general literature on the subject of flame photometry.

## C. ATOMIC ABSORPTION TECHNIQUE

Atomic absorption spectroscopy is a relatively new analytical technique, although the principle has been known for many years. As in flame photometry, the sample is aspirated in the flame, but the absorption of radiation from a secondary source provides the quantitative measurement. Since absorption is due to ground-state atoms rather than excited atoms, the sensitivity is much greater. The technique is highly specific, due to the nature of the light source (11,53). Two such instruments are illustrated in Figs. 3 and 4.

Atomic absorption is ideally suited to the determination of metallic ions in water, since liquid samples are used. Analysis can be made without prior sample preparation, except for calcium and magnesium, where

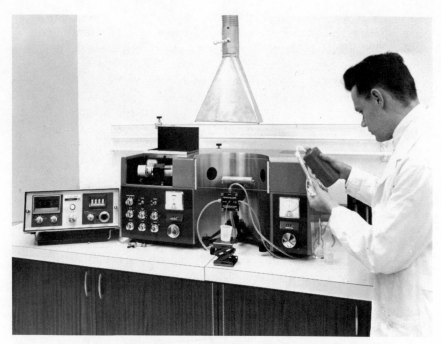

Fig. 3. Perkin-Elmer Atomic Absorption Spectrometer, Model 303. Photograph courtesy of the Perkin-Elmer Corporation.

dilution in 1% lanthanium chloride is required. As many as 50 determinations per hour are possible (28,84).

In contrast to emission spectroscopy, only a single metal may be deter-

TABLE X

| Metal | Sensitivity for 2% absorption, mg/liter |
|---|---|
| Cadmium | 0.06 |
| Calcium | 0.2 |
| Chromium | 0.10 |
| Copper | 0.2 |
| Iron | 0.2 |
| Lead | 0.6 |
| Nickel | 0.3 |
| Zinc | 0.06 |

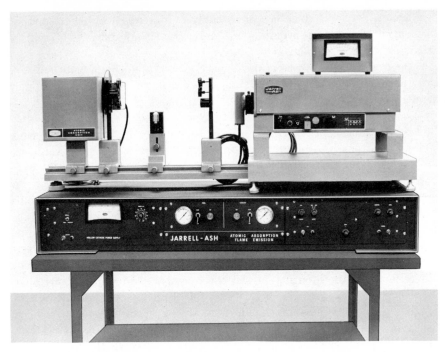

Fig. 4. Jarrell-Ash Atomic Absorption Spectrophotometer. Photograph courtesy of Jarrell-Ash Company.

mined at a time. Thus the technique is better suited to repetitive analysis than to scanning for the presence of possible contaminants.

With most metals, sensitivity is adequate for control purposes, although somewhat less than in colorimetric methods. Typical sensitivities, in milligrams per liter, are shown in Table X. When the sensitivities listed are not adequate, concentration by evaporation, ion exchange, or solvent extraction may be used. Extraction is preferred, since organic solvents enhance the absorption in the flame (18).

## D. EMISSION SPECTROSCOPY

The emission spectrograph (78), which has long been a favorite analytical tool of metallurgical and soil chemists, has only recently been used by water chemists to any great extent. Whereas the time-honored colorimetric procedures permit measurement of only one element at a time, the emission spectrograph is capable of detecting and measuring more than 60 elements simultaneously in a single sample. This not only enables the chemist to perform a complete analysis in a relatively short period, but also furnishes information on the presence of difficult-to-identify toxic or nutritional elements.

Spectrographic analysis is based on the measurement of light emitted by individual elements in a sample that has been volatilized in a high energy source.

During excitation by a thermal or electrical source, the orbital electrons of an element absorb energy by moving to higher energy orbits. These electrons return to their normal energy levels (ground state) by a single jump or a series of jumps. The energy emitted with each jump produces a spectral line of characteristic wavelength for the particular element. Each element has a large number of spectral emissions which occur in the spectrum from the infrared through the ultraviolet.

Several different optical arrangements have been devised for recording these emission lines on film. After recording the spectrum of an element on film, the presence of various emission lines are used for qualitative identification; the intensity of the lines, compared to similarly prepared standards, can be used for quantifying the elements. Some elements have high energy emissions in the portion of the spectrum most sensitive to photographic response and are therefore easily measured. Beryllium and silver emissions, for example, are very sensitive to photographic detection, whereas the opposite is true of zinc and arsenic.

More sophisticated instruments have been designed in recent years in which the photographic plate is replaced by a series of phototubes located to detect spectral emissions from specific elements. The so-called "direct reader" spectrographs eliminate the complexities of film development, emulsion calibration, and microphotometer readings (Fig. 5). They also permit efficient measurement of some elements which are not amenable to the photographic procedures. Zinc, for example, is found in almost all natural waters, using a direct reader technique, but it is rarely found when a photographic procedure is used. Because of space limitations imposed by the physical size of the phototubes and crowding of tubes on the spectral arc, very few direct reading spectrographs have been manufactured that are capable of measuring as many as 25 elements.

For measurement of trace elements, Haffty (38) uses a method in which a sample containing about 50–60 mg of dissolved solids is evaporated to dryness in a quartz or Vycor vessel. The residue is then scraped from the sides of the dish, pulverized, mixed with spectroscopically pure graphite, weighed onto a cratered electrode and excited with a direct current arc to complete consumption of the sample. Standards are pre-

Fig. 5. Jarrell-Ash Direct-Reader Spectrograph with sequential readout. Photograph courtesy of the Jarrell-Ash Company.

pared by blending a number of standard trace elements salts into a matrix of calcium, magnesium, sodium and potassium salts.

The proportions of the matrix salts are chosen to approximate the average composition of waters of North America (14). All the operations of weighing, mixing, and electrode preparation are performed in a warm, dry atmosphere to prevent moisture absorption by hygroscopic materials in the residue. With this procedure, it is possible to detect about 60 elements, many at concentration levels in the microgram per liter range.

Kopp and Kroner (60) have developed a method that utilizes a liquid sample which dispenses with the weighing operations used in the residue procedures. A volume of sample containing 100 mg of dissolved solids is evaporated to 5.0 ml and arced using a rotating disk electrode arrangement. Standards are prepared by spiking known concentrations of elements into a matrix solution of calcium, magnesium, sodium, and potassium salts similar to Haffty's. Kopp's procedure is adapted to use on a direct reading instrument programmed for 19 elements. This method is restrictive as to the number of elements that may be measured and also lacks sensitivity on samples containing large amounts of dissolved solids, but it is capable of accurate analyses of large numbers of samples in a short time. Table XI summarizes the levels of sensitivity for various elements obtained by Kopp by several different water systems of the United States.

TABLE XI

Approximate Levels of Detection for Trace Elements
by Direct Reader Spectrograph for Various Water
Systems of the United States ($\mu$g/liter)

| Group | Colorado River | Columbia River | Ohio River | Mississippi River | Great Lakes River |
|---|---|---|---|---|---|
| Beryllium | 0.5–1.0 | 0.05–0.1 | 0.1–0.15 | 0.1–0.2 | 0.05–0.1 |
| Barium<br>Boron<br>Silver<br>Strontium | 0.5–10 | 0.5–1.0 | 1.0–1.5 | 1.0–2.0 | 0.05–1.0 |
| Copper<br>Manganese | 15–30 | 1.5–3.0 | 3.0–5.0 | 3.0–6.0 | 1.5–3.0 |
| Chromium<br>Iron | 25–50 | 2.5–5.0 | 5.0–8.0 | 5.0–10 | 2.5–5.0 |
| Cadmium<br>Cobalt<br>Nickel<br>Zinc | 50–100 | 5.0–10 | 10–15 | 10–20 | 5.0–10 |
| Aluminum<br>Lead<br>Molybdenum<br>Vanadium | 100–200 | 10–20 | 20–30 | 20–40 | 10–20 |

## E. AUTOMATIC REPETITIVE INSTRUMENTS

There are two systems for conducting automatic, or "robot," types of analyses. These systems are based on repetitive measurement of a single constituent on successive samples using either a colorimeter–recorder or an electrode–recorder device. Either system may be modified to monitor a continuous stream rather than discrete samples.

The colorimeter–recorder system (120) consists of four integral parts, each of which performs a separate function (Fig. 6). The parts are (1) a sampler–timer, (2) a roller-type pump, (3) a flow through colorimeter, and (4) a recorder. The sampler–timer consists of a perforated circular plate which holds a large number of test tubes. The plate is solenoid actuated to move one stop at a time as controlled by the timer. Samples are pumped from each successive test tube through flexible tubing, through a manifold construction on the pump. The reagents required

Fig. 6. Technicon Auto Analyzer. Photograph courtesy of the Technicon Instruments Corporation.

for performing a colorimetric reaction are also pulled from their respective containers by the same pump and brought together in the proper sequence in the manifold. All solutions used in the reaction are moved at the same rate, but volumes of reagents are varied by proper selection of tubing sizes. A variety of accessories, especially spirals of glass tubing, are employed to obtain mixing time delay and temperature control. When the color reaction has reached the desired stage, the solution passes into the flowthrough colorimeter. The phototube in the colorimeter senses the amount of color in the sample and transmits the signal to a recorder. Concentrations are calculated by comparing peak heights of the unknown with peak heights of standard solutions.

With this type of instrumentation, it is theoretically possible to measure any element, ion, or compound which can be determined colorimetrically. Consequently, almost all the conventional water measurements have been successfully automated. It is also possible, with this equipment, to combine manifolds so that several parameters may be measured simultaneously.

The second type of automatic analyzer, the electrode–recorder (24), employs an electrode-sensing system, capable of responding to pH, emf, or ionic concentrations. Such systems are not capable of performing the variety of measurements as are the colorimeter–recorder instruments, but they are less complicated and easier to operate. Also, they are more compatible to volumetric measurements.

The electrode–recorder devices also consist of four integral parts: (1) a piston-operated buret, (2) an electrode-sensing system, (3) an automatic turntable sample holder, and (4) a readout device, such as a digital printer or recorder. In operation, samples are placed in beakers on the turntable and the sensing circuit adjusted to detect a preselected pH or emf which represents the endpoint of a titration. The electrodes are mechanically lowered into the sample and the piston-operated buret delivers titrant to the automatically stirred sample. When the preselected endpoint is reached, the electrode signal activates a solenoid which closes the buret and terminates the titration. The volume of titrant used is a function of piston travel in the buret, which is, in turn, digitally translated into concentration on the readout device or on the recorder.

## F. PROBE-TYPE INSTRUMENTS

Recently developed electrodes capable of sensing specific ions may be used to measure the ionic concentration in terms of emf. At the time of this writing, specific electrodes have been developed for measurement of chloride ions, fluoride, sulfide, sulfate, nitrate, cyanide, sodium potassium, calcium, total monovalent cations, total divalent cations, and several of the heavy metals (6,17,81). With these electrodes, the volumetric titration is eliminated and the emf of the specific ion is measured directly.

For both the colorimeter–recorder and the electrode–recorder types of equipment, the advantages are obvious. After the measurement operation is perfected and the instrument made ready, repetitive determinations may be made on a large number of samples without supervision by the analyst. The instruments may be left unattended after working hours. In special situations, the instruments may be employed for continuous operation on a week-to-week schedule. Several modifications of the probe-type instruments have been used as monitoring instruments for plant outfalls, process streams, river waters, and finished waters (23,49,101). The monitoring instruments have been used for data collection in remote locations, with telemetering capabilities for transmission of information to a central data-gathering point.

## V. METHODS OF REPORTING RESULTS

Over the years a variety of units and terms have been used for reporting results of water analyses. Some of these methods, such as "per cent weight of residue," were found to be unwieldy and have gradually fallen into general discard. Other methods were developed for special purposes and are used only in rare instances. For the methods in popular use there is a trend toward standardization of reporting units, but it may be expected that at least several methods will continue as modes of expression because of their definite usefulness (46).

## A. WEIGHT PER WEIGHT UNITS

Many laboratories routinely report all results as parts per million (ppm) by weight. One part per million is 1.0 mg of solute per kilogram of solution. Where constituents are measured at very low concentrations, data is often presented as parts per billion (ppb), which is equivalent to 1.0 mg/kg.

For expression of results on sea water analysis the term "parts per thousand" is used, which is the same as grams per kilogram. In this respect, the terms "chlorinity" and "salinity" are used, especially for designating the concentration of chloride and total dissolved solids in sea water.

## B. WEIGHT PER UNIT VOLUME

Since water is a liquid, the quantities used for analysis in the laboratory are most conveniently obtained by use of volumetric glassware rather than by weighing. Results, therefore, are commonly (and more properly) expressed as weight of constituent per unit volume of sample. Milligrams per liter (mg/liter) is the most frequently used expression; for trace elements, micrograms per liter ($\mu$g/liter) is used to avoid use of cumbersome decimals, i.e., 0.00001 mg/liter becomes 0.01 $\mu$g/liter.

For all practical purposes, it may be assumed that 1 liter of water weights 1 kilogram, in which case 1 mg/liter is equivalent to 1 ppm. As the dissolved solids content increases, the density of the sample increases. If unit density is assumed, errors become significant at about 10,000 ppm of dissolved solids. It is therefore more correct to report results in terms of weight per unit volume which avoids the need for density correction.

The term, "tons per acre foot," is sometimes used for reporting quality of irrigation water.

Another weight per unit volume which still persists is "grains per gallon" where 1.0 grain is equal to 0.0023 ounces. This term is most often used for reporting hardness and alkalinity.

## C. EQUIVALENT WEIGHT UNITS

A refinement in units of expression which takes into account not only the weight concentrations of the ions, but also the idea of chemical

TABLE XII
Conversion Factors (milligrams/liter—millequivalents/liter)

| Cations | meq/liter = mg/liter × | Anions | meq/liter = mg/liter × |
|---------|------------------------|--------|------------------------|
| $Al^{3+}$ | 0.1112 | $Br^-$ | 0.0125 |
| $Ba^{2+}$ | 0.0146 | $Cl^-$ | 0.0282 |
| $Ca^{2+}$ | 0.0499 | $CO_3^{2-}$ | 0.0333 |
| $Cr^{2+}$ | 0.0577 | $CrO_4^{2-}$ | 0.0172 |
| $Cu^{2+}$ | 0.0315 | $F^-$ | 0.0526 |
| $Fe^{2+}$ | 0.0358 | $HCO_3^-$ | 0.0164 |
| $Fe^{3+}$ | 0.0537 | $HPO_4^{2-}$ | 0.0208 |
| $H^+$ | 0.9921 | $H_2PO_4^-$ | 0.0103 |
| $K^+$ | 0.0256 | $I^-$ | 0.0079 |
| $Mg^+$ | 0.0823 | $NO_2^-$ | 0.0217 |
| $Mn^{2+}$ | 0.0364 | $NO_3^-$ | 0.0161 |
| $Mn^{4+}$ | 0.0728 | $OH^-$ | 0.0588 |
| $Na^+$ | 0.0435 | $PO_4$ | 0.0316 |
| $NH_4^+$ | 0.0554 | $S^{2-}$ | 0.0624 |
| $Pb^{2+}$ | 0.0096 | $SIO_3^{2-}$ | 0.0263 |
| $Sr^{2+}$ | 0.0228 | $SO_3^{2-}$ | 0.0250 |
| $Zn^{2+}$ | 0.0306 | $SO_3^{2-}$ | 0.0208 |

equivalence is the equivalent weight concept. Parts per million or milligrams per liter values may be converted to "equivalents per million" (epm) by multiplying parts per million or milligrams per liter by the reciprocals of the combining weights of the individual ions. The combining weight is equal to the atomic or molecular weight of an ion divided by the ionic charge. Table XII gives the conversion factors for a number of cations and anions listed alphabetically.

When the analysis of a water sample is expressed in equivalents per million, unit concentrations of all ions are chemically equivalent. If all the major constituents have been determined, the total equivalents of the cations should very nearly equal the total equivalents of anions.

If the sum of equivalents per million of the cations and anions is not equal, or nearly so, it may be assumed that the analysis is not accurate or that a prominent ion has not been measured.

## REFERENCES

1. Adams, R. C., R. E. Barnett, and D. E. Keller, *Field and Laboratory Determination of Dissolved Oxygen,* Proceedings, American Society for Testing and Materials, Reprint 90, 1943.

2. Alsterberg, G., "Methods for the Determination of Elementary Oxygen Dissolved in Water in the Presence of Nitrite," *Biochem.*, **159**, 36 (1925).

3. Ballinger, D. G., "Polarographic Methods for Water and Wastes," *J. Water Pollution Control Federation*, **35**, 116 (1963).

4. Barnes, H., and A. R. Folkard, "The Determination of Nitrites," *Analyst*, **76**, 599 (1951).

5. Baylis, J. R., "Turbidimeter for Accurate Measurement of Low Turbidities," *Ind. Eng. Chem.*, **18**, 311 (1926).

6. Beckman Instruments Co., Fullterton, California.

7. Bellack, E., "Simplified Fluoride Distillation Methods," *J. Amer. Water Works Assoc.*, **50**, 530 (1958).

8. Bellack, E., and P. J. Schouboe, "Rapid Photometric Determination of Fluoride with SPADNS-Zirconium Lake," *Anal. Chem.*, **30**, 2032 (1958).

9. Burriel-Marti, F., and J. Ramirez-Munoz, *Flame Photometry: A Manual of Methods and Applications,* VanNostrand, Priceton, New Jersey, 1957.

10. Busch, A. W., and C. N. Sawyer, "Determination of the BOD of Sewage and Industrial Wastes with the Polarograph" *Anal. Chem.*, **24**, 1887 (1952).

11. Butler, L. R. P., and D. Brink, "The Determination of Magnesium, Calcium, Potassium, Sodium, Copper and Iron in Water Samples By Atomic Absorption Spectroscopy," *S. African Ind. Chem.*, **17**, 152 (1963).

12. Carritt, D. E., and J. W. Kanwisher, "An Electrode System for Measuring Dissolved Oxygen," *Anal. Chem.*, **31**, 5 (1959).

13. Chamot, E. M., Pratt, D. S., and Redfield, H. W., "A Study on the Phenoldisulfonic Acid Method for the Determination of Nitrates in Water," *J. Amer. Chem. Soc.*, **31**, 922 (1909); **32**, 630 (1910); **33**, 366 (1911).

14. Clarke, F. W., *The Composition of River and Lake Waters of the United States*, U.S. Dept. of the Interior, Geological Survey, Water Supply Paper #135, U.S. Government Printing Office, Washington, D.C., 1924.

15. Cleary, E. J., "Introducing the ORSANCO Robot Monitor Proc. Water Quality Measurements and Instrumentation," *U.S. Public Health Serv.*, page 108, **108**, (1962).

16. Cohen, J. M., L. J. Kamphake, E. K. Harris, and R. E. Woodward, "Taste Threshold Concentrations of Metals in Drinking Water," *J. Amer. Water Works Assoc.*, **52**, 660 (1960).

17. Corning Glass Works, Medfield, Massachusetts.

18. David, D. T., "Recent Developments in Atomic Absorption Analysis," *Spectrochim. Acta*, **20**, 185 (1964).

19. Dean, J. A., *Flame Photometry*, McGraw-Hill, New York, 1960.

20. Dean, J. A., *Flame Photometry*, McGraw-Hill, New York, 1960.

21. Domask, W. C., and K. A. Kobe, "Mercurimetric Determination of Chlorides and Water-Soluble Chlorohydrins," *Anal. Chem.*, **24**, 989 (1952).

22. Epperson, A. W., "The Pyrophosphate Method for the Determination of Magnesium and Phosphoric Anhydride," *J. Amer. Chem. Soc.*, **50**, 321 (1928).

23. Fairchild Camera & Instrument Co., Woodbury, Long Island, New York.

24. Fisher Scientific Co., New York, New York.

25. Fontaine, T. D., "Spectrophotometric Determination of Phosphorus," *Ind. Eng. Chem., Anal. Ed.*, **14**, 77 (1942).

26. Fortune, W. B., and M. G. Mellon, "Determination of Iron with o-Phenanthroline: a Spectrophotometric Study," *Ind. Eng. Chem., Anal. Ed.*, **10**, 60 (1938).

27. Fox, C. L., "Stable Internal-Standard Flame Photometer for Potassium and Sodium Analyses," *Anal. Chem.*, **23**, 137 (1951).

28. Frabicand, B. P., R. R. Sawyer, S. G. Unger, and S. Adler, "Trace Metals Concentrations in the Ocean by Atomic Absorption," *Geochim. Cosmockim. Acta*, **26**, 1023 (1962).

29. Frant, M. S., and T. W. Ross, "Electrode for Sensing Fluoride Activity in Solution," *Science,* **154**, 1553 (1966).

30. Gales, M. E., Jr., E. C. Julian, and R. C. Kroner, "Method for the Quantitative Determination of Total Phosphorus in Water," *J. Amer. Water Works Assoc.*, **58**, 1363 (1966).

31. Geldrich, E. E., H. J. Clark, P. W. Kabler, C. B. Huff, and R. H. Bordner, "The Coliform Group II Reactions in E. C. Medium at 45°C," *Appl. Microbiol.*, **6**, 347 (1958).

32. Goetz, C. A., and R. C. Smith, "Evaluation of Various Methods and Reagents for Total Hardness and Calcium Hardness in Water," *Iowa State J. Sci.*, **34**, 104 (1959).

33. Goetz, C. A., and R. C. Smith, "Evaluation of Various Methods and Reagents for Total Hardness and Calcium Hardness in Water," *Iowa State J. Sci.*, **34**, 81 (August 15, 1959).

34. Goldman, E., "Modification of the Standard Methods Procedure for Turbidimetric Determination of Sulfate," (1958, unpublished).

35. Goldman, E., "New Indicator for the Mercurimetric Chloride Determination in Potable Water," *Anal. Chem.*, **31**, 1127 (1959).

36. Greenberg, A. E., "Study of Methods for the Determination of Nitrates," *J. Amer. Water Works Assoc.*, **50**, 821 (1958).

37. Hach Chemical Company, Ames, Iowa.

38. Haffty, J., *Residue Methods for Common Minor Elements*, U.S. Dept. of the Interior, Geological Survey, Water Supply Paper No. 1540-A, U.S. Government Printing Office, Washington, D.C., 1960.

39. Haffty, J., *Residue Method for Common Minor Elements*, U.S. Dept. of the Interior, Geological Survey, Water Supply Paper No. 1540-A, U.S. Government Printing Office, Washington, D.C., 1960.

40. Hallinan, F. J., "Determination of Iron in Water," *Ind. Eng. Chem., Anal. Ed.*, **15**, 510 (1943).

41. Haney, P. D., and Schmidt, J., "Representative Sampling and Analytical Methods in Stream Studies; Sewage and Ind. Wastes," **30**, 812 (1958).

42. Harley, J. H., and S. F. Wiberley, *Instrumental Analysis*, Wiley, New York, 1954.

43. Hazen, A. "On the Determination of Chlorine in Water," *Amer. Chem. J.*, **11**, 409 (1889).

44. Hazen, A., "A New Color Method for Natural Waters," *Amer. Chem. J.*, **14**, 300 (1892).

45. Hem, J. D., *Study and Interpretation of the Chemical Characteristics of Natural Waters*, U.S. Dept. of the Interior, Geological Survey, Water Supply Paper No. 1473, U.S. Government Printing Office, Washington, D.C., 1959.

46. Hem, J. D., *Study and Interpretation of the Chemical Characteristics of Natural Waters*, U.S. Dept. of the Interior, Geological survey, Water Supply Paper No. 1473, U.S. Government Printing Office, Washington, D.C., 1959.

47. Hillebrand, W. F., *Applied Inorganic Analysis*, 2nd ed., Wiley, New York, 1953.

48. Hillebrand, W. F., *Applied Inorganic Analysis,* 2nd ed., Wiley, New York, 1953.
49. Honeywell Instruments, Fort Washington, Pa.
50. Iler, R. K., *The Colloid Chemistry of Silica and Silicates,* Cornell University Press, Ithaca, N.Y. 1955.
51. Kabler, P. W., "Water Examinations by Membrane Filter and MPN Procedures," *Amer. J. Public Health,* **44,** 379 (1954).
52. Kabler, P. W., and T. F. Clark, "Coliform Group and Fecal Coliform Organisms as Indicators of Pollution in Drinking Water," *J. Amer Water Works Assoc.,* **52,** 1577 (1960).
53. Slavin, W., *Atomic Absorption Spectroscopy,* 25, Interscience Publishers, New York (1968), Int. Science and Analysis.
54. Kenner, B. A., H. F. Clark, and P. W. Kabler, "Fecal Streptococci II Quantification of Streptococci in Feces," *Amer. J. Public Health,* **50,** 1553 (1960).
55. Kitson, R. E., and M. G. Mellon, "Further Studies of the Molybdenum Blue Reaction," *Ind. Eng. Chem., Anal. Ed.,* **16,** 466 (1944).
56. Knight, A. G., "The Photometric Estimation of Color in Turbid Waters," *J. Inst. Water Eng.,* **5,** 623 (1951).
57. Kolthoff, I. M., and E. B. Sandell, *Textbook of Quantitative Inorganic Analysis,* 3rd ed., Macmillan, New York, 1952.
58. Kolthoff, I. M., and E. B. Sandell, *Textbook of Quantitative Inorganic Analysis,* 3rd ed., Macmillan, New York, 1952.
59. Kolthoff, I. M., and V. A. Stenger, *Volumetric Analysis,* Vol. 2, 2nd ed., Interscience, New York, 1947, p. 242.
60. Kopp, J. F., and R. C. Kroner, "A Direct Reading Spectrochemical Procedure for the Measurement of Nineteen Minor Elements in Water," *Anal. Spectrpy.,* **19,** No. 5, 155 (1965).
61. Kopp, J. F., and R. C. Kroner, "A Direct Reading Spectrochemical Procedure for the Measurement of Nineteen Minor Elements in Water," *Appl. Spectry.,* **19,** No. 5, 155 (1965).
62. Kroner, R. C., and J. F. Kopp, "Trace Elements in Six Water Systems of the United States," *J. Amer. Water Works Assoc.,* **57,** 2 (1965).
63. Langelier, W. F., "Chemical Equations in Water Treatment," *J. Amer. Water Works Assoc.,* **38,** 169 (1946).
64. Mancy, K. H., and W. C. Westgarth, "A Galvanic Cell Oxygen Analyzer," *J. Water Pollution Controlled Federation,* **34,** 1037 (1962).
65. *Manual on Industrial Water and Industrial Waste Water,* 2nd. ed., ASTM Technical Publication No. 148-G, American Society for Testing and Material, Philadelphia, Pennsylvania, 1962.
66. *Manual on Industrial Water and Industrial Waste Water,* 2nd ed., ASTM Technical Publication No. 148-G, American Society for Testing and Materials, Philadelphia, Pennsylvania, 1962.
67. Mason, B., *Principles of Geochemistry,* Wiley, New York, 1952.
68. Mavrodineau, R., "Bibliography on Analytical Flame Spectroscopy," *Appl. Spectrpy.,* **16,** 51 (1956).
69. Megregian, S., "Rapid Spectrophotometric Determination of Fluoride with Zirconium-Eriochrome Cyanine-R Lake," *Anal. Chem.,* **26,** 1161 (1954).
70. Megregian, S., and F. J. Maier, "Modified Zirconium-Alizarin Reagent for Determination of Fluoride in Water," *J. Amer. Water Works Assoc.,* **44,** 239 (1952).

71. Mehlig, J. P., "Colorimetric Determination of Manganese with Periodate," *Ind. Eng. Chem., Anal. Ed.,* **11**, 274 (1939).
72. Mehlig, R. P., and R. H. Hulett, "Spectrophotometric Determination of Iron with *o*-Phenanthroline and with Nitro-*o*-Phenanthroline and with Nitro-*o*-Phenanthroline," *Ind. Eng. Chem. Anal. Ed.,* **14**, 869 (1942).
73. Middleton, F. M., "Taste and Odor Sources and Methods of Measurement," *Taste Odor Control J.,* **26**, 1 (1960).
74. Mills, R. M., and V. G. Stack, *Biological Oxidation of Synthetic Organic Chemicals,* Proc. Eighth Industrial Waste Conf., Purdue University, 492 1953, Lafayette, Ind.
75. Moss, M. L., and M. G. Mellon, "Color Reactions of 1,10-Phenan-throline Derivatives," *Ind. Eng. Chem., Anal. Ed.,* **14**, 931 (1942).
76. Moss, M. L., and M. G. Mellon, "Colorimetric Determination of Iron with 2,2'-Bipyridine and with 2,2'-2''-Tripyridine," *Ind. Eng. Chem., Anal. Ed.,* **14**, 862 (1942).
77. Murphy, J., and J. P. Riley, "A Modified Single Solution Method for the Determination of Phosphate in Natural Water," *Anal. Chim. Acta,* **27**, 31 (1962).
78. Nachtrieb, N. H., *Principles and Practice of Spectrochemical Analysis,* McGraw-Hill, 1950.
79. Noll, C. A., "Determination of Nitrate in Boiler Water by Brucine Reagent," *Ind. Eng. Chem., Anal. Ed.,* **17**, 426 (1945).
80. Nydahl, F., "Determination of Manganese by the Persulfate Method," *Anal. Chim. Acta.,* **3**, 144 (1949).
81. Orion Research, Inc., Cambridge, Massachusetts.
82. Palin, A. T., "Photometric Determination of the Colour and Turbidity of Water," *Water Water Eng.,* **59**, 341 (1955).
83. Placak, O. R., and C. C. Ruchoft, "Copper and Chromate Ions in Sewage Dilutions," *Ind. Eng. Chem.,* **41**, 2238 (1949).
84. Platte, J. A., and V. M. Marcy, "A New Tool for the Water Chemist," *Ind. Water Eng.,* **2**, 26 1965.
85. Precision Scientific Co., Chicago, and Yellow Springs Instrument Co., Yellow Springs, Ohio.
86. *Public Health Service Drinking Water Standards,* United States Public Health Service Publication #956, U.S. Govt. Printing Office, Washington, D.C., 1962.
87. Rainwater, F., H., and L. L. Thatcher, *Methods for Collection and Analysis of Water Samples,* U.S. Dept. of Interior, Geological Survey, Water Supply Paper No. 1454, U.S. Government Printing Office, Washington, D.C., 1960.
88. Rainwater, F. H., and L. L. Thatcher, *Methods for Collection and Analysis of Water Samples,* U.S. Dept. of Interior Geological Survey, Paper No. 1454, U.S. Government Printing Office, Washington, D.C., 1960.
89. Rainwater, F. H., and L. L. Thatcher, *Methods for Collection and Analysis of Water Samples,* U.S. Dept. of Interior Geological Survey, Water Supply Paper No. 1454, U.S. Government Printing Office, Washington, D.C., 1960.
90. Rennerfelt, J., "Determination of Dissolved Oxygen in Watercourses Containing Sulfite Waste Liquors," *Svensk Papperstidn.,* **58**, 86 (1955).
91. Rideal, S., and G. G. Stewart, "The Determination of Dissolved Oxygen in

Waters in the Presence of Nitrites and Trganic Matter," *Analyst,* **26,** 141 (1901).

92. Rider, B. F., and M. G. Mellon, "Colorimetric Determination of Nitrates," *Ind. Eng. Chem., Anal. Ed.,* **18,** 96 (1946).

93. Rosen, A. A., R. T. Skeel, and M. B. Ettinger, "Relationship of River Water Odor to Specific Organic Contaminants," *J. Water Pollution Control Federation,* **35,** 777 (1963).

94. Rossum, J. R., "Conductance Method for Checking Accuracy of Water Analyses," *Anal. Chem.,* **21,** 631 (1949).

95. Roy, C. J., "Silica in Natural Waters," *Amer. J. Sci.,* **243,** 393 (1945).

96. Ruchoft, C. C., "Report on Cooperative Studies of Dilution Waters," *Sewage Works J.,* **13,** 669 (1941).

97. Ruchoft, C. C., W. A. Moore, and O. R. Pacak, "Determination of Dissolved Oxygen by the Rideal-Stewart and Alsterberg Modifications of the Winkler Method," *Ind. Eng. Chem., Anal. Ed.,* **10,** 701 (1938).

98. Rudolfs, W., and W. D. Hanlon, "Color in Industrial Wastes and Determination by Spectrophotometric Method," *Sewage Ind. Wastes,* **23,** 1125 (1951).

99. Sanchis, J. M., "Determination of Fluorides in Natural Waters," *Ind. Eng. Chem., Anal. Ed.,* **6,** 134 (1934).

100. Schellenberger, R. D., "Procedures for Determining Treshold Odor Concentrations in Aqueous Solutions" *Taste Odor Control J.,* **24, 5** (1958).

101. Schneider Instrument Co., Cincinnati, Ohio.

102. Schwarzenbach, G., *Complexometric Titrations,* Interscience, New York, 1957.

103. Schwarzenbach, G., *Complexometric Titrations,* Interscience, New York, 1957.

104. Schwarzenbach, G., *Complexometric Titrations,* Interscience, New York, 1957.

105. Scott, R. D., "Modification of Fluoride Determination," *J. Amer. Water Works Assoc.,* **33,** 2018 (1941).

106. Sletten, O., and C. M. Bach, "Modified Stannous Chloride Reagent for Orthophosphate Determination," *J. Amer. Water Works Assoc.,* **53,** 1031 (1961).

107. Staff Report, "The Threshold Odor Test," *Taste Odor Control J.,* **29, 6** (1963).

108. *Standard Methods for the Examination of Water, Sewage, and Industrial Wastes,* 10th ed., American Public Health Assoc., New York, 1954.

109. *Standard Methods for the Examination of Water and Wastewaters,* 11th ed., American Public Health Association, New York, 1960.

110. *Standard Methods for the Examination of Water and Wastewaters,* 11th ed., American Public Health Association, New York, 1960.

111. *Standard Methods for the Examination of Water and Wastewaters,* 11th ed., American Public Health Association, New York, 1960.

112. *Standard Methods for the Examination of Water and Wastewaters,* 11th ed., American Public Health Association, New York, 1960.

113. *Standard Methods for the Examination of Water and Wastewaters,* 11th ed., American Public Health Association, New York, 1960.

114. *Standard Methods for the Examination of Water and Wastewaters,* 12th ed., American Public Health Association, New York, 1965.

115. *Standard Methods for the Examination of Water and Wastewaters,* 12th ed., American Public Health Association, New York, 1965.

116. *Standard Methods for the Examination of Water and Wastewaters,* 12th ed., American Public Health Association, New York, 1965.

117. *Standard Method of Test for Calcium Ion and Magnesium Ion in Industrial*

*Water-D511-52,* American Society for Testing and Materials, Philadelphia, Pennsylvania, 1952.

118. Taras, M. J., "Phenoldisulfonic Acid Method of Determining Nitrate in Water: Photometric Study, *Anal. Chem.,* **22,** 1020 (1950).

119. Taras, M., "Photometric Determination of Magnesium in Water with Brilliant Yellow," *Anal. Chem.,* **20,** 1156 (1948).

120. Technicon Instruments Corporation, Ardsley, New York.

121. Theriault, E. J., and P. D. McNamee, "Dissolved Oxygen in the Presence of Organic Matter, Hypochlorides, and Sulfite Wastes," Public Health Rep., **48,** 1363 (1933).

122. Thomas, J. F., and J. E. Cotton, "A Turbidimetric Sulfate Determination," *Water Sewage Works,* **101,** 462 (1954).

123. Weber, W. W., and W. Stumm, "Mechanism of Hydrogen Ion Buffering in Natural Water," *J. Amer. Water Works Assoc.,* **55,** 1553 (1963).

124. West, P. W., P. Folse, and D. Montgomery, "Application of Flame Spectrophotometry to Water Analysis," *Anal. Chem.,* **22,** 667 (1950).

125. Whipple, G. C., and D. D. Jackson, "A Comparative Study of the Methods Used for Measurement of Turbidity in Water," *Mass. Inst. Technol. Quart.,* **13,** 274 (1900).

126. Wilcox, L. V., "Electrical Conductivity," *J. Amer. Water Works Assoc.,* **42,** 775 (1950).

127. Winkler, L. W., "The Determination of Dissolved Oxygen in Water," *Ber. Deut. Chem. Ges.,* **121,** 2843 (1888).

128. Woods, J. T., and M. G. Mellon, "Molybdenum Blue Reaction," *Ind. Eng. Chem., Anal. Ed.,* **13,** 760 (1941).

# ANALYSIS OF INDUSTRIAL WASTE-WATERS

K. H. Mancy and W. J. Weber, jr., *The University of Michigan Ann Arbor, Michigan*

**Contents**

**Contents** (*continued*)

# I. INTRODUCTION

The quantity of water used annually for industrial operations in any highly developed society represents a significant part of the total water requirements of that society. Moreover, there is little reason to believe that with constant expansion and development of technology there will ever be a decrease in the relative use of water by industry. In 1960 an average of approximately 270 billion gallons of water was withdrawn daily from ground and surface water supplies in the United States; of this, industry accounted for 138 billion gallons per day, or about 51% of the total (278). In the same period, the average daily quantity of water consumed, i.e., not returned directly to ground or surface supplies, was 61 billion gallons, or about 23% of the total daily withdrawal. The major portion, 85%, of the daily consumption of water was for irrigation, while industry consumed 5%, and public and private water-use accounted for 10% of the total. These figures indicate that slightly more than 2% of the water used by industry was consumed and nearly 98% was returned to surface or underground sources.

Rarely is water, which has been subjected to industrial use, of the same quality as it was at the time of withdrawal from its source; rather, its quality generally has been degraded to some degree. This degradation, which may range from a simple temperature increase in the case of cooling waters to introduction of high concentrations of toxic materials in the case of some process waters, most often renders the water unfit for direct reuse in the same application, thereby necessitating its disposal as a waste. The distinction between industrial water supplies and industrial wastewaters is often not clear, for what is considered as waste for one industrial application may be suitable as a source of supply for another, and, with contiguous location of industry along a water course, multiple reuse of water is fairly common practice.

From an analytical standpoint it is desirable to strike a distinction between the two types of industrial water. In the case of industrial water supplies, chemical analyses are usually performed either for determination of the suitability of a water for use in a particular industrial process or for provision of information required for fixing the degee of treatment needed for removal of undesirable materials and/or addition of certain desirable constituents. Chemical analyses of industrial wastewater also are generally directed either to determination of the suitability of the water, in this case for reuse or disposal, or to determination of the degree of treatment required prior to disposal or for recovery of secondary products. While there seems little difference in the overall objectives of chemical analyses of industrial water supplies and wastewaters, the differences which do exist, coupled with the usually quite different nature of these two types of industrial water, often require specific test procedures of different levels of sophistication.

The present chapter deals with the chemical analysis of industrial wastewaters, with due recognition of the fact that the methodology involved is applicable, in a general sense, to all kinds of waters. An attempt has been made to present a fairly comprehensive, documented discussion of certain operating principles which are useful as guidelines for the analysis of industrial wastewaters. In this respect, the present chapter should not be considered as a substitute for any of the standard manuals on analytical procedures for waters and/or wastewaters (20,21,29,85,112, 177,212,427,428,450,456), which indeed are used as reference sources for detailed description of the more common analytical methods. The present discussion is meant to serve as a guide for the effective use of the methods described in these manuals and is intended primarily for the chemist, engineer, or other professional person concerned with all aspects of industrial wastewater analysis. Concern, therefore, is mainly with the design of measurement systems and theory of analysis rather than with stepwise procedures for analysis.

Analytical programs for industrial wastewaters must include some consideration of the major problems of water pollution associated with the discharge of wastes to streams, rivers, and other receiving waters, for these are the problems to which analysis for treatment and disposal must ultimately be related. Six major types of pollutants, any one or more of which may be associated with a particular industrial waste, are: (*1*) organic materials, (*2*) inorganic dissolved solids, (*3*) fertilizing elements, (*4*) heat, (*5*) suspended solids, and (*6*) pathogenic organisms.

Many organic pollutants undergo biochemical oxidation in receiving waters to which they are discharged, thus decreasing levels of dissolved oxygen in these waters and rendering them unsuitable for support of their natural biota and flora. Gross aesthetic damage, such as colors and odors, may also result directly from organic pollution. On the other hand, one of the most alarming aspects of organic pollution is that of the resistance of certain materials to biochemical oxidation. Such substances often escape removal by conventional treatment methods and persist for long periods, thus accumulating in receiving waters. Health and conservation agencies are presently studying the toxicity and carcinogenicity of some of these materials and their short-term and long-term effects on both man and aquatic animals and plants. The results of some recent studies have revealed, for example, that a rather definite cause and effect relationship existed between an industrial waste effluent containing pesticides and a serious fish kill in the Mississippi River (72,73). The long-term effects of such materials have not as yet been established.

Increases in the salinity of receiving waters is a water pollution problem of major concern, particularly in the southwestern parts of the United States and in most arid countries. Salinity is an expression of the total mineral content of a water, commonly expressed in per cent by weight. Increases in the salinity of fresh waters can result from such natural phenomena as intermixing with saline springs or ground waters of high salt content, from salt-water intrusion, and by evaporation from reservoirs. Certain industrial wastewaters, such as mine drainage, oil field brines, residual water from saline water conversion plants, and drainage from irrigation water, are major sources of salinity. Perhaps the greatest economic burden of saline water pollution falls on the agricultural industry, which often cannot afford the expensive process of treating very large volumes of water for salt removal.

The increased fertility of certain receiving waters, which often results in abundant blooms of algae and attached aquatic plants, can be traced to the disposal of wastewaters which are rich in phosphates and nitrates. This fertilization commonly results in the deterioration of an otherwise high quality water to the point where it may be unsuitable for domestic, industrial, or recreational uses or for the support of desirable fish and wild life.

The disposal of large volumes of high temperature wastes to receiving waters is recognized as one of the major current water pollution problems in the United States. Increases in the temperature of receiving waters may result in accelerated chemical and biological reactions, the net effects of which may be harmful to the ecological balance of streams and lakes. Prediction of the effects of thermal pollution on water quality in a given situation is difficult, requiring knowledge of such factors as physical mixing, heat exchange relationships, and biochemical reactions associated with the particular situation.

The influences of discharges of large quantities of suspended solids to receiving waters are obvious. Turbidity and excessive sediment buildup can have deleterious effects on the ecology of rivers, lakes, and streams, on the recreational value of these waters, and on their value as sources of water supply.

Advances in the technology of drinking water purification have greatly reduced the incidence of human disease resulting from bacterial pollution of receiving waters. However, outbreaks of water-borne disease still occur from time to time, usually in connection with shellfish contamination, small private water supplies, and bathing in polluted waters. There is evidence that conventional water purification processes are not completely effective in removing water-borne virus, especially if high concentrations of organic material are present. Viral and bacterial pollution usually results from the discharge of domestic, agricultural, and food processing wastewaters.

Water pollution may take many forms, but regardless of the type of pollution of concern in any instance, one may say with a fair degree of confidence that it will increase as a natural consequence of population expansion and industrial development unless definite abatement measures are taken. Industry has, for the most part, recognized the urgency of protecting our natural water resources, and, to a considerably increasing extent, is effecting treatment of wastewaters to this end. The proper control of treatment processes and the evaluation of the pollution potential of industrial wastewaters are highly dependent upon precise and accurate measurement of impurities. Thus, industrial wastewater analysis is a vital part of water pollution control.

## A. DESIGN OF MEASUREMENT SYSTEMS

The comprehensive analysis of industrial wastewaters is one of the most challenging problems with which the analytical chemist is likely to be confronted. It requires not only considerable knowledge of the application of standard analytical methods, procedures, and instrumentation, but also a keen insight into the nature of interferences and other problems, which may be quite unique to a particular waste and which may in many cases render analytical data misleading. The industrial-waste analyst must have the ability to properly interpret analytical results, pertinent observations, and the history of the water for design of an overall analytical program which will best serve for definition of a complex system which is often subject to rather wide variation in composition.

### 1. Objectives of Analysis

Definition of the purpose and objectives of analysis is the first step in the design of any measurement system; this includes the definition of particular problems to which solutions are sought. Some of the more common objectives of industrial wastewater analysis are as follows:

*a.* Estimation of possible detrimental effects of the waste effluent on the quality of a receiving water for subsequent downstream use.

*b.* Determination of the compliance of the wastewater with quality standards for water reuse, production control, or disposal in municipal sewers.

*c.* Evaluation of treatment requirements in view of water reuse.

*d.* Recovery of valuable by-products from the waste effluent.

The first objective directly concerns the problem of water pollution. The Federal Water Quality Act of 1965, Public Law 89-234, provides stringent rules prohibiting the discharge of waste effluents into interstate waters—directly or indirectly—which may result in deterioration of the quality of such waters to levels below established standards (470). Such standards are being set to protect present and future uses of our natural waters, based on economic, health, and aesthetic considerations. Furthermore, the Federal Water Quality Act of 1965 prohibits the use of any stream or portion thereof for the sole or principal purpose of transporting wastes. This strong legislative action on the part of the Federal Government has accompanied increased public and private demands for abatement of water pollution. Conscientious efforts on the part of industry are presently being made to correct problems of water pollution, and, as a result, comprehensive chemical analysis of waste effluents for better control is being emphasized strongly in most industrial waste treatment and disposal programs.

Natural bodies of fresh water can be classified according to intended use, including public water supply, fish or shellfish propagation, recreation, agricultural use, industrial water supply, hydroelectric power, navigation, and disposal of sewage and industrial wastes. Under the terms of the new Water Quality Act (470), industries which discharge liquid wastes directly or indirectly to receiving waters are obligated by Federal law to conform to specific water quality criteria or standards set by local and state agencies and approved by the Federal Water Pollution Control Administration (470). Water quality criteria, which have been reviewed rather extensively by McKee (298), Camp (84), and others may be prescribed by regional authorities within a given state, by the state itself, by interstate compacts, or by the Federal Government in cases involving interstate waters.

Methods for implementing and enforcing compliance to water quality standards vary from one state to another. Quality criteria may be established for receiving waters into which wastes are discharged; such criteria are termed "stream standards." A second method for controlling quality of receiving waters is that of setting quality standards on the effluent itself. Conservation and Public Health agencies in general favor the so-called "effluent standards." Conversely, industry in general prefers establishment of stream standards, since effluent standards most often do not provide for full use of the capacity of streams for assimilation of wastes.

Chemical analyses associated with control and treatment of industrial wastewaters for purposes of conforming to standards of water quality for streams, lakes, ocean outfalls, or underground aquifers are often more complicated than those required in instances where the standards are set for the waste effluent itself; indeed, the respective, methods of analysis and interpretation may be quite different in these two cases. In the former case the analysis is directed not only to characterization of the quality of the waste effluent, but also to determination of its effect on the ecosystem of the receiving water, while in the latter case the quality of the specific waste is the only matter of concern.

Quality standards on industrial waste effluents vary from one place to another and are primarily dependent on whether the effluent is disposed of into a natural body of water (i.e., river, lake, ocean) or into a municipal sewage treatment plant.

One common method for estimation of the deleterious effects a waste effluent will have on the quality of a receiving water is to treat the wastewater as a complete entity, thus avoiding analyses for particular constituents. For this type of evaluation the wastewater is first diluted to a level corresponding to that which would occur in the receiving water, and then certain gross parameters, such as taste, odor, color, and toxicity to fish, are measured, depending on the intended water use. While this procedure may give a preliminary indication of the ability of the waste to be assimilated harmlessly into the receiving water, its effectiveness for providing sufficient basis for any significant conclusion is highly doubtful. Among other things, the rate of self-purification of the receiving water is not accounted for in such a test procedure. Self-purification of streams and other receiving waters is a dynamic process in which the rate of biochemical transformation of pollutants is often much more significant than the ultimate assimilative capacity of the stream per se. For example, in evaluating the biochemical oxygen demand (BOD) of a particular wastewater, determination of the rate constant is at least as important as determination of the 5-day BOD. This method of analysis will be discussed in detail in a later section of this chapter.

The analysis of wastewaters which are to be discharged to municipal sewers is done principally for the purpose of evaluating compliance with certain effluent criteria set by the municipality. Effluent standards in this case are established for the purpose of protecting municipal waste treatment plants from operational interference which might be caused by industrial waste discharges and for protection of the sewer structure from damage. Both the municipality and the industry may carry out periodic analysis of the waste effluent for purposes of control and assessment of charges, which are usually related to the strength and volume of a particular waste. It is important to point out that wastewater which is discharged to municipal sewers becomes the responsibility of the municipality (484). The general requirements for acceptable wastewater for joint treatment with municipal wastes have been discussed in some detail by Byrd and others (83,484).

As far as in-plant operations are concerned, chemical analyses of industrial wastewaters are performed for one or more of the following purposes:

*a*. Estimation of material balances for processes to permit evaluation of unit efficiencies and to relate material losses to production operations.

*b*. Evaluation of continuing conformance to limits set for performance efficiency of certain unit processes.

*c*. Evaluation of the effectiveness of in-plant processes, modifications, and other measures taken for reduction of losses.

*d*. Determination of sources and temporal distributions of waste loads for purposes of by-product recovery or segregation of flows, relative to strength and type, for separate treatment.

*e*. Provision for immediate recognition of malfunctions, accidents, spills or other process disturbances.

*f*. Determination of the type and degree of treatment required for recovery of certain substances from waste effluents.

*g*. Evaluation of conformance to standards set for effluent quality and/or stream quality.

*h*. Provision for control of treatment and discharge of waste effluents according to present standards and/or according to variations in the conditions of the receiving water.

*i*. Provision of a current record of costs associated with discharge of waste effluents to municipal sewers when such costs are at least partially based on the chemical characteristics of the waste.

Some of the objectives of industrial wastewater analysis listed above are, of course, exploratory in nature and therefore occasional in frequency, while others are related to continuous or regular monitoring and control.

## 2. Choice of Parameters for Analysis

After definition of the objectives of analysis, the next step in the design of measurement systems is to decide on particular constituents for which analyses are to be made and what methods are to be employed. The analyst experienced in water quality characterization can often make the proper decision based on practiced intuition. In most cases, however, certain rather well defined guidelines should be followed.

Depending on the intended subsequent use of a receiving water, the parameters listed in Tables IA and IB are of significance for water

TABLE IA
Parameters for Water Quality Characterization—Domestic Water Supplies

| Quality parameter | Permissible criteria | Desirable criteria |
|---|---|---|
| Color (Co–Pt scale) | 75 units | <10 units |
| Odor | Virtually absent | Virtually absent |
| Taste | Virtually absent | Virtually absent |
| Turbidity | — | Virtually absent |
| Inorganic chemicals | | |
| pH | 6.0–8.5 | 6.0–8.5 |
| Alkalinity (CaCO$_3$ units) | 30–500 mg/liter | 30–500 mg/liter |
| Ammonia | 0.5 | <0.01 |
| Arsenic | 0.05 | Absent |
| Barium | 1.0 | — |
| Boron | 1.0 | |
| Cadmium | 0.01 | |
| Chlorides | 250 | <25 |
| Chromium (hexavalent) | 0.05 | Absent |
| Copper | 1.0 | Virtually absent |
| Dissolved oxygen | ≥4.0 | Air saturation |
| Fluorides | 0.8 to 1.7 mg/liter | 1.0 mg/liter |
| Iron (filtrable) | <0.3 | Virtually absent |
| Lead | <0.05 | Absent |
| Manganese (filtrable) | <0.05 | Absent |
| Nitrates plus nitrites (as mg/liter N) | <10 | Virtually absent |
| Phosphorus | 10–50 μg/liter | 10 μg/liter |
| Selenium | 0.01 | Absent |
| Silver | 0.05 | — |
| Sulfates | 250 | <50 |
| Total dissolved solids | 500 | <200 |
| Uranyl ion | 5 | Absent |
| Zinc | 5 | Virtually absent |
| Organic chemicals | | |
| Carbon chloroform extract (CCE) | 0.15 | <0.04 |
| Cyanides | 0.20 | Absent |
| Methylene blue active substances | 0.5 | Virtually absent |
| Pesticides: | | |
| Aldrin | 0.017 | — |
| Chlordane | 0.003 | — |
| DDT | 0.042 | — |
| Dieldrin | 0.017 | — |
| Endrin | 0.001 | — |
| Heptachlor | 0.018 | — |

*(continued)*

TABLE IA (continued)

| Quality parameters | Permissible criteria | Desirable criteria |
|---|---|---|
| Organic chemicals (continued) | | |
| Heptachlor expoxide | 0.018 | — |
| Lindane | 0.056 | — |
| Methoxyehlor | 0.035 | — |
| Organic phosphates plus | | |
| carbamates | 0.1 | — |
| Taxophane | 0.005 | — |
| Herbicides | | |
| 2,4,D plus 2,4,5-T, plus | | |
| 2,4,5-TP | 0.1 | — |
| Radioactivity | | |
| Gross beta | 1000 pc/liter | <100 pc/liter |
| Radium 226 | 3 pc/liter | <1 pc/liter |
| Strontium-90 | 10 pc/liter | <2 pc/liter |

quality characterization, and these should serve as guidelines for analysis of wastewater quality for purposes of treatment and control.

The choice of parameters for analysis depends primarily on the type of information sought. Certain tests are frequently used for the identification of various types of pollution associated with industrial wastewaters. Table II lists a number of tests and their significance.

## 3. Choice of Methods of Analysis

Choice of methods of analysis should be based on familiarity with the purpose of analysis and on the origin, properties, and intended future

TABLE IB
Parameters for Water Quality Characterization

A. Recreation and aesthetics

The general requirements are that surface waters should be capable of supporting life forms of aesthetic and recreational values. Hence, surface waters should be free from (a) materials that may settle to form objectionable deposits or float on the surface as debris, oil, and scum; (b) substances that may impart taste, odor, color, or turbidity; (c) toxic substances, including radionuclides, physiologically harmful to man, fish, or other aquatic plants or animals; and (d) substances which may result in promoting the growth of undesirable aquatic life.

Presently, there are no well defined water quality criteria for recreation or aesthetic purposes.

(continued)

TABLE IB     (Continued)

B. Aquatic life, fish and wildlife

1. *Turbidity.* Discharge of waste in receiving waters should not cause change in turbidity in the order of 50 Jackson units in warm water streams, 25 Jackson units in warm lakes, and 10 Jackson units in cold water streams and lakes.

2. *Color and transparency.* Optimum light requirements for photosynthesis should be at least 10% of incident light on the surface.

3. *Settleable matter.* Minor deposits of settleable matter may inhibit growth of flora and biota of water body. Such materials should not be discharged in surface waters.

4. *Floating matter.* All foreign floating matter should not be discharged in surface waters. A typical pollution problem is that of oil waste discharges which may (a) result in the formation of visible objectionable color film on the surface, (b) alter taste and odor of water, (c) coat banks and bottoms of water course, (d) taint aquatic biota, and (e) cause toxicity to fish and man.

5. *Dissolved matter.* The effect of dissolved matter on aquatic biota can be due to toxicity at relatively low concentrations or due to osmotic effects at relatively high concentrations. In general, total dissolved matter should not exceed 50 milliosmoles (the equivalent of 1500 mg/liter NaCl).

6. *pH, Alkalinity and acidity.* The pH range of 6.0–9.0 is considered desirable. Discharge of waste effluents should not lower the receiving water alkalinity to less than 20 mg/liter.

7. *Temperature.* Heat should not be added to a receiving water in excess of the amount that will raise the temperature by 3–5°F. In general, normal daily and seasonable temperature variations should be maintained.

8. *Dissolved oxygen.* It is generally required to maintain a dissolved oxygen level above 4–5 mg/liter. In cold water bodies it is recommended to maintain the dissolved oxygen above 7 mg/liter.

9. *Plant nutrients.* Organic waste effluents, such as sewage, food processing, canning and industrial wastes containing nutrients, vitamins, trace elements, and growth stimulants, should be carefully controlled. It is important not to disturb the naturally occuring ratio of nitrogen (nitrates and ammonia) to total phosphorus in the receiving water.

10. *Toxic matter.* Waste effluents containing chemicals with unknown toxicity characteristics should be tested and proven to be harmless in the concentration to be found in the receiving waters. Discharging pesticides in natural waters should be avoided if possible or kept below 1/100 of the 48-hr $TL_m$ values. Levels of ABS and LAS should not exceed 1.0 and 0.2 mg/liter, respectively, for periods of exposures exceeding 24 hr. It should be noticed that the presence of two or more toxic agents in the receiving water may exert a synergistic effect.

11. *Radionuclides.* No radionuclides should be discharged in natural waters to produce concentrations greater than those specified by the *United States Public Health Service Drinking Water Standards.*

C. Agricultural water use

1. *Total dissolved solids or "salinity."* This is the most important water quality consideration since it controls the availability of water to the plant through osmotic pressure regulating mechanisms. The effect of salinity on plant growth varies from one type to another and is dependent on environmental conditions.

*(continued)*

## TABLE IB (continued)

2. *Trace elements.* Trace elements tolerance for irrigation waters may be summarized as follows:

| Element | Continuous water use, mg/liter | Short-term water use, fine texture soil, mg/liter |
|---|---|---|
| Aluminum | 1.0 | 20.0 |
| Arsenic | 1.0 | 10.0 |
| Beryllium | 0.5 | 1.0 |
| Boron | 0.75 | 2.0 |
| Cadmium | 0.005 | 0.05 |
| Chromium | 5.0 | 20.0 |
| Cobalt | 0.2 | 10.0 |
| Copper | 0.2 | 5.0 |
| Lead | 5.0 | 20.0 |
| Lithium | 5.0 | 5.0 |
| Manganese | 2.0 | 20.0 |
| Molybdenum | 0.005 | 0.05 |
| Nickel | 0.5 | 2.0 |
| Sellenium | 0.05 | 0.05 |
| Vanadium | 10.0 | 10.0 |
| Zinc | 5.0 | 10.0 |

3. *pH Acidity and alkalinity.* pH is not greatly significant and waters with pH values from 4.5 to 9.0 should not present problems. Highly acidic or alkaline waters can induce adverse effects on plant growth.

4. *Chlorides.* Depending upon environmental conditions, crops, and irrigation management practices, approximately 700 mg/liter chloride is permissible in irrigation waters.

5. *Temperature.* Very high, as well as very low, temperatures of irrigation waters can interfere with plant growth. Temperature tolerance is highly dependent on the type of plant and other environmental conditions.

6. *Pesticide.* A variety of herbicides, insecticides, fungicides, and rodenticides can be present in irrigation waters at concentrations which may be detrimental to crops, livestock, wildlife, and man. As far as the effect on plant growth and permissible levels are concerned, these variables are highly dependent on the type of chemical, type of plant, environmental factors, and exposure time.

7. *Suspended solids.* Suspended solids in irrigation waters may deposit on soil surface and produce a crust which inhibits water infiltration and seedling emergence. In waters used for sprinkler irrigation, colloids and suspended matter may form a film on leaf surfaces which impairs photosynthesis and defers growth.

8. *Radionuclides. United States Public Health Service Drinking Water Standards* are usually applied to irrigation waters.

TABLE II
Significance of Parametric Measurements

| Test or determination | Significance |
|---|---|
| Dissolved solids | Soluble salts may affect aquatic life or future use of water for domestic or agricultural purposes |
| Ammonia, nitrites, nitrates, and total organic nitrogen | Degree of stabilization (oxidation) or organic nitrogenous matter |
| Metals | Toxic pollution |
| Cyanide | Toxic pollution |
| Phenols | Toxic pollution, odor, and taste |
| Sulfides | Toxic pollution, odor |
| Sulfates | May affect corrosion of concrete, possible biochemical reduction to sulfides |
| Calcium and magnesium | Hardness |
| Synthetic detergents | Froth, toxic pollution |

use of the water under test. Some of the factors regarding informational requirements that should be considered in establishing methods of analysis are: (a) the required degree of sensitivity and accuracy; (b) the required frequency of analysis; and (c) the relative desirability of field and laboratory analysis.

Another point for consideration in selecting analytical methods concerns the collection, transportation, and storage of samples. Screening tests should be conducted for purposes of approximating required sample volumes, establishing desirable sites for and frequency of sampling, and providing a rough estimate of the waste composition and strength.

Listings of "standard" and "recommended" methods for analysis of natural waters and wastewaters are to be found in a variety of publications sponsored by several water works, pollution control, and public health agencies and organizations in this country and abroad (29,456). In addition, in several instances certain private industries have found it desirable to formalize listings of more specific methods for analysis of particular types of industrial wastewater (112,450).

While general procedures of analysis for specific waste constituents are highly useful, the industrial-wastewater analyst must be careful to guard against overreliance upon such procedures and against the possibility of being lulled into a false sense of security by results obtained from application of such procedures in instances where they may not be applicable. Indiscriminate application of general purpose methods for analysis without due consideration of specific interferences and other problems must be avoided. Standardization upon procedures should be made only after these procedures have been thoroughly evaluated in terms of particular analytical requirements. Continuing use of such standard methods without modification should then be subject to the condition that the characteristics of the waste being analyzed do not change significantly over the duration of the analytical program. Just as the skilled medical doctor will not prescribe treatment or medication until he has carefully examined the patient *in toto*, so the analytical chemist should select his approach to the analysis of an industrial wastewater only after making a careful diagnosis of the total problem. This diagnosis should include consideration of: (a) objectives of the analysis; (b) requirements of speed, frequency, accuracy, and precision of analysis; (c) effects of interferences; and (d) effects of systematic and environmental conditions on sampling and measurements.

## 4. Measurement Characteristics

It is desirable in the chemical analysis of industrial wastewaters to differentiate between intensive and extensive measurements. The distinction between intensive and extensive properties per se is clear. By definition, extensive properties are additive in the sense that the total value of the property for the whole of a system is the sum of the individual values for each of its constituent parts. Conversely, intensive properties are not additive and can be specified for any system without reference to the size of that system. In chemical systems, the total number of moles of a substance in a sample is considered an extensive property, while the chemical potential or molal free energy, $\mu$, of the substance is an intensive property. Consequently, analytical methods based on the titration of the number of moles of a given substance in a water sample are "extensive measurements" and they are distinctly different from "intensive measurements" based on the determination of the chemical potential or activity* of the same substance. Because of basic differences in measurement techniques, one may anticipate somewhat different

* Activity is an intensive parameter and is usually defined in terms of the relative fugacity. In this discussion, the term activity is used as a direct measure of difference between the partial molal free energies or the chemical potentials of a chosen and a reference state, i.e.,

$$\mu - \mu° = RT \ln a \qquad (1)$$

where $\mu°$ is the standard chemical potential, $R$ is the gas constant, $T$ is the absolute temperature, and $a$ is the activity.

results from the two methods. Hence, potentiometric measurements of pH, pX, or pM, where X and M refer to anions and cations, respectively, may give results in contradiction to those obtained from titrimetric determinations of acidity, anions, or metal cations. This is common in the presence of certain interferences, which may cause the activity coefficient in the test solution to deviate from unity.

Similarly, in the case of voltammetric membrane electrode systems, such as the galvanic cell oxygen analyzer, the measured parameter is essentially an intensive factor, since the diffusion current is solely dependent on the difference in the chemical potentials of molecular oxygen across the membrane (286). Accordingly, values derived from measurements with a galvanic cell oxygen analyzer do not have to be equal to results obtained by titration methods for dissolved oxygen, such as the Winkler test. In the former case, the activity of molecular oxygen is the parameter measured (284,286) ; in the latter case, the total number of oxygen molecules present in the test volume is measured. For the majority of natural and wastewaters it is unlikely, for a variety of reasons, that the two kinds of measurements will give exactly the same results, although in many applications the difference may be negligible for all practical purposes.

The analyst should also be aware of the differences—and the significance of such differences—between the concentration (number of moles in a given volume) of a species and its chemical activity. Activity measurements are most significant in characterizing biochemical and physiochemical dynamics in aquatic environments. Consider, for example, the case of dissolved molecular oxygen, which may be involved in a variety of physical, chemical, and biological reactions in natural waters and in wastewaters. Oxygen transfer across the air–water interface or within the bulk of the aqueous phase is an example of a physical process. Under constant temperature and hydrodynamic conditions the rate of oxygen transport is solely dependent on the gradient in dissolved oxygen activity, and not always in the direction of diminishing concentration. Thus, under certain conditions, "uphill" diffusion, counteracting equilization of concentration, may occur. This is possible, if, for instance, a component not participating in diffusion causes a decrease in activity combined with an increase in concentration (salting-in effect) or an increase in activity combined with a decrease in concentration (salting-out effect). Accordingly, determination of the rate of oxygen transfer based solely on concentration measurements can be in error. In a similar fashion, in biological systems the availability of molecular oxygen for reaction depends primarily on the activity level, for diffusion through biological membranes is more precisely described in terms of oxygen activity than in terms of concentration.

For evaluation and prediction of rates of chemical reactions in waters and wastewaters, determination of the chemical activity of the substances involved is indeed highly significant. Whether a given reaction is diffusion controlled or activation controlled, knowledge of the activity is essential whenever the effects of environmental factors, such as pressure, ionic strength, solvent–solute or solute–solute interactions, are to be considered.

In addition, activity measurements can be used to provide a phenomological description of the dynamics of a system, in the form of appropriate proportionalities (e.g., Fourier's law, Ficks law, and the chemical reaction law). Description of complicated cross phenomena, such as the Soret effect and the Dufour effect are also possible based on such measurements.

### a. In Situ Analyses

Perhaps the most meaningful type of analytical program for water quality characterization is that involving *in situ* measurements. In general, methods for *in situ* analyses are to be preferred over analytical procedures which involve removal of the water from its natural environment, in the form of "grab" samples or in the form of a diverted stream, for subsequent analysis in the laboratory or field station. The main problems associated with the latter procedure can be related to the process of collecting samples, which in most cases cannot be done in such fashion as to give true representation of the test solution, and to the fact that the analyses are then usually performed under conditions quite different from those which exist at the sampling site. For example, changes in temperature and pressure may result in the escape of gases with consequent chemical or biological transformation of the species under test. When monitoring is the principal objective of the analytical program, the grab sample method usually does not provide sufficient data for a satisfactory degree of statistical significance and also can be relatively expensive on a cost per sample basis.

The use of *in situ* analysis for water quality characterization is not a novel concept. One of the classical methods for analysis of toxic compounds in water is based on the survival of fish in the natural environment. In a fashion similar to the 19th century practice of using canaries to monitor the presence of toxic gases in coal mines, *"Gambusia affinis"* has been used to monitor industrial waste effluents. In this procedure, the toxicity of the wastewater is continuously gauged by placing a certain number of fish in a net or screen box in the receiving stream and observing the number of dead or live fish at daily intervals. Death of the fish in 4–5 days is indicative of the presence of toxic substances (109). The fish, in this case, may be considered as biological indicators or sensors. Because of lack of specificity, techniques of this type find only limited application, although the "fish test" is still in fairly common use both in this country and abroad. Current methods of using biological indicators for water quality characterization will be discussed in more detail in a later part of this chapter.

Instrumental methods of *in situ* analysis are generally based upon the use of input transducers or sensors which, upon immersion in the test solution, transform responses to physical and/or chemical changes to a transmittable signal, most commonly an electrical signal. This signal is then transferred, over attenuating, amplifying, or transforming components, to a final display or readout device. The measuring system as a whole may be considered as being composed of a series of transducers, classified as (a) input or measuring transducers, (b) modifying transducers, and (c) output or read-out transducers.

Input transducers may be self-generating (active) devices, which produce an energy output for a single energy input, or non-self-generating (passive or impedance based) modules, which require more than one energy input in order to produce a single energy output. Examples of the former type are the glass electrode, the galvanic cell oxygen analyzer, and the thermocouple; conductivity cells, voltammetric cells, and resistance thermometers are examples of the latter type. Bollinger (66) and Stein (434) have recently discussed the classification and application of input transducers in measurement systems for environmental control.

*In situ* measuring systems may be based either on imbalance or on reference techniques. In the former case the output signal from the input transducer is measured directly (e.g., with a galvanometer). In the latter case, the output signal is compared to a known or reference quantity, the reference system output being varied until the difference between it and the output from the measurement system is zero.

Because such systems often involve intensive-type measurements, careful consideration should be given to the interpretation of the analytical results, especially when determinations of material balance or stream capacity for waste assimilation are concerned.

Much recent attention has been given to *in situ* analysis in conjunction with continuous monitoring systems. A partial list of parameters and sensors commonly determined *in situ* by continuous monitoring systems in surface waters and certain industrial waste effluents (309) is given in Table III.

TABLE III

Water Quality Parameters Commonly Measured by *in situ* Methods

| Quality parameters | Sensor system |
|---|---|
| Temperature | Thermistors; resistance thermometers; radiation pyrometers; thermocouples; pneumatic or capillary devices |
| Turbidity | Photoelectric cell |
| pH | Glass electrode |
| Dissolved oxygen | Voltammetric or galvanic membrane electrodes; dropping mercury electrode; gold electrode |
| Conductivity | Platinum electrode |
| Chlorides | Ag/AgCl electrode |
| Oxidation reduction potential | Platinum electrode |
| Alkalies, alkaline earths, fluorides, cyanides, and sulfides | Potentiometric membrane electrodes (specific ion electrodes) |

b. Instrumental and Automated Methods for Analysis

The preceding brief introduction to the use of instrumental systems for *in situ* analysis leads logically to a somewhat more detailed discussion of instrumental methods in general. During the last two decades there has been a noticeable increase in the use of instrumentation in all fields of chemical analysis. In the water and wastewater field, however, highly sophisticated analytical instruments and automatic analyzers have not had extensive application to date, probably due in large part to the relatively high costs involved. However, as the value of more rigid control of water quality becomes more evident, one may expect a gradual increase in the use of such instrumentation.

Instrumental methods can be very useful for obtaining the information about the physicochemical and biochemical properties of a water required for prescription of proper treatment and for control of quality. However, the analyst concerned with water quality characterization should avoid unnecessary use of complicated automatic instrumentation. Many analytical procedures lend themselves to simple manual operations without loss in accuracy or sensitivity. Such methods should be investigated thoroughly before any decision is made to use complex automated techniques. Use of the most simple instrumentation suitable for accomplishing the objectives of the analytical program is recommended, especially for water and waste treatment plants lacking personnel fully qualified to maintain and operate complicated instruments. Needless to say, small industrial and municipal treatment plants are frequently left unattended for several days; this is also true for water quality monitoring systems stationed on streams or on industrial waste effluents.

In general, the selection and use of instruments for analysis should be based on the following considerations: (1) a thorough understanding of the principle of operation of the sensor and its response characteristics; (2) a general understanding of the basic properties of the instrumental elements, their functions, and modes of operation; (3) the method of calibration of the system (certain instruments require only static calibration; others require dynamic calibration in order to determine the response of the system to rapidly fluctuating variables); (4) proper installation and use of instruments; and (5) periodic maintenance and calibration checks.

Sensors (input transducers) can generally be characterized according to their input, transfer, and output properties. The input characteristics of a sensor are specified by the type of input, the useful range of input for which the sensor can be used, and the effect of the sensor on the material under investigation. The transfer characteristics are defined by the sensitivity of the element, which is a function of the differential quotient of the output to the input quantities. Thus the sensitivity of the sensor is related to the smallest change in the measured variable that causes a detectable output.

For cases in which the transfer function is linear, the sensitivity will be constant over the range of the sensor response. The transfer function is also sometimes called the "gain," the "attenuation factor," or the "scaler factor."

Errors in measurement are generally caused by failure of the sensor to behave according to given transfer characteristics. Errors may, however, be more complex. So-called "scale errors" result from deviation of the output quantity from the true value by a constant value (e.g., zero displacement), or, on the other hand, the deviation may be a variable function of the input quantity. The output may, in certain cases, depend not only upon the applied input, but also upon the past history of the sensor. "Dynamic errors" can result when the variation of output with time does not follow precisely that of the input or when output depends upon such time functions as a time derivative or the frequency of the input (462).

The "speed of response" of a sensor refers to the time required for the sensor to undergo a certain per cent response to a sudden change in the measured variable; 90, 95, and 99% responses are common, and the particular one used for defining response speed should be specified. For sensors having first-order response rates, the term "time constant" in this case is the period required for the sensor output to respond to 63.2% $(100-100/e)$ of the stepwise change in input.

Often the difference between instrumental methods of analysis and automated chemical techniques is not sufficiently clear. Instrumental methods involve the use of sensor devices, but regardless of the degree of sophistication or complexity of the instrument, it is the analyst who initiates and controls the analytical event. Automated chemical devices, on the other hand, may or may not employ instrumental methods of analysis; they are quite often merely automated forms of classical wet chemical methods (147,292,318,338,339,482,506). Blaedel and Laessig (61) have discussed automation of analytical procedures in some length. Continuous and batch analyses have been compared and the design considerations such as response time and sample size have been presented. These authors have given a survey of continuous methods of analysis, including many of interest for the water quality area.

Colorimetric or spectrophotometric procedures are among those most suitable for automated operation. A typical automatic system of this type might be comprised of several basic components: a sample turntable, a proportioning pump, a mixing coil, a separator, a heating bath, a colorimeter, and a recorder or digital printout unit. Two schematic diagrams of two automatic analyzers are given in Fig. 1.

Samples placed on the turntable are pumped at constant rate through narrow tubing, consecutive samples being separated from each other by air bubbles. Appropriate reagents and diluents are added to each sample and allowed to mix in a coil. The sample is then driven to the separator compartment where certain interfering compounds are removed by means of dialyzing membranes, by filtration, or by other procedures. Following this, chromogenic agents are added to the sample, which then goes to a heating bath where color formation takes place. Finally, the solution is transferred automatically to a continuous flow colorimeter, in which transmittance at a preset wavelength is measured and recorded on a strip chart recorder. Known standards are periodically run through the system for measurement of transmittance. Concentrations are determined by comparing spectrophotometric data for the samples with those for the known standards. Accuracy and precision are therefore dependent upon effecting exactly the same treatment for the reference standards as for the samples to be measured. Under these conditions reactions are not necessarily carried to completion, but if exactly the same treatment is given the unknown and reference samples, the measurements are nonetheless valid on a comparative basis.

The literature concerning the use of automatic analyzers for analysis

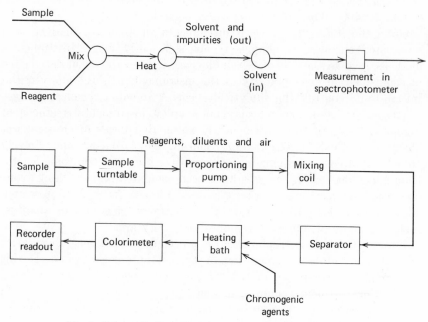

Fig. 1. Schematic flow diagrams for automated analyses.

of natural waters and wastewaters is rapidly increasing. Automatic analysis for chemical oxygen demand (COD) in domestic raw sewage and
in effluents from trickling-filter and activated-sludge processes has been
reported (318). The automated technique was compared both with the
manual COD test reported in *Standard Methods* (29) and with the
digestion method for total organic carbon reported by Weber and Morris
(487). The results of the comparisons indicated good correlation between
the manual and automatic COD procedures, but, as the authors have
pointed out, it is essential to first evaluate the suitability of a particular
automatic analyzer for each potential application and to establish correlation between the manual and automated methods. Other investigators
have reported on the use of similar automated chemical techniques for
the analysis of pesticides (506), nitrates, chlorides, and nitrogen
(252,292).

The use of automated chemical techniques for analysis of natural
waters and wastewaters should not be undertaken without careful consideration of the suitability of the underlying chemical procedure, the
physicochemical characteristics of the test solution, and the susceptibility

of the technique to pertinent interferences. If it appears feasible to employ an automatic analyzer, then the question of flexibility should be considered. It is possible to obtain equipment capable of performing more than one automatic analytical procedure. The development and operation of an automated system capable of simultaneous analysis of up to 12 different parameters has been described by Marten et al. (292).

One of the main advantages of automatic analysis is elimination of a large share of the element of human error involved in so many chemical procedures, thus enhancing reproducibility of the steps in the procedure and of the accuracy and precision of the test in general. The analyst should be aware, however, that changes in the properties of the test solution may go undetected in automated chemical procedures, leading to erroneous results. The inability of most automatic analyzers to recognize and adjust for changes in the chemical nature of test solutions is probably the principal drawback of such procedures. Because of the complex characteristics and changing nature of the test solution, it is often quite difficult, if not impossible in certain cases, to apply completely automated chemical techniques for water and waste analysis. Each sample may require a particular type of pretreatment, depending on the source, objectives of analysis, and presence of interfering substances. Because of the complexity of most automatic analyzers, required modifications of the system to this end may be difficult and costly.

### c. Continuous Monitoring

Whenever the chemical characteristics of an industrial wastewater or receiving water are variable or whenever it is necessary to maintain close control over waste treatment processes, continuous, rather than periodic analyses are to be preferred.

The process control industry has been largely responsible for development and perfection of the equipment and "hardware" required for continuous monitoring. By far the largest application of continuous analytical measurement systems has been for industrial process control. Sophistication of continuous monitoring systems in the application has advanced to the point where not only can analyses be performed automatically and continuously, but the analytical data can be processed and translated by computer to operational control information (46). Further, this information can then be fed into automatic control devices for actual process operation.

Recently there have been substantial increases in the use of continuous monitoring systems in the wastewater treatment and quality control field (95,309,345,471). Automatic, on-line, continuous monitoring systems have been used for surveillance and remote control of wells, treatment facilities, pumping stations, storage tanks, etc. (49,105). A number of industries, including the petrochemical, pulp and paper, pharmaceutical, and a variety of chemical industries, have gone into complete or partial automation of their waste treatment facilities (46,482). Several municipal waste treatment plants also are using continuous monitoring systems for control of activated-sludge, trickling filter, and anaerobic digestion processes.

Increasing emphasis on water pollution control has led to establishment of continuous water quality monitoring stations on most of the major rivers, tributaries, lakes, and estuaries in the United States. The Public Health Service and the Geological Survey maintain a number of continuous monitoring installations, as do most interstate agencies, such as the Ohio River Valley Water Sanitation Commission (ORSANCO) and the Interstate Commission on the Delaware River Basin (471).

Industries often find it desirable to continuously monitor water quality of rivers and streams which are used as sources for water supply or for disposal of waste effluents. In the latter case, monitoring is usually done both upstream and downstream of the point of discharge for the purpose of proportioning the quality and quantity of the discharge according to the assimilative capacity of the stream and for maintenance of stream quality standards.

Continuous analytical measurements may be of the *in situ* type or may involve automated measurements made on a diverted portion of the water or waste system. In a system of the latter type the water may be pumped from the river or estuary to a small tank in which appropriate sensing elements are contained, whereas for *in situ* type systems the sensing elements are suspended directly into the river or estuary. Each of these methods has certain advantages and drawbacks. In the diversion-type stream the sensing elements are readily accessible for frequent cleaning and calibration. This convenience may, however, be gained at the expense of a truly representative monitoring system. During pumping certain changes in temperature, pressure, agitation, etc. may induce changes in the test solution which lead to absorption or release of gases or to dissolution or precipitation of salts. Other problems commonly associated with pumping the water to the monitoring station, such as clogging of the sampling lines with suspended aquatic plants, silt, etc., pump failure, and the freezing of the lines at low temperatures, may be greatly reduced by employing *in situ* techniques.

*In situ* measurements, as mentioned previously, are considered to give more significant and meaningful results, since the species under test are determined in their own environment. The main operational problems involved in *in situ* analytical systems relate primarily to protection of submerged sensors from damage by floating debris, aquatic plants, ice, etc., while still maintaining fairly easy access to the sensor equipment for purposes of frequent cleaning and checking.

It is essential for the proper design of a continuous monitoring system that the objectives of the analytical program be clearly defined, that the parameters to be measured be carefully selected, and that a well formulated plan be established for data collection, retrieval, and utilization. Design characteristics of water quality monitoring systems have been discussed in detail by Mentink (309). There are two basic variations in design, each of which has advantages for particular applications. The first is based on electronically, or mechanically and electronically, independent parametric systems, while the second is a form of an integrated system. In the first type each parametric signal is detected, transformed, amplified, and recorded independently, while the integrated system is based on the use of flexible module components for the measurement of several parameters. A well designed integrated system, beside providing all the advantages of parametric systems, is flexible, simple to maintain, and has a lower initial and operating cost (309). Modularity, by providing for simple plug-in type operation, obviates the need for design of complex operational networks, whether passive or active. Modularity in the output phase of the monitoring system extends its usefulness and application. Thus the output may not be limited to an analog strip chart recorder, but rather the addition of either telemetry or digital output equipment may be possible, this being desirable whenever large quantities of data are to be accumulated.

## II. CHARACTERIZATION OF INDUSTRIAL WASTEWATERS

The diversity of modern industry and of industrial processes makes rigid classification of wastewaters according to composition virtually impossible. Single-product industries are rare, that is, most industries process or manufacture a variety of products. Seldom is the particular combination of products processed or manufactured at a given industrial installation identical to that at another, even within the same general product field. Further, a given product is often not produced by exactly the same process at each installation at which its manufacture or preparation is carried out. Competition among industries and slight variations in grade, composition, or quality among raw materials used in production of a given product often require continuing process innovation and modification. Variations in process type and operation usually lead to variations in the composition of the liquid waste produced. It is apparent then that very nearly every industrial wastewater is, at least in fine detail, unique in its composition.

Broadly, however, liquid industrial wastes may be categorized according to their principal constituents. Certain industries produce wastes which contain primarily mineral impurities. Included in the group are the oil field and refining, mining, steel, metal plating, foundry, and similar industries. On the other hand, liquid wastes commonly produced by the food, beverage, and pharmaceutical industries consist primarily of organic impurities. A number of industrial processes and operations lead to wastewaters which contain both mineral and organic impurities in equally significant concentrations; such wastes are common to the paper, textile, leather, and laundry industries. Liquid waste containing primarily radioactive impurities are associated for the most part with water-cooled nuclear reactors and with industries involved in processing of ores and reactor fuels. On a smaller scale as concerns both volume and activity levels, radioactive wastes also originate in research laboratories, hospitals, and laundry operations serving such facilities. A final category of industrial wastewater includes those of sufficiently high temperature and volume to cause thermal pollution of receiving waters into which they are discharged. Such wastes are limited almost exclusively to the steam power industry and to certain cooling operations within other industries.

It must be recognized that certain complex industrial wastewaters may fall into more than one of the above categories, but in general the five groups listed provide a rather comprehensive classification of liquid wastes according to their principal impurities. It should be evident, however, even to the reader with only a casual awareness of the technology of industrial processes that marked differences must exist among the wastes produced by the various industries which fall within any one of the given categories.

While a broad classification of wastewaters according to the nature of the principal constituent provides a useful sphere of reference, the present discussion relates to analytical methods and procedures appropriate for specific industrial situations. It is appropriate then to approach a more detailed characterization of wastewaters in terms of those typically produced by specific industries. For this purpose, six major classes of industry are designated:

a. The chemical manufacturing industries.
b. The food, beverage, and pharmaceutical industries.

c. The apparel industries.
d. The materials industries.
e. The energy- and power-related industries.
f. The services industries.

It is entirely beyond the scope of the present discussion to consider the nature of the wastewaters associated with each of the many specific industries within the six designated classes. Rather, examples of some of the more significant types will be given. For more extensive coverage of the nature of wastes produced by specific processes and industries, the reader is advised to consult appropriate scientific periodicals, references and text books on the subject of industrial wastes. Reference works by Nemerow (332) and Gurnham (176) are examples of books in which the characterization and treatment of industrial wastewaters are discussed in detail. Such reference books also provide bibliographic listings of periodicals, reports, and other sources of information which the reader will find most useful in further exploration of this subject.

## A. CHEMICAL MANUFACTURING INDUSTRIES

There is considerable diversity among wastes produced by the various industries concerned with the manufacture and processing of chemicals. While certain similarities in particular characteristics often exist (for example, wastes originating from production of acids are of course quite low in pH while wastewaters from the manufacture of explosives, pesticides, and phosphate and phosphorus also tend to be acidic in nature), few generalities may be drawn concerning such wastes as a group.

Liquid wastes from the explosives industry are generally highly colored, quite odorous, and contain organic acids, alcohols, oils, soaps, trinitrotoluene, and dissolved metals. An average phenolphthalein acidity of about 330 mg/liter and an average pH of 2.6 have been reported for wastes from the production of TNT (423). The same report lists average concentrations of 638 and 130 mg/liter for sulfate and total nitrogen (primarily nitrate), respectively. Wastes from power plants typically contain high concentrations of mixed acids and relatively high concentrations of ether–alcohol from solvent recovery systems, as well as aniline from the manufacture of diphenylamine (332). Reports of average analytical results for wastes from ammunition production gives pH values of 3.5, a phenolphthalein acidity of 239 mg/liter, total solids of about 1700 mg/liter, suspended solids of about 400 mg/liter, and grease and copper concentrations of 709 and 86 mg/liter, respectively (423).

In addition to being acidic, pesticide wastes generally contain high concentrations of dissolved organic substances, such as benzene and other ring structures, which are quite toxic to bacteria and fish. One of the major and most troublesome constituents of wastes from the insecticide industry is dichlorophenol, resulting from the production of 2,3-dichloro-phenoxyacetic acid (332). The production of DDT leads to highly acid wastes containing approximately 55% sulfuric acid, 20% ethyl hydrogen sulfate, and 20% chlorobenzene sulfuric acid (332).

The acidic wastes from production of phosphate and phosphorus typically contain slimes and tall oils. They are usually high in both suspended and dissolved solids, which consist for the most part of phosphorus, fluorides, and silica. Horton et al. (207) have described wastes from the phosphate industry as having pH values between 1.5 and 2.0 and temperatures ranging from 120 to 150°F. These investigators have reported concentrations of elemental phosphorus of between 400 and 2500 mg/liter, of total suspended solids between 1000 and 5000 mg/liter, of fluoride between 500 and 2000 mg/liter, of silica between 300 and 700 mg/liter, of $P_2O_5$ between 600 and 900 ppm, and of reducing substances between 40 and 50 mg/liter as iodine.

Several of the liquid wastes produced by the chemical manufacturing industries are characterized by high biochemical oxygen demands. Wastewaters having high BOD's include those involved in the production of cornstarch, detergents, and formaldehyde. While exhibiting high levels of BOD, formaldehyde wastes in high concentration are quite toxic to bacteria. The high BOD of cornstarch wastes is mainly attributable to starch and related materials appearing in this waste, the dry substance of the corn kernel being composed approximately of 80% carbohydrates, 10% proteins, 4.5% oil and fats, 3.5% fiber, and 2% minerals (332). Detergent wastes, which originate in the washing and purification of soaps and detergents, contain high concentrations of saponified soaps and fatty acids, as well as detergents lost in the manufacturing process.

## B. FOOD, BEVERAGE, AND PHARMACEUTICAL INDUSTRIES

Almost without exception wastewaters produced in the food, beverage, and pharmaceutical industries are high in biochemical oxygen demand, in suspended organic solids, and in dissolved organic matter. This classification of industry concerns the production and processing of canned goods, dairy products, meat and poultry products, beet sugar, yeast, pickles, coffee, fish, rice, brewed and distilled beverages, soft drinks, and pharmaceutical products.

High levels of proteins and fats are commonly found in the waste from the dairy, meat, and poultry industries, lactose additionally being high in concentration in dairy wastes and blood contributing considerably to the organic matter found in meat and poultry wastes. Process wastes from the dairy industry have been reported to have an average total solids concentration of about 4500 mg/liter, with a 5-day BOD of approximately 1900 mg/liter (332). Of the total solids, approximately 2700 mg/liter consists of organic matter and approximately 1800 mg/liter of ash solids. Approximately 4000 mg/liter of the solids are soluble, while about 500 mg/liter are suspended. These process wastes contain approximately 800 mg/liter of sodium, 112 mg/liter of calcium, 116 mg/liter of potassium, 60 mg/liter of phosphorous, 25 mg/liter of mercury, 75 mg/liter of total organic nitrogen, and about 6 mg/liter of free ammonia (332). Slaughterhouse wastes are generally quite strong, usually containing about 1000 mg/liter of total solids, 2000 mg/liter of 5-day BOD, and 500 mg/liter of total nitrogen (332). By comparison, a typical stockyard waste has been reported as having a BOD of 64 mg/liter, total suspended solids of 173 mg/liter, 8 mg/liter ammonia nitrogen, and organic nitrogen concentration of 11 mg/liter (473).

Cannery wastes are extremely variable in composition, depending upon the particular food product being processed. For example, liquid wastes from the canning of asparagus have a 5-day BOD of approximately 100 mg/liter and a suspended solids concentration of about 30 mg/liter, while wastes from the canning of pumpkin and whole kernel corn may range as high as 6000 or 7000 mg/liter in 5-day BOD, with suspended solids concentrations as high as 3000–4000 mg/liter (394). Great differences in both volume and characteristics of wastewaters from the cannery industries will be found from plant to plant, and even within the same plant from day to day. The wastewaters from all canning processes are usually made up of washwater and spillage from filling and sealing machines, which contain solids from the various sorting, peeling, and coring operations.

Beet sugar wastes are high in protein as well as sugar. Pearson and Sawyer (348) have reported that process wastewater from the beet sugar industry has a total solids concentration of about 3800 mg/liter, of which 75% is volatile and 1300 mg/liter is suspended solids. The BOD of this waste is in the neighborhood of 1600 mg/liter, while the COD is about 1500 ppm. These wastes contain about 1500 mg/liter sucrose and have a total nitrogen concentration of about 80 mg/liter, of which 65 mg/liter is protein nitrogen and 15 mg/liter is ammonia nitrogen.

Liquid wastes from the rice processing industries contain high concentrations of starch. Heukelekian has described composite rice wastes as having a BOD in the neighborhood of 1000 mg/liter with a starch level of about 1200 mg/liter and a concentration of reducing sugars of approximately 70 mg/liter (197). The total solids concentration is approximately 1500 mg/liter, of which about 11% is ash. According to Heukelekian, composite rice wastes contain about 30 mg/liter total nitrogen, and 30 mg/liter phosphates and have a pH between 4.2 and 7.0.

Fermented starches or their products are present in high concentrations in wastes from the brewed and distilled beverages industry, along with considerable concentrations of nitrogen. According to Porges and Struzeski (355) a typical waste from the carbonated beverage industry has a pH of about 10.8, with a total alkalinity of 290 mg/liter and a phenolphthalein alkalinity of 150 mg/liter. These investigators have indicated that the 5-day BOD of such wastes is about 430 mg/liter, while the suspended solids concentration is approximately 220 mg/liter.

Spent nutrient wastes from yeast plants range in total solids concentration from 10,000 to 20,000 mg/liter, with approximately 50–200 mg/liter of this being suspended solids and approximately 7000–15,000 mg/liter being volatile solids (461). This waste typically has a 5-day BOD ranging between 2000 and 15,000 mg/liter and a pH between 4.5 and 6.5, and it contains between 3800 and 5500 mg/liter total organic carbon, 500–700 mg/liter organic nitrogen, 800–900 mg/liter total nitrogen, 2000–2500 mg/liter sulfate expressed as $SO_4$, and 20–140 mg/liter phosphate expressed as $P_2O_5$.

Horton et al. (207) have reported on a coffee fermentation washwater waste having a BOD of 1700 mg/liter and a pH of 4.5, with a total solids concentration of 2100 mg/liter and a suspended solids concentration of 900 mg/liter. By comparison, coffee depulping wastes, according to Horton et al., have an average BOD of 9400 mg/liter and a pH of 4.4. The total solids concentration for the coffee depulping waste is approximately 11,500 mg/liter on the average, with approximately 800 mg/liter of this being suspended solids.

Liquid wastes from the fish processing industry can be quite odorous, while those from industries involved in the processing of pickles tend to be high in color. Pharmaceutical products can contain a broad variety of dissolved organic substances, including vitamins, trace antibiotics, and numerous other impurities, depending upon the particular product involved.

## C. APPAREL INDUSTRIES

The two principal apparel industries are those involved in the production of textiles and leather goods. Wastes originating in the textile industry from the cooking of fibers and desizing of fabrics are high in BOD, suspended solids, and temperature. In addition, such wastes tend to be high in pH and color.

Masselli et al. (294) have reported that total impurities in typical woolen mill wastes are on the order of 3800 mg/liter, of which approximately 3000 mg/liter consists of natural impurities, such as grease, suint, and dirt. Of the remaining 800 mg/liter or so of impurities contributed by process chemicals, soda ash from the scouring and fulling processes accounts for approximately 350 mg/liter, while approximately 200–250 mg/liter consists of fatty acid soaps, solvents, and detergents. These wastes also contain about 25 mg/liter of acetic acid and approximately 50 mg/liter of high carbohydrates and enzymes used in the finishing process. Other impurities to be found in lesser quantities in woolen mill wastes are pine oil, mineral oils, sulfates, chromates, phosphates, ammonia, and monochlorobenzene.

Principal waste constituents from textile mills producing synthetic fibers derive from the process chemicals used in preparing the synthetic fibers. Depending upon the particular type of synthetic fiber being processed, such wastewaters contain varying concentrations of sulfonated oils, soaps, synthetic detergents, aliphatic and fatty esters, acetic acid, ortho- and para- phenylphenol, benzoic acid, salicylic acid, phenylmethyl carbinol, formic acid, miscellaneous phenolic compounds, copper, sulfate, and ammonia (294).

Liquid wastes from the leather goods industries are also high in biochemical oxygen demand (about 1000 mg/liter), total solids (about 9000 mg/liter), pH (11–12), and total hardness (about 1600 mg/liter) (332). Typically these wastes contain about 1000 mg/liter of sulfide, approximately 1000 mg/liter of protein, 60 mg/liter ammonia nitrogen, 40 mg/liter chromium, about 300 mg/liter of sodium chloride, and about 1200 mg/liter of precipitated lime (293,332).

## D. MATERIALS INDUSTRIES

The industries included in this classification are the pulp and paper industry, the steel industry, the metal plating industry, the iron-foundry industry, the rubber industry, and the glass industry.

Wastes from the pulp and paper industries may be very high or very low in pH, depending upon the particular process used. These wastes contain inorganic fillers and are generally high in suspended colloidal and dissolved solids and in color. Pulp-mill wastes, from grinding, cooking, bleaching, and other treatment of pulps, contain sulfite, liquor, sulfides, carbonates, mercaptans, bleach, sizing, casein, ink, dyes, waxes, grease, oils, fiber, and clay (332). Paper-mill wastes, from the screens, showers, and felts of the paper machines, beaters, and mixing and regulating tanks, contain fibers, sizing, dye, and other loading material (332).

There are essentially three chemical processes for the preparation of pulps: (1) the soda process, (2) the kraft or sulfate process, and (3) the sulfite process. In place of the chemical methods either mechanical pulping or a semichemical soda process is often employed. The semichemical soda process characteristically produces wastes containing pentosans, $NaC_2H_3O_2$, formate, fine particles of bark and wood, and some dissolved solids. Moggio (317) has reported that efficiently operated kraft process plants discharge effluents containing no more than 100 lb of the sodium sulfate equivalent of the cooking liquor per ton of pulp produced. According to Moggio, the nature of the wastewater will depend to some extent on the bleaching processes employed, but, in general, suspended solids concentrations will range between 20 and 60 mg/liter (primarily fiber), with dissolved solids concentration ranging from 1000 to 1500 mg/liter. Typical kraft process wastes are highly colored and have a 5-day BOD ranging from about 100 to 200 mg/liter. Wastes from the soda pulping process may be expected to be quite similar to those from the kraft process in that the processes themselves are quite similar, the greatest difference being that in the soda pulping process either sodium hydroxide alone or a lower concentration of sodium sulfide is used in the cooking step; thus, the waste from this process will have a lower total concentration of sulfur (394). Solids concentrations of spent sulfite liquors are generally of the order of 10–12% (372), consisting mainly of lignosulfonic acid and reducing sugars (59). The sulfite liquor contains both free and combined sulfur dioxide and related sugar–sulfur dioxide derivatives, sugars, lignin, furfural, acetone, alcohols, and volatile acids (372).

Liquid wastes from the steel industry are low in pH due to the presence of considerable concentrations of mineral acids. These wastes contain a large number of dissolved and suspended materials, including limestone, oils, coke, ore, alkali, cyanogen, phenol, and mill scale. Metal-plating wastes also contain high concentrations of acid, metals, and mineral impurities, while iron-foundry wastes are high in suspended solids, mainly attributable to sand, clay, and coal.

Ammonia-still wastes from by-product coke plants represent one of the most important classes of effluent waters from steel-mill operations. Phenolic compounds represent one of the primary classes of constituents of ammonia-still wastes, with cyanides and organic and ammonia nitrogen of importance also (28). Typical BOD's for these wastes are of the order of 4000 mg/liter, with phenol levels of 2057 mg/liter, cyanide concentrations of 110 mg/liter, organic and ammonia nitrogen levels of 281 mg/liter, total suspended solids concentrations of 356 ppm, and volatile suspended solids levels of 153 ppm having been reported (28). Flue solids in wet scrubber effluents in steel mills consist primarily of iron oxide and silica, with significant percentages also of alumina, carbon, lime, and magnesia (195). Major contaminants in the wastes from the pickling and washing of steel are sulfuric acid and ferrous sulfate. Sulfuric acid concentrations are about 0.5–2.0% in pickling liquors and about 0.02–0.5% in wash waters, while corresponding concentrations of ferrous sulfate are approximately 15–22% and 0.03–0.45% respectively (332).

As far as other metal plants are concerned, the two primary wastes are those from bright-dip and pickle-bath operations. Pickle-bath wastes contain between 59.7 and 163.3 g of sulfuric acid per liter, 4.0–22.6 g of copper per liter, 4.3–41.4 g of zinc per liter, from traces to 0.56 g of chromium per liter, and from 0.1 to 0.21g of iron per liter (507). Bright-dip wastes from the brass and copper industry contain the same contaminants as do pickle bath wastes, but sulfuric acid levels are generally somewhat lower, copper levels somewhat higher, and chromium levels significantly higher, on the order of 13.5–47.7 g/liter (507).

Metal-plating wastes, generally low in volume, are extremely heterogeneous and dangerous because of their high concentrations of toxic metals. Stripping baths usually consist of mixtures of sulfuric, nitric, and hydrochloric acids and are therefore generally quite acidic in nature, although some stripping baths are alkaline, containing hydroxides, sulfides, and cyanides (332). Typical metal plating wastes have been reported as ranging in pH from as low as 2.0 to as high as 11.9, in copper concentration as high as 300 mg/liter, in iron as high as 21 mg/liter, 32 mg/liter in nickel, 82 mg/liter in zinc, 612 mg/liter total chromium, and 15 mg/liter in copper (394). Also to be found in metal plating wastes are grease, oil, and alkaline cleaners. Organic solvent cleaners are generally petroleum or coal tar emulsions, while alkaline cleaners consist of phosphates, silicates, carbonates, hydroxides, wetting agents, and emulsifiers (332).

Wastes from the production of rubber, originating from the washing of latex and coagulated rubber, generally contain high levels of suspended solids and chlorides. Rubber wastes tend to be quite variable in pH and exhibit high levels of biochemical oxygen demand and odor. Liquid wastes from the polishing and cleaning of glass have a distinctive red color, are alkaline, and contain considerable quantities of suspended solids.

Reclaimed rubber wastes have been reported with total solids concentrations as high as 63,400 mg/liter, suspended solids up to 24,000 mg/liter, BOD's up to 12,500 mg/liter, chloride concentration as high as 2000 mg/liter hydroxide alkalinities ranging to 2700 mg/liter, and pH's ranging from 10.9 to 12.2 (401). Wastes from the production of synthetic rubber are considerably less objectionable in terms of total solids and BOD. Schatz has reported synthetic rubber wastes with concentrations of total solids as high as 9600 mg/liter, suspended solids of up to 2700 mg/liter, BOD's up to 1600 mg/liter, chlorides ranging up to 3300 mg/liter, and pH ranging between 3.2 and 7.9 (401).

## E. ENERGY AND POWER-RELATED INDUSTRIES

For purposes of the present discussion this category includes those industries concerned with the processing of coals and oils, the steam power industry, and those industries concerned with nuclear power and the handling of radioactive materials.

Wastes from the coal processing industry, originating largely in the cleaning and classification of coal and in the leaching of sulfur strata with water, are high in suspended solids, due largely to the presence of coal in the liquid waste. These wastes, which include acid mine drainage wastes, are quite low in pH due to the presence of high concentrations of sulfuric acid and of ferrous sulfate. Concentrations of contaminants in acid mine drainage wastes vary considerably, with acid concentrations ranging from less than 100 mg/liter to nearly 50,000 mg/liter, sulfuric acid concentrations from 100 to 6000 mg/liter, ferrous sulfate concentrations from 10 to 1500 mg/liter, aluminum sulfate concentrations up to 350 mg/liter, and manganese sulfate from up to 250 mg/liter (332). These wastes also usually contain various concentrations of silica, sulfates, fluorides, and oxides of iron, aluminum, manganese, calcium, magnesium, and sodium (202).

Liquid wastes from the oil industry derive primarily from drilling muds, salt, oil, some natural gases, acid sludges, and miscellaneous oils from the refining process. All these wastes are high in biochemical oxygen demand, odor, and concentration of phenol. Wastes from field operations are high in dissolved salts, while those from refinery operations contain high concentrations of sulfur compounds.

A report of analyses of the mineral contents of typical oil field brines has given calcium concentrations ranging from 1507 to 12,888 mg/liter, magnesium from 346 to 4290 mg/liter, sodium from 8260 to 63,275 mg/liter, bromide from 32 to 633 mg/liter, bicarbonates from 43 to 644 mg/liter, chlorides from 12,750 to 127,220 mg/liter, sulfates as high as 1578 mg/liter, and total solids ranging from 25,210 to 248,600 mg/liter (473). Combined refinery wastes also contain crude oil and fractions thereof and dissolved and suspended mineral and organic compounds discharged in the liquors and sludges from various stages of processing (332). All refinery wastes also contain various organic sulfur compounds and organic nitrogen compounds. Typical organic sulfur compounds include mercaptans, dialkyl-sulfides, throphenes, etc. Amines, amides, quinolines, and pyridines are among the major organic nitrogen compounds found in various combinations and concentrations in oil refinery wastes.

Liquid wastes from the steam power industry, which include cooling water, boiler blowdown, and cold water drainage, are high volume wastes at elevated temperatures and contain considerable quantities of dissolved inorganic solids. Wastes other than the cooling waters which must be disposed of from steam power plants include the solutions used for cleaning boilers. These cleaning solutions, and consequently the waste discharges from the cleaning operation, contain fairly high concentrations of trisodium phosphate, sodium carbonate, sodium hydroxide, sodium sulfite, sodium nitrate, and various detergents (358). Certain waste problems can also arise from the concentration and buildup of minerals in the circulating water due to windage, leakage, and blowdown. Powell (358) has reported a concentration factor of approximately 4 for such dissolved mineral constituents as calcium, magnesium, sodium, chloride, sulfate, nitrate, bicarbonate, silica, fluoride, and boron from makeup water to circulating water.

Nuclear wastes, of course, contain radioactive elements and tend to be on the acid side. These wastes originate from the processing of ores, from the processing of nuclear fuels, from power plant cooling waters, and from research and hospital laboratory wastes.

## F. SERVICES INDUSTRIES

Two principal industries included in this classification are the laundry trades and the photographic processing industries. Laundry waste from the washing of fabrics contain considerable concentrations of soaps and detergents. These wastes are also high in turbidity, alkalinity, and organic solids. Liquid wastes from the photographic processing industries, which involves spent solutions of developer and fixer, contain various organic and inorganic reducing agents, including silver. In addition, these wastes tend to be quite alkaline.

Rudolfs (394) has reported that commercial laundry wastes have a pH of approximately 10, with a total alkalinity of about 500 mg/liter. Total solids in these wastes are in the neighborhood of 2000 mg/liter with volatile solids representing about 1500 ppm of the total. Commercial laundry wastes tend to be relatively high in grease content, at about 500 mg/liter, with a 5-day BOD in the neighborhood of 2000 mg/liter. Liquid waste from laundromats and small laundry operations, as reported from a study by Eckenfelder and Barnhart (124), generally contain between 50 and 100 mg/liter sulfonated alkylbenzenes, with a pH of between 7 and 8 and a suspended solids concentration of about 150 mg/liter. These wastes typically have a turbidity between 200 and 300 and a chemical oxygen demand between 350 and 450 mg/liter.

## III. SAMPLING

Development of a reliable system for sampling of an industrial wastewater is an important step in the overall analytical program—one which deserves the careful consideration of the analyst. The significance of a chemical analysis is no greater than that of the sampling program employed. In general, a good sampling program can be designed only by an analyst who is familiar with the physicochemical characteristics of the water to be sampled. There is no universal procedure for sampling which would be entirely suitable for all industrial wastes applications. As indicated in the preceding section, industrial wastewaters are not uniform in composition, but show appreciable changes depending on source, presence of specific or nonspecific interferences, and the effects of environmental parameters, such as temperature and pressure. There are, however, certain basic criteria or guidelines which are essential for the design of an effective sampling program. The most important requirements for a satisfactory sample are that it be both valid and representative. For a sample to be valid, it has to be one which has been collected by a process of random selection. Random selection is one of the most basic, yet most frequently violated, principles in development of a sampling program. Any method of sampling that sacrifices random selection will impair statistical evaluation of the analytical data. If nonrandom sampling procedures are contemplated, perhaps for significant reasons of convenience, it is highly desirable to first demonstrate that the results of the analysis check those which would be obtained by random sampling. This check would be essential prior to any statistical evaluation of the data.

A satisfactory sample is not only randomly drawn, but also is representative. This means that the composition of the sample should be identical to that of the water from which it was collected; the collected sample should have the same physicochemical characteristics as the sampled water at the time and site of sampling.

Planning for a sampling program should be guided by the overall objectives of analysis. Major factors of concern for any sampling program are: (a) frequency of sample collection, (b) total number of samples, (c) size of each sample, (d) sites of sample collection, (e) method of sample collection, (f) data to be collected with each sample, and (g) transportation and care of samples prior to analysis.

Frequency of sampling will depend to large extent upon the frequency of variations in composition of the water to be sampled. There are two principal types of sampling procedures commonly used for analysis of industrial wastewaters. The first type is that which yields instantaneous spot or grab samples, while the second type yields integrated continuous or composite samples. A grab sample is a discrete portion of a wastewater taken at a given time; a series of grab samples reflects variations in constituents over a period of time. The size of such individual samples will depend on the objectives and methods of analysis and on the required accuracy. The total number of grab samples should satisfy the statistical requirements of the sampling program.

Composite samples are useful for determining average conditions, which when correlated with flow can be used for computing the material balance of a stream of wastewater over a period of time. A composite sample is essentially a weighted series of grab samples, the volume of each being proportional to the rate of flow of the waste stream at the time and site of sample collection. Samples may be composited over any time period, such as 4, 8, or 24 hr, depending on the purposes of analysis.

Selection of sampling sites should be made with great care. A field survey is often useful in planning for site selection. In the case of sampling of a stream, special consideration should be given to sources of waste discharge, dilution by tributaries, and changes in surrounding topography. Sampling of streams has been discussed adequately by Velz (478) and by Haney and Schmidt (183).

Sampling of wastewater from pipes or conduits is more complicated than stream sampling, especially when the water to be sampled is under pressure. For example, in the case of a chemical treatment plant, selection of sampling sites may require extensive investigation and preliminary checking of samples from a number of effluent outlets. Proper positioning of the sampling outlet within the cross section of a conduit is essential for obtaining a representative sample, particularly for conduits of large diameter. The choice of a sampling site within the cross section of a conduit is best done by examining and comparing samples drawn from several points along the vertical and horizontal diameters of the conduit. The cross-sectional area of the opening or inlet of the sampling line should be such that the flow of water in this line is proportional to the flow of the water in the conduit. An elaborate discussion on sampling of water from pipes and conduits can be found in the ASTM *Manual on Industrial Water and Industrial Waste Water* (20).

Sampling of industrial wastewaters which contain immiscible liquids requires special consideration. Ordinary sampling techniques cannot be used in this case, since the proportionate ratio of the two immiscible liquids (e.g., mineral oil and water) usually cannot be maintained in such a sample.

The most satisfactory method of sampling two-phase or multi-phase industrial effluents is to employ a sampling tube which is capable of withdrawing a complete section of the effluent from its discharge channel or pipe. When, as is most often the case, wastewater samples are collected from the outfall of a pipe or a stream, it is suggested (427) that a large volume of the effluent be collected in a large container and left to separate, and a sectional sampling tube be used to draw the test sample.

As discussed previously, wastes discharged by industry are of great variety, and sampling must be tailored to suit the particular characteristics of a given wastewater. Sampling procedures can be expected to vary widely from one wastewater to another. Special procedures have been reported for use with waters sampled under reduced or elevated pressure and/or temperature (20). Procedures and equipment used for the sampling of waters containing dissolved gases and volatile constituents susceptible to loss upon aeration have been described by Rainwater and Thatcher (370).

A certain amount of precaution is sometimes required in sampling processes for reasons of safety. For example, strict precautionary measures (369) should be followed in taking samples from deep manholes to guard against accumulation of toxic and explosive gases and insufficiency of oxygen.

Sampling can be accomplished by either manual or automatic means, again depending on the purpose of analysis and method of sampling.

A grab sample is usually collected manually. When it is necessary to extend sampling over a considerable period of time, or when a continuous (repetitive) record of analysis at a given sampling point is required, automatic sampling equipment is commonly used.

Continuous sampling equipment, correctly designed and installed, will provide more frequent samples, tend to eliminate human errors, and in many cases be economically more feasible. A variety of automatic sampling equipment suitable for water sampling under variable conditions and for different purposes, is presently available (10,20,58,299,369,370).

The maintenance of complete records regarding the source of the sample and the conditions under which it has been collected is an inherent part of a good sampling program. This is of particular importance in field, river, or in-plant surveys, where a great number of samples are collected from different sources and under variable conditions. For illustrative purposes, the U.S. Geological Survey has defined the minimum data required for samples of surface and ground waters (370) as follows:

One of the most important aspects of the sampling process is the care and preservation of the sample prior to analysis. This point cannot be overemphasized. A water analysis is of limited value if the sample has undergone physicochemical or biochemical changes during transportation or storage. These changes are time dependent, but they usually proceed slowly. In general, the shorter the time that elapses between

| Surface Waters | Ground waters |
| --- | --- |
| Name of water body | Geographical and legal locations |
| Location of station or site | Depth of well |
| Point of collection | Diameter of well |
| Date of collection | Length of casing and position of screens |
| Time of collection | Method of collection |
| Gage height or water discharge | Point of collection |
| Temperature of the water | Water bearing formation(s) |
| Name of collector | Water level |
| Weather and other natural or other man-made factors that may assist in interpreting the chemical quality | Yield of well in normal operations |
| | Water temperature |
| | Principal use of water |
| | Name of collector |
| | Date of collection |
| | Appearance at time of collection |
| | Weather or other natural or man-made factors that may assist in interpreting chemical quality |

collection of a sample and its analysis, the more reliable will be the analytical results. Certain constituents may, however, require immediate analysis at the sample site.

Certain determinations are more sensitive than others to the method of handling of water samples before analysis. Changes in temperature and pressure may result in the escape of certain gaseous constituents (e.g., $O_2$, $CO_2$, $H_2S$, $Cl_2$, $CH_4$) or the dissolution of some atmospheric gases (e.g., $O_2$). It is recommended, therefore, that determinations for gases be done in the field, or, to "fix" such materials as $O_2$, $Cl_2$, and $H_2S$, the sample should be treated upon collection with stable oxidizing or reducing agents (284). It is also recommended that the temperature and pH of the water be determined at the site of sampling. Changes in temperature and pH may cause changes in the solubility of dissolved gases and certain nonvolatile constituents, resulting in their separation from aqueous phase. Carbonic acid–bicarbonate–carbonate equilibria may be shifted to release gaseous $CO_2$ or to precipitate certain metal carbonates. Similarly, shifts in hydrogen sulfide–sulfide equilibria due to changes in pH and/or temperature may result in the escape of $H_2S$ or the precipitation of metal sulfides.

Heavy metals ions may undergo a variety of physicochemical transformations during sample handling. It has been recommended that for analyses for Al, Cr, Cu, Fe, Mn, and Zn, samples should be filtered at the site of collection and acidified to about pH 3.5 with glacial acetic acid (370). Acidification tends to minimize precipitation, as well as sorption on the wall of the sample container. Since acetic acid may stimulate growth of molds, it may be necessary to add a small quantity of formaldehyde to the sample solution as a preservative.

Another major point of interest for handling water samples is the effect of biological activity on the sample characteristics. Microbiological activity may be effective in changing the nitrate–nitrite–ammonia balance, in reducing sulfate to sulfide, and in decreasing the dissolved oxygen content, BOD, organophosphorous compounds, and any readily degraded organic compound. Freezing of water samples is helpful in minimizing changes due to biological activity. Certain chemical preservatives, such as chlorofrom or formaldehyde, are sometimes added to water samples for this purpose (370).

That it is practically impossible to handle and process a water sample without changing its characteristics should be recognized. The best chance for error-free procedure lies in the use of *in situ* analyses. In the end, the dependability of even a well planned sampling program rests upon the experience and good judgment of the analyst.

## IV. ANALYSIS FOR MAJOR PHYSICAL CHARACTERISTICS

Methods for the analysis of industrial wastewaters have been variously classified according to: (a) the purpose of the analysis (e.g., determination of toxicity or biodegradability), (b) the nature of the constituent under test (e.g., gases, alkali metals, and heavy metals), and (c) the nature of the analytical procedure itself (e.g., titrimetric, gravimetric, and electrometric). In the present discussion, methods of analysis are somewhat arbitrarily classified according to the analytical information desired and whether it pertains primarily to the physical, chemical, or biological characteristics of the test solution. The discussion includes a survey of new methods and techniques, as well as a review of important classical analytical procedures for characterization of industrial wastewaters.

The significant physical properties of a given industrial wastewater might include: (a) density and viscosity; (b) temperature; (c) electrical conductivity; (d) turbidity; (e) particulate, volatile, and dissolved matter; (f) oils, grease, and other immiscible liquids; (g) color; (h) odor; and (i) radioactivity.

### A. DENSITY AND VISCOSITY

Literature concerning determinations of density, viscosity, and surface tension for industrial wastewaters is sparce. This probably results from the fact that the last of these tests is not frequently performed and the procedures for the first two are rather straightforward.

Differences between absolute density and specific gravity and the effect of temperature and salinity on these parameters have been discussed by Cox (99). Density determinations are of particular interest for characterization of brine wastes, for which concentrations of dissolved materials are commonly indicated by density measurements.

Density measurements of high salinity wastewaters are also significant for relating concentration on a weight basis to concentration on a volume basis. By definition, concentration expressed in terms of parts per million represents the weight of dissolved matter per one million equal weights of solution (i.e., milligrams of solute per kilogram of solution). A concentration of 1000 ppm will increase the density of solution by only approximately 0.1%, which may not be significant. At high concentrations, however, corrections must often be made to account for changes in density. The U.S. Geological Survey (370) has arbitrarily selected a concentration level of 7000 ppm, below which corrections for changes in density are not necessary.

Density determinations may be accomplished by measuring the weight of an exact volume of solution at a given temperature, commonly 20°C (the same temperature at which volumetric glassware is calibrated). Results are accurate to 10.0005 g (370). More commonly, density is measured with a hydrometer, at the temperature of the sample with appropriate correction to 20°C. Nomographs are usually provided to facilitate conversion.

Viscosity is a direct measure of the resistance of the liquid to flow or fluidity, which is of interest for certain industrial wastewaters of high solid content, waste slurries, and sludges. Results are usually expressed in centipoise units at 20°C. The viscosity of pure water is taken to be approximately equal to unity 20°C (1.009 cp).

Several instruments are available for viscosity determinations, e.g., the canal viscometer (Ostwald) or the couette viscometer (Brookfield). Viscosity can also be measured by determining the time of fall of a spherical ball of known weight and dimension through a column of the test solution (212,370).

## B. TEMPERATURE

Temperature is an intensive measure and should not be confused with the extensive property of heat capacity. Measurement of temperature in industrial waste effluents is of particular importance in cases where biochemical activity in the receiving water or the heat budget of the stream are matters of concern. Such is the case with waste cooling waters from the power industry, which may cause significant thermal pollution of receiving streams.

Liquid-in-glass thermometers, in which mercury is often used, are the simplest temperature-measuring devices. The response time of such simple thermometers is one of the longest of common temperature-measuring devices. Needless to say, liquid-in-glass thermometers are not very suitable for continuous monitoring systems. In certain cases differential temperature measurements are more significant than absolute values, and a number of commercially available thermometers can be employed.

Other temperature-measuring devices include bimetallic thermometers, radiation pyrometers, resistance thermometers, thermistors, and thermocouples. An excellent discussion of the application of temperature transducers for environmental measurements has been presented by Bollinger (66).

## C. ELECTRICAL CONDUCTIVITY

Electrical conductivity has been conveniently used as a measure of the total concentration of ionic species in a water sample (393). Much confusion exists in the literature regarding interpretation of conductivity data and the calibration of conductivity salinometers. The electrical conductance, $L$, of a solution can be represented by the expression

$$L = K_c \sum_{i}^{n} C_i \lambda_i Z_i \qquad (2)$$

where $K_c$ is a constant, characteristic of the geometry and size of the conductance cell, $C$ the molar concentration of the individual ions in solution, $\lambda$ the equivalent ionic conductance, and $Z$ the ionic charge. Thus the electrical conductance will vary with the number, size, and charge of the ions and also with some solvent characteristics, such as viscosity. For this reason a meaningful comparison of the electrical conductance of two different types of industrial wastewaters may be difficult. Equality in electrical conductance may not mean equality in total dissolved solids. Nonetheless, conductance measurements can be used to good advantage for continuous monitoring of the strength of a given wastewater. In this case a change in conductance may be assumed to be due to a change in the number of ions rather than a change in the type of ions.

Conductance measurements are used extensively for monitoring the quality of surface waters (501) and in chemical oceanography for salinity determinations (99).

Conductivity determinations are usually based on alternating current measurements using either electrodes or inductive systems, depending on how the current is generated in solution. In the more conventional system of the former type, measurement is based on the application of an alternating current (or ac potential difference) across two or more electrodes immersed in the test solution. The major disadvantages of this type of system are the possibilities for polarization and poisoning (fouling) of the electrodes. In systems of the second type, the electrodes do not come in contact with the test solution, but are isolated by a layer of glass or some other dielectric (insulating) material. A very high frequency current in the megacycle per second range is used. In such systems the conductivity cell represents a series combination of a capacitance (the dielectric material separating the electrode from the solution) and a parallel-connected capacitance and resistance (the solution capacitance and resistance, respectively). Although the cell response is less direct because the electrodes are not in contact with the solution, the problems of electrode fouling and polarization are eliminated. Conductivity measurements based on high frequency inductive systems are fundamentally more sound than those based on conventional electrode systems and eventually will gain wider acceptance for laboratory and field applications (99).

It should be noted that one of the basic problems in precision conductivity is temperature control. Temperature effects on ionic conductance in heterogenous solutions are quite complex. The temperature coefficient for a solution of constant ionic strength varies with temperature. The conductivity of sea water, for example, increases by 3% per degree increase in temperature at 0°C and only 2% per degree increase at 25°C. At 30°C the conductivity of a solution is about double the value at 0°C. Likewise, the temperature coefficient of conductivity for sea water varies appreciably with large variations in ionic strength (99,100). In oceanographic work, therefore, relative conductance is determined rather than absolute conductance. In this case the ratio of the conductance of the sample to that of a reference solution at the same temperature is measured. In certain modifications, a thermistor or a resistance is used instead of a reference solution (99).

Conductivity measurements are quite well suited for *in situ* and continuous-type analyses. Great care should be taken, however, to account for changes in temperature, pressure, and other such factors.

## D. TURBIDITY

Turbidity is a measure of the light scattering characteristics of a water and is attributable to colloidal and particulate matter suspended in the water. Reference is to a standard suspension of fine silica (20). The Jackson Candle Turbidimeter is the standard reference instrument for turbidity measurements. The Jackson turbidity test is based on measuring that length of light path through the solution at which the outline of the flame of a standard candle becomes indistinct. Results are reported in arbitrary turbidity units (48,346).

Wastes of turbidity in excess of 1000 Jackson units are diluted prior to measurement. For waters of low turbidity (less than 25 Jackson turbidity units) nephelometric or light scattering techniques are most commonly used (60,20). Black and Hannah (60) have discussed the theoretical and procedural aspects of turbidity measurements with the Jackson Candle method and more sophisticated methods. A simple low angle photometer that may be calibrated with clay suspensions in terms of Jackson turbidity units is described and recommended for use with low turbidity waters. Several commercial turbidity monitoring systems are available and have found wide use for monitoring wastewater quality (95).

## E. PARTICULATE, VOLATILE, AND DISSOLVED SOLIDS

Particulate suspended matter consists of fine, solid materials which are dispersed in water to give a heterogenous suspension. This material can be separated by filtration. Dissolved solids, on the other hand, consist of nonvolatile compounds and salts in true solution, i.e., homogeneous phase (29).

Particulate matter is usually determined by filtering a given volume of wastewater, extracting the residue with a solvent (carbon tetrachloride, benzene, or chloroform), drying at 103°C, igniting at 180°C, and weighing the final residue (29).

Dissolved solids are determined by weighing the residue from the filtrate after evaporation and extraction with organic solvent and ignition at 180°C (29).

*Standard Methods for the Examination of Water and Wastewaters* (29) classifies particulate, volatile, and dissolved matter as follows: (*a*) residue on evaporation, (*b*) total volatile and fixed residue, (*c*) total suspended matter, and (*d*) dissolved matter. Although this classification is particularly suitable for domestic wastes and municipal sewage treatment plant effluents, it is applied frequently to a variety of industrial waste effluents.

*Residue on evaporation* is determined by evaporating a given sample, drying at 103°C, and weighing the residue. *Total volatile residue* is determined by igniting the sample at 600°C after determining the residue on evaporation and calculating the weight loss due to ignition. The weight of the residue after ignition is reported as *total fixed residue.*

The *total suspended matter* is the *nonfilterable residue* and is determined by filtering a sample through a membrane filter or an asbestos mat in a Gooch crucible. The dry residue remaining after evaporation of the filtrate at 103°C is reported as *dissolved matter* of *filterable residue.* This can also be obtained by calculating the difference between the *residue on evaporation* and the *total suspended matter* (29).

Analysis for residue in an industrial wastewater generally is of little direct value in estimating its effect on a receiving water. Residue determinations are probably more valuable for control of plant operation.

## F. OILS, GREASE, AND IMMISCIBLE LIQUIDS

The gross determination of volatile and nonvolatile oily material is of particular interest for industries such as oil refineries (21). Tests for oils and grease are based on solvent extraction procedures using common solvents, such as hexane, petroleum ether, benzene, chloroform, or carbon tetrachloride. The amount of oily matter determined is primarily dependent on the type of solvent used and the extraction procedure. Needless to say, the test is not selective for immiscible oils and grease; other organic matter in solution (e.g., phenols, organosulfur compounds) will also be measured.

The procedure for determination of volatile and nonvolatile oily matter in wastewater is based on refluxing a given volume of sample and collecting the volatile oily matter, which is then measured volumetrically. The remaining sample is extracted with an immiscible solvent. The extracts are distilled to remove the solvent, and the residue is weighed and reported in units of parts per million by weight. Oily matter, measured according to this procedure, is defined (21) as hydrocarbons, hydrocarbon derivatives, and other fractions with a boiling point of 90°C or above which are extracted from water at pH 5.0 or lower using benzene as a solvent. Various extraction techniques and equipment have been reported.

Nonvolatile oily material may also be determined by flocculation of the wastewater with an iron salt, followed by extraction of the oily matter from the flocs. The sample is first acidified to pH 4 and treated with an iron salt to form a flocculent ferric hydroxide precipitate in the sample. The floc is separated from the sample by filtration and is then extracted with ether. The ether is then evaporated in a specially designed U-tube with a calibrated capillary (21). The oil is displaced into the graduated section of the tube and measured volumetrically.

An infrared spectrometric method for gross determination of volatile and nonvolatile oily matter has been described (21,420). This method is based on extraction of the oily matter with carbon tetrachloride. By means of absorption measurements of the extract at 3.4 and 3.5 $\mu$, the oily matter concentration is determined from calibration curves. This method is especially suitable for routine monitoring of effluents which are known to contain relatively constant amounts and types of oily matter (21).

## G. COLOR

It is customary to differentiate between true and apparent color in waters and wastewaters. True color is due only to matter which is in true solution, while apparent color includes the effects of matter in suspended and coloidal states as well.

The major problem associated with this aspect of the analysis of industrial wastewaters is how to define and express color. Classically, the color of a trade effluent has been determined by visual comparison with colored solutions of known concentration or with special colored glass disks. In laboratory operations, comparison is made to standard platinum–cobalt color solutions, and the standard unit of color is that produced by 1 mg of platinum per liter, in the form of chloroplatinate ion. For field use, comparison is made with colored glass disks calibrated to correspond to the platinum–cobalt scale (112).

Color determinations by visual comparison are subject to a number of interferences and variables. The main drawback to this method is the subjectivity and variation in response of different individuals to color. It is obvious also that certain industrial wastes may produce colors which cannot be matched well by the standard platinum–cobalt scale.

A more accurate determination of color in wastewaters can be accomplished by application of tristimulus colorimetry techniques (222,307,395). The color of a filtered waste can be expressed in terms which approximately describe the visual response of an individual. One of these terms relates to the brightness of color, or *luminosity*. The hue of the color (e.g., red, yellow, green) is characterized in terms of a *dominant wavelength,* and the degree of saturation (pastel, pale, etc.) is characterized by *purity.* Luminosity and purity are usually reported in units of per cent and the dominant wavelength in millimicrons.

Tristimulus parameters are commonly determined from measurements of the light transmission characteristics of a filtered sample of wastewater. Transmission data are converted to color classification terms by using standards adopted by the International Commission on Illumination (307). Chromaticity diagrams are used to describe the color numerically in terms of the tristimulus parameters (29).

Trichromatic color characteristics of filtered wastewater are measured with ordinary absorption spectrophotometers. A photometric technique has been proposed for routine work (29). This method is based on the use of three special tristimulus light filters, which, when combined with a specific light source and photoelectric cell in a filter photometer, will give effective energy distribution curves similar in shape to the "CIE" tristimulus curves (222).

## H. ODOR

Odor, like color, is a measure of a physiological response (141,165,385). Determination of odor is based solely on the olfactory senses of the analyst, or on those of a group of individuals, and on the ability of the analyst (or group) to distinguish between different levels and kinds of odors. The testing is based entirely on arbitrary comparison since no absolute units or base for odor exist (20,21).

Several authors have attempted to characterize and classify the origin of odor in wastewaters (20,39,141,387,388,432). Most of these studies treat taste and odor as closely connected human responses. Taste determinations are generally not recommended for wastewater or untreated industrial effluents and thus are excluded from the present discussion.

Odor can always be related to the presence of volatile organic and/or inorganic species present in water. Odor intensity is a function of the volatility and the concentration of the odor-causing species, as well as of certain environmental factors, such as temperature, ionic strength, and pressure. It has been claimed that there are only four basic types of odor: (a) sweet, (b) sour, (c) burnt, and (d) goaty, realizing that the many odors are in fact combinations of two or more of these groups.

Odors often can be related to the presence of certain biological forms in the wastewater, such as algae and actinomycetes. Such odor-causing organisms are believed to secrete characteristic volatile oils during growth and upon decomposition and decay. Such poetic terms as musty, earthy, woody, moldy, swampy, grassy, fishy and wet-leaves have been used to describe odors (141,387). Odors have also been classified by chemical type (20) as shown in Table IV.

Recent studies of odor characteristics and human response have led to a proposal of a steriochemical theory of odor (39,165). This theory relates the response to odor to the geometry of molecules. It has been postulated that the olfactory system is composed of receptor cells of certain different types, each representing a distinct "primary" odor, and that odorous molecules produce their effects by fitting closely into "receptor sites" on these cells. This concept is similar to the "lock and key" theory used to explain certain biochemical reactions, e.g., enzyme with substrate, antibody with antigen, and deoxyribonucleic acid with ribonucleic acid in protein synthesis.

Seven primary odors are distinguished (387), each of them by an appropriately shaped receptor at the olfactory nerve endings. The primary odors, together with reasonably familiar examples are: (a) camphoraceous, e.g., camphor or moth repellent; (b) musky, e.g., pentadencanolactone as in angelica root oil; (c) floral, e.g., phenylethyl methyl ethyl carbinol as in roses; (d) pepperminty, e.g., menthone as in mint candy; (e) pungent, e.g., formic acid or as vinegar; and (g) putrid, e.g., butyl mercaptan as in rotten eggs.

TABLE IV

Odors Classified by Chemical Types

| Odor class | Chemical types included | Odor characteristics | | | | | Odors and algae and fungi |
|---|---|---|---|---|---|---|---|
| | | Fragrance | Acidity | Burntness | Caprylicness | | |
| Estery | Esters; lower ketones | High | Medium | Low to medium | Medium | — | |
| Alcoholic | Phenols and cresols; alcohols; hydrocarbons | High | Medium to high | Low to high | Medium | Asteriomella Coelosphaerium | |
| Carbonyl | Aldehydes; higher ketones | Medium | Medium | Low to medium | Medium | Mallemonas | |
| Acidic | Acid anhydrides; organic acids; sulfur dioxide | Medium | Very high | Low to medium | Medium | Anabaena | |
| Halide | Quinones; oxides (including ozone); halides; nitrogen compounds | High | Medium to high | Medium to high | Low to high | Dinobryon Actinomycetes | |
| Sulfury | Selenium compounds; arsenicals; mercaptans; sulfides and hydrogen sulfide | Medium | Medium | Very high | Very high | Aphanizomenon | |
| Unsaturated | Acetylene derivatives; butadiene; isoprene; vinyl monomers | High | Medium | Medium | High | Synura | |
| Basic | Higher amines; alkaloids; ammonia and lower amines | High | Medium | Low to medium | High | Uroglenopsis Dinobryon | |

461

It has been claimed that every known odor can be made by mixing the seven primary odors in certain combinations and proportions (388).

Odors resulting from mixtures of two or more odoriferous substances are extremely complex. The mixture may produce an odor of greater or lesser intensity than might be expected from summing the individual odors, or a completely different kind of odor may be produced (39,387,388). Accordingly, it is frequently necessary to characterize the odor of the wastewater and that of the receiving stream both separately and in combination if the actual relationship and effect are to be determined.

Odor intensity is expressed in terms of the *threshold odor number* (20,21,29). By definition, the threshold odor number is the greatest dilution of the sample that still leaves a perceptible residual odor. The test procedure is based on successive dilution of a sample with odor-free water, disregarding any suspended matter or immiscible substances, until a dilution is obtained which has a barely perceptible odor. It has been recommended that odor tests be run at 25 and 60°C (29) or 40 and 60°C (20). In all cases the sampling and test temperature should be reported, since the threshold odor is a function of temperature. A given sample, under fixed conditions, will emit a characteristic odor stimulus, but the response to this stimulus and the judgment based upon this response are purely subjective matters, and their interpretation may vary considerably from individual to individual (39,388,432). Consequently, it is desirable to use a panel or group of judges rather than a single analyst for both qualitative and quantitative evaluation of odors in water or wastewater samples (20).

## I. RADIOACTIVITY

Developments in the useful application of nuclear energy and its by-products have focused increasing attention on problems connected with water pollution by radioactive materials. Liquid wastes from the operation of nuclear reactors, wastes from the use of radioisotopes, and fallout from the detonation of nuclear weapons already have added measurable quantities of radioactivity, in excess of the natural or background level, to some natural waters.

Wastewaters from nuclear energy industries commonly contain materials which are in a state of nuclear instability and emit ionizing radiation. The health aspects of ionizing radiation in man's drinking water, in the air he breathes, and in the plants and animals he eats make the analysis and treatment of radioactive wastewaters of paramount importance.

Radioactive wastewaters are commonly classified as: (*a*) low level (radiation in the order of microcuries per liter); (*b*) intermediate level radiation in the order of millicuries per liter); and (*c*) high level (radioactivity measured in curies per liter) (**439**). There are, however, no rigid classifications for characterizing the strength of radioactive wastewaters. Oak Ridge National Laboratory defines high level wastes as those in the range of $2 \times 10^{-2}$ to $10^{-3}$ Ci/gal and low-level wastes as those having radiation levels of 10 to $10^{-1}$ $\mu$Ci/gal. On the other hand, Hanford Atomic Products Operation of General Electric Company adopts the following categorization: high level $>100$ $\mu$Ci/mg; intermediate level $10^{-5}$ to $10^{2}$ $\mu$Ci/ml, and low level $<10^{-5}$ $\mu$Ci/ml (**128**). Simple classification of radioactive wastewaters as low level, intermediate, or high level can be somewhat misleading since the radiotoxicity of specific nuclides, the quantities discharged, and certain other important relative factors are not defined by these terms.

Sources of radioactive wastewater are numerous. Operations involved in the mining and processing of radioactive ores may result in the release of liquid wastes of low level radioactivity to the environment. Wastes from the processing of irradiated reactor fuel elements are very high in radioactivity, but are usually not released directly to the environment. Rather, these are generally stored in large underground tanks.

Because of their public health significance, radioactive waste effluents must be monitored continuously, and accurate records must be maintained regarding the amount of material release. Radioactive wastes are usually separated from nonradioactive wastes prior to treatment. This is common practice in the nuclear energy industry. Analyses of radioactive wastewater are directed toward: (*a*) determination of the level of radiation and the type and quantity of radioactive materials present and (*b*) determination of the effect that the release of the waste would have upon the environment. The first objective is accomplished by analyses performed at or close to the source of release. The second objective, which is more difficult to accomplish, involves sampling and analysis of various elements of the aquatic environment to which the waste is discharged. In the latter case, the physiochemical and biological characteristics of the receiving stream must be characterized before and after discharge. Samples of the receiving water, fish, phytoplankton, zooplankton, algae, aquatic plants, bottom deposits and shellfish must be collected and analyzed for radioactive content. The results of these analyses should present an overall picture of the effect of the radioactive waste discharge on the stream. Great care should be practiced in interpreting the results of analyses performed on these different types of samples. Table V lists some of the problems to be encountered and

TABLE V
Advantages and Disadvantages of Sampling Specific Media

| Medium sampled | Advantages | Disadvantages |
|---|---|---|
| Water | Simplicity, quantitative Legal standard, human consumption | Low activity levels; varying chemical composition; fallout contamination |
| Fish | Simplicity, cumulative intake, human consumption | Low activity levels; specific differences; seasonal variation; temperature effects; varying food habits |
| Mud | Cumulative intake, concentration[a] | Qualitative; movement of bottom; sampling difficulties |
| Algae (sessile) | Cumulative intake, concentration,[a] ease of collection, fixed (nonmobile) organisms | Semispecific; nonquantitative |
| Plankton | Semicumulative, concentration[a] | Sampling difficulties; seasonal variations; mobility, contamination with silt, debris, etc.; nonquantitative |
| Vegetation (aquatic) | Ease of sampling | Little knowledge, seasonal |
| Shellfish (aquatic invertebrates) | | Highly variable depending on species, feeding habits, temperature, etc. |

[a] Signifies removal from water by surface absorption, ion exchange, precipitation, etc.

information to be derived from the sampling and analysis of various elements of the aquatic environment (439).

Sampling programs for radioactive wastewaters should follow the general procedures discussed earlier. There is, however, one additional requirement not commonly imposed on the sampling of other industrial waste effluents. This is the need to prevent loss of the radioactive material to the sample container. It is sometimes necessary, therefore, to add carrier materials or chelating agents to the sample to minimize loss by sorption on the walls of the container. This is particularly significant when the amounts of nuclide present are only of the order of $10^{-12}$ g or less (20). Glass or plastic containers present less of a problem in this regard than do those made of metal (20).

Sampling of radioactive wastewater can be done manually or automatically. Manual sampling provides more flexibility for exploratory work and for spot-check surveys. It is, however, relatively expensive, time consuming, and more subject to human errors.

Automatic sampling is commonly associated with permanent installations. It can be designed to collect water samples intermittently or continuously and in proportion to the flow of the waste effluent (31).

Sampling equipment for biological tracing material and bottom deposits has been discussed by Straub (439) and others (20).

It is often necessary to measure extremely small quantities of radioactive materials in wastewaters, in which case the problem of sensitivity becomes more significant. The sensitivity of a radioactive measurement is limited by the randomness of the disintegration process, which results in setting a lower limit to the precision of analysis. Sensitivity is also a function of sample preparation, instrument type, and test procedure.

With regard to sample preparation, two types of analyses are frequently performed on radioactive waste effluents. The first is the determination of gross alpha, beta, or gamma radioactivity. The second is analysis for specific radionuclides. Sampling and sample pretreatment differ for each type of analysis.

When sampling water for gross activity purposes, representative samples of 1–2 liters are collected in polyethylene or chemically resistant containers. It is not advisable to add preservatives to suppress biological activity, but if they are added, they should be accounted for, separately, in the analysis. The radioactivity detected in the water sample can be categorized as being associated either with insoluble solids or with soluble fractions. To analyze for both types of radioactivity, the sample is vacuum filtered through cellulose acetate paper and the solids and the filter paper are then dried, saturated with ethyl alcohol, ignited, redried, and counted. Similarly, the dissolved fraction is evaporated, dried, and counted (20,36,327). It is estimated that with this procedure an appreciable part of beta radiation and as much as 50% of alpha radiation are lost by self-absorption (36).

Analyses for specific radionuclides require chemical separation. Several techniques are applicable e.g., precipitation, complexation, ion exchange, and centrifugation (20,36,50,96,400,411).

After concentration and/or separation of the sample, gross radioactivity or specific radionuclide levels are counted. With proper calibration of instruments for a given geometry of the sample container, sample size, volume, etc. quantitative measurements can be made. As far as counting instruments are concerned, detection efficiency is governed by:
(a) "geometry," or fraction of radiation emitted toward the detector;

(b) "self-absorption," or failure of part of the radiation to penetrate the sample solid; and (c) "detector efficiency," or the actual fraction of radiation entering the detector and causing a response. Background suppression is usually attained by shielding the detector with lead blocks.

Commercially available instruments are reported in several articles and manufacturers' advertisements. The end-window Geiger counter is sometimes used for detection of beta and gamma activity. The internal proportional counter may be preferred, however, since it can also detect alpha activity. Automatic sample-changer and print-read-out equipment is frequently used for routine work. "Anticoincidence" counters are used for low level beta activity (43). Direct measurements of gamma-emitting radionuclides are frequently accomplished with spectrometers equipped with crystal sodium cesium iodide. Liquid scintillation and alpha scintillation counters are sometimes used (50,96,151,324,400).

A variety of specialized instruments and monitoring equipment for the analysis of radioactivity in natural waters and wastewaters have been described (337). Automatic analyzers have been described for continuous monitoring of predominant nuclides and total beta emitters in reactor coolant water (20,31,70,163,327,334).

A certain amount of precaution is, of course, required when working with radioactive wastewaters. Safety procedures and control measures have been summarized by several authors (326,328,329,439,510).

## V. ANALYSIS FOR ORGANIC COMPOUNDS

Organic constituents of industrial wastewaters are of general concern for one or more of a number of effects they may have upon receiving waters. The most readily apparent effect is that exerted directly on aesthetic quality by certain organic pollutants as a result of foaming, formation of slicks and films, offensive odors and tastes, discoloration, etc. Of equal significance are the effects of biologically oxidizable organic wastes on the depletion of dissolved oxygen levels in receiving waters, with concomitant disruption of the natural ecology of these waters. Other organic wastes may not degrade biochemically, but may rather persist and accumulate, thus constituting insidious long-term potential health hazards. The damaging effects of organic wastes on the quality of water for particular uses are summarized in Table VI.

Certain industries characteristically discharge waste effluents which are high in organic content; these include those industries concerned with petroleum refining, coke production, food processing, pharmaceutical

TABLE VI
Characteristics of Organic Pollution

| Water use | Damage to water quality for particular use |
|---|---|
| Domestic[a] or industrial process supply | Taste and odor; carbon demand; chlorine demand; interference with coagulation; color; corrosion promotion; carcinogenic properties; toxicity to humans |
| Production of fish | Toxicity to fish or fish food; taint fish flesh; deoxygenation of water; promotion of filamentous organisms; sludge deposits |
| Recreation | Odor; color; floating matter; suspended matter; sludge deposits |
| Agricultural irrigation | Toxicity to plants |
| Watering of livestock | Toxicity to animals |

[a] This damage applies in cases where industrial waste is discharged to municipal sewers for combined treatment with domestic waste.

preparation, and the production of fertilizers and organic chemicals in general. The waste materials are mostly impurities which have been removed during purification of the raw materials, unmarketable or uneconomically recoverable by-products, spillage and leakage, equipment wastings, water condensates, spent extracting or absorbing solutions, etc.

Organic material may exist in the form of settleable particulate matter, in the form of colloidal matter, or in the dissolved state. Dissolved organic matter can be roughly defined as that which is not retained by a membrane filter. The present discussion is concerned principally with organic matter which is present in true solution, and, to a lesser extent, with that which exists in the form of a colloidal suspension. It should be realized that the degree of solubility of an organic pollutant is highly dependent on factors such as temperature and pressure and on the physicochemical characteristics of the aqueous phase, such as the presence of salting-in or salting-out agents.

Several approaches are commonly used for characterization of organic matter in industrial waste effluents. These can be classified into two main categories. In the first category the damaging effect (pollutional effect) of the organic waste matter on the receiving water is estimated. This may be accomplished by diluting the waste effluent with the receiving water to a level corresponding to the dilution which will result in the receiving stream and by then characterizing apropriate pollution parameters, such as odor, color, carbon demand, chlorine demand, fish-flesh tainting, persistence (resistance to biodegradation), and treatability.

The second approach is based on both qualitative and quantitative analyses for the organic compounds present in the waste effluent. Analyses for organic compounds may involve either nonspecific or specific analytical methods. In the former case, analysis is done by measurement of oxidizable organic matter, such as the biochemical oxygen demand or the chemical oxygen demand, or by determining the total organic carbon or total organic nitrogen present in a given sample. Specific analysis, on the other hand, includes identification and quantitative determination of specific species present in the test solution.

## A. NONSPECIFIC ANALYSIS

Nonspecific analytical methods are often based upon measurement of quantities of oxidizable organic material, either by biologically mediated oxidation or by strictly chemical oxidation (by wet or dry combustion procedures). The procedure most commonly employed for measurement of the susceptibility of a waste to biological oxidation is the biochemical oxygen demand (BOD) test, while the chemical oxygen demand (COD) test is widely used for measurement of concentrations of organic matter oxidizable by a dichromate reflux method. Detailed descriptions of standard procedures employed for BOD and COD measurements are readily available in the literature (20,29).

## 1. Biochemical Oxygen Demand

The biochemical oxygen demand test is essentially a bioassay method involving measurement of quantities of oxygen consumed during biological oxidation of organic waste matter under controlled conditions. Because the amount of oxygen required to convert a given quantity of biologically oxidizable organic compound to carbon dioxide and water is fixed, it is possible to interpret BOD data semiquantitatively in terms of gross concentrations of organic matter, as well as oxygen-consuming tendency.

Because the concentration of dissolved oxygen present in a stream, river, or lake is of major concern from the standpoint of water pollution control, the BOD test is useful for providing an estimation of the amount of oxygen likely to be consumed by a given amount of waste upon discharge to a receiving water. By utilizing a "seed" taken directly from the receiving water in question, actual conditions can be closely paralleled in that the measured consumption of oxygen will be that corresponding to the biological activity of the particular organisms indigenous to that receiving water. There are several distinct disadvantages to the BOD test. First, a relatively long period of time (usually 5 days) is required to obtain test results. Second, it is generally assumed that oxygen utilization by nitrification is of little consequence during the first 5 days: this is not always the case; indeed, incipient nitrification often may account for a considerable portion of the 5-day oxygen demand. Third, the BOD test is subject to interference from certain substances which exhibit toxic effects on the organisms involved in the biological breakdown of organic matter. There are certain complex organic compounds usually found in industrial wastes which are at least partially resistant to biochemical oxidation; the BOD test does not provide for measurement of the concentrations of such substances.

The standard "dilution" method for determining the BOD of a wastewater is based on the general observation that the rate of biochemical degradation of organic matter is closely proportional to the amount remaining to be oxidized. Thus the rates at which oxygen is consumed in a series of dilutions of a particular wastewater should be in proportion to the respective dilution factors, provided that all other factors are equal. It must be recognized that certain inorganic constituents of industrial wastewaters, such as ferrous iron, sulfite, and sulfide, will be oxidized by molecular oxygen. Thus one must take care to differentiate between a strictly biochemical oxygen demand and a total oxygen demand. To differentiate, an "immediate 15-min. dissolved oxygen demand" (IDOD) may be determined separately, the total oxygen demand then being the sum of the IDOD and the 5-day BOD.

The IDOD may represent either immediate oxidation of substances such as ferrous iron by molecular oxygen, or it may be attributable to oxidation by iodine produced in the acidification step of the Winkler method for determining dissolved oxygen, thus decreasing the amount of iodine that would be included in the final titration with thiosulfate.

The principal disadvantages of the dilution method for BOD include the time involved in obtaining the analytical information and the so-called "sliding effect." The sliding effect, which is evidenced when different ultimate BOD levels are obtained for different dilutions, is often due to the presence of toxic substances, lack of nutrients, or lack of proper seed.

In the "manometric" method for BOD a sample is placed in a closed system at constant temperature and agitation, and oxygen consumption is measured directly, by change in pressure at constant volume if the Warburg respirometer is used and by change in volume at constant pressure if the Sierp apparatus is used.

The advantages and limitations of both the dilution and manometric methods for BOD have been discussed in some detail. Gillman and Heukelekian (164) have reported that reproducibility is approximately the same for both methods, although values obtained by the manometric method tend to be somewhat higher than those obtained by the dilution method. According to Jaeger and Niemitz (218) the manometric method provides better reproducibility along with the advantage of continuous observation. Lee and Oswald (259) have expressed the opinion that manometric methods are useful if a complete demand curve is desired, but that they are unsuitable for large scale testing programs. Arthur (34) has stated that it is unrealistic and uneconomical to use conventional monometric methods to determine 5-day BOD, but that the advantage of a continuous record of oxygen demand as obtained by manometric methods can be achieved by using an automated respirator to determine the oxygen demand over periods shorter than 5 days. Arthur claims that the advantage of this method for automatically recording oxygen consumption over conventional manometric methods is the elimination of tedious gathering of data, and over the dilution method the advantage is the simplicity of the test and the fact that it provides a complete record of BOD, it being possible to determine the oxygen demand at any time without destroying the sample.

Hiser and Busch have presented a test for what they call the "total biological oxygen demand" (TBOD) of a wastewater (204). The TBOD test, which measures the disappearance of food from a biological system, according to Hiser and Busch, measures the total soluble organic content of a waste or substrate that is amenable to microbiological metabolism.

In the conventional BOD test, the oxygen-consuming tendency of a waste is measured in terms of the change in concentration of dissolved oxygen, as a function of time over an extended period, in a diluted sample held at constant temperature in a completely filled, closed container. The test provides a measure of the oxygen utilized for biological stabilization of the organic matter in the sample under the specific test conditions. However, its usefulness for predicting conditions in a receiving water to which the waste is to be discharged is limited, first by the relatively small, and possibly nonrepresentative, sample generally used and, second, by the absence during the test of mixing and reaeration which would normally occur in the receiving water.

The progression of the oxygen change in the BOD test has been observed to approximate a first-order reaction, disregarding any initial lag in oxygen uptake due to lack of seed or need for acclimation of the system. Streeter and Phelps (440) have described the nature of this reaction: "The rate of the biochemical oxidation of organic matter is proportional to the remaining concentration of unoxidized substance, measured in terms of oxidizability." Mathematically this may be expressed,

$$\frac{dL}{dt} = -k_1 L \qquad (3)$$

which upon integration yields,

$$L_t = L_0 e^{-k_1 t} \qquad (4)$$

$$Y_t = L_0(1 - e^{-k_1 t}) \qquad (5)$$

where $L_0$ is the total amount of oxidizable organic matter present at initiation of the test, i.e., the ultimate BOD, $L_t$ is the amount of oxidizable organic matter remaining at time, $t$, $k_1$ is the reaction rate constant, $t$ is the elapsed time from initiation of the test, and $Y_t$ is the amount of BOD "exerted" up to time $t$.

One may certainly question—and many have—the use of such a simple expression for description of a complex biochemical process. The formulation of the BOD reaction has been widely discussed, and numerous modifications have been proposed. It is beyond the scope of the chapter to cover this aspect of the BOD test, and the reader is referred to other sources for detailed discussions of this matter (140,142,320,342,343,440,-454,457,485,509,512). Suffice it to say for the present that the expressions given in eqs. (2) and (3) are most commonly used for calculation of the standard BOD reference parameters, namely $L_0$ and $K_1$.

BOD tests are normally carried out at an incubation temperature of 20°C. The reaction is, of course, strongly dependent upon temperature, the rate of oxygen utilization increasing with increasing temperature to a maximum value beyond which further rise in temperature cannot be tolerated by the bacteria. Fair has summarized the nature of the temperature dependence of the BOD reaction (142).

Another factor which must be considered in conducting the BOD test is the factor of illumination. If the test solution contains photosynthetic bacteria or algae, care must be taken to carry out the test either in the absence of light or under uniform conditions of illumination so that the effects of these organisms are held relatively constant from one run to the next.

Toxic materials in an industrial waste can seriously affect determinations of BOD. If such materials are present one may obtain low values for BOD which are grossly in error simply because biological activity was retarded or even completely arrested by the toxic substance(s).

One way to determine whether this influence is present is to mix a quantity of the waste with a well-seeded solution of glucose, [dextrose], or some other readily oxidized organic material. If this mixture does not exert an appropriate BOD, then one must conclude that toxic materials are inhibiting the biochemical oxidation of the organic matter. If the toxic substance cannot be easily separated from the solution prior to running the BOD test (e.g., by precipitation, etc.) and if the toxic effect persists upon dilution of the waste, then the analyst should discard the BOD test in favor of a chemical method, such as the COD test.

Of considerable importance for the application of biological methods for assessment of total organic waste load is a consideration of the susceptibility of the organic constituents of a particular industrial waste to biochemical oxidation. Ludzack and Ettinger have reported on rather extensive studies of the resistance of various types of organic pollutants to biological attack (269). The results of these studies, along with reports by other investigators, are summarized below.

Most hydrocarbons on which  information is available are at least moderately resistant to biological oxidation. Alkylbenzene structures with short side chains appear to exhibit fairly high resistance to oxidation. There have been reports that aromatic compounds are degraded more rapidly in natural bodies of water than are aliphatics (472). Infrared data suggest that ring opening occurs rather readily when aromatic materials are discharged to natural waters, resulting in an increase in aliphatic species (269). Davis in 1956 described tests in which cyclic hydrocarbons were found to be more resistant than aliphatic materials (110).

Most alcohols appear to be rather readily metabolized (269). Data for methanol have been found to exhibit quite a high degree of variation, with susceptibility to oxidation depending mainly on acclimation. Iso or secondary structures behave in much the same fashion as normal alcohols. Tertiary butyl and amyl alcohols and pentaerythritol are strongly resistant to biological action. Within a rather broad range, chain length does not appear to be of great importance. The diols (e.g., glycol and 1,5-pentanediol), although often reported as being highly resistant to biological oxidation, have been found by Ludzack and Ettinger to be rather readily degraded (269).

Data for only a small number of phenolic compounds can be found in the literature. Mono- and dihydric phenols or cresols seem to be quite susceptible to biological attack, and many, but not all, chlorophenols behave similarly (269). For example, 2,4,5-trichlorophenol is extremely resistant, while pentachlorophenol can be assimilated.

With the exception of benzaldehyde and 3-hydroxybutenal, the aldehydes show relatively low resistance to assimilation in acclimated systems (110). The aldehydes, however, along with the alcohols, are more resistant as a group than are the acids, salts, and esters.

Esters as a group show high resistance to biological degradation. However, if sufficient acclimation is provided, oxidation of these carbon–oxygen–carbon linkage compounds can be accomplished. Dioxane, for example, can be oxidized by specifically acclimated organisms, and diphenyl ether can also be biochemically eliminated, although it persists longer than most contaminants (110,269).

What little work that has been done with ketones indicates that they are more readily degraded than ethers, but are more resistant than alcohols, aldehydes, acids, and esters.

Amino acids are readily assimilated, with the exceptions of cystine and tyrosine. The latter structures can be broken down if sufficiently long acclimation periods are provided.

Nitrogen compounds display a wide range in metabolic availability. For amines, resistance has been noted to increase with a decrease in the number of hydrogen atoms associated with each atom of nitrogen (312). Triethanolamine, acetanilide, and purine are rather readily available to biological attack, whereas the morpholenes, with a heterocyclic ring containing both nitrogen and oxygen atoms, are highly resistant (269).

Cyanides, with the exception of iron complexes thereof, show relatively low resistance to acclimated cultures. Long acclimation times are required, however.

Nitriles are, for the most part, readily metabolized in acclimated systems. The required acclimation period varies with the specific nitrile, particularly in natural waters.

Compounds containing the vinyl group are in general degraded fairly readily, with some notable exceptions. Crotonaldehyde is unique in that at low concentrations oxidation is apparently inhibited, whereas at high concentrations it is favored (269). Side reactions may form resistant substances which are masked when an adequate excess of crotonaldehyde is present (313). Methyl vinyl ketone is one of the highly resistant exceptions referred to above. Resistance apparently increases with the formation of higher molecular weight polymers. Size and changes in reactive centers of the polymer are two contributing factors. Mills has suggested that a molecular-size borderline between resistance and availability to biochemical oxidation exists somewhere in the region of molecular weights between 250 and 600 (312).

Results from experiments on the surfactant family and analogous materials indicate that low molecular weight normal sulfonated alkylaryl compounds are not strongly resistant to biochemical oxidation, although data from Warburg and BOD studies with such materials are frequently dissimilar (269). Sulfonation appears to create a marked difference in metabolic activity of the alkylaryl compounds. Normal sulfonated butylbenzene is easily degraded, for example, while normal butylbenzene is resistant. Tertiary butylbenzene and its sulfonate derivative have both been observed to be highly resistant. This trend seems to extend through the range of 12- to 15-carbon alkyl-group compounds commonly used for the manufacture of surfactants. Restated, the normal compounds seem readily available, while tertiary compounds are not. No detergent compound tested to date has been found totally biologically inert (64,269). Sulfates, esters, and low molecular weight polyethoxy amides and esters are readily assimilated, while the higher molecular weight polyethoxy esters and amides are relatively resistant (269).

Various chlorinated compounds show wide assimilation diversity and require much more thorough study than has yet been attempted. Carbohydrates show fairly low resistance, which increases with increasing molecular weight. Lignin resistance is apparently rather high, but definitive research on this material has been impeded by the variability of the natural material and by the difficulty in obtaining unmodified lignin for purposes of study (269). Changes which occur in the material during purification generally act to increase resistance. Lignin, however, is related to coniferal alcohol or oxygenated phenylpropene structures, and it is known that both the ether and propene group contribute to resistance in other compounds (173,269).

Recently, Gates et al. (161) have pointed out the advantage of determining the rate of biochemical oxygen demand, rather than the $BOD_5$ per se. In an attempt to predict the effect of disposal of organic matter on the oxygen balance in the stream, the authors described a laboratory procedure to evaluate the assimilative capacity of receiving waters. The technique is based on the simultaneous determination of the rate of biochemical oxygen utilization and the rate of atmospheric oxygen uptake, using stream and wastewaters, in appropriate ratios.

## 2. Chemical Oxygen Demand

The standard chemical oxygen demand test measures concentrations of organic materials which may be oxidized by dichromate when refluxed for 2 hr or less in a 50% sulfuric acid medium. Depending upon the nature of the organic compounds present in a particular industrial waste, the COD test may, in the two extremes, provide either a total or a negligible measure of the organic content of the waste; more often COD data represents a fractional measure of total organic content somewhere between these two extremes.

A number of oxidants other than dichromate have been tested for possible use in the COD method, including permanganate, persulfate, ceric sulfate, perchloric acid, periodic acid, nitric acid, and numerous combinations of these and other reagents. Dichromate has been selected for the standard method on the basis of comparative testing with other reagents, such as those listed above (322). A 50% solution of sulfuric acid is employed, since it has been observed that oxidation under anhydrous conditions is more complete for the majority of compounds normally found in municipal and industrial wastewaters.

The efficiency of the dichromate reflux method for oxidation of many organic materials is enhanced considerably by the presence of a catalyst such as silver. A catalyst is required particularly for low molecular weight fatty acids and their respective salts, such as acetic acid and acetate, which are otherwise not oxidized. Since the COD method is based on measurement of dichromate consumed, ferrous iron and other oxidizable inorganic materials commonly found in industrial wastewaters present certain interferences for this test, as do chlorides. Appropriate corrections for these materials can of course be made, provided that their respective concentrations are known. In the presence of a silver catalyst, however, oxidation of chloride by dichromate is not complete, and a simple correction for chloride equivalent is not applicable. This particular interference, a very significant one for many industrial wastes, can be avoided by addition of mercuric sulfate prior to addition of the oxidant (118). The mercuric ion forms a slightly dissociated complex with the chloride and thus prevents oxidation of the latter. This method for eliminating chloride interference is applicable for chloride concentrations up to about 2000 mg/liter or slightly greater. For higher concentrations of chloride it is generally wise to reflux the sample for approximately 30 min before adding the silver catalyst. Within this period complete oxidation of chlorides is accomplished and appropriate corrections may then be applied to account for this interference. Other procedures for COD determinations in wastewaters with saline concentrations as high as 3% have been discussed by Burns and Marshall (80).

Other sources of error in the COD test include reduction of dichromate by organic nitrogen, which is in turn converted to ammonia or even nitrate in some cases, and loss of volatile organics during initial heating of the sample prior to refluxing. For application of the COD test to industrial wastes containing significant amounts of volatile organic matter, slow addition of the acid through the condenser during heating and initial stages of refluxing is recommended.

The COD test was originally intended to serve the combined functions of providing a more complete measure of the organic content of wastewaters than is afforded by the BOD test, while at the same time giving a rapid approximation to the ultimate oxygen requirements of the waste. Unfortunately, the test as presently described accomplishes neither of these objectives completely, since oxidation of many organic compounds is not complete under the conditions of the test and because certain biologically oxidizable substances are not measured as COD, while others which are not available for biological oxidation are oxidized by the dichromate–sulfuric acid mixture.

In many instances, the COD test is much more useful as a nonspecific analytical method even for estimating the oxygen requirements of industrial wastewaters than is the BOD test. It is very valuable for evaluation of wastes for which the BOD test is not applicable due to the presence of toxic materials, low rate of oxidation, or other similar factors. One can make estimates of theoretical oxygen requirements based on prior knowledge of the nature of the principal organic constituents of an industrial wastewater. For example, a sample mass balance for the reaction described in eq. (6) indicates that 192 g of molecular oxygen is required for complete oxidation of 1 mole of glucose to yield 264 g of carbon dioxide and 108 g of water. A simplified general relationship for oxidation

$$C_6H_{12}O_6 + 6O_2 \rightarrow 6CO_2 + 6H_2O \tag{6}$$

of organic matter by molecular oxygen is given by eq. (7). By comparing the percentage of the theoretical oxygen demand for a particular waste

$$C_aH_bN_cO_d + \frac{n}{2}O_2 \rightarrow aCO_2 + \frac{b}{2}H_2O + \frac{c}{2}N_2 \tag{7}$$

component obtained by the COD method with that given by the BOD test, one can evaluate the relative applicability of each of these tests for a given situation. For example, both the BOD test and the COD test (without catalyst) typically measure approximately 80% of the theoretical oxygen requirement for phenol (approximately 90% is obtained by using silver sulfate in the COD test). For a compound such as acetic acid, the percentage of the theoretical value yielded by the COD test without a catalyst is negligible, while that given by the BOD is about 80% (about 90% for the COD with silver sulfate).

As far as using the comparatively rapid COD test for estimating the 5-day biological oxygen requirement is concerned, great care must be taken not to overextend observed relationships between COD and BOD. Ratios of COD to BOD should be employed only in instances where both determinations are applicable to a given wastewater, and it should be recognized that these ratios will vary with time, with variations in the composition of the waste, with changes in prior degree of treatment of the waste, etc. If such a ratio is to be employed, and it does have certain very useful applications for predicting BOD values from measured values for COD, frequent rechecks should be made to ensure that the ratio does not change significantly over the period of concern. Normally the effect of treatment of waste on reduction of its BOD is more marked than on reduction of the COD. Thus the ratio of COD/BOD should be expected to increase with increasing degree of treatment. Dilution upon discharge of a waste to a receiving water will tend to have the same effect of increasing the COD/BOD ratio.

### 3. Total Organic Carbon

There are certain classes of perdurable organic materials occurring in increasing numbers and concentrations in industrial wastewaters which are susceptible neither to biological oxidation nor readily to chemical attack. Branched-chain synthetic surfactants, chlorinated hydrocarbons, compounds containing aromatic or heterocyclic rings, condensed ethers, and many other types of organic compounds are included in this category. Nonspecific analyses for these materials generally cannot be accomplished satisfactorily by either BOD or COD measurements. When such resistant organics are present in industrial wastewaters—indeed, even when the organics present are not particularly resistant—a most useful measure of the overall level of pollution is the total concentration of organic carbon, for carbon is, by definition, the characteristic element of organic matter.

That total organic carbon is a useful measure of pollution has been recognized for some time, and a number of techniques have been developed for this nonspecific method analysis. Without practical exception, methods for the determination of total organic carbon are based upon complete oxidation of the carbon with resultant evolution and measurement of carbon dioxide. Differences among techniques appear primarily in procedures employed for oxidation and in the particular methods used for measurement of the carbon dioxide evolved upon combustion of the organic matter.

The literature is replete with descriptions of different wet oxidation methods, and innovations thereto, in which strong oxidizing agents are used to convert organic carbon to carbon dioxide. Mohlman and Edwards (316), Van Slyke and Folch (476), Lindenbaum et al. (264), and Archer (30) have described the oxidation characteristics of various mixtures of chromic and sulfuric acids. Lindenbaum and his co-workers, one of the few groups to record data on the temperature at which the oxidation was carried out, employed digestion temperatures of 140–160°C, but, as others, failed to note the effect of temperature on the completeness of the oxidation attained. In efforts to enhance the oxidative power of the digestion medium, fuming sulfuric and orthophosphoric acids have been used in combination with chromic acid in some instances (264,476). Dichromate–sulfuric acid mixtures have received considerable attention from a number of investigators. Adeney and Dawson (11), Schulz (408), Ingols and Murray (213), and Moore et al. (321,322) have reported on studies with this medium. Ingols and Murray have suggested a digestion temperature of 145°C, reporting a rapid decrease in the oxidizing capacity of dichromate at temperatures in the neighborhood of 155°C and higher (213). Experimenting with two different concentrations—33 and 50% by volume—of sulfuric acid in the digestion mixture, Moore et al. reported better results with the 50% mixture, but did not link the increased oxidation to the fact that the more concentrated acid mixture boiled at a higher temperature (321). In this same study, Moore and his co-workers investigated the effects of adding selenium, copper, iron, nickel, and platinum to the digestion mixture, but even with these catalysts they were unable to obtain any measurable oxidation of pyridine, only about 5% recovery for acetic acid, and approximately 10% for benzene. In later work with a silver catalyst, Moore was able to obtain better results for compounds such as acetic acid (322). Description of the use of a mixture of dichromate, permanganate, and ceric sulfate has been given by Klein (237). Halate and perhalate acids have been studied by Johnson and Halvorson (221), Smith (424), and Popel and Wagner (354). Van Slyke has provided a fine summary of the historical development of wet oxidation methods (477).

Weber and Morris have described a wet oxidation method in which the oxidation is accomplished at a temperature considerably higher than temperatures normally used in other wet procedures (487). The high temperature oxidation method, effective for a large number of the types of resistant organic compounds likely to occur in industrial wastewaters, is accomplished at 175°C in a chromic acid–concentrated sulfuric acid medium.

Elimination of possible interferences from chloride in concentrations up to at least 5 g/liter is accomplished by inclusion of a saturated acidic silver arsenite trap in the combustion train, after the procedure of Pickhardt et al. (350). Interference from oxides of sulfur and nitrogen is eliminated by passing the gas stream through a solution of barium chloride in hydrochloric acid and through a tube containing silver metal and lead dioxide heated to 193°C. The method has been described as applicable over a wide range of concentrations of organic carbon and as free from interferences normally encountered in methods such as the BOD and COD. At the elevated temperature at which combustion is carried out, more complete oxidation of organic carbon is accomplished by this method than is normally achieved with other wet oxidation methods. Temperatures as high as 175°C are not practical for measurement of values of COD because reduction of the dichromate occurs with evolution of oxygen, leading to spuriously high values for COD.

A number of excellent methods for dry combustion of organic matter in the presence of a catalyst (e.g., cupric oxide, cobaltic oxide, or asbestos-supported silver permanganate at elevated temperatures of 900–1000°C) have been described, but usually these involve procedures and equipment which are relatively too sophisticated for routine analysis in the laboratories of most water and waste treatment facilities. The small samples required because of problems resulting from the evolution of large volumes of steam at the high temperatures at which combustion is carried out may be impractical from sampling and reproducibility standpoints in many instances. Furthermore, rapid combustion at very high temperature occasionally leads to incomplete oxidation to carbon monoxide rather than carbon dioxide, thus yielding spuriously low results (477). Gorbach and Ehrenberger (172), Montgomery and Thom (319), and Van Hall et al. (474) recently have described modifications of dry combustion methods. Although usually employed independently, wet and dry oxidative techniques have sometimes been used in combination (350).

There are a number of techniques for measurement of the quantity of carbon dioxide evolved upon oxidation of organic matter. One of the more elaborate means has been the use of an infrared analyzer (319,350,474). Gravimetric (504) titrimetric (94,300) conductometric (129,245), and gas chromatographic (344) methods have been employed quite commonly, and manometric procedures also have been used (476).

The carbon dioxide measured in the TOC determination cannot be correlated directly to the "oxygen demand" using the general relationship given in eq. (5) because the values for both $b$ and $d$ are unknown. Stenger and Van Hall (435) have proposed the use of carbon dioxide as an oxidizing gas in place of oxygen. Under these conditions the oxidation of organic matter may proceed as follows:

$$C_aH_bN_cO_d + mCO_2 \rightarrow (m + a)CO + \frac{b}{2}H_2O + \frac{c}{2}N_2 \tag{8}$$

Balancing both eqs. (7) and (8) with respect to oxygen yields

$$d + n = 2a + \frac{b}{2} \tag{9}$$

$$f + 2m = m + a + \frac{b}{2} \tag{10}$$

Then, by subtraction and rearrangement

$$n = m + a \tag{11}$$

From eq. (11), the number of moles of carbon monoxide produced in eq. (8) is the same as the number of oxygen atoms utilized in eq. (7). Stenger and Van Hall (435) use the above argument to show the advantage of using $CO_2$ instead of $O_2$ as an oxidizing gas to obtain a more exact stoichiometric evaluation of the "chemical oxygen demand." This procedure is best suited for oxygen demands in the range of 10–300 mg/liter.

One drawback to any method for the determination of total organic carbon is that this quantity is not a measure of the oxygen consuming capacity of an industrial waste, hence the analytical value so obtained does not directly indicate the effect of a discharge of waste on the oxygen balance of a receiving water. However, determinations of total organic carbon do offer a valuable supplement to BOD and COD determinations for estimation of the pollution potential of an industrial waste. While the concentration of organic carbon is a different type of measure of organic matter than that afforded by the BOD and the COD and, therefore, cannot be directly correlated with these other quantities, the relationship for a particular wastewater is generally close enough so that similar inferences may often be drawn and additional information obtained by comparison of determinations of organic carbon with either of the other quantities.

## 4. Total Organic Nitrogen

Organic nitrogen determinations are commonly done by the Kjeldahl method, first described some 75 years ago (243). This method is applicable to many types of organic compounds, although it is sometimes referred to as a method for aminoid or albuminoid nitrogen.

According to Kjeldahl, organic material is destroyed with sulfuric acid in the presence of various catalysts, and the nitrogen is converted to ammonium acid sulfate. The ammonia is liberated and either titrated or determined colorimetrically (20,29). One of the principal problems of this method is that certain organic-bound nitrogen structures cannot be easily transformed to ammonia (406). Four main groups can be characterized: (a) compounds with N—H linkages, (b) compounds with heterocycles, (c) compounds with N—N linkages, and (d) compounds with NO and $NO_2$ groups. The main factors which determine the degree of digestion are time, temperature, and the concentration of potassium sulfate. Mercury is considered an adequate catalyst for the digestion of group a and group b type compounds.

Compounds of groups c and d, e.g., N—N, NO, and $NO_2$, must be reduced prior to digestion. Hydroiodic acid and red phosphorous zinc (157) and other metal powders (117,276) have been used as reducing agents.

For the determination of total organic nitrogen, gaseous ammonia in solution is usually removed by distilling a buffered sample prior to the test (20,29).

Several methods utilizing various combustion techniques separately or in conjunction with the Kjeldahl procedure have been proposed. The reader is referred to the recent review articles by Schoniger (406) and Feigl et al. (146).

Automated chemical techniques are quite suitable for continuous analysis of Kjeldahl nitrogen (452). It is possible by these means to continuously monitor total nitrogen in the concentration range between 0.1 mg/liter to in excess of several thousand milligrams per liter with good correlation to classical manual methods. Appropriate procedures for homogenizing and diluting samples also have been described.

## 5. Total Organic Phosphorus

For determination of organic phosphorus, organic material is first broken down by wet combustion with mixtures of sulfuric and nitric acids. The phosphoric acid produced then can be determined either gravimetrically as ammonium phosphomolybdate or colorimetrically (20,29,449). More extensive discussion of this subject is provided in the section dealing with the anlysis of inorganic phosphates.

## B. SPECIFIC ANALYSIS

In general, specific analysis of the organic constituents of an industrial waste effluent is complicated. Direct application of conventional analytical techniques is frequently not possible because the quantities present may be well below detectable limits. Additionally, the presence of interferences may create difficulties for the application of certain separation techniques. One of the major problems associated with the isolation and separation of organic compounds from wastewaters is the biochemical degradation or chemical transformation of these compounds resulting from bacterial action, temperature effects, surface catalysis, solvent–solute and solute–solute interactions, etc.

Because of the complex nature of the majority of industrial waste effluents, specific analyses for organic compounds are not readily amenable to general regimentation and schematization. Selection of appropriate analytical and separation procedures should be based not only on the general degree of specificity and sensitivity of the test, but also on factors relating to the nature of the waste itself, factors which of course vary from one waste effluent to another.

Few analytical tests can be applied directly to an industrial wastewater without prior sample pretreatment; those which can, include the nonspecific methods discussed above together with certain methods for the analysis of phenols, proteins, and carbohydrates. In the majority of cases, however, the water sample must be subjected to one or more concentration or separation procedures prior to analysis.

## 1. Concentration Techniques

It is frequently necessary to concentrate sample solutions to bring them within the detectable limits of certain analytical procedures. Concentration by removal of water can be achieved by either evaporation or freezing. For evaporation, vacuum distillation at low temperatures is generally preferred. Partial distillation and steam distillation techniques also have been employed (308), and freeze concentration techniques have been used very effectively (41,91,416). One of the main advantages of freeze concentration is that the materials to be concentrated are kept at low temperature during the entire process, thus the chances for loss of volatile constituents and/or alteration of the nature of organic substances of interest are minimized.

Attention has recently been focused on the use of membranes for concentration of organic material in water samples (23). Reverse osmosis with cellulose acetate membranes can be used effectively to concentrate both low and high molecular weight organic compounds. In this technique, pressure greater than the osmotic pressure is applied to the sample solution, resulting in the flow of water through the membrane, with a high degree of retention of the organic solute. The advantage of the membrane-osmotic method for concentrating dilute solutions of organics is that it is an *in situ* separation technique which does not involve changes in phase or changes in temperature.

Carrying the same concept further, all the water can be removed from the sample by evaporating till dryness or freeze-drying. These techniques, however, are used primarily to get a rather rough estimate of the nonvolatile organic content.

## 2. Separation Techniques

A variety of separation techniques may be used, singularly or in combination, for isolation and concentration of organic solutes in industrial wastes. Among these are distillation (308), solvent extraction (72,391,479), precipitation and crystallization (341,353), adsorption (40), gas chromatography (41,217,491), paper chromatography (270), and thin layer chromatography (92,425).

Distillation is commonly used to separate volatile fractions. Partial distillation, in which the sample flows through the distillation cell continuously and only a small portion is distilled (10%), has been applied to oil refinery waste effluents (308). A large number of hydrocarbons can be separated from petroleum refinery effluents by a combination of distillation, selective absorption, extraction, and crystallization. Most techniques utilize fractional distillation to separate mixtures of paraffins, cycloparaffins, and aromatic hydrocarbons into fractions of roughly equal molecular weights. These groups then may be further subdivided by means of other separation techniques. Final purification may be achieved by fractional crystallization or by high efficiency distillation. Alternatively, the separate fractions from distillation may be analyzed directly, by such techniques as mass spectroscopy (308).

Precipitation techniques are useful for only a few specific applications, e.g., silver salts of acids, chloroplatinates, or tetraphenylboron derivatives of ketones and aldehydes. The precipitates may then be analyzed by X-ray diffraction, infrared spectroscopy, or other appropriate techniques (202,203). In practice, precipitation techniques find limited use because of lack of selectivity and because of the number of other substances present in the sample that may coprecipitate.

Adsorption chromatography is one of the best methods available for rapidly concentrating or extracting solutes from dilute aqueous solution. Compared with the volume of the solution used, a relatively small volume of absorbent is required for the separation. The solute normally can be recovered from the absorbent in a small volume of eluting agent.

Adsorption chromatography with activated carbon has been used for more than a decade for separating organic compounds from surface waters and certain industrial effluents (40,68,145,425). Much of the work leading to the development of this procedure was done at the Robert A. Taft Sanitary Engineering Center, Cincinnati, Ohio, in the early 1950's (72). For this procedure, a carbon column, often referred to as the "carbon filter" is used in conjunction with a sand prefilter and/or a presettling tank. The efficiency of the method is a function of the rate of flow of the sample solution, particle size of the absorbent, type and characteristics of the adsorbate(s), and physicochemical properties of the sample solution, such as temperature, pH, ionic strength, and turbidity.

The organic matter collected on the adsorption column is recovered by solvent extraction. Chloroform and ethyl alcohol have been used most commonly for extraction of organics from carbon filters (390). These two extracts are further fractionated by means of various solvent extraction schemes.

It is important to emphasize that the carbon filter technique, as it is used now (20,29,371,390), does not quantitatively separate the total organic content of a water or waste solution. Recoveries may range from approximately 50 to 90%, and replicate samples may agree within only about ±10% (29). In spite of these drawbacks, the carbon filter technique is useful for qualitative collecting of organic matter from dilute waste effluents. It can be used to advantage for screening purposes, as well as for monitoring industrial waste effluents.

Solvent extraction has been used widely for separation of fats, oils, waxes, hydrocarbons, pigments, and other organic waste products from a multitude of waste effluents. This technique can be applied in the form of batch or multiple stage processes, continuous extraction processes, or countercurrent processes. The applicability and selectivity of countercurrent extraction processes has been demonstrated by Craig and Craig (102).

Several procedures have been devised for the systematic separation of organic fractions from wastewaters by successive extraction techniques (91). Some of these techniques are associated with the carbon filter extraction procedure. In this case, the organic compounds commonly are extracted from the carbon filter with chloroform and ethyl alcohol. The weight of the residue remaining after evaporation of the solvent gives a first approximation to the total organic matter present. Further fractionation may follow Schemes 1 and 2, a procedure frequently used for separation of organic matter from river water (72).

WEIGHED SAMPLE

add ether, filter

Ether solution;
extract with H₂O

Residue;
evaporate, weigh
ETHER INSOLUBLES

Ether layer;
extract with HCl

Water layer;
evaporate, weigh
WATER SOLUBLES

Water layer;
make basic, extract
with ether

Ether layer;
extract with NaHCO₃

Ether layer;
dry, evaporate
and weigh
BASES

Water layer;
discard

Water layer;
make acid
extract with
ether

Ether layer;
dry, evaporate
and weigh
STRONG ACIDS

Water layer;
discard

Ether layer;
extract with NaOH

Water layer;
make acid
extract with ether

Ether layer;
dry, evaporate

NEUTRALS

Ether layer;
dry, evaporate
and weigh

WEAK ACIDS

Water layer;
discard

Scheme 1. Liquid extraction scheme for organic compounds.

NEUTRALS

Adsorb on silica gel column

1  Elute with isooctane

2  Elute with benzene

3  Elute with chloroform/methanol (1:1)

ALIPHATICS           AROMATICS          OXYGENATED COMPOUNDS

Scheme 2. Chromatographic separation of neutrals.

A countercurrent batch extraction technique has been reported for concentration of trace organic materials from large volumes of water (205). In this technique, continuous extraction is carried out with $n$-butanol for 40 hr at adjusted pH levels of 2, 7, and 10. The three extractions are then combined and condensed by vacuum distillation for further separation and identification by gas chromatography.

Gas chromatography has proven to be a useful tool for analysis of natural waters and wastewaters, being used in the majority of cases to separate and identify components of extracts from carbon filters or from other separation processes (5,25,40,175,209,330,333,341,391,483). In a few cases, however, water samples have been directly injected for analysis of organic content (38,144,491).

The successful application of gas chromatography for analysis of the organic content of a wastewater depends upon careful selection of an appropriate set of operating parameters; these parameters include column temperature, gas flow rate, type of carrier gas, gas pressure, column length and diameter, nature and particle size of the solid phase, and nature and amount of the liquid phase. Other factors requiring careful consideration include temperature programming sample injection device and type of detector. Discussions of the selection of detectors, columns, and operating conditions for certain types of waste effluents are provided in the references cites above.

Some of the factors that must be considered in selection of a detector are: sensitivity, linearity of response, frequency of calibration, response time, reproducibility, and temperature range. Both primary and secondary methods of detection have been used. Primary detectors, such as thermal conductivity and ionization detectors (sometimes referred to as nonspecific detectors), cannot specifically identify the individual organic components as they emerge from the chromatographic column. Thermal conductivity detectors are used primarily for analysis of volatile hydrocarbons, organic acids, and the components of gas streams (25). Flame ionization detectors find wider use for analysis of a variety of organic compounds by direct-injection techniques (38,491). The main advantage of the flame ionization detector for this type of analysis is that it is relatively insensitive to water and thus permits direct injection of aqueous samples.

Secondary detection involves specific analysis by such techniques as ultraviolet, infrared, and mass spectroscopy. These techniques are frequently used for the subsequent identification of organic fractions which have been separated by gas–liquid chromatography.

Paper chromatography and thin layer chromatography also find application for separation and identification of organic constituents in wastewaters. Phenols, cresols, xylenol, and other industrial and biological phenols have been determined in microgram per liter concentrations in polluted waters by paper chromatography (171). Chlorinated hydrocarbon pesticides have been determined at concentrations of 2 $\mu$g/liter or less in carbon–chloroform extracts (5).

Thin layer chromatography has been used effectively for removing interfering substances from pesticides prior to gas chromatographic analysis (425). Christman has discussed the advantages of thin layer chromatography over paper chromatography for separation and identification of organic chromogenic agents in natural waters (91). The separation and detection of various herbicides (e.g., 2,4-D; 2,4,5-T MCPA; MCPB; 2,4-DB; Dalapan, etc.) can be effectively done by thin layer chromatographic techniques (425).

Methods for continuous concentration and separation of organic material have been used in connection with automated analytical techniques and continuous monitoring systems. Continuous distillation units are suitable for removal of low boiling organic fractions from a wastewater stream (107,308). Continuous filtration and dialysis units have been used with the Technicon Autoanalyzer (451). Similarly, continuous liquid–liquid extraction (205,227,398) and continuous gas chromatographic techniques (349) have been applied for separation of low boiling organics.

## 3. Identification Techniques

One of the more common methods for identification of organic compounds is the detection of functional groups by means of color reactions. Many schemes for classification by solvation, general chemical reactions, and special tests are found in most texts on organic analysis. Chelation methods have been used recently for detection of functional groups in various compounds (430). Several comprehensive surveys dealing with this aspect of organic analysis are available in the literature (87).

Spectrometric identification of organic compounds by infrared, ultraviolet, mass spectroscopy, and nuclear magnetic resonance techniques have been reviewed in previous chapters of this Treatise. For analysis of natural water and wastewaters, analytical spectrometry must generally be preceded by separation of the organic material from the water sample by one or more of the techniques discussed previously (72,92,308,391,479,496). Special procedures are necessary for collection and concentration of the sample after separation. Liquid samples in a solvent matrix, or solid potassium bromide mulls or paste in mineral oil, may be analyzed for typical infrared absorption bonds to provide structural identification. Near-infrared spectrometry offers some advantages when interferences occur in the "fingerprint" region from 7 to $12\mu$. Measurement in the near-infrared region $(1–3\mu)$ consists of overtone of hydrogen stretching vibration. These spectra are useful only for detecting and subsequently identifying functional groups which contain unique hydrogen atoms and are not characteristic of the organic molecule as a whole. Most useful are the stretching modes of vibration of the hydrogen bond in combination with carbon, oxygen, nitrogen, or sulfur.

A modification of infrared spectrometry which offers unique possibilities for analysis of organic matter in water involves attenuated total reflectance (139,186,187). This method is based on the passage of a monochromatic or monochromatically scanned light into a crystal of suitable material, in contact with the test solution, and detection of the transmitted light intensity. Changes in light intensity are related to changes in the type and concentration of "light active" substances in contact with the crystalline material. The principle is based on energy reflection at the interface between media of different refractive indices. Little sample preparation is required, and the use of two attenuation attachments permits differential spectral attachment (291,502).

Infrared scanning has been used recently for pollution surveillance (475). This technique is particularly applicable for determination of the origin and distribution of thermal pollution. The procedure involves noncontact, infrared aerial mapping. By means of air-borne detector systems, energy in the nonvisible portion of the electromagnetic spectrum (wavelength 8–14 $\mu$) is converted, recorded, and correlated with broad-band emission properties of the materials viewed. Such properties are a function of temperature and material emissivity characteristics, and a theory has been developed to separate temperature and emissivity contributions (475).

Ultraviolet spectrometry has not been widely used for analysis of natural waters and wastewaters, despite an abundance of literature on the application of uv-visible spectrometry for organic analyses. Exhaustive coverage of this subject can be found in reviews appearing in some recent periodicals (e.g., *Journal of Molecular Spectroscopy, Spectrochimica Acta, Applied Spectroscopy, Talanta,* and *Analytica Chimica Acta*).

Phenolic compounds in wastewaters may be determined by uv spectrometry by a technique based on comparing the bathochromatic shifts in wavelength in alkaline solutions and in neutral solutions (496). This method is particularly useful when organic separation is difficult.

Ultraviolet spectrometry finds wide application in industrial processes for monitoring the composition of reaction mixtures. Monitoring of trace organic material in industrial effluents by uv spectrometry has been reported by Bramer et al. (71). The method is based on measuring uv absorption spectra for compounds having aromatic or conjugated unsaturated molecular configurations. The instrument employed for these analyses uses a mercury discharge lamp with a principal uv radiation at 2537 Å. The author has reported a sensitivity of 10 mg/liter of phenol in water.

Mass spectrometry has not as yet been widely used for analysis of wastewaters. Melpolder et al. (308) have described the distillation of volatile organic compounds from oil refinery wastewater and subsequent identification by mass spectrometry. Because of the high training level required for operating personnel, the data handling problems, and the cost of instrumentation, this technique has been restricted primarily to research applications, and then only at a few major water pollution control laboratories. The technique does, however, offer considerable possibilities; for example, mass spectrometry has been used to detect phenols in nanogram quantities in the effluent from a gas chromatographic column (169).

Fluorescence spectrophotometry has significant potential for trace organic analysis in waste effluents. Christman (90) has applied this technique for analysis of lignin sulfonates in the waste effluents from Kraft sulfite pulping operations. The author has discussed the analytical feasibility of *in situ* fluorescent spectrophotometry versus conventional analytical techniques. Spent-sulfite effluents from the Kraft process have been monitored in concentrations as low as 0.2 mg/liter. Christman (90) has also applied the same technique for analysis of organic color-forming compounds in natural waters.

Traces of carbohydrate in the nanogram per liter range have been determined in water samples using spectrofluorometry (386). The test is based on the Seliwanoff reaction for the determination of ketones. The sensitivity of the method and the effects of environmental factors have been discussed (386).

The ensuing discussion of analytical methods for specific organic substances is subdivided into major groups of compounds (e.g., phenols, detergents or surfactants, insecticides, etc.). Analytical procedures for miscellaneous compounds found in wastewaters are listed in Appendix I.

## 4. Analysis for Phenols

Phenolic matter in industrial waste effluents is generally comprised of monohydroxy derivatives of benzene and homologous and condensed nuclei (20). Phenols in wastewaters, sometimes referred to as "tar acids," include cresols, xylenols, chlorophenols, naphthols, and other phenolic derivatives. Phenols are found in a variety of industrial wastes (e.g., coal tar, gas liquor, plastic wastes, rubber-proofing wastes, cutting-oil wastes, and the wastes from manufacture of disinfectants and pharmaceuticals).

The discharge of phenolic wastes to a receiving stream is undesirable because of the toxicity of this material to aquatic life, including fish. Further, chlorination of a phenol-containing water for use as a water supply results in the formation of chlorophenols and the resultant production of objectionable taste and highly intense odor.

One of the early methods for analysis of phenolic compounds in natural and wastewaters was that of Fox and Gauge (154). The method is based on coupling of the phenol, in caustic soda solution, with a freshly prepared diazotized sulfanilic acid. Various shades of color are produced, depending on the particular phenols present. Generally, the color varies from yellow to orange. For example, monohydroxy derivates of benzene give a yellow color, mixed cresols give a yellowish-orange color, and xylenols give a deep orange color. The reproducibility of this test can be improved by carrying out the diazotization in ice-cooled solutions, using freshly prepared diazonium compounds, and by properly controlling the pH of the reaction. For waste samples containing interfering "tannins" (which contain phenolic groupings), chloroform extraction of the acidified solution will separate phenols from tannins.

Phenols in wastewaters from coke and gas works have been determined by a more sensitive photometric procedure based on substituting sulfanilic acid for the $p$-nitroaniline normally used in the Fox-Gauge test (53).

The more recent Gibbs method (168) for phenol has been applied extensively to natural waters and wastewaters (137,381). The method is based on the interaction of phenols with $2:6$-dibromoquinone chloroimide and the formation of an indophenol dye, i.e.,

$$O:C_6H_2Br_2:NCl + C_6H_5OH \rightarrow O:C_6H_2Br_2:N \cdot C_6H_4OH + HCl \qquad (12)$$

Although the Gibbs method is more sensitive than the Fox-Gauge test, it also suffers from the formation of different shades of color for different phenolic compounds. For example, monohydroxy benzene and cresols give a blue color, $o$-cresol a purple color, and $p$-cresol gives no color at all. Amines interfere with the test, and sulfides prevent color development. Several modifications of the Gibbs method have been proposed to overcome some of these difficulties (7,200,336).

The standard method for the analysis of phenols in industrial wastewaters is based on the interaction of phenols with 4-amino antipyrine and oxidation under alkaline conditions to give an intense colored product. The reaction is dependent on the pH and type of buffer used (135a,135b). Variations of the pH value between 8.0 and 11.0 and the use of different buffer systems greatly influenced the sensitivity of the test to a particular phenol by shifting wavelength of maximum absorbance (144).

The reaction is also dependent on the type of phenol and the number of substitutions on the phenol ring (145a,145b). The position, type, and number of substitutions on the phenol ring were found to be greatly significant. Substitutions in the *para* position by alkyl, aryl, ester, nitro, benzoyl, nitroso, amino, and aldehyde appear to block or inhibit the reaction, the degree of which is dependent on pH. Faust and Mikulewicz (145a,145b) concluded that the determination of "total" phenol content in a water sample by the 4-amino antipyrine method is not possible since a number of phenols are either weakly reactive or do not react at all. The authors indicated, however, that best results are obtained when the test is done at pH 8.0 instead of 10.0 as recommended by *Standard Methods* (29).

Because the 4-amino antipyrine test cannot detect *para*-substituted phenols, other colorimetric procedures have been proposed for analysis for this substance (199,282). Water samples containing mixtures of phenol are first subjected to the 4-amino antipyrine test, then passed through an ion exchange column containing the hydroxide-form of Dowex 1-X8. The dye complexes pass through the column, while the *para*-substituted phenols remain sorbed. Elution with methyl alcohol, sodium chloride solution, and acetic acid removes the sorbed phenols, which are then diazotized with sulfanilic acid and determined spectrophotometrically at 495 m$\mu$. This method has been used for analysis for *p*-cresol, 2,3-xylenol, *o*,4-xylenol, and *p*-ethylphenol in various waters. Aromatic amines interfere with the reaction, and phenols containing *para*-substituted alkylaryl, nitro, and many other groups do not react. Oxidizing and reducing agents which react with the ferricyanide must be absent from the test solution. Despite these difficulties, the method is considered to be the best colorimetric test for most industrial wastewaters (121).

When phenols are present in fairly high concentration (e.g., more than 20 mg/liter), a titrimetric method based on bromination may be used (74). The waste sample is treated with excess standard bromine solution, which is then back-titrated iodometrically. The test is based on reaction

$$C_6H_5OH + 3Br_2 = C_6H_2Br_3 \cdot OH \text{(tribromophenol)} + 3HBr \qquad (13)$$

(13). The titrimetric method for phenols is susceptible to a variety of interferences from other organic species which may react with bromine.

Various modifications of the colorimetric procedure have been devised in attempts to reduce the effects of interferences. Double distillation techniques have been used to remove interferences from trade effluents (3). This has been followed by color development with 4-aminophenezone in an ammonium persulfate–alkaline borate solution. In other cases, the distillation of phenol was done after the water sample had been treated with CuSO$_4$. The distillate was then buffered to pH 8.3 and treated with alcoholic pyramidone and K$_3$Fe (CN)$_6$ solution for color development (106). Phenols in waste effluents have been determined in the presence of resorcinol by taking advantage of the fact that dimethylamine-benzaldehyde (DBA), which is used to detect resorcinol, is insensitive to phenols. Because resorcinol interferes in an additive fashion, phenol in waste liquor samples can be determined by subtracting light absorption values obtained with DBA from those obtained with DBC (420).

Gas chromatography has been used successfully for analysis of a variety of substituted phenols which do not respond to the colorimetric test, at concentrations less than 1.0 mg/liter (38,144,351). Concentration by vacuum distillation and solvent extraction prior to chromatographic analysis have been reported (405). Paper chromatography has also been used for analysis of simple phenolic compounds in coal distillation waters (260), with $n$-heptane and cyclohexane being used to separate and clearly define spots of *meta*- and *para*-cresols.

Ultraviolet differential spectrometry has been used for analysis of phenolic substances in some instances (405). This technique is based on comparison of the B band (benzenoid bands) of alkaline forms of phenolic substances with those in neutral solutions. Differences in spectra can be detected and enable identification in the presence of interfering materials which mask direct spectra.

Near ir spectroscopy has been employed for analysis of phenolic derivatives in industrial wastewaters from oil refineries (21). The procedure is based on measuring ir spectra of the hydroxyl group stretching vibrations in monohydroxyphenols at 2.84 $\mu$ after bromination (420). The method is applicable to phenolic compounds which can be brominated in the *ortho* position with respect to the hydroxyl group. *Ortho*-substituted or sterically hindered phenolic compounds will not respond to this procedure. Polarographic determination of nitrochlorobenzenes in water using the standard addition technique has been reported (149). The method is based on separation on activated carbon and liquid extraction with acetone followed by extraction in $0.2M$ $C_5H_5N \cdot HCl$ in $C_4H_5N$ mixed 2:3 with 7% barium chloride. After removal of molecular oxygen by bubbling nitrogen and using alkaline pyrogallol solution, the polarographic wave is determined from 0.2 to 0.9 V versus an internal mercury electrode. The polarogram is repeated with a standard addition of nitrochlorobenzene.

## 5. Analysis for Pesticides

Pesticides are chemical substances employed for regulation of noxious fauna and flora. Although pesticides contribute significantly to the welfare of mankind, the indiscriminate use and discharge of these materials to the environment may constitute a very serious health hazard. There are approximately 300 organic pesticide chemicals, marketed in more than 10,000 different formulations (315). The national consumption in 1965 has been estimated to be about 750 million pounds of insecticides and herbicides (315). The points of concern in the use of pesticides are amounts of discharged toxicities, persistence, and rates of detoxification.

Chlorinated hydrocarbons, organophosphorus, carbamate insecticides, dithiocarbamate fungicides, dinitrocresols, and certain inorganic compounds are among the main types of pesticides. Pesticides are considered toxic in trace concentrations, and because of their persistence and cumulative effects, considerable emphasis has been placed on devising methods for separation and detection of trace quantities of these substances.

Liquid–liquid extraction (72,79) and adsorption on carbon (72,488) have been primary methods for the concentration and separation of pesticides from large volumes of natural waters and wastewaters. Methods of extractions vary; for example, many of the nonionic pesticides of the chlorinated hydrocarbon and organic phosphate classes can be extracted from either acid or basic solution with nonpolar solvents such as $n$-hexane. On the other hand, anionic compounds, such as phenoxyalkanoic acid herbicides, are extracted with a more polar solvent, from a solution which has been acidified to suppress the ionization of carboxylic groups. Quite often compounds are separated into nonionic and anionic fractions by adjusting the pH of the sample between extractions. Since large volumes of both water and solvent are often used for extraction, the solvent containing the residue must be reduced in volume or removed entirely in order to further concentrate the residue prior to separation and identification. Removal of solvent is often accomplished by evaporation under a current of air, by reflux distillation, or by vacuum evaporation.

Certain ionic compounds may require chemical modification to change their volatility prior to determination by gas chromatography. Burchfield and Johnson (79) have suggested treatment with diazomethane, reaction with a mixture of methanol and $BF_3$ and esterification with methanol and $H_2SO_4$.

There are four general methods for identification of pesticide residues: (a) spectrophotometric analysis, (b) elemental analysis, (c) measurement of biological activity, and (d) chromatographic analysis. One of the early colorimetric methods for the determination of concentrations of DDT as low as 0.003 ppm is the Schechter-Haller method (56,402). After preliminary isolation by extraction with a mixture of ether and $n$-hexane, the residue is nitrated to a polynitro derivative, a benzene solution of which gives an intense blue color with sodium methoxide dissolved in methyl alcohol. $\alpha$-Isomers of benzene hexachloride (gamexan) have been identified after extraction with carbon tetrachloride and dechlorination to benzene followed by nitration to $m$-dinitrobenzene. This last compound is then allowed to react with methylethylketone and alkali to give a reddish-violet color which may be measured photometrically (403).

Direct identification of pesticide residue after extraction and concentration has been done by infrared spectrometry (389) and by ultraviolet spectrometry (334).

Elemental analysis of a pesticide residue commonly is used to determine large amounts of certain compounds. The method relies on special properties which certain pesticides possess which are not shared by most naturally occurring metabolites, e.g., the organically bound chlorine in chlorinated hydrocarbons. If the organic fraction containing bound chlorine is combusted, the liberated chloride ions can be measured colorimetrically or titrimetrically (175). The total amount of pesticide will be expressed then in terms of gram-atoms of chlorine. Similarly, organophosphorus compounds can be determined by measuring the amount of phosphorus liberated. It must be realized, however, that this method not only lacks specificity, but also is subject to interferences from other chlorinated or phosphorus-containing compounds.

A more specific test for certain pesticides is to measure their anti-enzyme activity. Organophosphorus compounds are, for example, specific inhibitors for acetylcholinesterase. Methods are available for measuring the extent of enzymatic inhibition (382). These procedures have certain shortcomings, since different compounds exhibit different inhibitory action, and for the same phosphate content one may get different anti-cholinesterase activities. Fish bioassay (bluegill) has been used, however, to detect pesticide residues in the part per billion range (490). The test is based on measuring the inhibition of acetylcholinesterase in the brain of fish.

Chromatographic techniques probably provide the most sensitive procedure for the analysis of pesticides. Paper and thin layer chromatography (5,171,217,425) have been used separately or together with gas chromatography for pesticide analysis. An increasing number of articles are appearing in the literature describing new and more sensitive chromatographic techniques (72,79,130,255,296,334,483). Electron capture detectors have been used to detect as little as a picogram of chlorinated hydrocarbons and organophosphorus pesticides.

When the extreme sensitivity of the electron capture detector is not required, the microcoulometric titrator detector is preferred because of its high selectivity to halogens (except fluorides), sulfur, and phosphorus. With such high specificity the problems associated with the presence of impurities are minimized.

Identification of pesticides is usually based on chromatographic retention-time data coupled with the response of specific detectors. More confirmation is sometimes sought through correlating results from more than one chromatographic column or through comparing chromatographic data with data from thin layer or paper chromatography measurements. Comparison of infrared spectra is considered the ultimate identification procedure. Column eluents are collected, repetitively, and micropellets or microcavity cells are used for measuring the infrared spectra. Rapid scan infrared spectrometers connected directly to chromatographic columns have been used. Complete infrared spectra in the gas phase are obtained within 30 sec or less for the column effluent.

## 6. Analysis for Surfactants

As a result of the widespread use of synthetic detergents in domestic and various industrial applications, these materials are found commonly in sewage and industrial effluents. The objectionable tendencies of detergents to cause persistent foam in streams and at sewage plants and the possible toxicity of some of their constituents to fish and aquatic flora make it quite important to have suitable methods for their analysis.

Surfactants may be categorized as: (a) anionic, e.g., alkylbenzene sulfonate (ABS); (b) nonionic, e.g., polyglycol ethers of alkylated phenols (Lissapol N); and (c) cationic, e.g., quaternary organic bases such as roccal. Commercial detergents for domestic and industrial use are usually mixed with other substances, called "builders," which serve to improve the cleansing action of the detergents. Some of the common builders are sodium triphosphate or polyphosphate, sodium sulfate, sodium carbonate, sodium perborate, sodium silicate, and sodium carboxymethylcellulose. Anionic-type surface active agents have been employed most commonly for both domestic and industrial detergents. Within this class, alkylbenzene sulfonates are particularly difficult to degrade biologically during sewage treatment, and about 50% of the original amount commonly passes in the final effluent to receiving waters.

Under pressure from the public and State and Federal Governments, the detergent industry has introduced more readily biodegradable surfactants, e.g., sugar esters of linear aliphatic monocarboxylic acids, alkyl ether sulfates, and fatty acid ester sulfonates. The most common of the so-called "biodegradable" surfactants is the linear alkylate sulfonate (LAS).

The standard analysis for alkylbenzene sulfonates in industrial wastewaters (20,35) is based upon formation of a chloroform-soluble colored complex with methylene blue. The intensity of the blue color is measured photometrically at a wavelength of approximately 650 m$\mu$. Compounds which combine with the surfactant molecule to inactivate the sulfonate site may block the methylene blue reaction, thus causing negative interference.

In an attempt to minimize the effects of interferences, extraction of the methylene blue complex with chloroform in an alkaline solution (phosphate–sodium hydroxide buffer at pH 10) instead of an acid medium has been introduced (267). The chloroform extracts are eventually washed with an acid solution of methylene blue. By using this double extraction procedure, interferences due to chloride, nitrate, thiocyanate, and proteins are minimized.

Anionic surfactants have been determined by solvent extraction of the 1-methyl-heptylamine salt and measurement of color intensity spectrophotometrically at 650 m$\mu$. The effects of interferences in this procedure are reduced by double extractions, at pH 7.5 with a chloroform solution of 1-methyl-heptylamine and, after acid hydrolysis, extraction at pH 4.8 with a hexane solution of 1-methyl-heptylamine (143).

Separation by carbon adsorption has been used to avoid interferences (20,29). This technique, capable of detecting ABS in the parts per billion range, is based on (a) adsorption of the syndets on activated carbon, (b) desorption with alkaline benzene–methanol, (c) acid hydrolysis to destroy interfering organic sulfates, etc., (d) treatment with light petroleum to remove hydrocarbons, alcohols, and sterols, (e) extraction of surfactant in chloroform as a complex 1-methyl-heptylamine salt, and, finally, (f) infrared identification in carbon tetrachloride solution at 9.6 and 9.9$\mu$.

A number of review articles (192,261) discussing analyses for nonionic and anionic surfactants in waters and waste effluents have been published. Some of the more pertinent analytical procedures reported in the recent literature are listed in Appendix II.

## 7. Analysis for Combined Nitrogen
### (Ammonia, Nitrites, and Nitrates)

$NH_3$, $NO_2^-$ and $NO_3^-$ in wastewaters may result from the degradation of organic nitrogenous compounds or may be entirely of inorganic origin.

The most widely used method for analysis for ammonia is the Nesslerization reaction. The test is based on the development of a yellow–brown (colloidal) color on addition of Nessler's reagent to an ammonia solution. The standard method (29) and the ASTM reference test (20) recommend the separation of the ammonia from the sample by distillation prior to the Nesslerization reaction. Direct Nesslerization is most often preferred, however, for rapid routine determinations.

For certain industrial wastewaters, it is often desirable to distinguish between "free" ammonia and "fixed" ammonia. The former is estimated by a straightforward distillation; the residual liquor is then treated with excess alkali (e.g., sodium carbonate, magnesium oxide or caustic soda) and distilled to determine fixed ammonia. Certain substances interfere with both the direct Nesslerization and distillation mtehods, e.g., glycine, urea, glutamic acid, acetamides, and hydrazines.

The standard method (20,29) for nitrites in water is based on forming a diazonium compound by the diazotization of sulfanilic acid by nitrite under strongly acidic conditions and coupling with α-naphthylamine hydrochloride to produce a reddish-purple color. Spectrometric measurement of the color of the azo dye is performed at 520 m$\mu$, or visual comparison with standards may be used. This method is sometimes known as the Griess-Ilosvay method (379). A frequently used alternative procedure for nitrite is based on formation of a yellowish-brown dye by the reaction of nitrite in acid solution with *meta*-phenylene diamine (238).

The Griess-Ilosvay method is most suitable for low nitrite concentrations, e.g., below 2.0 mg/liter. Another colorimetric procedure which is more suitable at high concentration involves reaction of the nitrites with *meta*-phenylene diamine in an acid solution to form a yellowish-brown dye. Chlorides in concentration below 500 mg/liter have no effect on either of the two procedures. High chloride concentrations (10,000 mg/liter) interfere more with the Griess-Ilosvay test. More distinct, pH-independent color development is achieved (418) by replacing the sulfanilic acid with sulfanilamide, and α-naphthylamine with 1-naphthylethylene diamine dihydrochloride within the Griess-Ilosvay test. The sulfanilamide undergoes diazotization in hydrochloric acid and the diazonium salt is then coupled with the diamine to give a stable red azo dye.

An excellent review of approximately 52 spectrophotometric methods for nitrite has been published by Sawicki et al. (399). The authors critically evaluate the sensitivity, color stability, conformity to Beer's law, simplicity and precision of a variety of methods.

Colorimetry, uv spectrometer, and polarography have frequently been used for nitrate determinations in natural waters and waste effluents. The phenoldisulfonic acid method and the brucine method are two colorimetric procedures more frequently used. In the former test, color development is based on the reaction between phenol disulfonic acid and nitrates in sulfuric acid solution to give a nitro derivative which causes a yellow coloration when the solution is made alkaline; the intensity of the color is measured at 470 m$\mu$. Nitrite ion interferes with the test in proportion to its concentration in the sample. Various inorganic ions above certain concentrations cause interference (20). Small amounts of chlorides do not interfere, but nitrites should be removed with sodium azide (20).

An alternate test for nitrates involves reaction of a brucine solution in glacial acetic acid with nitrates and acidification with dilute $H_2SO_4$. The color intensity changes with time and it is necessary to develop the color of standards and samples simultaneously and compare maximum color intensity. Chlorides above 1000 mg/liter interfere with color development. Nitrites, if present, should be separately estimated and an appropriate correction applied. A salt-masking technique which renders the test applicable to sea water and brackish water has been proposed by Jenkins and Medsker (219).

Nitrate analysis by reduction to ammonia, which is then detected by Nesslerization, has been reported by several authors. The procedure is based on expelling all ammonia from the water sample, followed by reduction of nitrogen ($NO_2^-$ and $NO_3^-$) by means of (a) aluminum foil in alkaline NaOH solution, (b) zinc–copper couple in acetic acid solution, (c) Devarda's alloy hydrazine (93), and (d) alkaline ferrous sulfates. The ammonia produced may be separated by steam distillation and estimated in the distillate by Nesslerization. Various procedures have been proposed to minimize interferences due to nitrites and chlorides.

Nitrate analysis by reduction to nitrites which are then detected by the Griess-Ilsovay method has been applied to both natural waters and wastewaters (127). Controlled reduction of nitrates to nitrites is accomplished with zinc powder in acid solution.

Ultraviolet analysis for nitrates offers the advantage of freedom from chloride interferences and a variety of other inorganic ions. However, dissolved organic compounds, nitrites, hexavalent chromium, and surfactants interfere with this procedure. The test is based on measuring uv adsorption spectra of the filtered, acidified sample at 220 m$\mu$. Measurements follow Beer's law up to 11 mg N/liter. Interference of dissolved organics is estimated by doing a second measurement at 275 m$\mu$, a wavelength at which nitrates do not absorb.

Simultaneous determination of nitrates, nitrites, and sulfates in water samples by infrared techniques has been reported (93). The test is based on concentrating the sample by ion exchange and removal of phosphates, carbonates, and organic matter. This is followed by separation by freeze-drying the aqueous solution in the presence of KBr; the infrared spectrum is determined in the resulting KBr disk.

The polarographic analysis of nitrates in wastewaters is based on the original work of Kolthoff, Harris, and Matsuyama (241a). Nitrate ion is catalytically reduced at the dropping mercury electrode in the presence of uranyl ion in an acid solution at $-1.2$ V versus SCE. The diffusion current is linearly proportional to the nitrate ion concentration. Nitrites, phosphates, ferric iron, and fluorides interfere with the test. Procedures to minimize interferences have been prescribed. The polarographic test offers the advantage of being adaptable to continuous monitoring (20,29,156).

The analytical procedures described above for ammonia, nitrites, and nitrates are those most commonly applied to wastewaters. Other pertinent procedures reported during the last few years are listed in Appendix III.

## 8. Analysis for Combined Phosphorus
### (Ortho-, Pyro-, and Polyphosphates)

Phosphorus may be present in industrial waste effluents either as inorganic phosphates (ortho-, meta-, or polyphosphates) or in organic combination. The most common analytical method for inorganic phosphorus is based on the colorimetric determination of the phosphomolybdenum blue complex (20,29). The test is sensitive to orthophosphates and not condensed phosphates. Polyphosphates and metaphosphates are then estimated as the difference between total phosphates (hydrolyzed samples) and orthophosphates (nonhydrolyzed samples).

Orthophosphates react with ammonia molybdate in acid medium to form the phosphomolybdic acid complex, which when reduced yields the molybdenum blue color which may be determined colorimetrically. The sensitivity of the test is largely dependent on the method of extraction and reduction of the phosphomolybdic acid aminonaphthol-sulfonic acid (29), stannous chloride (Deniges method) (6), metal sulfites (Tschopp reagent) (463), and ascorbic acid (150) have been used in the reduction step. The stannous chloride method is considered most sensitive and best suited for lower ranges of phosphate concentration.

A number of substances have been reported to interfere with the phosphate determination (29). Arsenic, germanium, sulfides, and soluble iron above 0.1 mg cause direct interferences. Tannins, lignins, and hexavalent chromium will cause errors only for analysis of phosphate concentrations below milligrams per liter.

Various modifications of the above procedures, as well as other new techniques, have been recently reported; some of the more pertinent ones are given in Appendix III.

## C. BIODEGRADABILITY OF ORGANIC COMPOUNDS

With increasing emphasis on water pollution control, and in view of recent legislation restricting the disposal of waste effluents, biodegradability is becoming the most significant test in the analysis for industrial wastewaters. Biodegradability tests are basically designed to estimate the extent to which organic compounds may be oxidized biochemically, and an industry must be concerned with the question of whether its products or waste materials can be degraded or assimilated efficiently by existing biological waste treatment processes.

Biodegradability may be considered as a measure of the susceptability of organic material to microbial metabolism. This property is not well defined and there is no single standard test for its measurement. It constitutes, however, a dominant mechanism for the removal of organic pollutants from water, both in self-purification processes in natural waters and in the accelerated biological processes of waste treatment. Biodegradation can occur aerobically or anaerobically, depending on the availability of atmospheric oxygen. The process is affected by a variety of environmental conditions. As discussed previously in this chapter, organic compounds are not equally susceptible to biodegradation; some are readily metabolized and others are more resistant (refractory compounds). Principal factors involved in any biodegradation process are as follows.

*a.* Type and number of microorganisms: a mixed culture of organisms, as in sanitary sewage, possesses a remarkable capacity to adapt to strange or different organic materials, while single cultures may not be effective.

*b.* Structure and concentration of organic materials: certain organic compounds, e.g., certain pesticides and surfactants, are relatively resistant to biodegradation in comparison to simple carbohydrates. The concentration of the organic material is also significant. High concentrations of "sugars" in certain wastewaters may inhibit biodegradation, yet upon dilution in a receiving water the sugars will be easily degraded, resulting in a water pollution problem due to oxygen depletion.

*c.* Environmental factors: factors such as temperature, mixing, and viscosity, of the wastewater are quite significant in dictating the extent and rate of biodegradation and its effect on the ecology of the receiving environment (air, water, or soil).

Much of the work which has been carried out on biodegradation has been concerned with surfactants and, in particular, with the "hard" branched-type ABS and the "soft" straight-chain LAS (18,26,27,301, 426,445,467). Surfactant (ABS or LAS) biodegradation begins at one end of the alkyl chain with oxidation of the terminal methyl group to a carboxyl group. Beta oxidation follows, shortening the chain by two carbons at a time. Then the benzene ring splits, yielding unsaturated intermediates (301,445). The rate of biodegradation is dependent on the degree of branching of the paraffin part of the surfactant molecule (301). Because of its linear configuration, linear alkylate sulfonate (LAS) degrades at a faster rate and requires less residence time in the biological treatment plant than does ABS.

A number of techniques have been used to test for biodegradability, such as the Warburg respiration technique (468), activated sludge tests (26,444), shake-flask experiments (444), and river die-away measurements (18,180). A comprehensive critique of various biodegradability tests has been presented recently by Bunch and Chambers (78). In some cases, investigators have tried to devise procedures to duplicate as closely as possible the conditions prevailing in the receiving stream or in the waste treatment plant (18,301). In other cases, simple static procedures have been employed (78). Sewage microorganisms are commonly used for biodegradability measurements because of availability and to avoid the need for maintaining standard cultures (78). Biological oxidation has been followed by measurement of one or more of the following parameters: (a) the rate of disappearance of the organic compound under test, (b) the rate of appearance of biodegradation by-products, (c) growth rate of microorganisms, and (b) dissolved oxygen consumption.

Analytical techniques used for estimating biodegradability have been reported by Allred et al. (18) and Bunch and Chambers (78). A number of laboratory-scale test environments have been proposed for measuring surfactant biodegradability (26).

Bunch and Chambers (78) have described a static biodegradation test and its application to a number of organic compounds. Gates et al. and Mancy (161,283) have investigated the mechanism and rates of biochemical assimilation of organic compounds in small laboratory batch reactors. Variable levels of turbulence were rated in terms of values of air–water oxygen transfer coefficients. The results point out the effect of the type and concentration of organic compounds and the type and number of microorganisms and assimilation rates.

# VI. ANALYSIS FOR METALS

This section is concerned with the analysis of metal ions commonly found in industrial wastewaters. The metals of interest include alkali metals, alkaline earths, transition metals, and heavy metals. Depending on the physicochemical characteristics of the solution phase in which they are dissolved, metal ions may occur in one or more aquometallic or organometallic complexes.

Metal analyses have undergone significant changes in the last three decades. Prior to about 1940, most analytical techniques for metals were either gravimetric or volumetric. Since the post-War era of the late 1940's there has been a considerable increase in the use of the spectrophotometric techniques, largely as a result of the development of various organic reagents such as dithizone, $o$-phenanthroline, sodium diethyldithiocarbamate, and diphenylcarbazide, which form color-producing compounds with metal ions in solution. Many of these reagents are highly specific for particular metals and find wide application in water analysis. Compleximetric titrations with ethylenediamine tetraacetate (EDTA) and a variety of specific metal ion indicators also are used extensively for analysis of metal ions in waters and wastewaters. Perhaps the most familiar example is the analyses for calcium, magnesium, and water hardness by titration with EDTA (29).

## A. SEPARATION AND CONCENTRATION TECHNIQUES

Various separation and concentration techniques are available for removing interferences, for extraction of colored organometallic complex compounds, or for concentration prior to titrimetric, spectrometric, electrometric, or radiometric analysis. In certain cases, the separation itself is sufficiently specific that it may be followed by a nonselective analytical procedure. In other cases, a mixture of two or more metals ions may be separated from solution and then subjected to analysis by more selective analytical procedures.

Separation by ion exchange has been used extensively for metal cations in natural and wastewaters. Perhaps the first analytical application of organic ion exchange was Kullgren's work on the separation of copper ions from wastewater for subsequent determination (244). The total free metal ion content of a wastewater can be determined by ion exchange (98,214,215). The technique involves passing a sample of water or waste through a hydrogen-form cation exchange resin and titrating the equivalent quality of $H^+$ released with a standard base. Another aliquot may be titrated with EDTA for the hardness metals. Analyses for $NH_4^+$, $K^+$, $Rb^+$, and $Cs^+$ ions in water have been carried out by precipitation with tetraphenylboron. The precipitate is dissolved in acetone and the solution passed through a cation exchange resin in the hydrogen form; the resulting free tetraphenylboron is then titrated (215).

Ion exchange also can be used effectively for removal of interfering ions or cations from a water sample. For example, the separation of complex cyanide ions which interfere with the titrimetric determination of alkali metals can be achieved by an ammonium-form cation exchange resin. This method also separates other interfering anions, such as vanadates, chromates, molybdates and tungstates (214). McCoy has presented an interesting discussion of the use of ion exchange for total separation of various anions and cations from industrial wastewaters (297).

Ion exchange chromatography offers an effective method for concentration and separation of ions from wastewaters. The ions are first concentrated on a suitable ion exchange column and then selectively eluted to be determined polarographically, radiometrically, spectrophotometrically, or spectrographically (126,178,302). Iron, commonly found in industrial waste effluents, may be collected on cation exchange columns as ferric iron, reduced to the ferrous state by a dilute ascorbic acid solution, and then eluted with a strong acid (214). The selective separation of metals by ion exchange chromatography often can be markedly improved by using complexing agents (158). For example, chromatographic separation of alkaline earth (magnesium, calcium, strontium, and barium) ions from a cation exchange column can be accomplished by elution with hydrogen chloride, ammonium acetate, ammonium formate, ammonium lactate, EDTA, diaminocyclohexanetetra-acetate, or ammonium -oxy-isobutyrate (214). The order of separation of ions is in all cases the same regardless of which of these complexing agents is used.

Attempts have been made recently to use ion exchange membranes for the separation and concentration of metal ions prior to analysis (131,283). The technique involved mounting a cation exchange membrane, of 2–5 mils thickness, on the surface of an indicator electrode (usually carbon, platinum or gold) in a voltammetric system. The membrane serves as an ion exchange preconcentration matrix, as well as a rigorously defined diffusion barrier for surface active or electroactive interferences present in the test solution. The exchange rate of metal ions between the test solution and membrane is accelerated by applying an appropriate emf across the membrane.

This technique was illustrated by Eisner and co-workers (131), who used a membrane-covered carbon electrode in $10^{-4}$ and $10^{-5}$ $M$ silver ion and 0.1 $M$ potassium nitrate solutions. Separation and concentration of the silver was done by potentiostating the membrane electrode at —0.4 $V$ versus SCE for 4 min; then the deposited metal was stripped by applying a 10 mV/sec anodic sweep. Well defined voltammetric peaks were obtained with a definite gain in sensitivity. When egg albumin at a concentration of 0.01% was added to the silver ion solution, the sensitivity obtained was ten times as great as that with the ion exchange membrane mounted on the electrode surface. In this case the membrane, being practically impermeable to protein molecules, served as a protective diffusion barrier for the indicator electrode.

Perhaps the most interesting aspect of ion exchange membranes in this application is their suitability for *in situ* separations. Hence, membrane-covered electrode systems can be used for analysis of metal ions in their natural environment. Additionally, the ion exchange membrane itself can be used as a preconcentration matrix for subsequent determinations by activation analysis, emission, or absorption spectrophotometry.

The main problem associated with using cation exchange membranes for transition and heavy metals in natural waters and wastewaters is their lack of specificity. This is particularly significant since the alkalies and alkaline earths are usually present in great excess. Recent exploratory studies (283) demonstrated the feasibility of using chelate ion exchange membranes made from Chelex 100. Such ion exchangers showed high selectivity for multivalent cations.

Another limitation to the use of cation-exchange membranes for natural waters and wastewaters is the fact that, except for the alkalies and alkaline earths, most metal ions will be found in the form of organometallic complexes. The separation of such complexed metal ions by ion exchange is sometimes not possible unless the complex is first disrupted.

Solvent extraction is commonly used for separation of metal ions from industrial wastewaters. Valuable schemes for the separation of a large number of metal ions by successive extractions employing different complexing agents and organic solvents at controlled pH have been reported (86,252,280,305,409,422,494). These discussions cover the colorimetry, sensitivity, and selectivity of principal reagents, e.g., dithizone (diphenylthiocarbazone), oxine, cuperferrons, diethyldithiocarbamate, tetraphenyl arsenium salts, quaterary ammonium compounds, and various chelating agents.

Selection of an appropriate solvent–extraction system depends on its specificity and its suitability for subsequent analytical procedures. By selection of appropriate ion-association and chelate solvent systems, almost any element can be separated from wastewaters. Examples of solvent extraction systems which have been or could be used for the analysis of industrial wastewaters are given in Table VII.

Partial freezing also has been used as a technique for cation concentration (239,256,281,415). The procedure involves the slow freezing of a water sample, the time required to achieve a certain concentration usually

TABLE VII

Solvent Extraction Systems Applicable to Wastewater Analysis

| Elements | Sample | Complexing agents | Solvent | Method of analysis | Ref. |
|---|---|---|---|---|---|
| Ce | Biological matter | Bis(2-ethyl hexyl)-hydrogen phosphate | n-Heptane | Radiochemical | 181 |
| Cr<sup>VI</sup> | Sea water Brines | Dithizone | Methyl isobutyl ketone (MIBK) | Atomic absorption | 113 |
| Cu | Sea water | Dithizone | CCl$_4$ | Polarographic | 459 |
| Cu | Sea water | Sodium diethyldithiocarbamate (DEDC) | CCl$_4$ | Spectrophotometric | 441 |
| Cu | Sea water | 2,2'-Diquinolyl neocuproine | n-Hexanol | Spectrophotographic | 268 |
| Fe | Sea water | Diphenylphenanthroline | Isobutyl alcohol | Spectrophotometric | 417 |
| Mn | Sea water | 1-Nitroso-2-naphthol | CHCl$_3$ | Spectrophotometric | 268 |
| Mo | Brines | Dithiol | MIBK | Atomic absorption | 113 |
| Pb | Environmental samples | NaI, dithizone | Isopropyl methyl ketone | Radiochemical | 448 |
| Zn | Urine | Dithizone | CCl$_4$ | Spectrophotometric | 226 |
| Co, Ni | Natural waters | Ammonium pyrrolidine | MIBK | Atomic absorption | 81 |
| Co, Zn | Sea water | Dithizone | CCl$_4$ | Spectrophotometric | 152 |
| Fe, Mn | Sea water | DEDC | MIBK | Atomic absorption | 223 |
| Cu, Mo, Zn | Sea water | 8-Quinolinol | CHCl$_3$ | Spectrochemical | 76 |
| Cu, Mo, Mn, V | Brines | APDC | MIBK | Atomic absorption | 289 |
| Cu, Fe, Mn, Ni | Brines | Cupferron | MIBK | Atomic absorption | 113 |
| Fe, Mn, Mo, Zn | Milk | APDC | CHCl$_3$ | Emission spectrographic | 480 |
| Ag, Cu, Fe, Mo, Ni, V | Sea water | DEDC | CHCl$_3$ | Emission spectrographic | 515 |

being judged by experience. The cation recovery by this technique is given by the following relationship:

$$\% \text{ recovery} = \frac{C_{L2}/C_{L1}}{V_1/V_2} \times 100 \tag{14}$$

where $C_{L2}$ and $C_{L1}$ are the initial and final cation concentrations in the liquid, respectively, $V_1$ is the initial sample volume, and $V_2$ is the final volume of liquid residue.

Partial freezing has been used for the concentration of Fe, Cu, Zn, Mn, Pb, Ni, Ca, Mg, and K in water samples in concentrations ranging from 0.1 to 10.0 mg/liter (281). Increasing the mixing rate up to some limiting value increases cationic recovery. The effect of initial pH on recovery efficiency depends on the nature of the cation. Alkali metals (K, Ca, and Mg) concentrate best at low pH, while heavy metal cations (Pb, Ni, and Cu) concentrate best under alkaline conditions (281).

### B. INSTRUMENTAL METHODS

#### 1. Absorption Spectrophotometry

Determination of metal ions in wastewaters by absorption spectrophotometry is based primarily on reaction of the metal ions with various organic reagents to form colored compounds which may be determined spectrophotometrically either directly or after appropriate separation. A compleximetric reaction between the metal ion and the organic molecule—acting often as a multidentate ligand—is usually involved. Some of the more common organic reagents used for separation by extraction are chelate compounds, e.g., dithizone (diphenylthiocarbazone), oxines, cupferron, and diethyldithiocarbamate (82,86,153,323,381,382,396). Examples of applications of this technique for analysis of metals in wastewaters are given in Table VIII.

The sensitivity of the test may be increased by selection of appropriate reagents, wavelength, and type and length of cuvette. The basic law of absorption spectrophotometry, the Beer-Lambert law, relates the absorbance, $A$, directly to the concentration of the absorbing species, $C$, the length of the light path through the absorbing solution, $l$, and the molar absorptivity of the absorbing species, $\epsilon$, i.e.,

$$A = \log (I_0/I) = \epsilon l C \tag{15}$$

where $I_0$ and $I$ are the intensities of the incident and emitted light, respectively. It would appear from eg. (15) that simply increasing $l$ for a

## TABLE VIII

### Examples of Molecular Absorption Spectrophotometry for Metals in Wastewater

| Metal | Complexing agent | Solvent extraction | Color of complex | pH range | Suitable wave-length, mu | Useful range mg/liter | Refs. |
|---|---|---|---|---|---|---|---|
| Cobalt | Diethyldithiocarbamate | Ethylacetate | Blue | pH: 3.0 | 367 | — | 20, 29 |
| Cadmium | Dithizone | Carbon tetrachloride | Red | pH: 10–12 | 518 | 0.1–5 | 20, 29 |
| Chromium | 1.5-Diphenyl carbohydrazide | Butanol | Violet | pH: 2–3 | 540 | 0.05–0.5 | 20, 29 |
| Copper | Dithizone | Carbon tetrachloride | Violet | pH: 0.5 | 510 | 0.04–14 | 37 |
| Copper | Diethyldithiocarbamate | Carbon tetrachloride | Yellow–brown | pH: 9.0 | 436 | 0.1–0.8 | 20, 29 |
| Copper | Cuprione (z-z′di-quinolyl) | Isoamyl alcohol | Purple | pH: 5–6 | 540 | — | 382 |
| Iron | 1,10-Phenanthroline | — | Orange–red | pH: 2–9 | 490 | 0.1–1.0 | 20, 29 |
| Iron | Thioglycollic acid | — | Purple | pH: 8–12 | 540 | 0.04–1.2 | 20, 29 |
| Iron | Tripyridyl | — | Red–purple | pH: 9–10 | 560 | 0.01–2.0 | 323 |
| Lead | Dithizone | Chloroform | Red | pH: 7–10 | 520 | — | 20, 29 |
| Mercury | Dithizone | Carbon tetrachloride | Yellow–orange | pH: 0–1 | 500 | — | 20, 29 |
| Nickle | Dimethylglyoxime | — | Reddish–brown | pH: 9.5–11 | 465 | — | 20, 29 |
| Zinc | Dithizone | Chloroform | Purple–red | pH: 4–5.5 | 530 | 0.1–1.0 | 20, 29 |
| Zinc | Zincon | — | Blue | pH: 9.0 | 620 | 0.1–2.4 | 396 |

given concentration will increase the sensitivity of an absorption measurement proportionally. This is reasonably true for small changes in $l$, but the background absorption by the other reagents in solution becomes limiting for very large light path lengths. Increasing the sensitivity of such determinations depends ultimately on the formation of color compounds of high molar absorptivity.

Typical sensitivities of metal analyses by absorption spectrophotometry are about $10^{-6}$ $M$. It is possible in certain cases to exceed normal limits of sensitivity by using "amplification reactions," which often result in a severalfold increase in sensitivity, e.g., the determination of phosphates in the nanogram range (469). Differential spectrophotometry (86) also allows for much more precise determinations than are possible by conventional techniques. Molecular absorption spectrophotometric procedures generally can be automated readily.

Molecular fluorescence spectrophotometry offers certain advantages over molecular absorption spectrophotometry with respect to selectivity and sensitivity. The technique is based on the spectral measurements of fluorescence or phosphorescence radiation emitted from luminescent compounds upon excitation by incident radiation. The reemitted radiation is of lower frequency than the absorbed light. Fluorescence spectra are characteristic of the compound in the sense that the emission spectrum is always the same irrespective of the wavelength of the incident light which promotes the fluorescence.

The fluorescence equation may be expressed as follows:

$$F = [2.303\phi I_0 \epsilon l p]C \qquad (16)$$

where $F$ is the amount of fluorescence generated, $\phi$ is a constant related to the efficiency of fluorescence, $I_0$ is the intensity of incident radiation, $\epsilon$ is the molar absorptivity at a given wavelength, $l$ is the pathlength in centimeters, $p$ is a fractional constant, and $C$ is the concentration. Hence, $F$ measured in terms of the signal response of a photomultiplier tube sensitive to fluorescence radiation is proportional to the analytical concentration $C$, while the parameters $I_0$, $l$, and $p$ are instrumental factors, and the parameters $\phi$ and $\epsilon$ are functions of the efficiency of the fluorescent reagent system.

It is evident from eq. (15) that for absorption spectrophotometry any increase in $I_0$ will be accompanied by a matching increase in $I$, with no net gain in the absorbance, $A$. However, for fluorescence spectrophotometry, any increase in $I_0$ will be matched by a corresponding increase in the analytical signal $F$, as indicated in eq. (16). Also, any increase in the amplifier gain in absorption spectrophotometry will amplify $I_0$ and $I$ correspondingly, whereas in fluorescence spectrophotometry, this will result in an increase in $F$. For these reasons the sensitivity of molecular fluorescence spectrophotometry is inherently greater than that of molecular absorption spectrophotometry.

Despite the fact that molecular fluorescence spectrophotometry has not been used to a very large extent for inorganic analysis, it offers an extremely useful technique which is applicable to solutions 100–10,000 times more dilute than those which can be analyzed by absorption spectrophotometry. There are a number of fluorometric reagents suitable for analysis of such metals as aluminum, rare earths, zinc, and calcium, which largely form colorless complexes. In those cases where the metals form colored complexes, such as iron, copper, nickel, and chromium, measurements are based on the extinction of the fluorescence of the reagents with which they react. A typical example of an effective fluorogenic agent is 8-hydroxyquinoline, which forms fluorescent complexes with aluminum, beryllium, etc., and nonfluorescent complexes with iron, copper, etc.

One of the most desirable characteristics of molecular fluorescence spectrophotometry for analysis of wastewaters is its selectivity. Only certain ions are capable of producing fluorescence. For example, few metal ions produce fluorescence with a non-selective reagent like 8-hydroxyquinoline, while over 30 produce absorption spectra.

Aluminum has been determined in natural and wastewaters by simple fluorometric techniques (120) using pentachrome blue–black to form a fluorescent complex. Trace quantities of aluminum have been determined by fluorometric techniques using 2-hydroxyl-3-naphthoic acid (234) and 2-pyridylazo-2-naphthol (443) as fluorogenic agents. Comprehensive discussions of fluorimetric analysis have been provided by White and Weissler (497,498) and West (494).

Perhaps the most dramatic achievement in inorganic analysis during the last decade has been the development of atomic absorption spectrophotometry. The similarity of atomic absorption spectrophotometry to molecular absorption spectrophotometry is based on the fact that atoms are capable of absorbing light in exactly the same way as molecules by interacting with a photon of the energy requisite to promote an electronic transition from ground state to one of the excited states of the atom. Hence the laws which govern the relationship between the amount of light absorbed and the concentration of the absorbing species, as well as the experimental apparatus and techniques, are basically the same for both atomic and molecular absorption spectrophotometry. As an analytical procedure, atomic absorption spectrophotometry has the unique advantage of virtual specificity. Exceptions are those few cases in which unfavorable matrix components are present in the sample solution. This is largely a result of the presence of certain compounds which combine with the metal under analysis to form relatively nonvolatile compounds, which do not break down in the flame. Calcium in the presence of phosphate exhibits this effect (55). This may be remedied by sequestering the calcium ion with EDTA. Matrix effects may be minimized by separation or by adding approximately the same amount of matrix component to the standard solutions.

In contrast to flame photometry, there is very little interelement interference in atomic absorption spectrophotometry. Also, while sensitivity in flame photometry is critically dependent on flame temperature, this is not the case for atomic absorption spectrophotometry.

Two excellent monographs on atomic absorption have been prepared recently by Robinson (383) and Elwell and Gidley (135). Review articles by Kahn (228), Fishman and Midget (148), and Boettner and Grunder (63) offer comprehensive surveys of applications in natural waters and wastewaters.

Over 60 elements can be determined readily by atomic absorption in the parts per million range without sample pretreatment and with an accuracy of $\pm 1$–2%. This sensitivity can be vastly increased to the parts per billion range by scale expansion or by extracting the metal in a nonaqueous solvent and spraying it into the flame. Microgram per liter quantities of cobalt, copper, iron, lead, nickel, and zinc have been determined in saline waters by extraction of metal complexes with ammonium pyrrolidine dithiocarbomate into methyl isobutyl ketone (148). The use of organic solvents may alter the flame temperature, which, in contrast to flame photometry, will generally have no significant effect. An increase of about 60% in the atomizer efficiency can be achieved with the use of certain organic solvents.

Although atomic absorption spectrophotometry is a relatively new technique, it is being applied widely for analysis of metal ions in natural waters and wastewaters. In addition to its selectivity and sensitivity, atomic absorpton spectrophotometry is a rapid and easy technique, suitable for routine analysis and easily automated for monitoring effluent streams (24,55). The detection limits to some common metals were reported by Kahn (228) and are given in Table IX.

From the above discussion, it would appear that molecular fluorescence spectrophotometry offers the advantages of greater sensitivity and selectivity over molecular absorption spectrophotometry. Relative to atomic

TABLE IX

Atomic Absorption Detection Limits[a]

| Metal | Detection limit | Analytical wavelength | Suggested resolution, Å |
|---|---|---|---|
| Silver | 0.005 | 3281 | 7 |
| Aluminum[b] | 0.1 | 3093 | 2 |
| Arsenic[c] | 0.1 | 1937 | 7 |
| Boron[b] | 6.0 | 2497 | 7 |
| Barium[b] | 0.05 | 5536 | 4 |
| Beryllium[b] | 0.002 | 2349 | 20 |
| Bismuth | 0.05 | 2231 | 2 |
| Calcium | 0.002 | 4227 | 13 |
| Cadmium[c] | 0.001 | 2288 | 7 |
| Cobalt | 0.005 | 2407 | 2 |
| Chromium | 0.005 | 3579 | 2 |
| Copper | 0.005 | 3247 | 7 |
| Iron | 0.005 | 2483 | 2 |
| Mercury | 0.5 | 2537 | 20 |
| Potassium | 0.005 | 7665 | 13 |
| Lanthanum[b] | 2.0 | 3928 | 4 |
| Lithium | 0.005 | 6708 | 40 |
| Magnesium | 0.0003 | 2852 | 20 |
| Manganese | 0.002 | 2795 | 7 |
| Molybdenum | 0.03 | 3133 | 2 |
| Sodium | 0.002 | 5890 | 4 |
| Nickel | 0.005 | 2320 | 2 |
| Lead | 0.03 | 2833 | 7 |
| Antimony | 0.1 | 2175 | 2 |
| Selenium[c] | 0.1 | 1961 | 20 |
| Silicon[b] | 0.1 | 2516 | 2 |
| Tin[c] | 0.02 | 2246 | 7 |
| Tellurium | 0.1 | 2143 | 7 |
| Titanium[b] | 0.1 | 3643 | 2 |
| Thallium | 0.025 | 2768 | 20 |
| Vanadium[b] | 0.02 | 3184 | 7 |
| Tungsten[b] | 3.0 | 4008 | 2 |
| Zinc | 0.002 | 2138 | 20 |
| Zirconium[b] | 5.0 | 3601 | 2 |

[a] The detection limit is given by the metal concentration in parts per million, which gives a signal twice the size of the peak to peak variability of the background.

[b] Nitrous oxide flame required.

[c] Indicates use of argon–hydrogen flame.

absorption spectrophotometry, however, no increase in selectivity can be gained by using atomic fluorescence, because the former is virtually specific for each element. It is possible, however, to increase the sensitivity of measurements with atomic fluorescence spectrophotometry by increasing the intensity of irradiation or by increasing the amplification until the system becomes noise limited (133). In this sense, atomic fluorescence spectrophotometry offers greater flexibility and sensitivity than atomic absorption spectrophotometry (347,505). The technique is inherently simple, and practically any flame spectrophotometer may be adapted for this purpose without interference with its normal mode of operation. A continuous source with simple monochromator may be used to readily generate atomic fluorescence. Where high sensitivities in the subnanogram range are required, it is necessary to use individual spectral discharge lamps (133).

## 2. Emission Spectrometry

Flame photometry has been used extensively for determination of alkaline metals and certain alkaline earths because of their low excitation energies. Reproducible results are obtained with careful control of flame temperature and sample composition and the use of internal standards.

Some of the main limitations of flame photometry are interelement interference (e.g., K and Mn) and the dependency of the energy of emission on the temperature of the flame. In some cases the temperature of the flame may be a limiting factor in determining whether or not the metal can be detected. With high temperature flames, such as those of $C_2H_2$—$O_2$ or $C_2H_2$—$N_2O$, up to 42 elements can be determined. The flame temperature, shape, background, and rate of sample consumption are critical factors controlling the sensitivity.

The majority of literature on the use of flame photometry for water analysis is concerned with sea water (88), river waters (220), and mineral waters (98). A number of investigators also have applied flame photometry to analysis of oil field effluents (98) and brine wastewaters (63). For certain applications separation by ion exchange has been used prior to determinations by flame photometry to remove anion and cation interferences or for concentration of certain elements (24,98).

With the advent of highly selective atomic absorption spectrophotometry, the applications of flame photometry to natural waters and wastewaters have been limited to a few alkalies and alkaline earth metals.

Emission spectroscopy is not frequently used for analysis of metals in wastewaters because of the highly specialized training required for proper operation and for interpretation of spectra. Further, few laboratories have the required instrumentation. It is often necessary to subject the water sample to separation and/or concentration procedures prior to the spectrographic analysis. Spectrographic procedures have been developed for routine analysis of 19 elements in river and ground waters (242) using rotating graphite electrodes and high voltage spark excitation. Wastewaters from oil fields have been analyzed for B, Be, Fe, Mn, and Sr by direct emission spectrography using a plasma arc (97).

X-ray fluorescence spectroscopy has had very limited application in natural water and wastewater analysis. The technique is relatively simple and offers a number of advantages over flame photometry and classical spectral emission analysis. While in flame photometry and classical emission spectroscopy the test sample is vaporized and excitation takes place by collisions of individual atoms with each other or with electrons, the sample in the case of X-ray fluorescence undergoes no phase change. The sample is irradiated by a constant X-ray source, and on absorption of primary X-rays, characteristic secondary X-rays are emitted. Measurement is based on the following relationship:

$$I_t = I_p \exp (\mu_m m) \qquad (17)$$

where $I_p$ is intensity of the primary radiation, $I_t$ is the intensity of the transmitted radiation, $\mu_m$ is mass absorption coefficient, and $m$ is the mass of irradiated material. The technique is capable of nondestructive analysis for elements in the parts per million range with $\pm 1\%$ accuracy. The test material may be spread in a thin layer prior to analysis (e.g., the sample solution may be applied to a filter paper which is then dried).

X-ray fluorescence has been used for the analysis for As, Se, Hg, Tl, Pb, and Bi in natural waters in concentrations as low as 0.01 ppm (290). The procedure is based on chelating the metals with pyrrolidine thiocarbamate and extracting into chloroform prior to X-ray analysis.

### 3. Activation Analysis

Activation analysis has been applied in many instances for the elemental analysis of natural waters and wastewaters. This technique involves irradiating a test sample (e.g., with thermal neutrons or gamma photons) to induce nuclear transformation of the elements under investigation; these then decay, each with a characteristic half-life. The induced activity is related to the quantity of reactive nuclide by the equation

$$A = \sigma f(W\phi/M)(1 - e^{-\lambda t})(6.2 \times 10^{23})    \qquad (18)$$

where $A$ is the activity (disintegrations/sec,) after irradiation; $f$ is the flux of particles used in the irradiation (number/cm$^2$/sec) ; $\sigma$ is the activation cross section for the nuclear reaction concerned (cm$^2$) ; $W$ is the weight of the element irradiated (g) ; $\phi$ is the fractional abundance of the particular isotope of the element concerned; $M$ is the atomic weight of that element; $\lambda$ is the decay constant of the induced radionuclide (sec$^{-1}$), and; $t$ is the irradiation time (sec).

Activation analysis is a technique which offers extreme sensitivity; sensitivities of the order of $10^{-12}$ g are obtainable with neutron fluxes of $10^{12}$ sec$^{-1}$ cm$^{-2}$ (75,240). Applications of activation analysis to natural waters and wastewaters generally require radiochemical separation of the sample and comparison of the activities of the unknown sample and of a known mass of standard treated under identical conditions.

A typical example of procedural format for activation analysis is as follows:

*1.* The water sample may be irradiated in the liquid state or it may be converted to a solid state (by precipitation or freeze-drying) prior to irradiation. This preliminary concentration and separation step is used with very dilute sample solutions or to eliminate interferences.

*2.* Weighed quantities of sample and standard are irradiated in suitable containers for a time sufficient to induce adequate radioactivity in the element to be determined.

*3* A known weight of the element being determined is added to both sample and standard as carrier. Sample and standard are then treated in such a way that the carrier and the element in the sample solution are in the same chemical form.

*4.* Chemical separation is carried out to isolate the element (or suitable compound) from all other nuclides. The chemical "yield" is determined by conventional methods. This makes it unnecessary for the chemical separation to be quantitative, since the final measured activity will be corrected for losses, using the chemical yield figure.

*5.* Measurement and comparison of the radioactivity of sample and standard are made under identical counting conditions, and, when necessary, corrections are applied for self-absorption dead-time losses, decay, etc.

*6.* The radiochemical purity of the separated compound may be checked by determining: (a) decay rate and half-life; (b) energies of emitted radiation, by measuring the activity through different thicknesses of aluminum; and (c) gamma energy by a scintillation counter or solid--state gamma spectrometer.

Depending on the type of sample and purpose of analysis, the use of a carrier and the determination of the chemical yield may be dispensed with.

Characterization of elements in a given water sample may be done by identifying type, energy, and half-life of emission. The concentration of a given element in a sample is determined by quantizing its characteristic emission, i.e.,

$$\frac{\text{Mass of element X in sample}}{\text{Mass of element X in standard}} = \frac{\text{total activity from element X in sample}}{\text{total activity from element X in standard}}$$

Some of the factors governing quantitative measurements are (a) the concentration of stable elements, (b) activation probability, (c) neutron flux, (d) relative abundance of stable isotopes, and (e) time of irradiation. A wide range of separation techniques have been associated with activation analysis procedures, some of which have been automated effectively (216). Considerable improvement in the resolution of individual peaks in spectra has been accomplished by replacement of sodium iodide detectors with germanium detectors (365) for gamma ray scintillation spectrometry.

Detailed procedures for activation analysis of natural waters and wastewaters have been reported (15,62). Generally, the accuracy and precision of these procedures are about $\pm 10\%$. Principal errors in analysis are due primarily to self-shielding, unequal flux at the sample and standard positions, and inaccurate counting procedures and counting statistics. A comparison of the sensitivity of activation analysis with several other analytical methods (304) was given by Meinke. Some of the main advantages of activation analysis are: (a) its very high sensitivity, (b) the rapidity of analysis, and (c) the nondestructive nature of the test.

The majority of the studies reported describe procedures for chemical treatment of water and wastewater samples for analysis similar to those discussed earlier (62,257,464,431). One technique which involves the addition of a carrier salt (high purity $Na_2CO_3$, freeze-drying, irradiation) of the recovered residue, and the separation and counting of the desired radioactive nuclides has been reported effective for the analysis of stream and lake waters (464).

The problem of identifying the components of a complex spectrum has led to the use of computers to facilitate interpretation of available data (340). Computers may also be used to determine optimum conditions for irradiation of particular samples (216).

## 4. Electrochemical Analysis

Electrochemical methods are often well suited for metal ion analysis in natural waters and wastewaters. A variety of electrode systems and electrochemical techniques have been used routinely for *in situ* analysis and continuous monitoring of waste effluents.

For purposes of this discussion, electrochemical methods are conveniently classified as being either based on the passage of a faradaic current, e.g., classical polarography, or based on electrode equilibrium, e.g., potentiometry.

Classical polarography has been used widely for water analysis since its development (279). Polarographic measurements are based on determining the time-averaged currents of the dropping mercury electrode under diffusion conditions. The response is described approximately by the Ilkovic equation,

$$i_d = (605nD^{1/2}m^{2/3}t^{1/6})C \qquad (19)$$

where $i_d$ is the average diffusion current ($\mu$A); $t$ is the drop-time (sec); $m$ is the mass rate of flow of mercury (mg/sec); $D$ is the diffusion coefficient of the electroactive species (cm$^2$/sec); $C$ is the concentration of electroactive species (mmoles/liter); and $n$ is the number of electrons per molecule involved in the electrode reaction. For a typical case in which $m = 2$ mg/sec, $t = 4$ sec, and $D = 10^{-5}$ cm$^2$/sec, the electrode response will be $i_d/C = 3.82$ $\mu$amp/mmole/liter.

As a result of the capacitance current used in charging the double layer, the sensitivity of classical polarography with the dropping mercury electrode is limited to approximately $10^{-5}$ $M$. However, by means of preconcentration techniques it may be possible to extend the sensitivity range significantly. Copper, bismuth, lead, cadmium, and zinc have been measured in the range of 0.01 mg/liter after extraction with dithizone and carbon tetrachloride (193). Preconcentration by ion exchange, freeze-drying, evaporation, or electrodialysis may be used.

A significant problem in the application of classical polarography to industrial wastewater analysis is the interference produced by electroactive and surface active impurities. Such impurities, frequently present in wastewaters, may interfere with electrode reaction processes and cause a suppression and/or a shift of the polarographic wave (285).

Modifications of polarographic techniques, such as "differential polarography" and "derivative polarography," may be used to increase the sensitivity and minimize the effect of interferences (407). Pulse polarography has the advantage of extending the sensitivity of determination to approximately $10^{-8}$ $M$. The technique is based on the application of short potential pulses of 50 msec on either a constant or gradually increasing background voltage. Following application of the pulse, current measurements are usually made after the spike of charging current has decayed. The limiting current in pulse polarography is larger than in classical polarography. The diffusion current equation for pulse polarography is given by eq. (20). Derivative pulse polarography, which

$$i_d = (nFA(D/\pi t)^{0.5})C \tag{20}$$

is based on superimposing the voltage pulse upon a slowly changing potential (about 1 mV/sec) and recording the difference in current between successive drops versus the potential, is even more sensitive than pulse polarography (407).

Cathode ray polarography or oscillographic polarography has been used for analysis of natural waters and wastewaters, with a sensitivity of $10^{-7}$ $M$ being reported (196,359,499). This technique involves the use of a cathode ray oscilloscope to measure the current–potential curves of applied (saw-tooth) potential rapid sweeps during the lifetime of a single mercury drop. Multiple sweep techniques are also applicable. The peak current ($i_p$) in the resulting polarogram is related to the concentration of the electroactive species for a reversible reaction in accordance with the following relationship:

$$i_p = (k_n^{3/2} m^{2/3} t^{2/3} D^{1/2} v^{1/2})C \tag{21}$$

where $v = dE/dt$ is the voltage sweep (about 6000 V/min).

Oscillographic polarography has the advantage of: (a) relatively high sensitivity, (b) high resolution, and (c) rapidity of analysis. Traces of Cu, Pb, Zn, and Mn can be determined at 0.05 mg/ml level in natural waters by this technique (499).

One of the most interesting electrochemical approaches to metal analysis in trace quantities is anodic stripping voltammetry (414). This technique involves two consecutive steps: (1) the electrolyte separation and concentration of the electroactive species to form a deposit or an amalgam on the working electrode; and (2) the dissolution (stripping) of the deposit. The separation step, best known as the preelectrolysis step, may be done quantitatively or arranged to separate a reproducible fraction of the electroactive species. This can be done by performing the preelectrolysis step under carefully controlled conditions of potential, time of electrolysis, and hydrodynamics of the solution.

The stripping step is usually done in an unstirred solution by applying a potential, either constant or varying linearly with time, of a magnitude sufficient to drive the reverse electrolysis reactions. Quantitative determinations are done by integrating the current–time curves (coulometry at controlled potential) or by evaluating the peak current (chronoamperometry with potential sweep). Several modifications of the separation and stripping steps have been reported (413).

Hanging-drop mercury electrodes of the Gerischer type (166) or Kemula type (232) have been widely used for anodic (or cathodic) stripping analysis. Greater sensitivity has been achieved by use of electrodes which consist of a thin film of mercury on a substrate of platinum, silver, nickel, or carbon (295). Errors due to nonfaradaic capacitance current components can be minimized by proper choice of stripping technique.

The main advantage of stripping voltammetry is its applicability to trace analysis. The technique has been applied for metal analyses in sea water (32), natural waters (277,279), and wastewaters (279).

Electroanalytical methods based on electrode equilibrium include a variety of membrane electrode systems which are applicable for analyses of metals in natural waters and wastewaters. Recent developments in glass electrodes make it possible to use these electrodes to analyze for certain metal ions, particularly sodium and potassium (132). The doping of ordinary glass pH electrodes with $Al_2O_3$ greatly enhances the "alkaline error" or the response of these electrodes to alkalies, and at the same time it reduces their pH response.

It has been found experimentally (132) that for a mixture of two cations, that is, $Na^+$ and $K^+$, the behavior of a modified glass electrode may be described by a modified form of the Nernst equation.

$$E = \text{const.} + RT/F \ln (^\alpha A^+ + K^\alpha B^+) \qquad (22)$$

where $^\alpha A^+$ and $^\alpha B^+$ are the activities of $A^+$ and $B^+$ ions, respectively, and $K$ is a selectivity constant which expresses the relative sensitivities of the glass electrode for ions $B^+$ and $A^+$. By varying the composition of the glass in the system $M_2O \cdot Al_2O_3 \cdot SiO_2$ where $M_2O$ is $Li_2O$, $Na_2O$, $K_2O$, $Rb_2O$, or $Cs_2O$, it is possible to vary the selectivity of response of the glass to each of the various alkali metal ions.

Liquid ion exchange has been used in conjunction with potentiometric specific-ion electrode systems. One example is the calcium-selective membrane electrode (392), which consists of the calcium salt of dodecylphosphoric acid dissolved in di-$n$-octylphenyl phosphate. This liquid ion exchanger is immobilized in a porous inert membrane, such as cellulose.

Below a solution concentration of $10^{-6}$ moles $Ca^{+2}$ per liter, the membrane potential is a constant, independent of the calcium ion activity. This has been attributed to the organic calcium salt solubility, which maintains a constant limiting activity of calcium ions at the membrane solution interface (22,392). Otherwise, the liquid ion exchange membrane electrode exhibits behavior similar to that of the glass electrode, which may be expressed in terms of the modified Nernst relationship given in Eq. (22).

Single crystal membrane electrode systems (solid-state membrane electrodes) have recently been applied to water analysis (22,155). The fluoride electrode (155), which is made of lanthanum fluoride crystal membrane doped with a rare earth, which presumably acts so that only fluoride carries current across the membrane, is a good example. This electrode system is highly selective for fluorides, but, at high pH, hydroxide ions constitute a major interference which limits its usefulness in this range. The introduction of anion-selective, precipitate-impregnated membrane electrodes (366,373) has been an important recent development for electrochemical analytical techniques. The membrane is made of a silicone rubber matrix which incorporates precipitated particles of silver halide or barium sulfate. The electrode is relatively insensitive to the nature of the cations. The most selective and sensitive electrode system of this type is the silver iodide membrane electrode, which responds to iodide concentrations as low as $10^{-7}$ $M$ with relatively little interference from common ions (373).

Although the last two membrane electrode systems described above are not sensitive to metal ions, they are included in this section to provide a unified coverage of potentiometric membrane electrodes.

From eq. (22) it is apparent that potentiometric membrane electrode systems are sensitive to the activity of the electroactive species. In order to use such electrode systems for determination of concentrations rather than activities, it is important to consider the effects of ionic strength on the activity coefficient of the electroactive species and the liquid junction potential between the test solution and the reference electrode. To avoid the uncertainty of estimating an activity coefficient, it is useful to determine the effect of an added known amount of species on the potential or adjust the ionic strength of the sample to that of a standard solution. Since the total ionic strength of the solution determines the activity coefficient for a specific ion, the activity coefficient of the ion being analyzed in the test sample will be identical to that in the standard solution. A constant ionic strength can be obtained by using a "swamping electrolyte." This technique, frequently referred to as the "ionic medium" method, has been effectively used to calibrate potentiometric membrane electrode systems for the analysis of natural waters and wastewaters (22,419).

The literature contains conflicting reports regarding the sensitivity limits for the various electroanalytical procedures discussed herein. A helpful discussion of this subject has been given by Laitinen (253); the conclusions of this discussion are in Table X. The sensitivity values given in Table X are defined as the lowest concentrations at which a determination can be made with a relative precision of 10% in the presence of a large concentration of major constituents (253).

A complete analysis of metal ions in natural waters and wastewaters should include definition of oxidation states and characterization of aquometallic or organometallic complexes. Aquometallic complexes in natural waters and wastewaters undergo exchange reactions in which coordinated water molecules are exchanged for certain organic ligands. The pH and the concentration of the organic ligands are important factors affecting such coordination reactions.

Electrochemical methods, in general, are more suited for elucidation of the oxidation state and complexed form in which metal ions exist in a particular sample than are spectrophotometric analyses. Organic polarography, in one or more of the various modes discussed previously, provides a useful method for such determinations. Recent studies have demonstrated the analytical feasibility of thin layer anodic stripping voltammetry for the quantitative estimation of free and bound metals in natural waters (17).

TABLE X

Quantitative Sensitivity Limits of Some Electroanalytical Methods

| Methods | Sensitivity limit, $M$ |
|---|---|
| AC polarography; chronopotentiometry; thin layer coulometry; potentiometry with metal-specific glass or membrane electrodes. | $10^{-4}$ to $10^{-5}$ |
| Classical polarography; coulometry at controlled potential; chronocoulometry; tensammetry; precision null-point potentiometry. | $10^{-5}$ to $10^{-6}$ |
| Test polarography; derivative polarography; square-wave polarography; second harmonic AC polarography; phase-sensitive AC polarography; linear sweep voltammetry; staircase voltammetry; derivative voltammetry; coulostatic analysis; chemical stripping analysis. | $10^{-6}$ to $10^{-7}$ |
| Pulse polarography; rf polarography; coulometric titrations; amperometry with rotating electrodes; conductivity (aqueous). | $10^{-7}$ to $10^{-8}$ |
| Anodic stripping with hanging-drop mercury electrodes. | $10^{-7}$ to $10^{-9}$ |
| Anodic stripping with thin film electrodes or solid electrodes. | $10^{-9}$ to $10^{-10}$ |

Membrane electrodes, either of the voltammetric or the potentiometric type, are usually sensitive only to free or unbound metal ions in a water sample. For example, in one case in which the calcium membrane electrode was used in a sea water sample, only 16% of the total calcium content was detected (458); the authors explained this in terms of the remainder of the calcium being complexed with sulfates and/or carbonates.

Future prospects for metal ion analyses in waters and wastewaters include the use of gas chromatography and NMR techniques. It would appear that more emphasis will be placed on the characterization of organometallics in wastewaters than on elemental analysis per se.


## VII. ANALYSES FOR NONMETAL INORGANIC SPECIES

Discussion in this section is directed to the analysis of nonmetal inorganic species other than nitrates and phosphates, which, because they are frequently classified as biochemical nutrients, have been discussed in the section on organic analysis.


### A. SEPARATION AND CONCENTRATION TECHNIQUES

The techniques discussed for separation and concentration of metal ions are generally applicable also for nonmetal inorganic species. Evaporation, precipitation, ion exchange, solvent extraction, and partial freezing are frequently used, ion exchange being particularly well suited for anion separations. Anion exchange chromatography has been used rather extensively for separations of species found in waters and wastewaters (495). Silicates, for example, can be effectively separated from natural waters by treating with hydrogen fluoride to form fluorosilicates, which are then removed by exchange (500).

Techniques for the chromatographic separation of ortho-, pyro-, tri-, trimeta, tetrameta-, and polyphosphates have been developed (174,492) with strongly basic anion exchange resins. Potassium chloride, in continuously increasing concentration (gradient elution technique), is used for elution. Sulfate, sulfite, thiosulfate, and sulfide ions can be separated by anion exchange chromatography using the gradient elution technique with an elution solution of nitrates (211). A more detailed discussion of the possible applications of anion exchange for such analytical separations has been given by Inczedy (214).

## B. INSTRUMENTAL METHODS

A number of instrumental methods are applicable to the analysis of nonmetallic inorganic species in natural waters and wastewaters. Many such analytical methods involve either the use of potentiometric membrane electrodes or the application of spectrophotometric techniques. New methods of absorption spectrophotometry using solid-phase ion (or ligand) exchange reagents have been devised for analyses for chloride, sulfates, phosphates, and other anions (44,57,188). These tests are based on using various salts of chloranilic acid as selective ion exchange reagents. Typical examples include the analysis for sulfates with barium chloranilate (57), for chlorides with mercuric chloranilate (44), and for phosphates with lanthanum chloranilate, i.e.,

$$BaCh + SO_4{}^{2-} \rightarrow BaSO_4 + Ch^{2-} \tag{23}$$
$$HgCh + 2Cl^- \rightarrow HgCl_2 + Ch^{2-} \tag{24}$$
$$La_2Ch_3 + 2PO_4{}^{3-} \rightarrow 2LaPO_4 + 3Ch^{2-} \tag{25}$$

This technique is subject to interferences which may be reduced by solvent extraction.

Many highly sensitive methods for nonmetallic inorganic species are based on the displacement of a ligand (usually colored) in a metal complex or chelate. The analysis for fluoride ions by displacement of a chelating dye anion from a zirconium complex is a typical example of this technique. The displaced dye differs sufficiently in color from its zirconium chelate to permit determination of the fluoride ion concentration as a function of the change in color of the solution (54).

Numerous indirect spectrophotometric methods have been developed (65). Heteropoly chemistry appears to offer important advances in analyses for phosphates, silicates, and arsenates (104). The reader is referred to recent reviews in *Analytical Chemistry* for an exhaustive survey on the subject matter (65).

Indirect uv spectrophotometry and atomic absorption methods have been developed for phosphates and silicates (210). These techniques are based on the selective extraction of molybdophosphoric acid and molybdosilicic acid followed by ultraviolet molecular absorption spectrophotometry and/or atomic absorption spectrophotometry. The molybdophosphoric and molybdosilicic acids are formed in acidic solution by addition of excess molybdate reagent. Molybdophosphoric acid is extracted with diethyl ether from an aqueous solution which is approximately 1 $M$ in hydrochloric acid. After adjusting the hydrochloric acid concentration of the aqueous phase to approximately 2 $M$, the molybdosilicic acid is extracted with 5:1 diethyl ether–pentanol solution. The extracts of molybdophosphoric and molybdosilicic acids are subjected to acidic washings to remove excess molybdate. Each extract is then contacted with a basic buffer solution to strip the heteropoly acid from the organic phase. The molybdate resulting from the decomposition of the heteropoly acid in the basic solution is then determined either by measurement of the absorbance at 230 $m\mu$ using ultraviolet spectrophotometry or by measurement of absorbance at the 313.3 $m\mu$ resonance line of molybdenum by atomic absorption spectrophotometry. The optimum concentration ranges are approximately 0.1–0.4 mg/liter of phosphorus or silicon for indirect ultraviolet spectrophotometry and 0.4–1.2 mg/liter for indirect atomic absorption spectrophotometry.

Electrochemical methods of analysis offer considerable promise for selective and specific measurements in wastewaters. Direct potentiometric techniques using electrodes of the second kind may be used for the analysis of chlorides or sulfides. Silver electrodes, coated with a layer of halides or sulfides, are available commercially for determination of chlorides, bromides, iodides, and sulfides at concentrations corresponding to the solubilities of the respective silver salts, as given by the following expressions:

$$E_{cell} = E^{\circ}_{Ag^+,Ag} - E_{ref} + \frac{RT}{nF} \ln K_{sp} - \frac{RT}{nF} \ln Cl^- \qquad (26)$$

and

$$E_{cell} = E^{\circ}_{Ag^+,Ag} - E_{ref} + \frac{RT}{nF} \ln K_{sp} - \frac{RT}{nF} \ln S^{2-} \qquad (27)$$

where $K_{sp}$ refers to the solubility products of AgCl and $Ag_2S$, respectively, in eqs. (26) and (27). Limitations on the use of such electrode systems are imposed by interferences from other potential-determining ions, by the problem of elimination of liquid junction potentials, and by the difficulty of satisfactorily resolving single ion activity coefficients.

Major developments in electrochemical analysis for anions have occurred in the area of ion-selective electrodes. Such electrode systems are primarily solid state or precipitate ion exchange membrane electrodes. Pungor and co-workers (366) have developed anion selective membrane electrodes by impregnating silicone gum rubber membranes with specific insoluble salts. Electrodes which are selective for $Cl^-$, $Br^-$, $I^-$, $S^{2-}$, $SO_4^{2-}$, and $F^-$ have been reported (367,368). Punger and Havas (367) have reviewed the literature of ion-selective membrane electrodes and discussed the preparation and characterization of the membrane. Response time, memory effects, and detection limits up to $10^{-4}$ $M$ have been discussed. Detailed studies on the sensitivity and selectivity of iodide, bromide, and chloride electrodes has been reported by Rechnitz et al. (373,374). The electrodes were prepared by incorporating AgI, AgBr, and AgCl into silicone rubber matrices. Selectivity ratios for the various electrodes were reported with response times ($t_{\frac{1}{2}}$) of 8, 14, and 20 sec, respectively. The lower limits of response (Eq. (22)) were $10^{-7}$ $M$ I$^-$, $5 \times 10^{-4}$ $M$ Cl$^-$, and $7 \times 10^{-5}$ $M$ Br$^-$.

Electrode systems prepared by incorporating metal oxides and hydroxides (167) or ion exchange resins (366) in polymeric membranes also have been reported. Solid-state ion exchange membrane electrodes for fluoride ion determinations have been reported (155). This type of membrane electrode is made of single crystals of LaF$_3$, NdF$_3$, and PrF$_3$ and is reported to be sensitive to fluoride ion concentrations as low as $10^{-5}$ M.

Anion-selective membrane electrodes can be used for direct potentiometry or for potentiometric titrations. For example, Lingane (265) used a commercially available fluoride electrode for the potentiometric titrations of Th$^{4+}$, La$^{3+}$, and Ca$^{2+}$ ions. Best results were obtained with La(NO$_3$)$_3$. The equivalence point potential was determined with $\pm 2$ mV, and an accuracy better than 0.1% noted in neutral, unbuffered solutions.

Cathodic stripping voltammetry can be also used for trace analysis of halides (414). Brainina and co-workers (51) have compared the limits of sensitivities of various anions using mercury electrodes and have given concentration limits of $5 \times 10^{-6}$ $M$ for Cl$^-$, $1 \times 10^{-6}$ $M$ for Br$^-$, and $5 \times 10^{-6}$ $M$ for $I^-$.

## C. SULFUR COMPOUNDS

Sulfides commonly occur in a variety of waste effluents (e.g., septic sewage, oil refinery wastes, tannery wastes, viscose rayon wastes, etc.). The presence of sulfides in wastewaters is usually indicated by the characteristic odor of hydrogen sulfide. The acidity constants for the diprotic acid H$_2$S are $K_1 = 1.0 \times 10^{-7}$ and $K_2 = 1.2 \times 10^{-13}$.

Detection of free sulfides in wastewaters is relatively straightforward; a small sample volume is placed in a 150-ml glass-stoppered conical flask and slightly moistened lead acetate paper is suspended between the stopper and the neck. On acidification of the sample a brown stain on the paper indicates the presence of sulfides. As low as 0.01 mg/liter H$_2$S in a 50-ml sample can be detected in this manner.

Total sulfides may be accurately determined in the range from 0.1 to 20 mg/liter H$_2$S by standard molecular absorption spectrophotometry (360). The test is based on the fact that hydrogen sulfide and sulfides react with $p$-aminodimethylaniline hydrochloride in the presence of sufficient hydrochloric acid and an oxidizing agent (ferric chloride) to produce methylene blue dye. The test is sensitive to free sulfides, as well as sulfides bound by iron, manganese, and lead. Sulfides of copper and mercury are too insoluble to react. Sulfites and thiosulfates interfere, but by increasing the amount of ferric chloride and lengthening the time of reaction, up to 50 mg/liter of these compounds may be tolerated.

Sulfides in industrial waste effluents may be precipitated by adding zinc or cadmium acetate or ammoniacal zinc chloride. The precipitated sulfide is then added to excess acidified standard iodine solution which is back-titrated with standard thiosulfate (233). Several modifications of iodometric determinations of sulfides in wastewaters have been reported (208,364).

The methods of analysis for sulfides described above give total sulfides, i.e., free and bound sulfides, polysulfides, and sulfanes. A specific test for only free sulfides can be accomplished using specific ion exchange membrane electrodes (283).

Specific ion electrode potential measurements of $S^{2-}$ can be related to the concentrations of $H_2S$, $HS^-$, and $S_T$ (analytical concentration of free sulfides) by the following equilibrium relationship:

$$\log [S_T] = \log [S^{2-}] + \log \left( \frac{[H^+]^2}{K_1 K_2} + \frac{H^+}{K_1} + 1 \right) \tag{28}$$

$$\log [H_2S] = \log [S^{2-}] + \log \frac{[H^+]^2}{K_1 K_2} \tag{29}$$

$$\log [HS^-] = \log [S^{2-}] + \log \frac{[H^+]}{K_1} \tag{30}$$

where $K_1$ and $K_2$ are the acidity constants for the weak acid $H_2S$.

Sulfites are commonly found in the wastewaters from pulp and paper mills, in which sulfites are used for the preparation of cellulose from wood. In the absence of thiosulfates, sulfites can be detected by heating an acidified water sample and identifying the evolved sulfur dioxide by the blue coloration produced when subjected to a piece of filter paper moistened with a mixture of potassium iodate solution and starch solution. Sulfites also may be detected in waste effluents by decolorization of triphenylmethane dyes by neutral sulfite solutions.

The iodometric titration of sulfites is done after sulfides are precipitated and filtered as zinc sulfides. This test is subject to interferences from organic matter and other reduced compounds, such as ferrous iron, in the test solution.

Sulfate determination in wastewaters is not called for except in connection with problems associated with corrosion of concrete pipes. Sulfates may be determined gravimetrically or turbidimetrically when precipitated as barium sulfate (20). Sulfites, sulfides, silica, and other insoluble solids may interefere with the gravimetric procedure. Turbidimetric measurements of $BaSO_4$ may be improved by using glycerin and sodium chloride to stabilize the suspension.

Titrimetric analysis of sulfates may be done by first precipitating the sparingly soluble benzidine sulfate, followed by titration of the washed precipitate with standard sodium hydroxide using phenolphthalein as an indicator (16). Interferences by phosphates can be minimized by using a colorimetric technique. The precipitated benzidine sulfate is washed with an alcohol–ether mixture to remove excess benzidine and is dissolved in 1% sodium borate, and the liberated benzidine is allowed to react with 1:2 naphthoquinone–4 sulfonate to give a red color which is determined photometrically at 490 $m\mu$ (236).

Sulfate ions can be also titrated in an alcoholic solution under controlled acid conditions with a standard barium chloride solution using thorin as an indicator. This test can be extended by use of ion exchange separation and concentration techniques. A number of anions and cations may cause interferences (e.g., potassium, iron, aluminum, phosphates, fluorides, and nitrates). Most metallic ions also interfere by forming colored complexes with the thorin indicator, especially in the alcohol–water solution. It is sometimes necessary to use ion exchange separation to remove interferences prior to sulfate titration (159).

## D. CYANIDES, THIOCYANATES, AND CYANATES

Cyanides may be found in significant quantities in industrial wastewaters from electroplating, steel, coke ovens, gold mining, and metal finishing industries. Cyanides are extremely toxic, even in low concentrations. In view of their toxicity, they can be detected easily by fish-kill incidence in concentrations as low as 0.03 mg/liter HCN.

Hydrogen cyanide is a volatile weak acid ($K_a = 4.8 \times 10^{-10}$). Both HCN and the conjugate base, $CN^-$, are called "free cyanides." Stable cyanide salts and metal cyanide complexes, such as $K_4Fe(CN)_6$ and $K_3Co(CN)_6$, also may be found in waste effluents. Total cyanide determinations include both free cyanides and complexed cyanides. The test for total cyanides (20) usually involves breaking down complex metal cyanides by distillation with (a) hydrochloric acid solution of cuprous chloride, (b) tartaric acid, (c) mercuric chloride, magnesium chloride, and sulfuric acid (410) (Serfass method); and (d) phosphoric acid in the presence of citric acid and ethylenediaminetetraacetic acid (248).

A simple procedure for detecting cyanides in a wastewater is based on treating a strip of filter paper with a drop of 10% ferrous sulfate and a drop of 10% caustic soda and suspending the paper strip over the acidified sample solution in a glass-stoppered flask for about 10 min. The liberated HCN reacts to form ferrocyanide on the paper, which, when immersed in hot dilute hydrochloric acid, yields the blue to blue–green stain of prussian blue dye. This test is sensitive to about 0.4 mg/liter of HCN.

Traces of cyanides can be determined by the Aldridge test, frequently known as the bromin–pyridine–benzidine method (12). The procedure utilizes the König synthesis, which is based on converting cyanide to cyanogen bromide (or chloride) and the reaction with pyridine and an aromatic amine (benzidine) to give an intense characteristic color. The di-anil derivative formed (orange to red) may be determined spectro-photometrically. Thiocyante will give the same reaction as cyanides with this test. Interference due to thiocyanide may be minimized by extracting cyanides from acid solution with isopropyl ether, which can be recovered by extraction in an aqueous sodium hydroxide solution (248). An alternate procedure (236) is based on cyanide conversion to cyanogen chloride by chloramine-T, which is allowed to react with pyridine containing 1-phenyl-3-methyl-5-pyrozolone to give a blue color which is determined spectrophotometrically (20).

A very sensitive and accurate method for the analysis of cyanides is based on the interaction of "ferroin" with cyanides at pH 9.2–9.7 (404). The violet complex [dicyano-bis-(1:10-phenanthroline)-iron] formed is extracted with chloroform and determined spectrophotometrically. This procedure is claimed to be subject to fewer interferences than any of the other methods discussed previously.

One of the oldest procedures for the analysis of cyanides in waste effluents is the Liebig test (20). This is based on the titration of cyanides with silver nitrate to form a soluble argentocyanide complex, $[Ag(CN)_2]^-$. After all cyanides have reacted, excess silver nitrate will cause turbidity due to precipitation of silver cyanide. The end point is characterized by the first appearance of turbidity, which in most cases is difficult to detect by eye. A colorimetric indicator, p-dimethyl-aminobenzylidine-rhodanine in acetone, can be used to aid in detection of the titration end point. In alkaline solution (pH 10–11) the end point is characterized by a change of color from yellow to salmon-pink. Dithi-zone may be also used for this titration (404).

Thiocyanates and cyanates are frequently present in plating and gasworks waste effluents. The cyanates may be easily detected by their interaction with ferric chloride in hydrochloric acid solution to give a characteristic wine-red color. This test is very approximate in nature and is subject to various interferences, such as those caused by mercury salts, fluorides, and organic hydroxy acids (6).

Thiocyanates, if present in relatively large quantities, can be estimated by precipitation as cuprous thiocyanate, which is either titrated with standard potassium iodate in acidic solution in the presence of chloroform or is decomposed with caustic soda, acidified with nitric acid, and titrated with silver nitrate using alum as indicator (233).

Thiocyanates may be determined colorimetrically in trace quantities by the formation of the copper pyridine thiocyanate complex $[Cu(C_5H_5N)_2(CNS)_2]$, which can be extracted in chloroform to yield a yellow solution (249). The test is sensitive to 0.5 mg/liter $CNS^-$ and is subject to interferences from cyanides. Cyanides may be removed by acidifying the solution with acetic acid and stripping HCN by aeration.

Cyanates may be determined by hydrolysis of the cyanates to ammonia by boiling with acid and estimation of ammonia so formed by means of Nessler's reagent (162). Any ammonia originally present in the sample should be removed.

## E. CHLORIDES

Chlorides are present in large quantities in certain pickle liquors, in spent regenerant solutions from softening plants, oil well waters, drainage from irrigation waters, and other waste effluents.

The terms "salinity" and "chlorinity" are frequently used to express chloride content in marine and estuarine waters. "Salinity" is defined as the weight in grams of dissolved solids (dried to constant weight at 480°C to remove organic matter and to convert carbonates to oxides) in 1000 g of sea water. "Chlorinity," on the other hand, is defined as the weight of halides, as measured by reaction with silver nitrate and computed on the basis of all halides being represented as chlorides. Both salinity and chlorinity are commonly expressed in parts per milli and are related in sea water as follows:

$$S\%_o = 0.03 + 1.805 \ Cl\%_o \tag{31}$$

where $S\%_o$ and $Cl\%_o$ refer to parts per milli salinity and chlorinity, respectively.

One procedure for chlorides in wastewaters is by titration with silver nitrate. In this method, which is commonly referred to as the Mohr method, the end point is detected by the formation of reddish silver chromate by the slightest excess of silver. The test is subject to interferences from substances such as sulfides, thiocyanides, phosphates, cyanides, sulfites, acids, alkalies, and any anion which may form a sparingly soluble silver salt. Some of these interferences can be eliminated by adjustment of pH or by potentiometric titration with a silver wire indicator electrode and a glass electrode as a reference (375). Volatile sulfur compounds which may be present in wastewaters from oil refineries and synthetic rubber manufacturing may be removed by evaporation. Sulfides and thiocyanates may be destroyed by addition of hydrogen peroxide and heating.

If the test solution contains large quantities of phosphates, the Volhard procedure is recommended (20). This involves addition of an excess of silver nitrate to a sample which has been acidified with dilute nitric acid, followed by coagulation of the silver chloride by shaking with nitrobenzene, and, finally, back-titration with standard thiocyanate using gerric alum as indicator.

Titration of chloride with mercuric nitrate offers a more sensitive procedure (20). The test is based on titration with mercuric nitrate to form a slightly dissociated mercuric chloride complex in an acid solution (pH $\approx$ 3.0). The end point is detected by the mixed indicator diphenylcarbazone and bromophenol blue, which turns blue–violet upon addition of a slight excess of mercuric ion.

## F. FLUORIDES

Fluorides occur in the wastewaters of industries involved in the production of aluminum from bauxite, in the production of phosphatic fertilizers, in oil field effluents, in nuclear power plant effluents, and in wastewaters from the scrubbing of flue gases and from the etching of glass.

Fluorides may be titrated with standard thorium nitrate in a solution buffered at pH $\approx$ 3.0 (67). Sodium alizarin sulfonate, solochrome brilliant blue, and chrome azurol S have been used as end point indicators (67, 314). Interferences from sulfate, phosphate, and carbonate can be minimized by sample pretreatment with barium chloride.

The most popular method of fluoride analysis is based on the bleaching action of fluorides on the reddish lake formed by zirconium oxychloride and sodium alizarin sulfonate (254). Visual color comparison is usually done with the zirconium alizarin test (20). Both color intensity and hue vary with fluoride concentration. A more stable colored complex is formed with fluorides and zirconium-Eriochrome cyanine R (20). The color intensity of the complex is diminished by addition of $F^-$ and is measured spectrophotometrically at 540 $m\mu$.

The preceding colorimetric procedures are subject to numerous interferences commonly found in industrial wastewaters. It is therefore recommended that fluorides be separated by distillation or ion exchange (20) prior to analysis by the above procedures.

Probably the most direct and simple method for the analysis of fluorides is based on the use of potentiometric ion selective membrane electrode systems. Lanthanum fluoride membrane electrodes have been successfully used for direct potentiometric measurements of fluorides in water supplies (155b) and industrial wastewaters (155a). The membrane electrode has also been used for precise end point detection in the titration of fluoride with lanthanum, calcium, and other fluoride-complexing agents (265).

Hydroxide ions at high concentrations interfere with the lanthanum fluoride electrode sensitivity, which limits its application at high pH values. The electrode sensitivity is estimated to be about $10^{-6}$ $MF^-$ or 0.02 ppm.

## VIII. DISSOLVED GASES

The present discussion of analyses for dissolved gases in waste effluent is concerned only with elemental gases, such as molecular nitrogen and oxygen. Analyses for important volatile inorganic weak acids and bases, such as $H_2S$, $CO_2$, and $NH_3$, have been discussed in earlier sections of this chapter.

### A. SEPARATION AND CONCENTRATION TECHNIQUES

Dissolved gases in waste effluents usually may be separated rather readily by vacuum degasification or by one or more of various stripping techniques. Stripping is essentially a gas–liquid extraction procedure in which an inert carrier gas is bubbled through a sample to carry off the dissolved gases for further separation, concentration, or detection. Gas transfer efficiency in such systems is dependent on the gas–liquid interfacial area and on the degree of mixing.

Gas exchange separation can be carried out as either a batch or a continuous flow process. In one design, a continuous mixed stream of sample and carrier gas (nitrogen or hydrogen) is forced through an aspirator nozzle under 50 lb of pressure (453). In another design, the dissolved gases are stripped from the test solution by means of multiple spinning disks rotating at high speed (446,503). Detection of the stripped gases in the stream of carrier gas may be done by measurement of paramagnetic susceptibility, thermal conductance, etc. (284).

The gas stripped from a wastewater sample may be separated into its various components by gas chromatography (503). Several modifications of this technique have been reported (442,446,447,453,503). By choosing appropriate detectors, it is usually possible to analyze simultaneously for almost all gases of interest in a water or wastewater sample.

## B. DISSOLVED OXYGEN

A detailed discussion of analytical methods for dissolved oxygen will serve to exemplify various techniques applicable to the analysis of most dissolved gases of interest. The analysis of dissolved oxygen in industrial wastewater has always been considered a highly significant test with respect to characterization of the physicochemical and biochemical characteristics of a waste effluent and its effect on a receiving water.

In situ analysis is probably the most effective way to analyze for dissolved oxygen. Certain precautions should be taken in cases where water samples are collected and stored for subsequent analysis. The sample must not remain in contact with air nor be agitated; either condition will cause a change in dissolved gas levels. Samples from any depth or from waters under pressure require special procedures to eliminate the effects of changes in pressure and temperature on sampling and storage. Detailed description of procedures and equipment for proper sampling of waters under pressure, as well as waters at atmospheric pressure, are available in the literature (20).

The time lag between sampling and analysis is of great significance. The longer the lag, the greater the chance that the oxygen content will change because of chemical or biological activity in the test solution.

The oldest and one of the most popular methods for the analysis of dissolved oxygen is the Winkler test (505a). Originally reported about 75 years ago, the Winkler procedure possesses most attributes of basic soundness and sensitivity. Improved by variations in equipment and techniques and aided by modern instrumentation, this test is still the basis for the majority of titrimetric procedures for dissolved oxygen. The test is based on the quantitative oxidation of manganese (II) to manganese(IV) under alkaline conditions. This is followed by the oxidation of iodide by the manganese(IV) under acid conditions. The iodine so released is then titrated with thiosulfate in the presence of a starch indicator. The reported precision of the standard Winkler test is $\pm 0.1$ mg/liter of dissolved oxygen (29).

In applying the Winkler test for oxygen determinations in wastewaters, full consideration must be made of the interfering effects of oxidizing or reducing materials in the sample. The presence of certain oxidizing agents liberates iodine from iodide (positive interference), and the presence of certain reducing agents reduces iodine to iodide (negative interference). Reducing compounds may also inhibit the oxidation of the manganous ion. Certain organic compounds have been found to interfere with the Winkler test in a different way. Surface active agents for example, have been reported to hinder the settling of manganic oxide floc, thus partially obscuring the end point of the final titration with thiosulfate (284).

Several modifications of the Winkler test have been devised to minimize the effect of interferences found in different wastewaters. The Alsterberger modification (19) was developed to eliminate the effect of nitrites, which interfere with the iodometric titration according to eqs. (32) and (33).

$$2NO_2^- + 2I^- + 4H^+ \rightarrow I_2 + N_2O_2 + 2H_2O \tag{32}$$

$$N_2O_2 + \tfrac{1}{2}O_2 + H_2O \rightarrow 2NO_2^- + 2H^+ \tag{33}$$

The nitrites formed in the reaction depicted in eq. (33) oxidize more iodide ions to free iodine; thus a cyclic reaction yielding erroneously high results is established. Also, the presence of nitrites in the test solution makes it impossible to obtain a permanent end point. As soon as the blue color of the starch–iodine complex disappears, the nitrites react with more iodide to form iodine, and the blue color of the indicator appears again.

The Alsterberg modification utilizes sodium azide, which reduces the nitrites according to eqs. (34) and (35).

$$NaN_3 + H^+ \rightarrow HN_3 + Na^+ \tag{34}$$

$$HN_3 + NO_2^- + H^+ \rightarrow N_2 + N_2O + H_2O \tag{35}$$

The effect of a wide variety of reducing agents may be overcome by the Rideal-Stewart modification (378) of treating the sample with potassium permanganate solution under acid conditions. However, the difficulty in manipulation of the Rideal-Stewart modification often results in low accuracy and precision.

The alkaline hypochlorite modification (455) was designed to overcome interferences caused by sulfur compounds. Wastes from the sulfite pulp industry, for example, usually contain appreciable quantities of sulfites, thiosulfates, polythionates, etc. This procedure involves pretreatment of the sample with alkaline hypochlorite to oxidize the sulfur compounds to sulfates and sulfur. Excess hypochlorite is destroyed by potassium iodide, and the iodine is then titrated by sodium thiosulfate. Again, this modification is difficult to perform, and the results obtained are of low accuracy (284).

Suspended solids in water samples may consume certain quantities of iodine during the Winkler test (284). This interference may be removed by flocculation with alum and ammonium hydroxide and settling of the solids prior to conducting the Winkler test.

For samples with biological activity (e.g., activated sludge or fermentation or food processing waste effluents) the addition of copper sulfate to the sample prior to the test coagulates the biological forms. Sulfamic acid is also added to inhibit biological activity. After allowing the floc to settle, an aliquot of supernatant liquor is siphoned and analyzed for dissolved oxygen by the standard Winkler test. The copper sulfate and the sulfamic acid are combined into a single solution in practice. This modification commonly suffers from relatively low precision (284).

The use of cerous salts in place of manganous salts has been reported to result in less interference by organic compounds (258). Attempts to minimize interferences by oxidizing agents have included sample treatment with sodium hydroxide and ferrous ammonium sulfate (136). Oxygen in the test solution oxidizes the ferrous iron to ferric iron, which is then titrated with ascorbic acid using 4-amino-4'-methoxydipenylamine as an oxidation–reduction indicator.

Interferences also may be minimized by the iodine-difference modification. This method (356) involves the addition of a small quantity of iodine solution to two portions of the water, one of which serves as a control and the other of which is analyzed by the standard Winkler method. Reducing substances in the wastewater react with the iodine in both the sample and the control; therefore, the difference between the standard titration of the sample and that on the control gives an accurate value for the dissolved oxygen in the sample. It is important to maintain the same experimental conditions and time of reaction for both the sample and control after addition of the iodine solution.

Another procedure has been used to compensate for interferences present in wastewaters, as well as those which might appear in the reagents (258). Two water samples, A and B, of equal volume are used. Sample A is analyzed by the standard Winkler test. The order of addition of reagents to sample B, the blank, is reversed, i.e., KOH and KI are added first, followed by $H_2SO_4$ and $MnSO_4$. In the case of sample B, dissolved oxygen is not first "fixed" by the manganous salt. Because the blank is initially made alkaline, allowance is made for substances that interfere specifically in an alkaline medium. Interfering substances in the test solution, as well as those in the reagents, react in both samples. Accordingly, the difference between the sample and the blank (A minus B) represents the oxygen in the sample plus the oxygen in the reagents.

If reducing substances such as sulfite are present in greater amounts than oxidants, it is possible to have a "negative" blank. In this case identical quantities of iodine or iodate are added to both sample and blank to provide an excess of iodine after acidification. The reverse-addition method is commonly used, but it does not correct for interferences caused by ferrous iron. This leads to low results due to the formation of ferrous hydroxide, which reacts with oxygen in the blank. The ferric ions formed do not produce an equivalent amount of iodine upon acidification.

The Winkler test may be modified to titrate dissolved oxygen chlorometrically instead of iodometrically. The test is called the "o-tolidine method" (310). After the dissolved oxygen has oxidized the divalent manganese in the conventional Winkler test, the solution then may be acidified with chlorine-free concentrated hydrochloric acid. This reaction results in the liberation of an equivalent quantity of chlorine according to reaction (36).

$$MnO_2 \cdot H_2O + 4H^+ + 4Cl^- \to Mn^{2+} + 3H_2O + 2Cl_2 \qquad (36)$$

The free chlorine then reacts with *ortho*-tolidine to form the characteristic yellow-colored haloquinone chloride. The intensity of the color of the haloquinone chloride is directly proportional to the oxygen content of the sample and is measured by comparison with standards or colored slides or by the use of absorption spectrometry. Recent studies have revealed that the intermediate chlorine is not necessary for oxidation of the *ortho*-tolidine. Colloidal manganese(IV), produced by air oxidation of manganese(II), is capable of reacting directly, even in neutral solution, with *ortho*-tolidine.

The precision and accuracy of titrimetric procedures for dissolved oxygen may be considerably improved by using better end-point detection techniques. Potentiometric detection of the iodometric end point improves sensitivity to about ±0.001 mg/liter of iodine (284). "Dead stop" end-point detection (an amperometric technique) offers an extremely sensitive, as well as accurate, measurement (284). The procedure is quite simple and utilizes two smooth platinum electrodes with a small potential difference (from 15 to 400 mV, depending on the sensitivity required). Diffusion current is measured during the course of the titration. No attempt is made to control the potential of either electrode; only the potential difference is controlled. The end point is indicated by discontinuation of current flow in the cell. As long as free iodine remains in the solution, the chief electrode reaction under the influence of the applied voltage is the oxidation of iodide to iodine at the anode and the reverse process at the cathode. At the end point, when all free iodine has been removed, the iodine to iodide reaction can no longer occur and the cell current comes to a "dead stop." Since the thiosulfate/tetrathionate reaction is highly irreversible and proceeds at only a minute rate under the influence of the applied voltage, no detectable current is observed at and beyond the end point. Ordinarily, the end point is so easily detected that there is no need for a graphical estimation of its position. By using sensitive current-measuring devices the end point can be established to an accuracy of $\pm0.01$ $\mu$g iodine in a 100-ml sample, or 1 part in 10 billion.

Coulometric titration of dissolved oxygen by *in situ* electrochemical generation of iodine has been used with considerable success (203). The procedure consists of the successive additions of standard solutions of $MnSO_4$, $KOH + KI$, $H_2SO_4$, and an excess of $Na_2S_2O_3$ to the test solution. The iodine formed electrolytically reacts with the residual thiosulfate in solution. The electrolytic current is held constant by varying the potential, and the equivalence point is conveniently detected by the dead-stop end-point method.

The procedure is very accurate, to within 0.02 g/liter. It has a distinct advantage in that, because the titrant is generated in solution, errors caused in conventional titrations by contact with air are eliminated.

Direct colorimetric methods of analysis for dissolved oxygen are based on the interaction of molecular oxygen with an oxidation–reduction indicator to give a color change. One of the most commonly used indicators for the detection of oxygen in solution is methylene blue; others are indigo carmine and safranin T.

In the presence of dissolved oxygen a reduced methylene blue solution exhibits a blue color, and in the absence of dissolved oxygen it is colorless. This indicator has been used in the relative stability test for sewage effluents (29). Quantitative colorimetric determinations of dissolved oxygen can be made with indigo carmine dyes. Indigo carmine in the reduced state reacts with oxygen to give a color change through orange, red, purple, blue, and finally a blue–green in the completely oxidized form. Colorimetric procedures are subject in general to a variety of interferences which limit their applicability to industrial wastewaters.

A radiometric procedure for monitoring dissolved oxygen is based on the quantitative oxidation of radioactive thallium-204 by oxygen in the test solution (377). Thallium-204 is primarily a beta emitter with a half-life of 3.6 years; therefore, decay over several months does not greatly reduce the sensitivity of the technique. The apparatus consists of a column of radioactive thallium electrodeposited on copper turnings, and two flow-type Geiger-Mueller counters.

The technique involves passing the test solution by one of the Geiger-Mueller counters to detect background beta activity, then through the column where reaction (37) occurs.

$$4Tl + O_2 + 2H_2O \rightarrow 4Tl^+ + 4OH^- \qquad (37)$$

The radioactive thallium in the effluent from the column is detected by the second Geiger-Mueller counter. One milligram of oxygen liberates $25.6 \times 10^{-3}$g of $^{204}Tl$. The counting rate is directly proportional to the oxygen concentration in the test solution.

The sensitivity of the test using a column with a specific activity of 2.04 mCi per gram of thallium is about 0.2 mg/liter. That is to say, a test solution containing 0.2 mg/liter produces a $^{204}Tl$ counting rate equal to the background counting rate of the detector. As a rule, because of the randomness of radioactive disintegrations, the precision of this method is $\pm 2\%$. It is important to note that oxidizing agents and changes in the pH of the test solution may interfere with the test.

A few coulometric methods of analysis for dissolved oxygen have been reported. For purposes or orientation, it is helpful to note that air-saturated water at 25°C and under 750 mm Hg air pressure contains 8.18 mg of dissolved oxygen per liter. This in terms of coulometric response is 0.1083 amp.sec/g, a rather large quantity. Two coulometric procedures are discussed here (42,284). In one method a deoxygenated solution of chromic ions is added to the water sample. During the test, chromous ions are generated electrolytically and are then reoxidized by the oxygen in solution. The apparatus immediately detects any excess of chromous ions, marking the end of the titration. This method is sensitive to 0.3 mg dissolved oxygen per liter and has an accuracy of $\pm 2\%$.

Another coulometric method is based on the interaction between oxygen and an ammonia–copper complex, $Cu(NH_3)_2^+$. This is followed by the reduction of the oxidized ammonia–copper complex on a platinum cathode. The amount of current used is equivalent to the oxygen concentration in the test solution.

Use of a constant-potential derivative coulometric system was reported recently (125). The working electrode was composed of tiny metal spheres packed in a ceramic tube. No field experience has been reported with this system, however.

Voltammetric analyses for dissolved oxygen in wastewaters have been carried out with various degrees of success using rotating platinum electrodes and dropping mercury electrodes. The main difficulty in using such electrode systems in industrial waste effluents is the presence of surface active and electroactive interferences which frequently cause "electrode poisoning." A detailed discussion of the effects of surface active agents on the polarographic oxygen determination is available in the literature (285).

Various modifications of the dropping mercury electrode system have been developed for continuous monitoring of dissolved oxygen (285,466). In the absence of interferences, the sensitivity of this technique ranges from 0.05 to 0.10 mg of dissolved oxygen per liter.

Oxygen-sensitive galvanic cells have been used for some time for analyses of water effluents (285). These are made of galvanic couples of an inert metal cathode (e.g., lead, zinc, or antimony) (460). The cathodic reduction of molecular oxygen results in a galvanic current proportional to the concentration of dissolved oxygen in the test solution. Changes in the pH and the conductivity of the test solution influence the oxygen measurement.

The usefulness of this type of cell is limited because the electrode system may be easily poisoned. The electrode is in direct contact with the test solution and surface-active compounds, as well as other suspended material, frequently adsorb on its surface, particularly in wastewaters. To prevent incrustation, a small amount of HCl may be added to the water by a dosing device ahead of the galvanic cell (285).

At the present time it appears that membrane electrodes offer one of the most useful techniques for analysis of dissolved oxygen in wastewaters. The unique feature of such electrode systems is that the membrane separates the electrode from the test solution and serves as a selective diffusion barrier with respect to electroactive and surface active interferences commonly found in industrial wastewaters. Two main types are presently available, the voltammetric type (189) and the galvanic cell type (190). The two types are similar in operating characteristics; however in the voltammetric type an appropriate emf source is needed, while the galvanic type is basically an oxygen energized cell.

With respect to circuitry, galvanic sensors are as simple to work with as thermocouples. All that is needed with the galvanic cell oxygen analyzer is a low impedance galvanometer or microammeter. For recording, an inexpensive galvanometer-type recorder is adequate in most cases. Also, the cell circuit may be closed with a known resistor and the potential drop fed to a pottentiometric recorder. The load resistance in the circuit has little effect on the cell sensitivity since it is in series with the large polarization resistance of the sensing electrode. At high values of external load, however, the galvanic current is affected.

A detailed discussion of the principle, operating characteristics, applicability, and limitations in the use of oxygen membrane electrodes may be found elsewhere (286,287). Similar to the membrane electrode systems discussed previously, the oxygen membrane is sensitive to the activity of the electroactive species and not necessarily the concentration. The steady-state current, $i_\infty$, is given as

$$i_\infty = [zFAD_mK_m(1/b)]a \qquad (38)$$

where $A$ is the cathodic surface area, $D_m$ is the diffusivity coefficient for oxygen in the membrane, $K_m$ is a partition coefficient for molecular oxygen at the membrane–solution interface, and $b$ is the thickness of the membrane. Concentration is related to activity by the activity coefficient,

$$a = \gamma C \qquad (39)$$

Hence,

$$i_\infty = [zFAD_mK_m(1/b)]C = \phi C \qquad (40)$$

where $\phi$ signifies the sensitivity coefficient in microamperes per unit dissolved oxygen concentration.

In the application of oxygen membrane electrodes to industrial wastewaters it is important to account for interferences caused by salting-in ($\gamma < 1.0$) and salting-out ($\gamma > 1.0$) agents, as well as for interferences from reactive species which can permeate the membrane, such as gaseous $H_2S$ and $CO_2$ (285). Industrial effluents from distilleries and pharmaceutical processes may contain salting-in agents. Wastewaters with high ionic strength, such as brine wastes, may cause a salting-out effect, which may be expressed as follows:

$$\ln \gamma = K_s I_s \qquad (41)$$

where $I_s$ is the ionic strength and $K_s$ is the salting-out coefficient. The salting-out effect on the sensitivity of the electrode system (285) is then

$$i_\infty = \phi(e^{K_s I_s})C \qquad (42)$$

The ionic strength of the test solution can be estimated by electric conductance measurements using appropriate calibration procedures. Automatic compensation for changes in ionic strength and temperature of the test solution using a simplified analog system has been described (285).

Polymeric membranes used with oxygen membrane electrodes show selective permeability to various gases and vapors. Gases reduced at the potential of the sensing electrode (e.g., $SO_2$ and halogens) cause erroneous readings, but these gases rarely exist in a free state in aqueous systems. Other gases capable of permeating plastic membranes may contaminate the sensing electrode or react with the supporting electrolyte, e.g., $CO_2$ and $H_2S$.

Another problem can arise if improper mounting of the membrane leads to trapping small air bubbles under the membrane. These bubbles cause slow electrode response and a high residual current.

## IX. CONCLUDING REMARKS

The preceding discussion provides a general survey of techniques and procedures for sampling, handling, storage, and analysis of industrial wastewaters.

Certain wastes and certain analytical methods have been examined in more detail than others. This has been determined partially by the relative significance of particular types of wastes, partially by the complexity of certain analytical problems, partially by the extent of use and availability of information on various analytical procedures, and doubtless in some small part also by the relative interests of the authors. Nonetheless, an attempt has been made to at least identify all major problems and available solutions for analysis of industrial wastes, if not discuss them all in depth.

An extensive list of sources of more detailed information and discussion of specific aspects of industrial wastewater analysis is provided by the reference list for this chapter. It is not possible within the confines of a single chapter to consider all aspects of each particular industrial wastewater situation. The reader is therefore encouraged to make use of the references cited herein to benefit fully from more complete consideration of specific analytical problems, methods, and procedures.

## APPENDIX I

### MISCELLANEOUS ORGANIC MATTER

| Substance | Occurrence | Mode of measurement | Method of analysis—Remarks | Refs. |
|---|---|---|---|---|
| Acetone | Chemical wastewater | Colorimetric | Colorimetric analysis of acetone or acetone–salicylic aldehyde or acetone furfural condensates. | 272 |
| Acrolein | Chemical wastewater | Colorimetric | The filtered sample is treated with ammonia, mixed with HCl—alcohol mixture, then treated with tryptophone in HCl. | 513 |

(continued)

| Substance | Occurrence | Mode of measurement | Method of analysis—Remarks | Refs. |
|---|---|---|---|---|
| Acrolein | Wastewaters | Colorimetric | Water filtered, treated with ammonia to remove iron salts, mixed with HCl and alcohol solution; interaction with 0.2 % of tryptophane causes color development. | 513 |
| Acrylonitrile | Chemical wastewater | Polarographic | Distillation with H₂SO₄ and CH₃OH to give an axeotropic mixture boiling at 61.4°C containing 38.7 liters acrylonitrile, which is determined polarographically (sensitivity 0.1 ppm). | 134, 108 |
| Amines | Steam condensate | Colorimetric | Test for dioctadecylamine and octadecylamines; both react with methyl orange at pH 3.4–3.6 to form yellow-colored complex soluble in ethyl dichloride. | 20 |
|  | Chemical wastewater | Colorimetric | Solution is treated with hypochlorite to form chloramine derivatives which are determined colorimetrically by reacting with starch–potassium iodide reagent. | 107 |
| Aniline | Chemical wastewater | Colorimetric | Color formation on reaction with chloramine-T. | 250 |
| Benzene | Chemical wastewater | Colorimetric | Benzene is converted to 1,3,-dinitrobenzene, which when reacted with methyl ethyl ketone under alkaline conditions will form a violet-colored compound (sensitivity 0.005 mg/liter and accuracy is 2–5 %). | 115 |
| Benzene | Chemical wastewater | Polarographic | Desorption by nitrogen as a carrier gas, followed by nitration and determination of the resulting $m$-dinitrobenzene polarographically. | 9 |
| Benzene hexachloride | Sewage and chemical wastewater | Spectrometric | Extraction on activated charcoal, determination as $m$-dinitrobenzene after dechlorination and nitrification by the method of Sehechtes and Hornstein, then measured by absorption spectrometry. | 182 |
| Chlortetracycline | Chemical wastewater | Fluorescence spectrometry | Compare fluorescence with standards at pH 8.5–9.0. | 397 |
| Creatinine | Infiltration water | Colorimetric | Color produced by reaction with picric acid and NaOH in the presence of sodium hexametaphosphate. | 1 |
| Dichloroethane | Chemical wastewater | Titrimetric | Sample neutralized, evaporated, burnt in a stream of air; products absorbed in NaOH, acidified, titrated with mercurous nitrate solution. | 429 |

*(continued)*

| Substance | Occurrence | Mode of measurement | Method of analysis—Remarks | Refs. |
|---|---|---|---|---|
| 2,4,-Dichloro phenoxy acetic acid | Surface waters | Colorimetric | 2,4,D heated with chromotropic acid to develop wine-red color (sensitivity 7 g/liter—range 0–30 g/liter). | 13 |
| | | Spectrometric (uv) | Direct measurement of 2,4,D uv spectra (sensitivity 30 g/liter). | 13 |
| Formaldehyde | Chemical wastewater and surface wastewater | Spectrometric | Sample is treated with phenylhydrazine hydrochloride, potassium ferricyanide, NaOH, and isopropyl alcohol for extraction. The absorption spectra in alcohol layer are determined. Acetaldehyde and ferrous iron interfere with test. | 433 |
| Formaldehyde | Plastic, tannery, and pharmaceutical wastewater | Colorimetric | Blue to greenish-blue color developed with 0.5 % of carbazole solution in conc. $H_2SO_4$ (spot test or ring test). | 160 |
| | | | Heating with chromtropic acid in 72 % $H_2SO_4$ at 60°C, develop violet color, compare with standards. | 376 |
| Furfuraldehyde | Chemical wastewater | Colorimetric | Reaction with aniline acetate and with acetophenone; another method based on benzidine reaction. | 273 |
| Heating oil and motor oil | Surface and wastewaters | Spectrometric | Liquid–liquid extraction followed by ir analysis. | 251 |
| Hexamethylene-tetramine | Chemical wastewater | Colorimetric | Hexamethylene-tetramine is hydrolyzed with dilute $H_2SO_4$ forming formaldehyde, which is measured colorimetrically using the Schiff reagent. Formaldehyde originally present can be removed by oxidation with $H_2O_2$ in alkaline solution. | 15 |
| Hydrazine | Wastewaters | Colorimetric | Sodium azide used to remove nitrite ions; 225 one part of sample treated with iodine and sodium sulfite to remove hydrazine, both parts of sample treated with p-dimethylaminobenzaldehyde in HCl for color development measurements based on differential absorption spectrometry of both parts of sample. | 225 |
| Hydroquinone | Wastewaters | Colorimetric | Based on reaction with 1,10-phenanthroline, sample pretreatment to eliminate interferences. | 274 |
| Lactose | Dairy wastewater | Colorimetric | After removal of proteins with sulfuric acid and sodium tungstate, alkaline copper tartarate and sodium bisulfite are added, and the cuprous copper so formed is allowed to reduce phosphomolybdic acid to molybdenum blue, which is determined colorimetrically (range 0–5000 ppm). | 201 |

(continued)

| Substance | Occurrence | Mode of measurement | Method of analysis—Remarks | Refs. |
|---|---|---|---|---|
| Lignin and ligno-sulfonic acid | Sea water | Spectrometric (uv) | Direct measurements of uv spectra in neutral and alkaline solutions. | 263 |
| Lipids | Domestic and industrial wastewaters | Gravimetric | New extraction procedures that can separate motor oils, tristeorin, sodium oleate, and various insoluble lipids. | 266 |
| Naphthalein | Industrial wastewater | Spectrometric (uv) | Extraction with heptane and differential uv spectrometric technique. | 511 |
| Naphthalene | Chemical wastewater | Colorimetric | Extraction with chloroform and NaOH, then mixing with anhydrous aluminum chloride to develop bluish-purple color in 2–3 min (range 0.2–200 ppm and accuracy + 5.6 %). | 303 |
| | | | Reaction with acetylacetone in presence of excess of ammonium salts at pH about 5.5–6.5, develops yellow color of pyridine derivative, compared with standards. | 325 |
| | | Titrimetric | Oxidation of formaldehyde by $H_2SO_4$ in presence of NaOH to form sodium formate or formation of hexamethylenetetramine by the action of ammonium chloride and caustic soda on formaldehyde. In both cases, the unused NaOH is back-titrated with HCl. | 241 |
| Nitrobenzene | Chemical wastewater | Colorimetric | Sample made alkaline, distilled, nitrobenzene is reduced to aniline, diazotized, reacted with sodium salt of 2-naphthol-3,6-disulfonic acid, and determined colorimetrically. | 170 |
| Oils and grease, chloroform-extractable matter | Oil refinery food processing | Gravimetric | Constitute a number of heavy oils, grease, rubber, certain resins, asphaltenes, and carbines. Test is based on the gravimetric determination of the residue of the chloroform extract of the sample. | 20 |
| Phthalic anhydride | Chemical wastewater | Colorimetric | Sample treated with alcohol and NaOH solution, evaporated till dryness, residue dissolved in $H_2SO_4$ and treated with acidic resorcinol; color is developed on dilution and made alkaline. | 514 |
| Proteins | Surface waters | Colorimetric | Folin–phenol reagent is reduced, in alkaline medium, by copper salt of protein, giving a blue color, the intensity of which is proportional to protein concentration (sensitivity to 0.3 mg/liter). | 357 |

(continued)

| Substance | Occurrence | Mode of measurement | Method of analysis—Remarks | Refs. |
|---|---|---|---|---|
| Pyridine | Oil refinery, road drainage | Colorimetric | Distillation of pyridine, buffer to pH 6–8, react with cyanogen bromide and benzidine hydrochloride and red color produced is extracted with butyl alcohol (range 0.005–1.0 ppm). | 246 |
| Pyridine | Chemical wastewater | Colorimetric | Reaction of pyridine with barbituric acid in presence of chlorocyanogen, and photocolorimetric analysis of color produced. | 123 |
| Sugars | Citrus wastewater, sulfite cellulose wastewater, beet sugar wastewater | Titrimetric | Conversion to reducing sugars by acid hydrolysis followed by heating with alkaline potassium ferricyanide; excess ferricyanide is determined idometrically. | 493 |
| Tar | Effluent gas works | Colorimetric | Extraction by chloroform in a weakly alkaline solution. Acid washing until neutral, drying over sodium sulfate, filtering, then measuring optical density (accuracy + 10 %). | 465 |
| Tar bases pyridine, quinoline, acridine | Oil refinery, coke ovens, gas works | Gravimetric | Extraction with chloroform, treated with picric acid, weighed as picrates. | 154 |
| Trichlorobenzene | Chemical wastewater | Titrimetric colorimetric | Digestion of the chloroorganic compounds in $H_2SO_4$ and $K_2Cr_2O_7$ in air, absorption of liberated chlorine by CdI solution, and determination of equivalent volume of iodine liberated titrimetrically; in cases of small amounts of liberated iodine, determinations are done colorimetrically (sensitivity = 30 g/liter and accuracy + 8 %). Interference by other chloroorganic substances. | 306 |
| Trichloroethylene | Chemical wastewater | Colorimetric | Sample is treated with pyridine and caustic soda and boiled for 5 min to develop orange color (range 1–20 ppm). | 275 |
| Trichloroethylene | Chemical wastewater | Titrimetric | Sample is treated with ammonium peroxydisulfate and nitric acid and boiled under reflux, hydrochloric acid released is titrated with $AgNO_3$ solution and potentiometric end-point detection. | 116 |
| Turpentine | Chemical wastewater | Colorimetric | Carbon dioxide passed through sample containing ethanol and phosphomolybdic acid immersed in ice; after temperature drops colorimetric determinations are done. | 271 |
| Wool wax | Textile effluents | Colorimetric | Reaction of stearine in wool wax with acetic anhydride and sulfuric acid. | 191 |

# APPENDIX II

## SYNTHETIC DETERGENTS

| Substance | Occurrence | Mode of measurement | Method of analysis—remarks | Refs. |
|---|---|---|---|---|
| Anionic surfactants | Sewage and river waters | Colorimetric | Procedure to distinguish between sulfate and sulfonate surfactants, based on hydrolyzing the sulfate detergents with boiling in sulfuric acid. | 111 |
| Anionic surfactants | Domestic and industrial effluents | Titrimetric | The titration is carried out with a standard solution of cationic surfactants (cetyl trimethylammonium bromide), in the presence of hexane; a solution of bromophenol blue or azophloxine is used as an indicator. | 128 45 |
| Anionic surfactants | Drinking water | Colorimetric | Complexation of methylene green with anionic surfactants. | 2 |
| Anionic surfactants | Surface and waste waters | — | Review article | 311 |
| Anionic surfactants | — | Polarographic | Based on dyestuff antagonist method. | 77 |
| Anionic surfactants | Surface and waste waters | — | Literature review—methods discussed are spectrometric and titrimetric methods. | 103 |
| Anionic surfactants | Textile wastewaters | Titrimetric | Surfactant is titrated with laur-2-pyridinium chloride using acid dye as indicator. | 438 |
| Anionic surfactants | — | Complexometric titration | Quantitative separation of alkyl sulfates and sulfonates as barium salt which is titrated with EDTA solution. | 185 |
| Anionic surfactants | Surface waters | Spectrometric (uv) | Separation followed by measuring uv absorption spectra. | 486 |
| Anionic surfactant | Surface waters | Ion exchange colorimetric | Separation on Amberlite IRA-68, elution with acetone and sodium hydroxide and determination by methylene blue method. | 261 |
| Anionic surfactant | Surface waters | Solvent extraction ac polarography | Separation by solvent extraction with chloroform and determination by ac polarography (range 0.07–0.028 mg ABS per 10 ml chloroform). | 228 |
| Mixed surfactants | Textile wastewaters | Colorimetric titrimetric | Review of methods for analysis for anionic, cationic, and nonionic surfactants, applicable to spent sulfate liquor. | 352 |
| Nonionic surfactants | Sewage effluents | Colorimetric | Extraction in ether, precipitation with barium phosphomolybdate in HCl–ethanol solution, digestion to form phosphates, which are measured colorimetrically by reduction to molybdenum blue. | 190 |
| Nonionic surfactants | — | Colorimetric | Surfactant reduces the optical density of dilute solutions of dichlorofluororescein in glacial acetic acid at a certain wavelength. | 437 |
| Nonionic surfactant | — | Surface tension | Surface tension measurements were made with stalagmameter at 20°C and compared with results from standard solutions. | 262 |
| Nonionic surfactant | Papermill wastewaters | Colorimetric | Separation and reaction with cobalt thiocyanate to develop a color complex. | 101 |
| Surfactants | — | Paper chromatography | Separation and identification of anionic, cationic, and nonionic surfactants by various paper chromatographic techniques. | 122 |

## APPENDIX III

## NUTRIENTS (AMMONIA, NITRITES, NITRATES AND PHOSPHATES)

| Substance | Occurrence | Mode of measurement | Method of analysis—remarks | Refs. |
|---|---|---|---|---|
| Ammonia | Water | Colorimetric | Ammonia determined in the presence of nitrates by the oxidation of nitrites to nitrates by $H_2O_2$, and subsequent distillation of ammonia from alkaline solution. | 14 |
| | | | Sample treated with chloramine-T and then allowed to react with pyridine pyrazolone reagent containing 3-methyl-1-phenyl-5-pyrazolone and a trace of the bis-pyrazolone; a purple color develops extracted with carbon tetrachloride (sensitivity 0.025 mg/liter). | 247 363 |
| | | | Based on formation of intensively blue indophenol by the reaction of ammonia, hypochlorite, and phenol; catalyzed by a manganous salt (sensitivity = 0.01 mg/liter, accuracy ± 5 %). | 69 |
| | Sea water | Colorimetric | Based on oxidation of ammonia to monochloramine; combination with phenol, extraction of resulting quinone chlorimide using $n$-hexanol, centrifugation, and determination of color intensity in the supernatant liquor. | 335 |
| Nitrites | Water and waste | Amperometric titration | Based on titration with chloramine-T (sensitivity 1 mg/liter). | 114 |
| | Surface waters | Colorimetric autoanalyzer | Hydrazine reduction test. | 156 |
| Nitrates | Natural and waste waters | Polarographic | Diffusion current measurements at $-1.2$ $V$ vs. SCE; nitrites, phosphates, and $Fe^{3+}$ interfere. | 47 |
| | Wastewaters | Colorimetric | Based on reaction of nitrates with chromotropic acid, reagent suitable for analysis in presence of formaldehyde. | 33 |
| | Waters | Spectrometric (uv) | Determine uv absorption spectra in acid solution; chlorides cause a shift in wavelength of maximum absorption measurements done at wavelength of minimum interference. | 138 |
| | Surface waters | Colorimetric | Nitrite interference prevented by preliminary treatment with urea. | 229 |
| Phosphates | Natural and wastewaters | Coulometric titration | Based on the argentometric titration of orthophosphates with $Ag^+$ ions coulometrically generated. Potentiometric and amperometric techniques were also discussed. | 89 |
| | | Colorimetric | Vanadium molybdate is used in this test and the yellow colored complex is determined colorimetrically, a technique is described to reduce interferences. | 4 150 |
| | | | Modified procedures for extraction and reduction of the phosphomolybdic acid (sensitivity 0.3 g/liter). | 436 194 |
| | | Activation analysis | Formation of phosphotungstic acid which is extracted and activated for 1 hr at a flux of $10^{13}$ neutrons/cm$^2$/sec. | 15 |

## REFERENCES

1. Abbott, D. C., *Analyst,* **87,** 494 (1962).
2. Abbott, D. C., *Analyst,* **88,** 240 (1963).
3. Abbott, D. C., *Proc. Soc. Water Treat. Exam.,* **13,** 153 (1964).
4. Abbott, D. C., G. E. Emsden, and J. B. Harris, *Analyst,* **88,** 814 (1963).
5. Abbott, D. C., H. Egan, E. W. Hammond, and J. Thompson, *Analyst,* **89,** 480 (1964).
6. Association of British Chemical Manufacturers and Society of Analytical Chemistry Joint Committee, *Analyst,* **83,** 50 (1958).
7. Association of British Chemical Manufacturers and Society of Analytical Chemistry Joint Committee, *Analyst,* **82,** 518 (1957).
8. Association of British Chemical Manufacturers and Society of Analytical Chemistry Joint Committee, *Analyst,* **83,** 230 (1958).
9. Adamovsky, M., *Vodni Hospodarstvi,* **16,** 102 (1966), *Chem. Abstr.,* **65,** 6908f (1966).
10. Adams, C. E., Southern Pulp Paper Mfr., **1,** 12 (1959).
11. Adeney, W. E., and B. B. Dawson, *Sci. Proc. Royal Dublin Soc.,* **18,** 199 (1926).
12. Aldridge, W. N., *Analyst,* **69,** 62 (1944).
13. Aly, O. M., and S. D. Faust, *J. Amer. Water Works Assoc.,* **55,** 639 (1963).
14. Alexandrov, G. P., and W. S. Tichonova, *Lavodsk. Lab.,* (*USSR*), **26,** 57 (1960).
15. Allen, H. E., Abstracts, 155th American Chemical Society Meeting, San Francisco, April 1968.
16. Allen, L. A., *J. Soc. Chem. Ind.,* **63,** 89 (1944).
17. Allen, H., W. R. Matson, and K. H. Mancy, *J. Water Pollution Control Federation,* in press.
18. Allred, R. C., E. A. Stezkom, and R. L. Huddleston, *J. Amer. Oil Chemists Soc.,* **41,** 13 (1964).
19. Alsterberg, G., *Biochem. J.,* **159,** 36 (1925).
20. American Society of Testing Materials, *Manual on Industrial Water and Industrial Waste Water,* 2nd ed., Philadelphia, 1964.
21. American Petroleum Institute, *Manual on Disposal of Refinery Wastes—Methods for Sampling and Analyses of Refinery Wastes,* American Petroleum Institute, New York, 1957.
22. Andelman, J. B., *Proc. 140th Annual Conference, Water Pollution Control Federation, Washington, D.C.,* **1967,** p. 6.
23. Andelman, J. B., and M. J. Suess, Abstracts, 151st Meeting, American Chemical Society, Pittsburgh, March 1966.
24. Anderson, N. R., and D. N. Hume, *Advan. in Chemistry,* **73,** 30 (1968).
25. Andrews, J. F., J. F. Thomas, and E. A. Pearson, *Water and Sewage Works,* **111,** 206 (1964).
26. Anon, *Chem. Eng. News,* **10,** 46 (1965).
27. Anon, *Ind. Eng. Chem.,* **57,** 45 (1965).
28. AISI, "Annual Statistical Report," American Iron and Steel Institute, 1949.
29. American Public Health Association, American Water Works Association, and Water Pollution Control Federation, *Standard Methods for the Examination of Water and Wastewater,* 12th ed., American Public Health Association, 1965.
30. Archer, E. E., *Analyst,* **79,** 30 (1954).

31. Argonne National Laboratory, "Management of Radioactive Wastes of Argonne National Laboratory," in *Hearings of Joint Committee on Atomic Energy,* Vol. 1, 86th Congress, Superintendent of Documents, U.S. Government Printing Office, 708 (1959).

32. Ariel, M., and U. Eisner, *J. Electroanal. Chem.,* 5, 362 (1963).

33. Armstrong, E. A., *Anal. Chem.,* 35, 1252 (1963).

34. Arthur, R. M., *Proc. Ind. Waste Conf. 19th, Purdue Univ.,* 628 (1964).

35. Association of American Soap and Glycerine Producers, *Anal. Chem.,* 28, 1822 (1956).

36. American Society for Testing Materials, "Symposium on Radioactivity in Industrial Water and Industrial Waste Water," *Amer. Soc. Testing Mater. Spec. Tech. Publ.,* 235 (1959).

37. Atkins, W. R. G., *J. Conseil, Conseil Perm. Intern. Exploration Mer.,* 22, 271 (1957).

38. Baker, R. A., *J. Amer. Water Works Assoc.,* 58, 751 (1966).

39. Baker, R. A., *J. Water Pollution Control Federation,* 34, 582 (1962).

40. Baker, R. A., *J. Amer. Water Works Assoc.,* 56, 92 (1964).

41. Baker, R. A., *J. Water Pollution Control Federation,* 37, 1164 (1965).

42. Barbi, G., and S. Sandroni, *Comit. Nazl. Energia Nucl.,* CNI-55, 3 (1960).

43. Barker, F. B., and B. P. Robinson, "Determination of Beta Activity in Water," *U.S. Geol. Surv. Water Supply Papers,* 1696-A, 36 (1963).

44. Barney, J. E. II, and R. J. Bertolacini, *Anal. Chem.,* 29, 1187 (1957).

45. Barr, T., J. Oliver, and W. V. Stubbings, *J. Soc. Chem. Ind.,* 67, 45 (1948).

46. Bartow, H., *Chem. Eng.,* 72, 177 (1965).

47. Batlen, J. J., *Anal. Chem.,* 36, 939 (1964).

48. Baylis, J. R., *Ind. Eng. Chem.,* 18, 311 (1926).

49. Baxter, S. S., and V. A. Appleyard, *J. Amer. Water Works Assoc.,* 54, 1181 (1962).

50. Bizollon, C. A., and R. Moret, *Chim. Anal.,* 46, 273 (1964).

51. Brainina, Kh. Z., *J. Anal. Chem. (USSR),* 19, 753 (1964).

52. Beckman Instrument Co., Fullerton, California.

53. Beier, E., *Gas-Wasserfach,* 98, 262 (1957).

54. Belcher, R., M. A. Leonard, and T. S. West, *Talanta,* 2, 92 (1954).

55. Bentley, E. M., and G. F. Lee, *Environ. Sci. Technol.,* 1, 721 (1967).

56. Berck, B., *Anal. Chem.,* 25, 1253 (1953).

57. Bertolacini, R. J., and J. E. Barney II, *Anal. Chem.,* 29, 281 (1957).

58. Black, H., *Sewage Ind. Wastes,* 24, 45 (1952).

59. Black, H. H., *Ind. Eng. Chem.,* 50, 10 (1958).

60. Black, A. P., and S. A. Hannah, *J. Amer. Water Works Assoc.,* 57, 901 (1965).

61. Blaedel, W. J., and R. H. Laessig, "Automation of the Analytical Process through Continuous Analysis," in *Advances in Analytical Chemistry and Instrumentation,* Vol. 5, C. N. Reilley, Ed., Interscience, New York, 1966, p. 69.

62. Blanchard, R. L., G. W. Leddicotte, and D. W. Moeller, *J. Amer. Water Works Assoc.,* 51, 61 (1959).

63. Boettner, E. A., and F. I. Grunder, *Advan. Chem. Ser.,* 73, 238 (1968).

64. Bogan, R. H., and C. N. Sawyer, *Proc. Ind. Waste Conf., 12th,* Purdue Univ. 1957, p. 156.

65. Boltz, D. F., and M. G. Mellon, *Anal. Chem.,* 40, 255R (1968).

66. Bollinger, L. E., *U.S. Publ. Health Serv. Publ.* 999-AP-15, 41 (1964).

67. Bond, A. M., and M. M. Murray, *Biochem. J.,* **53,** 642 (1953).
68. Booth, R. L., J. N. English, G. N. McDermott, *J. Amer. Water Works Assoc.,* **57,** 215 (1965).
69. Bossum, J. R., and P. A. Villarruz, *J. Amer. Water Works Assoc.,* **55,** 657 (1963).
70. Bovard, P., and A. Granby, *Chim. Anal.,* **44,** 439 (1962).
71. Bramer, H. C., M. J. Walsh, and S. C. Caruso, Abstracts, 151st Meeting, American Chemical Society, Pittsburgh, March 1966.
72. Breidenbach, A. W., *U.S. Publ. Health Serv. Publ.,* **1241,** (1964).
73. Breidenbach, A. W., C. G. Gunnerson, and F. Kawahara, "Chlorinated Hydrocarbon Pesticides in Major River Basins 1957–1965," Publication of Basic Data Program, Department of Health, Education and Welfare, April 1966.
74. British Standards Institution, *Brit. Std. Inst.,* **B. S. 2690** (1953).
75. Broda, E., and T. Schonfeld, *Acta Chim. Acad. Sci. Hung.,* **50,** 49 (1966).
76. Brooks, R. R., *Cosmochim. Acta,* **29,** 1369 (1965).
77. Buchanan, G. S., and J. C. Griffith, *J. Electroanal. Chem.,* **5,** 204 (1963).
78. Bunch, R. L., and C. W. Chambers, *J. Water Pollution Control Federation,* **39,** 181 (1967).
79. Burchfield, H. P., and D. E. Johnson, *U.S. Publ. Health Serv. Rept.* **1** and **2** (1965).
80. Burns, E. R., and C. Marshall, *J. Water Pollution Control Federation,* **37,** 1716 (1965).
81. Burrell, D. C., *Atomic Absorption Newsletter,* Perkin Elmer Corp., Norwalk, Conn., **4,** 309 (1955).
82. Butts, P. G., A. R. Gahler, and M. G. Mellon, *Ind. Wastes,* **22,** 1543 (1950).
83. Byrd, J. F., "Combined Treatment, *Proc. Ind. Waste Conf., Purdue Univ.,* **1962,** pp. 16, 109.
84. Camp, T. R., *Water and Its Impuities,* Reinhold, New York, 1963, p. 77.
85. CBEDE, *Livre De L'Eau,* Vol. 1, Centre Belge D'Etude Et De Documentation Des Eaux, Liege, Belgium, 1954.
86. Charlot, G., *Colorimetric Determination of Elements,* Elsevier, New York, 1964.
87. Cheronis, N. D., *Micro and Semimicro Methods, Technique of Oragnic Chemistry,* Vol. 6, Interscience, New York, 1954.
88. Chow, T. J., and T. G. Thompson, *Anal. Chem.,* **27,** 18 (1955).
89. Christian, G. D., E. C. Knoblock, and W. C. Purdy, *Anal. Chem.,* **35,** 1869 (1963).
90. Christman, R. F., *Proc. Water Pollution Control Federation Annual Meeting, 40th Symposium on Water Quality Analysis, New York,* 1967, p. 8.
91. Christman, R. F., and M. Ghassemi, "Progress Report to Public Health Services on Research Grant WP-00558," The University of Washington Press, Seattle, Washington, 1966.
92. Christman, R. F., and M. Ghassemi, *J. Amer. Water Works Assoc.,* **58,** 723 (1966).
93. Citron, I., H. Tsi, R. A. Day, and A. L. Underwood, *Talanta,* **8,** 798 (1961).
94. Clarke, F. E., *Ind. Eng. Chem.,* **19,** 889 (1947).
95. Cleary, E. J., *J. Amer. Water Works Assoc.,* **54,** 1347 (1962).
96. Coomber, D. I., *Proc. Soc. Water Treat. Exam.,* **12,** 100 (1963).
97. Collins, A. G., *Appl. Spectr.,* **21,** 16 (1967).

98. Collins, A. G., *U.S. Bur. Mines, Rept. Invest.,* **6641,** 18 (1965).
99. Cox, R. A., "The Physical Properties of Sea Water," *Chemical Oceanography,* Vol. 1, in J. P. Riley and G. Skirrows, Eds., Academic Press, New York, 1965, p. 73.
100. Cox, R. A., *Deep Sea Res.,* **9,** 504 (1962).
101. Crabb, N. T., and H. E. Presinger, *J. Amer. Oil Chemists' Soc.,* **41,** 752 (1964).
102. Craig, L. C., and D. Craig, in *Technique of Organic Chemistry,* 2nd ed., Vol. 3, Part I, R. Weissberger, Ed., Interscience, New York, 1956.
103. Cropton, W. G., and A. S. Joy, *Analyst,* **88,** 516 (1963).
104. Crouch, S. R., and H. V. Malmstadt, *Anal. Chem.,* **39,** 1084 (1967).
105. Crow, W. B., and F. A. Eidsness, *J. Amer. Water Works Assoc.,* **57,** 1509 (1966).
106. Csabadtm, N., *Hidrol. Kozl.,* **44,** 371 (1964).
107. Dahlgrene, G., *Anal. Chem.,* **36,** 596 (1964).
108. Daves, G. W., and W. F. Hammer, *Anal. Chem.,* **29,** 1035 (1957).
109. Davis, R. C., *J. Water Sewage Works,* **3,** 259 (1964).
110. Davis, J. B., *Ind. Eng. Chem.,* **48,** 1444 (1956).
111. Degens, P. N., Jr., H. Van Der Zee, and J. D. Kommer, *Sewage Ind. Wastes,* **25,** 24 (1953).
112. Degremont, E., *Memento Technique De L'Eau,* Degremont, Paris, 1959.
113. Delaughtor, B., *Atomic Absorption Newsletter,* Perkin Elmer Corp., Norwalk, Conn., **4,** 273 (1965).
114. Deshmukh, G. S., and S. N. Murty, *Indian J. Chem.,* **1,** 316 (1963).
115. Devlaminck, F., *Bull. Centre Belge Etude Doc. Eaux (Liege),* **101,** 135 (1959).
116. Deyl, Z., and M. Effenberger, *Voda,* **37,** 90 (1958).
117. Dickinson, W. E., *Anal. Chem.,* **26,** 777 (1954).
118. Dobbs, R. A. and R. T. Williams, *Anal. Chem.,* **35,** 1064 (1963).
119. Dostal, H. C., and D. R. Dilley, *Bio-Science (Eng.),* **14,** 35 (1964).
120. Donaldson, D. E., *U.S. Geol. Surv. Water Supply Paper* **550-D,** 258 (1966).
121. Drabek, R., *Chem. Tech. (Berlin),* **9,** 77 (1957).
122. Drewry, J., *Analyst,* **88,** 225 (1963).
123. Dyathovitskaya, F. G., *Gigiena i Sanit.,* **25,** 51 (1960).
124. Eckenfelder, W. W., and E. Barnhart, "Removal of Synthetic Detergents from Laundry and Laundromat Wastes," Research Report No. 5, New York State Water Pollution Control Board, (March 1960).
125. Eckfeldt, E. L., and E. W. Shaffer, *Anal. Chem.,* **36,** 2008 (1964).
126. Edge, R. A., R. R. Brooks, L. H. Ahrens, and S. Amdurer, *Geochim. Cosmochim. Acta,* **15,** 337 (1959).
127. Edwards, G. P., J. P. Pfafflin, L. H. Schwartz, and P. M. Lauren, *J. Water Pollution Control Federation,* **34,** 1112 (1962).
128. Edwards, G. P., and M. E. Ginn, *Sewage Ind. Wastes,* **26,** 945 (1954).
129. Effenberger, M., *Sci. Papers, Inst. Chem. Technol. (Prague), Technol. Water,* **6,** 471 (1962).
130: Egan, T., E. W. Hammond, and J. Thomson, *Analyst,* **89,** 175 (1964).
131. Eisner, U., M. Rottschaffer, F. J. Berlandi, and H. B. Mark, Jr., *Anal. Chem.,* **39,** 1466 (1967).
132. Eisenman, G., in *Advances in Analytical Chemistry and Instrumentation,* Vol. 4, C. N. Reilley, Ed., Interscience, New York, 1965, p. 213.
133. Ellis, David W., and D. R. Demers, *Advan. Chem. Ser.,* **73,** 326 (1968).

134. Ellis, M. M., B. A. Westfall, and M. D. Ellis, *U.S. Fish Wildlife Serv. Res. Rept.*, **9** (1948).
135. Elwell, W. T., and J. A. F. Gidley, *Atomic Absorption Spectrophotometry*, Pergamon Press, Oxford, 1966.
135a. Emerson, E., *J. Org. Chem.*, **8**, 417 (1943).
135b. Emerson, E., and K. Kelly, *J. Org. Chem.*, **13**, 532 (1948).
136. Erdey, L, and F. Szabadvary, *Acta. Chim. Acad. Sci., Hung.*, **4**, 325 (1954).
137. Ettinger, M. B., and C. C. Ruchhoft, *Anal. Chem.*, **20**, 1119 (1948).
138. Fadrus, H., and J. Maly, *Z. Anal. Chem.*, **202**, 164 (1964).
139. Fahrenfort, J., *Spectrochim. Acta.*, **17**, 698 (1961).
140. Fair, G. M., *Sewage Works J.*, **8**, 430 (1936).
141. Fair, G. M., *J. New Engl. Water Works Assoc.*, **47**, 248 (1933).
142. Fair, G. M., J. C. Geyer, *Water Supply and Waste Water Disposal*, New York, 1954.
143. Fairing, I. D., and F. R. Short, *Anal. Chem.*, **28**, 1827 (1956).
144. Faust, S. D., and O. M. Aly, *J. Amer. Water Works Assoc.*, **54**, 235 (1962).
145. Faust, S. D., and N. E. Hunter, *J. Amer. Water Works Assoc.*, **57**, 1028 (1965).
145a. Faust, S. D., and E. W. Mikulewicz, *Water Res.* **1**, 405 (1967).
145b. Faust, S. D , and E. W. Mikulewicz, *Water Res.*, **1**, 509 (1967).
146. Feigl, F., R. Belcher, and W. I. Setephen, in *Advances in Analytical Chemistry and Instrumentation*, Vol. 2, C. N. Reilley, Ed., Interscience, New York, 1963, p. 1.
147. Ferrari, A., *Ann. N. Y. Acad. Sci.*, **87**, 792 (1960).
148. Fishman, M. J., and M. R. Midget, *Advan. Chem. Ser.*, **73**, 230 (1968).
149. Fleszar, B., *Chem. Anal.*, **9**, 1075 (1964).
150. Fogg, D. N., and N. T. Wilkinson, *Analyst*, **83**, 406 (1958).
151. Folkendorf, E., *Kernenergie*, **7**, 108 (1964).
152. Fonselius, S. G., E. Kovoleff, *Bull. Inst. Oceanog.*, **61**, 1 (1963).
153. Foulke, D. G., *Metal Finish*, **47**, 58 (1949).
154. Fox, J. J., and J. H. Gauge, *J. Soc. Chem. Ind.*, **39**, 260T (1920).
155. Frant, M. S., and J. W. Ross, *Science*, **154**, 1553 (1966).
155a. Frant, M. S., *Plating*, **54**, 702 (1967).
155b. Frant, M. S., and J. W. Ross, *Anal. Chem.*, **40**, 1169 (1968).
156. Frasier, R. E., *J. Amer. Water Works Assoc.*, **55**, 624 (1963).
157. Friedrich, A., E. Kuhaas, and R. Schurch, *Z. Physiol. Chem.*, **2/6**, 68 (1933).
158. Fritz, J. S., and S. K. Karakker, *Anal. Chem.*, **32**, 957 (1960).
159. Fritz, J. S., and S. S. Yamamura, *Anal. Chem.*, **27**, 1461 (1955).
160. Furst, K., *Mikrochemie*, **33**, 348 (1948).
161. Gates, W. E., K. H. Mancy, F. Shafie, and F. Pohland, *Proc. Purdue Ind. Waste Conf.*, **1966**, p. 238.
162. Gardner, D. G., R. F. Muraca, and E. J. Serfass, *Plating*, **43**, 743 (1956).
163. Gebauer, H., and S. Muller, *Atomwirtschoft*, **1**, 487 (1962).
164. Gellman, I., and H. Heukelekian, *Sewage Ind. Wastes*, **23**, 1267 (1951).
165. Gerald, F. A., *The Human Senses*, Wiley, New York, 1953.
166. Gerischer, H., *Z. Physik. Chem. (Leipzig)*, **202**, 302 (1953).
167. Geyer, R., and W. Syring, *Z. Chem.*, **6**, 92 (1966).
168. Gibbs, H. D., *J. Biol. Chem.*, **72**, 649 (1927).
169. Gohlke, R. S., *Anal. Chem.*, **34**, 1332 (1962).
170. Golubeva, M. T., *Lab. Delo*, **1**, 6 (1964).

171. Goodenkamf, A., and J. Erdei, *J. Amer. Water Works Assoc.*, **56**, 600 (1964).

172. Gorbach, S., and F. Ehrenberger, *Z. Anal. Chem.*, **181**, 106 (1961).

173. Gotlieb, E., and J. T. Pelczar, Jr., *Bacteria Rev.*, **15**, 55 (1951).

174. Grande, J. A., and J. Beukenkamp, *Analyt. Chem.*, **28**, 1497 (1956).

175. Gunther, F. A., T. A. Miller, and T. E. Jenkins, *Anal. Chem.*, **37**, 1186 (1965).

176. Gurnham, C. F., *Industrial Wastewater Control*, Academic Press, New York, 1965.

177. Haase, L. W., and E. V. Gessellschaft, *Standard Methods for the Examination of Water, and Sludge,* (in German), Verlag Chemie, Wienheim, 1954.

178. Habashi, G., *Mikrochim. Acta*, **23**, 233 (1960).

179. Hallbach, P. F., "Radionuclide Analysis of Environmental Samples," A Laboratory Manual of Methodology, *U.S. Publ. Health Service, Div. Radiological Health, Rept.* **R50-6**, (1959).

180. Hammerton, C., *J. Appl. Chem.*, **5**, 517 (1955).

181. Hampson, B. L., *Analyst*, **89**, 651 (1964).

182. Hancock, W., and E. Q. Law, *Analyst*, **80**, 665 (1955).

183. Haney, P. D., and J. Schmidt, *U.S. Publ. Health Serv. Tech. Rept.*, **W58-2**, 133 (1958).

184. Hanna, George P., P. J. Weaver, W. D. Sheets, and R. H. Gerhold, *Water and Sewage Works*, **111**, 478 (1964).

185. Harada, T., and W. Kimura, *J. Japan Oil Chemists' Soc.*, **7**, 77 (1958).

186. Harrick, N. J., *J. Phys. Chem.*, **64**, 1110 (1960).

187. Harrick, N. J., Ann, *N.Y., Acad. Sci.*, **101**, 928 (1963).

188. Hayashi, K., T. Danzuka, and K. Ueno, *Talanta*, **4**, 244 (1960).

189. Hazen, A., *J. Amer. Chem. Soc.*, **12**, 427 (1892).

190. Heatley, N. G., and E. J. Page, *Water Sanit. Eng.*, **3**, 46 (1952).

191. Heidler, K., *Chem. Tech.*, **8**, 160 (1956).

192. Heinerth, E., *Tenside*, **3**, 109 (1966).

193. Heller, K., G. Kuhla, and F. Machek, *Mikrochemie*, **18**, 193 (1935).

194. Henriksen, A., *Analyst*, **88**, 898 (1963).

195. Henderson, A. D., and J. J. Baffa, *Proc. Amer. Soc. Civ. Eng.*, **80**, 494 (1954).

196. Hetman, J., *J. Appl. Chem.*, **10**, 16 (1960).

197. Heukelekian, H., *Ind. Eng. Chem.*, **42**, 647 (1950).

198. Higashiura, M., *Kagaku To Kogyo (Tokyo)*, **38**, 306 (1964).

199. Higashiura, M., *Kagaku To Kogyo (Tokyo)*, **40**, 90 (1966).

200. Hill, R. H., and L. K. Herdon, *Sewage Ind. Wastes*, **24**, 1389 (1952).

201. Hindin, E., *Sewage Ind. Wastes*, **25**, 188 (1953).

202. Hinkle, M. E., and W. A. Koehler, "Investigations of Coal Mine Drainage," West Virginia University Engineering Experiment Station, 1944, 1946.

203. Hissel, J., and J. Price, *Bull. Centre Belge Etude Doc. Eaux (Liege)*, **44**, 76 (1959).

204. Hiser, L L., and A. W. Busch, *J. Water Pollution Control Federation*, **36**, 505 (1964).

205. Hoak, R. D., H. C. Bramer, and S. C. Caruso, "Recovery of Organics by Continuous Countercurrent Extraction," Mellon Institute, Pittsburgh, 1962.

206. Horton, R. K., M. Pachelo, and M. F. Santana, *Proc. Inter-Amer. Reg. Conf., Sanitary Eng., Caracus, Venezuela*, **1946**, p. 205.

207. Horton, J. P., J. D. Molley, and H. C. Bays, *Sewage Ind. Wastes*, **28**, 70 (1956).

208. Houlihau, J. E., and P. E. L. Farina, *Sewage Ind. Wastes*, **24**, 157 (1952).
209. Hrivnak, J., *Vodni Hospodarstvi*, **14**, 394 (1964); *Chem. Abstr.*, **62**, 8822h (1965).
210. Hurford, T. R., and D. F. Boltz, *Abstracts of Papers, 154th Meeting, American Chemical Society*, Chicago, 1967.
211. Iguchi, A., *Bull. Chem. Soc. Japan*, **31**, 600 (1958).
212. Institution of Water Engineers, "Approved Methods for the Physical and Chemical Examination of Water," 3rd ed., W. Heffer & Sons, Ltd., Cambridge, England, 1960.
213. Ingols, R., and P. E. Murray, *Water Sewage Works*, **95**, 113 (1948).
214. Inczedy, J., *Analytical Applications of Ion Exchangers*, Pergamon Press, 1966, London, p. 151.
215. Inczedy, J., *Wasserchemie*, **9**, 80 (1964).
216. Isenhour, T. L., C. A. Evans, and G. H. Morrison, *Proc. Intern. Conf. Modern Trends in Activation Analysis, Texas A & M University, College Station*, **123**, 236 (1965).
217. Irudayasamy, A., and A. R. Natarajan, *Analyst*, **90**, 503 (1965).
218. Jaeger, K., and W. Niemitz, *Sewage Ind. Wastes*, **25**, 631 (1953).
219. Jenkins, D., and L. L. Medsker, *Anal. Chem.*, **36**, 610 (1964).
220. Joensson, G., *U.S. At. Energy Comm.*, **AE-105**, 9 (1963).
221. Johnson, D. W., and H. O. Halvorson, *J. Bacteriol.*, **42**, 145 (1941).
222. Jones, H., *The Science of Color*, Thomas Y. Crowell Co., New York, 1952.
223. Joyner, T., J. S. Finley, *Atomic Absorption Newsletter*, Perkin Elmer Corp., Norwalk, Conn., **5**, 21 (1966).
224. Kalalova, E., *Sb. Vysoke Skoly Chem. Technol. Praze, Fak. Technol. Vody*, **5**, 55 (1962).
225. Kalinia, N. M., *Emergetik*, **31**, 802 (1965); *Chem. Abstr.*, **62**, 7503c (1965).
226. Kagi, J. H. R., and B. L. Vallee, *Anal. Chem.*, **30**, 1951 (1958).
227. Kahn, Lloyd, and Cooper H. Wayman, *Anal. Chem.*, **36**, 1340 (1964).
228. Kahn, H. L., *Advan. Chem. Ser.*, **73**, 183 (1968).
228a. Kambara, T., and K. Hasebe, *Bunseki Kagaku*, **14**, 491 (1965).
229. Kamphake, L. J., S. A. Hannah, and J. M. Cohen, *Water Res.*, **1**, 205 (1967).
230. Katlofsky, B., and R. E. Keller, *Anal. Chem.*, **35**, 1665 (1963).
231. Kelley, T. F., *Anal. Chem.*, **37**, 1078 (1965).
232. Kemula, W., Z. Kublick, and Z. Galus, *Nature*, **184**, 1795 (1959).
233. Key, A., *Gas Works Effluents and Ammonia*, 2nd Ed., Institute of Gas Engineers, London, 1956.
234. Kirkbright, G. F., T. S. West, and C. Woodward, *Anal. Chem.*, **37**, 137 (1965).
235. Kirkbright, G. F., T. S. West, and C. Woodward, *Anal. Chem.*, **38**, 1558 (1966).
236. Kleeman, C. R., E. Taborsky, and F. H. Epstein, *Proc. Soc. Exptl. Biol.*, **91**, 480 (1956).
237. Klein, L. J., *Proc. Inst. Sewage Purif.*, 174 (1941).
238. Klein, L. J., *J. Inst. Sewage Purif.*, **2**, 153 (1950).
239. Kabayashi, S., and G. F. Lee, *Anal. Chem.*, **36**, 2197 (1964).
240. Koch, R. C., *Activation Analysis Handbook*, Academic Press, New York, 1960.
241. Kolthoff, I. M., and V. A. Stenger, *Volumetric Analysis*, Vol. 2, 2nd ed., Interscience, New York, 1942.
241a. Kolthoff, I. M., W. D. Harris, and G. Matsuyama, *J. Amer. Chem. Soc.*, **66**, 1782 (1944).

242. Kopp, J. F., and R. C. Kroner, *Appl. Spectr.*, **19**, 155 (1965).
243. Kjeldahl, J. *Z. Anal. Chem.*, **22**, 366 (1883).
244. Kullgren, C., *Svensk Kem. Tidskr.*, **43**, 99 (1931).
245. Kreg, J., and K. H. Szekielda, *Z. Anal. Chem.*, **207**, 388 (1965).
246. Kroner, R. C., M. B. Ettinger, and W. A. Moore, *Anal. Chem.*, **24**, 1877 (1952).
247. Kruse, J. M., and M. G. Mellon, *Anal. Chem.*, **25**, 1188 (1953).
248. Kruse, J. M., and M. G. Mellon, *Sewage Ind. Wastes*, **23**, 1402 (1951).
249. Kruse, J. M., and M. G. Mellon, *Sewage Ind. Wastes*, **24**, 1254 (1952).
250. Kuper, A. I., *Gigiena i Sanit.*, **22**, 61 (1957).
251. Ladendorf, P., *Vom Wasser*, **29**, 119 (1962).
252. Lakanen, E., *Atomic Absorption Newsletter*, Perkin Elmer Corp., Norwalk, Conn., **5**, 17 (1966).
253. Laitinen, H. A., *Natl. Bur. Std. (U.S.) Monograph*, **100**, 75 (1967).
254. Lamar, W. L., and P. G. Drake, *J. Amer. Water Works Assoc.*, **47**, 563 (1955).
255. Lamer, W. L., D. F. Goerlitz, and L. M. Law, *Advan. Chem. Ser.*, **60**, 305 (1966).
256. Leconite, M., *Rev. Gen. Thermique*, **4**, 629 (1965).
257. Leddicotte, G. W., *U.S. At. Energy Comm.*, **65-372-2**, 17 (1966).
258. Lederer, V. V., *Chem. Listy*, **41**, 230 (1947).
259. Lee, E. W., and W. J. Oswald, *Sewage Ind. Wastes*, **26**, 9, 1097 (1954).
260. Leibnitz, E., U. Behrens, and A. Gabert, *Wasserwirtsch.-Wassertech.*, **9**, 69 (1958).
261. LePeintre, C., and C. Romens, *Compt. Rend.*, **261**, 452 (1965).
262. Levchenko, O. N., A. D. Khudyakova, and N. D. Gadrivola, *Lavodsk. Lab.*, **27**, 408 (1961).
263. Lindberg, A., *Vattenhygien*, **19**, 106 (1963).
264. Lindenbaum, A., J. Schubert, and W. D. Armstrong, *Anal. Chem.*, **20**, 1120 (1948).
265. Lingane, J. J., *Anal. Chem.*, **39**, 881 (1967).
266. Loehr, R. C., and G. C. Higgins, *Air Water Pollution*, **9**, 55 (1965).
267. Longwell, J., and W. D. Maniece, *Analyst*, **80**, 167 (1955).
268. Loveridge, B. A., G. W. E. Milner, G. A. Barnett, A. Thomas, and W. M. Henry, *A.E.R.E.* (Harwell), **R-3323** (1960).
269. Ludzack, F. J., and M. B. Ettinger, *Proc. Ind. Wastes Conf., 14th, Purdue Univ.*, **1959**, p. 14.
270. Luré, Yu Yu, and Z. V. Nikolaeva, *Zavodsk. Lab.*, **30**, 937 (1964); *Chem. Abstr.*, **61**, 13035e (1964).
271. Luré, Yu Yu, and V. A. Panova, *Zavodsk. Lab.*, **29**, 293 (1963).
272. Luré, Yu Yu, and Z. W. Nikolajeva, *Zavodsk. Lab.*, **21**, 410 (1955).
273. Luré, Yu Yu, and V. A. Panova, *Zavodsk. Lab.*, **28**, 281 (1962).
274. Luré, Yu Yu, and Z. V. Nikolaeva, *Zavodsk. Lab.*, **31**, 802 (1965); *Chem. Abstr.*, **63**, 12859a (1965).
275. Lyne, F. A., and T. McLachlan, *Analyst*, **74**, 513 (1949).
276. Ma, T. S., R. E. Lang, and J. D. McKinley, *Mikrochim. Acta*, **36**, 57, 368 (1957).
277. Macchi, G., *J. Electroanal. Chem.*, **9**, 920 (1965).
278. MacKichan, K. A., *J. Amer. Water Works Assoc.*, **53**, 1211 (1961).
279. Maienthal, E. J., and J. K. Jaylor, *Advan. Chem. Ser.*, **73**, 172 (1968).
280. Malissa, H., and E. Schoffmann, *Microchim. Acta*, **40**, 187 (1955).

281. Malo, B. A., and R. A. Baker, *Advan. Chem. Ser.*, **73**, 149 (1968).
282. Malz, W., *Foederation Europaeischer Gewaesserschutz Informationsbl.*, **11**, 19 (1964); *Chem. Abstr.*, **64**, 1808g (1966).
283. Mancy, K. H., Unpublished work, School of Public Health, University of Michigan, 1968.
284. Mancy, K. H., and T. Jaffe, *U.S. Public Health Serv. Publ.*, **999-WP-37**, 1966.
285. Mancy, K. H., and D. A. Okun, *Anal. Chem.*, **32**, 108 (1960).
286. Mancy, K. H., D. A. Okun, and C. N. Reilley, *J. Electroanal. Chem.*, **4**, 65 (1962).
287. Mancy, K. H., and W. C. Westgarth, *J. Water Pollution Control Federation*, **34**, 1037 (1962).
288. Manecke, G., C. Bahr, and C. Reich, *Angew. Chem.*, **73**, 299 (1961).
289. Mansell, R. E., and H. W. Emmel, *Atomic Absorption Newsletter*, Perkin Elmer Corp., Norwalk, Conn., **4**, 365 (1965).
290. Marcie, F. J., *Environ. Sci. Technol.*, **1**, 164 (1967).
291. Mark, H. B., private communications, Chemistry Department, The University of Michigan, 1967.
292. Marten, J. F., E. W. Cantanzaro, and D. R. Grady, *Proc. Technicon Symp. Automation Anal. Chem., New York City*, p. 259, October 1966.
293. Masselli, J. W., N. W. Masselli, and M. G. Burford, *New England Interstate Water Pollution Control Commission*, 1958.
294. Masselli, J. W., N. W. Masselli, and M. G. Burford, *New England Interstate Water Pollution Control Commission*, 1959.
295. Matson, W. R., D. K. Roe, and D. E. Carritt, *Anal. Chem.*, **37**, 1594 (1965).
296. May, D. S., Jr., and G. H. Dunstan, *Proc. Purdue Ind. Waste Conf.*, **15**, 321 (1963).
297. McCoy, J. W., *Anal. Chim. Acta*, **6**, 259 (1956).
298. McKee, J. E., and H. W. Wolf, *Water Quality Criteria*, Publication No. 3-A, State of California, State Water Quality Board, Sacramento, 1954.
299. McKeown, J. J., "Procedures for Conducting Mill Effluent Surveys," Technical Bulletin 183, National Council for Steam Improvement, 1965.
300. McKinney, D. S., and A. M. Amorosi, *Ind. Eng. Chem.*, **16**, 315 (1944).
301. McKinney, E., and J. M. Symons, *Sewage Ind. Wastes*, **31**, 549 (1959).
302. McNutt, N. W., and R. H. Maier, *Anal. Chem.*, **34**, 276 (1962).
303. Medin, A. L., and L. K. Herndon, *Sewage Ind. Wastes*, **24**, 1260 (1952).
304. Meinke, W. W., *Science*, **121**, 177 (1955).
305. Meites, L., *Handbook of Analytical Chemistry*, McGraw-Hill, New York, 1963.
306. Meleshchenko, K. F., *Gigiena i Sanit.*, **25**, 54 (1960).
307. Mellon, M. G., *Analytical Absorption Spectroscopy*, Wiley, New York, 1950, Chapter 9.
308. Melpolder, F. W., C. W. Warfield, and C. E. Headington, *Anal. Chem.*, **25**, 1453 (1953).
309. Mentink, A. F., "Instrumentation for Water Quality Determination," *ASCE Water Resources Eng. Conf., Reprint* **153** (1965).
310. Meyer, H. J., and C. Brack, *Chem. Eng. Techol.*, **22**, 545 (1950).
311. Michelsen, E., and E. Marki, *Mitt Gebiete Lebensm. Hyg.*, **52**, 557 (1961).
312. Mills, E. J., Jr., and V. T. Stack, Jr., *Proc. Ind. Waste Conf., 9th, Purdue Univ.*, **57**, 1954.

313. Mills, E. J., and V. T. Stack, Jr., *Proc. Ind. Waste Conf., 8th, Purdue Univ.,* **273,** 1953.

314. Milton, R. F., *Analyst,* **74,** 54 (1949).

315. Mitchell, L. E., *Advan. Chem. Ser.,* **60,** 1 (1966).

316. Mohlman, F. W., and F. P. Edwards, *Ind. Eng. Chem ,* **3,** 119 (1963).

317. Moggio, W. A., *Proc. Amer. Soc. Civil Engs.,* **80,** 420 (1954).

318. Molof, A. H., and N. S. Zaleiko, *Proc. Purdue Ind. Waste Conf., 19th, Purdue Univ.,* **1964,** p. 56.

319. Montgomery, H. A. C., and N. S. Thom, *Analyst,* **87,** 689 (1962).

320. Moore, E. Q., H. A. Thomas, Jr., and W. B. Snow, *Sewage Ind. Wastes,* **22,** 1343 (1950).

321. Moore, W. A., R. C. Kroner, and C. C. Ruchhoft, *Anal. Chem.,* **21,** 953 (1949).

322. Moore, W. A., F. J. Ludzack, and C. C. Ruchhoft, *Anal. Chem.,* **23,** 1297 (1951).

323. Morris, R. L., *Anal Chem.,* **24,** 1376 (1952).

324. Myers, L. S., and A. H. Brush, *Anal. Chem.,* **34,** 342 (1962).

325. Nash, T., *Biochem. J.,* **55,** 416 (1953).

326. National Bureau of Standards, "Recommendations of the National Committee on Radiation Protection and Measurements," Handbook 49, *U.S Government Printing House,* November 1951.

327. National Bureau of Standards, "Radiological Monitoring Methods and Instruments," Handbook 51, U.S. Government Printing House, April 1952.

328. National Bureau of Standards, "Maximum Permissible Amounts of Radioisotopes in the Human Body and Maximum Permissible Concentrations in Air and Water," Handbook 52, U.S. Government Printing House, March 1953.

329. National Bureau of Standards, "Permissible Dose from External Sources of Ionizing Radiation," Handbook 59, U.S. Government Printing House, September 1954.

330. Naucke, W., and F. Tarkmann, *Brennstoff-Chem.,* **45,** 263 (1964); *Chem. Abstr.,* **62,** 322b (1965).

331. Navone, R., and W. D. Fenninger, *J. Amer. Water Works Assoc.,* **59,** 757 (1967).

332. Nemerow, N. L., *Theories and Practices of Industrial Waste Treatment,* Addison-Wesley, Reading, Mass., 1963.

333. Nemtsova, L. I., A. D. Semenov, and V. G. Datsko, *Gidrokhim. Materialy,* **38,** 150 (1964); *Chem. Abstr.,* **62,** 15902x (1965).

334. Newell, J. C., R. J. Mazaika, and W. J. Cook, *J. Agr. Food Chem.,* **6,** 669 (1958).

335. Newell, B., and G. D. Pont, *Nature,* **201,** 36 (1964).

336. Nusbaum, I., *Sewage Ind. Wastes,* **25,** 311 (1953).

337. Oak Ridge National Laboratory and Robert A. Taft Sanitary Engineering Center, PHS, "Report of the Joint Program of Studies on the Decontamination of Radioactive Waters," *U.S. At. Energy Comm., Rept.,* **ORNL-2557,** 45 (1959).

338. O'Brien, J. E., and J. Fiore, *Wastes Eng.,* **33,** 352 (1962).

339. O'Brien, J. E., and J. Fiore, *Wastes Eng.,* **33,** 128 (1962).

340. O'Kelley, G. D., "Application of Computers to Nuclear and Radio Chemistry," *U.S. At. Energy Comm. Rept.,* **NASNS 3017,** p. 156 (1962).

341. Otsuki, A., and T. Hanya, *Nippon Kagaku Zasshi*, **84**, 798 (1963); *Chem. Abstr.*, **60**, 2640e (1964).
342. Orford, H. E., and W. T. Ingram, *Sewage Ind. Wastes*, **25**, 419 (1953).
343. Orford, H. E., and W. T. Ingram, *Sewage Ind. Wastes*, **25**, 424 (1953).
344. Oppenheimer, C. H., E. F. Corcoran, and J. Van Arman, *Limnol. Oceanog.*, **8**, 478 (1963).
345. Palange, R. C., and S. A. Megregian, *J. Sanit. Eng., Amer. Soc. Civil Engs.*, **84**, 1606 (1958).
346. Palin, A. T., *Water Water Eng.*, **59**, 341 (1955).
347. Parsons, M. L., W. J. McCarthy, and J. D. Winefordner, *J. Chem. Ed.*, **44**, 214 (1967).
348. Pearson, E., and C. N. Sawyer, *Proc. Ind. Waste Conf., 5th, Purdue Univ.*, **1949**, p. 26.
349. Pichler, H., and H. Schulz, *Brennstaff-Chem.*, **39**, 148 (1958); *Chem. Abstr.*, **57**, 1978 (1959).
350. Pickhardt, W. P., A. M. Oemler, and I. Mitchell, Jr., *Anal. Chem.*, **27**, 1784 (1955).
351. Pillion, E., *J. Gas Chromatog*, **3**, 238 (1965).
352. Pitter, P., *Sci. Papers Inst. Chem. Technol., Water (ČSSR)*, **6**, 547 (1962).
353. Ponomarenko, A. A., and L. N. Amelina, *Zh. Analit. Khim.*, **18**, 1244 (1963); *Chem. Abstr.*, **60**, 3494h (1954).
354. Popel, F., and C. Wagner, "Determination of Organic Carbon," unpublished manuscript, *Forschungs und Entwicklungsinstutut fur Industrie—und Siedlungs-wasserwirtschaft sowie Abfallwertschaft e.B.*, Stuttgart, Germany.
355. Porges, R., and E. J. Struzeski, *J. Water Pollution Control Federation*, **33**, 167 (1961).
356. Potter, E. C., and J. F. Moresky, "The Use of Cation-Exchange Resin in the Determination of Copper and Iron Dissolved at Very Low Concentrations in Water," in *Ion Exchange and Its Applications*, Society of Chemical Industry, London, 1955, p. 93.
357. Povoledo, D., and M. Gerletti, *Mem. Inst. Ital. Idrobiol. Dott. Marco de Marchi*, **15**, 153 (1962).
358. Powell, S. T., *Ind. Eng. Chem.*, **46**, 112A (1954).
359. Pohl, F. A., *Z. Anal. Chem.*, **197**, 193 (1963).
360. Pomeroy, R., *Sewage Works J.*, **8**, 572 (1936).
361. Potter, E. C., and G. E. Everitt, *J. Appl. Chem.*, **9**, 642 (1959).
362. Precision Scientific Co., Chicago, Illinois.
363. Prochazkova, L., *Anal. Chem.*, **36**, 865 (1964).
364. Promeroy, R., *Petroleum Eng.*, **15**, 156 (1944).
365. Prussin, S. G., T. A. Harris, and T. M. Hollander, *Proc. Intern. Conf. Mod. Trends Activation Anal., Texas A & M University, College Station*, **123**, 132 (1965).
366. Pungor, E., K. Toth, and J. Havas, *Acta Chim. Acad. Sci. Hung.*, **41**, 239 (1964).
367. Pungor, E., and J. Havas, *Acta Chim. Acad. Sci. Hung.*, **50**, 77 (1966).
368. Pungor, E., K. Toth, and J. Havas, *Acta Chim. Acad. Sci. Hung.*, **48**, 17 (1966).
369. U.S. Department of Public Works, *Public Works*, 85 (1954).

370. Rainwater, F. H., and L. L. Thatcher, *U.S. Geol. Surv., Water, Supply Paper,* 1454 (1960).

371. Rambow, C. A., *J. Amer. Water Works Assoc.,* 55, 1037 (1963).

372. Rayonier's, Inc., *Paper Mill News,* 82, 12 (1959).

373. Rechnitz, G. A., M. R. Kiesz, and S. B. Zamochnick, *Anal. Chem.,* 38, 973 (1966).

374. Rechnitz, G. A., M. R. Kresz, *Anal. Chem.,* 38, 1786 (1966).

375. Reilley, C. N., and D. T. Sawyer, *Experiments for Instrumental Methods,* McGraw-Hill, New York, 1961.

376. Reynolds, J. G., and M. Irwin, *Chem. Ind. Rev.,* 419 (1948).

377. Richter, H. G., and A. S. Gillespie, Jr., *Anal. Chem.,* 34, 1116 (1962).

378. Rideal, S., and G. Stewart, *Analyst,* 26, 141 (1901).

379. Rider, B. F., and M. F. Mellon, *Ind. Eng. Chem. (Anal.),* 18, 96 (1946).

380. Riehl, M. L, and E. G. Will, *Sewage Ind. Wastes,* 22, 190 (1950).

381. Riehl, M. L., *Sewage Works J.,* 20, 629 (1948).

382. Riley, J. P., and P. Shinhaseni, *Analyst,* 83, 299 (1958).

383. Robinson, J. W., "Atomic Absorption Spectroscopy," Marcell Dekker, Inc., New York, 1966.

384. Robertson, G., *Analyst,* 89, 368 (1964)

385. Roderick, W. R., *J. Chem. Ed.,* 43, 510 (1966).

386. Rogers, C. J., C. W. Chambers, and N. A. Clarke, *Anal. Chem.,* 38, 1853 (1967).

387. Rosen, A. A., R. T. Skeel, and M. B. Ettinger, *J. Water Pollution Control Federation,* 35, 777 (1963).

388. Rosen, A. A., J. B. Peter, and F. M. Middleton, *J. Water Pollution Control Federation,* 34, 7 (1962).

389. Rosen, A. A., and F. M. Middleton, *Anal. Chem.,* 31, 1729 (1959).

390. Rosen, A. A., personal communication, Cincinnati Water Pollution Control Laboratory, FWPCA, USDI, 1966.

391. Rosen, A. A., and F. M. Middleton, *Anal. Chem.,* 27, 790 (1955).

392. Ross, J. W., *Science,* 156, 1378 (1967).

393. Rossum, J. R , *Anal. Chem.,* 21, 631 (1949).

394. Rudolfs, W., *Industrial Waste Treatment,* Reinhold, New York, 1953.

395. Rudolfs, W., and W. D. Hanlon, *Sewage Ind. Wastes,* 23, 1125 (1951).

396. Rush, R. M., and J. H. Yoe, *Anal. Chem.,* 26, 1345 (1954).

397. Shabunin, I. I., and V. I. Lavrenchuk, *Gigiena i Sanit.,* 30, 63 (1965); *Chem. Abstr.,* 62, 14320f (1965).

398. Sanderson, W. W , and G. B. Ceresia, *J. Water Pollution Control Federation,* 37, 1177 (1965).

399. Sawicki, E., T. W. Stanley, J. Pfaff, and A. D. Amico, *Talanta,* 10, 641 (1963).

400. Sax, N. I., M. Beigel, and J. C. Daly, *Ann. Rept. N.Y. Dept. Health Res. Lab.,* 1962, 75.

401. Schatze, T. C., *Sewage Works J.,* 17, 497 (1945).

402. Schechter, M. S., S. B. Soloway, R. A. Hayes, and H. L. Haller, *Ind. Eng. Chem.,* 17, 704 (1945).

403. Schechter, M. S., and I. Hornstein, *Anal. Chem.,* 24, 544 (1952).

404. Schilt, A. A., *Anal. Chem.,* 30, 1409 (1958)

405. Scholz, L., *Vom Wasser,* 30, 143 (1963).

406. Schoniger, W., in *Advances in Analytical Chemistry and Instrumentation*, Vol. I, 199, C. N. Reilley, Ed., Interscience, New York, (1965).
407. Schmidt, H., and M. von Stackelbert, *Modern Polarographic Methods*, Academic Press, New York, 1963.
408. Schulz, N. F., *Anal. Chem.*, **25**, 1762 (1953).
409. Schweitzer, G. K., and W. Van Willis, *Advances in Analytical Chemistry and Instrumentation*, Vol. 5, C. N. Reilley, Ed., Interscience, New York, 1966, p. 169.
410. Serfass, E. J., R. B. Freeman, B. F. Dodge, and W. Zabban, *Plating*, **39**, 267 (1952).
411. Setter, L. R., A. S. Goldin, and J. S. Nader, *Anal. Chem.*, **26**, 1304 (1954).
412. Setter, L. E., and A. S. Goldin, *J. Amer. Water Works Assoc.*, **48**, 1373 (1956).
413. Shain, I., "Stripping Analysis," in *Treatise on Analytical Chemistry*, Part I, Vol. 4, I. M. Kolthoff and P. J. Elving, Eds., Interscience, New York, 1959, p. 50.
414. Shain, I., and S. P. Perone, *Anal. Chem.*, **33**, 325 (1961).
415. Shapiro, J., *Science*, **133**, 2063 (1961).
416. Shapiro, J., *Science*, **133**, 3470 (1963).
417. Sherwood, R. M., and F. W. Chapman, *Anal. Chem.*, **27**, 88 (1955).
418. Shinn, M. B., *Ind. Eng. Chem.*, **13**, 33 (1941).
419. Sillen, L. G., *Advan. Chem. Ser.*, **67**, 45 (1967).
420. Simard, R. G., I. Hasegawa, W. Bandaruk, and C. E. Headington, *Anal. Chem.*, **23**, 1384 (1951).
421. Sirois, J. C., *Analyst*, **87**, 900 (1962).
422. Slavin, W., *Atomic Absorption Newsletter*, Perkin Elmer, Norwalk, Conn., **3**, 141 (1964).
423. Smith, R. S., and W. W. Walker, "Surveys of Liquid Wastes from Munitions Manufacturing," United States Public Health Service, Reprint 2508, Public Health Reports, 1965.
424. Smith, G. F., *Mixed Perchloric, Sulfuric and Phosphoric Acids and Their Applications in Analysis*, 2nd ed., G. Frederick Smith Chemical Company, Columbus, Ohio, 1942.
425. Smith, D., and J. Eichelberger, *J. Water Pollution Control Federation*, **37**, 77 (1965).
426. Soap and Detergent Association, Subcommittee on Biodegradation Test Methods, *J. Amer. Oil Chemists' Soc.*, **42**, 987 (1965).
427. Society for Analytical Chemistry, *Official, Standardized and Recommended Methods of Analysis*, S. C. Jolly, Ed., W. Heffer & Sons, Ltd., Cambridge, England, 1963.
428. Society of Public Analysts and Other Analytical Chemists, *Bibliography of Standard Tentative and Recommended or Recognized Methods of Analysis*, Society of Analytical Chemists Publication, London. 1951.
429. Sokolov, V. P., and K. A. Labashov, *Zavodsk. Lab.*, **28**, 285 (1962).
430. Soloway, S., and P. Rosen, *Anal. Chem.*, **29**, 1820 (1957).
431. Souliotis, A. G., R. P. Belkas, and A. P. Grimanis, *Analyst*, **92**, 300 (1967).
432. Spaulding, *J. Amer. Water Works Assoc.*, **34**, 277 (1942).
433. Stankovic, V., *Chem. Zvesti*, **16**, 683 (1962).
434. Stein, P. K., *U.S. Publ. Health Serv. Publ.*, **999-AP-15**, 65 (1964).
435. Stenger, V. A., and C. E. Van Hall, *Anal. Chem.*, **39**, 205 (1967).

436. Stephens, K., *Limnol. Oceanog.,* **8,** 361 (1963).

437. Stewart, R. G., *Analyst,* **88,** 468 (1963).

438. Stojkovic, I., and H. Kukovec, *Textil,* **13,** 69 (1964).

439 Straub, C. P., *U.S. At. Energy Comm., Div. of Tech. Inform.,* **1966,** p. 88.

440. Streeter, H. W., and E. B. Phelps, *U.S. Public Health Bull.,* **146** (February 1925).

441. Strickland, J. D. H., and T. R. Parsons, *Bull. Fisheries Res. Board Can.,* **125,** 210 (1960).

442. Sullivan, J. P., "Determination of Dissolved Oxygen and Nitrogen in Sea Water by Gas Chromatography," Marine Science Department, Report No. **0-17-63,** U.S. Naval Oceanographic Office, Washington, D.C., 1963.

443. Surak, J. G., M. F. Herman, and D. T. Haworgh, *Anal. Chem.,* **37,** 428 (1965).

444. Sweeney, W. A., and J. K. Foote, *J. Water Pollution Control Federation,* **36,** 14 (1964).

445. Swisher, R. D., *Soap Chem. Specialties,* **39,** 47, 57 (1963).

446. Swinnerton, J. W., V. J. Linnenbom, and C. H. Cheek, *Anal. Chem.,* **34,** 483 (1962).

447. Szekely, G., G. Raoz, and G. Traply, *Periodica Polytech.,* **10,** 231 (1966); *Chem. Abstr.,* **67,** 500 (1967).

448. Talvitie, N. A., and W. J. Garcia, *Anal. Chem.,* **37,** 851 (1965).

449. Taylor, A. E., and C. W. Miller, *J. Biol. Chem.,* **18,** 215 (1914).

450. Technical Association of the Pulp and Paper Industry, "Analysis of Industrial Process and Waste Waters," Tappi **12,** 32 (1955).

451. Technicon Instruments Corp., Bulletin, Technicon AutoAnalyzer, Channeey, New York.

452. Tenny, A. M., reprint from paper presented at Technicon Symposium on Automation in Analytical Chemistry, New York, October 19, 1966.

453. Thayer, L. C., and D. A. Robinson, *Proc. First Intern. Cong. Instr. Soc. Amer. 1st, Philadelphia,* **9,** 2 (1954).

454. Theriault, E. J., *U.S. Public Health Bull.,* **173** (July 1927).

455. Theriault, E. G., and P. D. McNamee, *Ind. Eng. Chem.,* **4,** 59 (1932).

456. Therous, F. R., E. F. Eldridge, and W. L. Mallmann, *Laboratory Manual for Chemical and Bacterial Analysis of Water and Sewage,* 3rd ed., McGraw-Hill, New York, 1943.

457. Thomas, H. A., Jr., *Sewage Works J.,* **9,** 425 (1937).

458. Thompson, M. E., and J. W. Ross, *Science,* **154,** 1643 (1966).

459. Tikhonov, M. K, and V. K. Zhavoronkina, *Soviet Oceanog.,* **3,** 22 (1960).

460. Todt, F., and R. Freier, Ger. Pat. No. 1-012-764 (1957).

461. Trubnik, E. H., and W. Rudolfs, *Proc. Ind. Waste Conf., 14th, Purdue Univ.,* **1948,** p. 266.

462. Trimmer, J. D., *Response of Physical Systems,* Wiley, New York, 1950.

463. Tschopp, E., and E. Tschopp, *Helv. Chim. Acta.,* **15,** 793 (1932).

464. Turekian, K. K., *U.S. At. Energy Comm.,* **2912-12,** 60 (1966).

465. Turski, Y. I., A. V. Masov, and L. E. Samolova, *Gaz. Prom.,* **4,** 20 (1959).

466. Tyler, C. P., and J. H. Karchmer, *Anal. Chem.,* **31,** 499 (1959).

467. Underwood, E. S., *Chem. Specialities Mfrs. Assoc. Proc.,* **1965,** 141.

468. Umbreit, W. W., R. H. Burris, and J. F Stanffer, *Manometric Techniques,* Burgess Publishing Co., Minneapolis, 1957.

469. Umland, F., and G. Z. Wunsch, *Anal. Chem.,* **213,** 186 (1965).

470. U.S. Department of the Interior, *Guidelines for Establishing Water Quality Standards for Interstate Waters—Under the Water Quality Act of 1965,* Public Law 89–234," Federal Water Pollution Control Administration, U.S. Department of the Interior (May 1966).

471. U.S. Public Health Service, National Water Quality Network, Annual Completion of Data, *Public Health Serv. Publ.,* 663 (1963).

472. U.S. Public Health Service and Ontario Department of Health, "A Study of Organic Contaminants in Boundary Waters Using Carbon Filter Techniques, Lake Huron—Lake Erie (1953–1955)," 1960.

473. United States Public Health Service, "Industrial Waste Guides: Supplement D," Ohio River Pollution Survey, *United States Public Health Service, Federal Security Agency,* 1942.

474. Van Hall, C. E., J. Safranko, and V. A. Stenger, *Anal. Chem.,* 35, 315 (1963).

475. Van Lopik, J. R., G. S. Rambie, and A. E. Pressman, *Proc. Symp. Water Quality Analysis, New York,* 1967, p. 7.

476. Van Slyke, D. D., and J. Folch, *J. Biol. Chem.,* 136, 509 (1940).

477. Van Slyke, D. D., *Anal. Chem.,* 26, 1706 (1954).

478. Velz, C. J., *Sewage Ind. Wastes,* 22, 666 (1950).

479. Voege, F. A., and H. L. Vanesche, *J. Amer. Water Works Assoc.,* 56, 1351 (1964).

480. Voth, J. L., *Anal. Chem.,* 35, 1957 (1963).

481. Walker, J. Q., *J. Gas Chromatograph,* 2, 46 (1964)

482. Ward, J. C., and R. W. Klippel, *Chem. Process. Mag.,* p. 69 (October 1965).

483. Warnick, S. L., and A. R. Gaufin, *J. Amer. Water Works Assoc.,* 57, 1023 (1965).

484. Water Pollution Control Federation, D.C., "Regulations of Sewer Use," Manual of Practice-3, 1955.

485. Weber, W. J., Jr., and R. H. Carlson, *J. Sanit. Eng. Div. Amer. Soc. Civil Eng.,* SA3, 140 (1965).

486. Weber, W. J., Jr., J. C. Morris, and W. Stumm, *Anal. Chem.,* 34, 1844 (1962).

487. Weber, W. J., Jr., and J. C. Morris, *J. Water Pollution Control Federation,* 36, 573 (1964).

488. Weber, W. J., Jr., and J. P. Gould, *Advan. in Chem. Ser.,* 60, 305 (1966).

489. Weiss, C. M., *Trans Amer. Fisheries Soc.,* 90, 143 (1961).

490. Weiss, C. M., and J. H. Gakstatter, *J. Water Pollution Control Federation,* 36, 240 (1964).

491. Weiss, C. M., J. D. Johnson, and B. Kwan, *J. Amer. Water Works Assoc.,* 55, 1367 (1963).

492. Weiker, W., *Anal. Chem.,* 185, 457 (1962).

493. Wells, W. N., P. W. Rohrbaugh, and G. A. Dotty, *Sewage Ind. Wastes,* 24, 212 (1952).

494. West, T. S., *Anal. Chim. Acta.,* 25, 405 (1961).

495. Westland, A. D., and R. R. Langford, *Anal. Chem.,* 33, 1306 (1961).

496. Wexler, A. S., *Anal. Chem.,* 35, 1936 (1963).

497. White, C. E., *Anal. Chem.,* 30, 729 (1958).

498. White, C. E., and J. Weissler, *Anal Chem.,* 36, 116R (1964).

499. Whitnack, G. C., *J. Electroanal. Chem.,* 2, 110 (1961).

500. Wickbold, R., *Z. Anal. Chem.,* 171, 81 (1959).

501. Wilcox, L. V., *J Amer. Water Works Assoc.,* 42, 775 (1950).

502. Wilks Scientific Corp. Publication, South Norwalk, Conn.

503. Williams, D. D., and R. R. Miller, *Anal. Chem.*, **34**, 657 (1962).

504. Wilson, R. F , *Limnol. Oceanog.*, **6**, 259 (1961).

505. Winefordner, J. D., and T. J. Vickers, *Anal. Chem.*, **36**, 161 (1964).

505a. Winkler, L. W., *Ber. Deut. Chem. Ges.*, **21**, 2843 (1888).

506. Winter, G. D., and A. Ferrari, "Automatic Wet Chemical Analysis as Applied to Pesticides Residues," in *Residue Rev. V*, W. Gunther, Ed., Springer-Verlag, Berlin, 1963.

507. Wise, W., B. F. Dodge, and H. Bliss, *Ind. Eng. Chem.*, **39**, 5, 632 (1947).

508. Witmer, A. W., and N. W. H. Addink, *Science Ind.*, **12**, 1 (1965).

509. Woodward, R. L., *Sewage Ind. Wastes,* **25**, 918 (1953).

510. World Health Organization, *World Health Organ. Tech. Rept. Ser.*, **173** (1959).

511. Yazhemskaya, V. Ya, *Gigiena i Sanit,* **29**, 58 (1964); *Chem. Abstr.*, **62**, 8305h (1965).

512. Young, J. C., and J. W. Clark, *J. Sanit. Eng. Div., Amer. Soc. Civil Engs.,* SA1, 43 (1965).

513. Yorko, N. A., and Z. A. Volkova, *Khim. Prom. Inform. Nauk-Tekh,* **2**, 77 (1964); *Chem. Abstr.*, **62**, 2611b (1965).

514. Yorko, N. A., and Z. A. Volkova, *Khim. Prom. Inform. Nauk-Tekh,* **2**, 77 (1964).

515. Zhavoronkina, T. K., *Soviet Oceanog.*, **3**, 27 (1960).

# SEWAGE, EFFLUENTS, AND SLUDGE ANALYSES

By ROBERT L. BUNCH, *Department of the Interior, Robert A. Taft Water Research Center, Cincinnati, Ohio*

## Contents

## I. INTRODUCTION

The analyses of sewage, effluents, and sludge are meaningful only if the analyst has a basic concept of sewage characteristics and sewage treatment processes. Many of the determinations are not analysis per se, but certain empirical tests used to evaluate the performance of sewage treatment plants. Without these analytical determinations sewage plants cannot be run intelligently; therefore, more and more installations are using the fundamental principles of hydraulics, bacteriology, and chemistry in their operations. In addition to giving guidance to the operator, a record of analysis is useful in court in the event of suits by landowners downstream for alleged damages. Well documented records also serve as a basis for determining future treatment requirements. Almost every municipality will sooner or later have to extend or rebuild its present treatment plant. Characteristics of the local sewage and past plant performance will be of inestimable value to the designing engineer.

In presenting the analysis in this chapter, the emphasis is on the purpose and on the interpretation of the results rather than step by step procedures. For those trained in chemistry, specific directions for making most analyses encountered in domestic waste can be found in the British and American standard methods (1,2,19,34). Reference 2 is commonly known as *Standard Methods*. Chemists who have only infrequent occasion to make laboratory determinations on sewage and students in sanitary engineering will find these references sparse in the interpretation of results in relationship to specific problems. This treatise will then serve as an adjunct for those new in the field.

It is well to emphasize that sewage is too complex and variable from place-to-place, hour-to-hour, and day-to-day to permit the determination of the extract quantities of all constituents. For this reason chemists will find the examination of sewage matter is unlike most other chemical analyses with which they are familiar.

## A. CHEMICAL CHARACTERISTICS OF SEWAGE

Sewage is the used water supply of a community. This may include waste from residences or domestic sewage, waste from industrial establishments or industrial waste, and drainage water if the community has combined sewers. Although sewage is over 99% water, it carries a large variety of dissolved, dispersed, and floating substances. These range from the minerals present in the water supply to unusual chemicals from industrial wastes.

In sewage disposal problems the sanitary engineer is generally not too concerned with the mineral content; therefore, the concentration or strength of the sewage is based on the organic matter. The organic matter can be divided into carbonaceous and nitrogenous materials. The main non-nitrogenous substances are sugars, starches, cellulose, fats, oils, and lignins. The nitrogen-containing compounds include proteins, amines, amino acids, and urea. Fresh sewage has the appearance of dishwater with paper, lumps of feces, and miscellaneous materials floating in it. Fresh sewage becomes stale in about 2 hr and soon afterwards develops a dark color with a hydrogen sulfide odor. The constituents of sewage are not static, but change as time progresses. From the above description, one can appreciate the difficulties in obtaining a truly representative sample.

## B. SEWAGE TREATMENT PROCESSES

Fundamentally there are two types of sewage treatment, primary and secondary. Primary treatment is the removal of solid particles by physical or mechanical means and the disposal of the residual sludge. Solids removal is done by screens, grit chambers, settling tanks, and skimming devices. Sedimentation is the most important process in the primary treatment. Chemical precipitation with lime, alum, or other flocculents is an adjunct that is sometimes used to increase the effectiveness of the primary process. Primary treatment removes about 35% of the biological oxygen demand from waste water if chemical precipitation is not used. Up to 85% removal can be accomplished with chemical precipitation, but the increased cost and the disposal of the sludge become problems.

In a primary treatment plant the chemist is concerned with the determination of the efficiency of solids removal and the condition of the sludge.

Secondary sewage treatment is based on the action of bacteria in removing the putrescible matter remaining after the primary treatment. Secondary treatment methods are so varied that only the two main methods will be discussed without various ramifications. The analyst who has need of additional knowledge on these ramifications should read a textbook on sewage treatment practice.

Most small towns with sewage treatment plants use trickling filters as the means of secondary treatment. The principle of this method is that the supernatant from the primary settling tank is sprayed upon a bed of crushed stones about 6 ft deep. The sewage trickles through the bed to underdrains which lead to a final settling tank. The action of the filter consists in mechanically removing the lighter solids not removed by sedimentation and in the oxidation of the sewage by contact with the zoogloeal film that forms on the filter stones with oxygen provided in the void space in the bed. Suspended solids sloughed from the filter are removed from the effluent by sedimentation before the effluent is discharged into the river.

The activated sludge process is the method most frequently used by large cities; however, it is sometimes used by small towns where a high degree of purification is required. In this process the settled sewage is mixed with a biologically active mass called "activated sludge" that was produced previously by this process. The mixture flows through a tank where compressed air is added to furnish the necessary oxygen and agitation. From the aeration tank, the mixture goes to a tank where the sludge settles. Almost all the sludge is returned to the inlet end of the aeration tank, and the clear effluent is discarded to the waterway. The activated sludge process is a true biological process in which a large amount of the organic matter in the sewage is assimilated by the microorganisms.

Irrespective of the method used, comparative tests upon the sewage before and after treatment are needed not only to evaluate the efficiency of the treatment, but they are necessary to control the operation. For the most part, the amount of impurity present can only be accurately determined by chemical analysis. Often an effluent will be relatively free from suspended matter, yet it will contain organic matter in solution which will undergo putrefaction later.

In secondary sewage treatment plants, the chemist must determine not only the efficiency of solid removal, but also the oxidizing efficiency of the plant. Certain routine control tests must also be run to assure that the proper conditions for bacterial growth are being maintained. At times, special determinations are necessary if industrial wastes are suspected to be causing treatment difficulties.

An important part of any sewage treatment operation is the solids disposal. All the suspended solids removed by sedimentation and the excess activated sludge must be disposed of by burying, burning, drying, digesting, or other means. The method used is usually determined by the size of the plant. Sludge digestion with drying on sand beds is the most common method used by small and medium size plants.

Sludge digestion is an anaerobic biological process which transforms a portion of the sludge into liquids and gases, thereby reducing the sludge volume. The resulting "humus" is stable, compact, and easily filtered. The gas evolved during sludge digestion is high enough in methane to be used for heating and operating gas engines.

Digestion occurs automatically in nature when nonliving organic matter accumulates in the presence of moisture. To adapt this natural process to sludge digesters and intensify it requires laboratory control. The efficiency of sludge digestion is measured by the solids reduction and the gas production.

## II. LABORATORY CONTROL OF SEWAGE TREATMENT

The tests made at any sewage treatment plant depend on the personnel and equipment available. Large cities usually have a completely equipped laboratory with trained chemists and engineers. On the other hand, many small treatment plants have no trained operators, and laboratory facilities are meager or entirely lacking. It is unfortunate that in the past designing engineers neglected to provide space for routine tests. Today it is well known that the lack of proper laboratory controls will adversely affect the performance of any treatment plant, large or small; yet many small communities fail to provide the necessary funds for personnel. They expect a lone attendant to be a chemist, an engineer, and an able-bodied laborer capable of performing all the duties of technical control, routine operation, and maintenance.

It is obviously impractical to establish a complete laboratory at every treatment plant, yet to operate a plant efficiently requires that the operation be on a laboratory control basis. The solution for small municipalities is to train the plant operator to make simple tests and have additional tests made periodically by some technically trained person retained by the town. A few very simple tests can be of great aid in the operation of a small plant. For example, consider a small plant which has only primary sedimentation with sludge digestion and chlorination of the plant effluent. The Imhoff cone test on the influent and effluent will show how much material can be removed by sedimentation and what efficiency is being obtained. This test requires very little equipment and no special skill. The efficiency of a digestion tank is measured by the reduction of the volatile solids. Determination of the quantity of dry solids in the sludges, and the proportion of such solids that are volatile will tell the operator the amount of solids to be digested and how well this is achieved. A simple, easily operated pH color comparator can be of value to the operator in maintaining the proper conditions for digestion. Chlorination of sewage effluent is generally practiced to destroy bacteria. Bacteriological examination is impractical at a small plant. If sufficient chlorine is added to sewage effluents to have a residual of 0.5 mg/liter, 15 min after the chlorine has been applied effective disinfection should be accomplished. Kits are available at moderate cost for this determination. Thus, a small plant can, with only about $400 worth of equipment and care in sampling, secure operating information. None of these tests require standard solutions or an analytical balance.

The tests discussed are routine operational tests which tell nothing about the strength of the effluent and its effects on the receiving stream. Therefore, they should be periodically supplemented by analytical determinations that are more exact and encompassing.

The laboratory tests required for any particular plant will be governed by the type of treatment process. Whether the minimum or total number of tests are performed will depend on the laboratory facilities, personnel, and use made of the analyses. From the standpoint of control, the following tests should be performed if possible:

Raw and settled sewage
    Biochemical oxygen demand
    Chemical oxygen demand
    Suspended solids
    Volatile suspended solids
    Kjeldahl nitrogen
    Settleable solids
    Chlorides
    Temperature
Activated sludge aeration tank
    Suspended solids
    Settleable solids
    Dissolved oxygen
    Sludge volume index or sludge density index
Sludge
    Return activated sludge
        Suspended solids
    Primary and wasted activated sludge
        Total solids
        Volatile solids
        pH
Final treatment effluents
    Biochemical oxygen demand
    Chemical oxygen demand
    Suspended solids
    Volatile suspended solids
    Dissolved oxygen
    Nitrate nitrogen
    Nitrite nitrogen
    Ammonia nitrogen
    Chlorine residuals

Sludge digestion
  pH
  Gas production—% $CO_2$
  Alkalinity of the liquid
  Volatile acids
  Total solids
  Volatile solids
Stream or other dilution body
  Biochemical oxygen demand
  Chemical oxygen demand
  Dissolved oxygen

It should not be inferred that the above tests are the only ones that can be run in a treatment plant. If funds are available, the plant laboratory can be a proving ground for the study of new methods and processes. There are many problems unsolved in wastewater treatment, and who is closer to the problem than the plant operator and plant chemist?

## A. SAMPLING AND VOLUME MEASUREMENT

The importance of good sampling cannot be overrated in dealing with heterogeneous matter. Care must be exercised in maintaining the true proportion of suspended solids to liquid. Samples should not be taken near the top or sides, but taken at mid-depth in the channels or tanks. Dippers, cans, or wide-mouth bottles can be used for sampling; however, the samples should be stored only in borosilicate glass containers. In general, samples should be analyzed within a few hours after collection, but if this is not possible, they should be kept in the dark at 5°C. If a chemical preservative is used, the analyst should make certain that it does not affect the determination. For many analyses, samples can be preserved for a short time by adjusting the acidity to pH 2 with sulfuric acid.

A single or "grab" sample of sewage or sewage effluent will not be a truly representative sample of the average conditions. The composition of sewage varies throughout the day and night, corresponding to the habits of a community. A composite sample made up of portions of hourly individual samples measured in proportion to the flow at the time are more desirable. Many plants have automatic sampling devices for taking composite samples at different places in the treatment process. These individual samples should be kept cool until the end of the total sampling period. If it is not possible to obtain a 24-hr composite, samples collected at certain hours will give a fair indication of the average conditions if the past flow patterns are available. Single samples are necessary for analyses, such as dissolved oxygen, chlorine demand, and residual chlorine, that must be made immediately after the samples are collected.

Pipettes with small openings are not suitable for measuring sewage and effluents. The suspended matter may block the tip causing it to act as a filter or slow the discharge of the contents, permitting sedimentation to take place in the bulb of the pipette. Rotating the pipette while it is being discharged acts to keep the solids in suspension. Large-tip pipettes or ones having a small amount of the delivery end cut off will permit the measurement of a more representative sample. Pipettes so modified should be recalibrated before they are used. It is not advisable to use the mouth in pipetting sewage. A rubber bulb or some other means of applying suction should be used.

Samples containing settleable solids can be homogenized in a blender for ease in obtaining a representative sample. When only a small volume of sample is needed, it is advisable to make an initial dilution in a volumetric flask in order to reduce the error in measuring small volumes.

Good quality graduated cylinders of the appropriate size can be used for large volumes.

## B. DETERMINATIONS AND INTERPRETATIONS

### 1. Temperature

The temperature of a sample should be taken at the time of collection. It is usually sufficiently accurate to record the temperature of sewage to the nearest half degree centigrade. For more accurate work, especially in calculating the percentage of saturation of dissolved oxygen and various forms of alkalinity, a standardized thermometer graduated in tenths of a degree centigrade should be used.

The mean annual temperature of most American sewages ranges between 11 and 22°C. The sewage temperature is higher than the air temperature all year except during the summer months. The temperature of incoming sewage, if higher than normal, indicates discharge of warm industrial waste. The seepage of ground water into the sewer lines can give lower than the normal temperatures.

Excessively high temperatures stimulate septic action in sewers and in primary settling tanks, causing increased odors at the treatment plant. In addition, septic conditions accelerate the deterioration of cement and bituminous joints in the sewers and tanks.

Lastly, temperature measurements will often explain differences in treatment and sedimentation efficiencies encountered during the year. An increase in temperature of 10°C approximately doubles the rate of microbial action within the range of 10–40°C. Sedimentation results may be 10% better in the summer than in the winter because with a higher temperature there is a decrease in viscosity and density of the liquid.

## 2. pH Value

Formerly the acidity or basicity of sewage was determined by titration, and this was shown by alkalinity to methyl organge or acidity to phenolphthalein. The amount of alkalinity and acidity are still important determinations in water treatment, but for the control of various biological waste treatment processes, the intensity of acids or alkalies is more important than the amount.

The pH value of sewage may be determined either colorimetrically or with any good commercial pH meter. The potentiometric method is the method of choice because of limitations of the colorimetric method in the presence of suspended solids, oxidizing agents, reducing agents, and color.

This is one of the easiest tests to perform, yet this single test will give very valuable information on the condition of the sewage. Normal fresh sewage is slightly alkaline, and stale or septic sewage is usually acid. In passing through a settling tank, the pH of sewage will drop a few tenths of a pH unit. More change than this would indicate too long a retention period, with the sewage becoming too septic.

Excessive deviation from the normal pH value of raw sewage would be a sign that unneutralized industrial wastes are being discharged to the sewer.

## 3. Chlorides

The Volhard method is the preferred chloride method for sewage and sewage effluents. Many laboratories that run both water and sewage analyses use the Mohr method. The amount of orthophosphates contained in wastewater will interfere with the Mohr method. Other ions, such as sulfide, thiosulfate, and sulfite, will also cause interference if not eliminated beforehand. In the Volhard method, bromide, iodide, and sulfide are registered as equivalent chloride; however, they are usually not present in significant amounts.

The chloride test is a simple inexpensive way of obtaining a crude index of the strength of sewage. Sewage will contain a higher amount of chlorides than the raw water because of chloride added from food and human urine. A high increase in chlorides can be caused by industrial waste, such as that from food processing plants and plating shops. In the winter time, it can give an indication of the amount of surface water intrusion when the chlorides are used for ice control. Along the sea coast, the determination of chlorides in raw sewage is helpful in ascertaining the leakage of the tide water into the sewerage system.

Sodium chloride has been used as a means of determining the detention time in tanks. It is added to the influent, and the effluent is periodically tested for chlorides. An increase above the normal content is noted when the flow has passed through the tank. Chlorides, being soluble inorganic substances, are not affected by sedimentation or biological actions.

### 4. Chlorine

The chlorine existing in water as hypochlorous acid, hypochlorite ions, and molecular chlorine is defined in sanitary chemistry as *free available chlorine*. When chlorine in water is chemically combined with ammonia or other nitrogenous compounds, it is known as *combined available chlorine*. The *chlorine demand* is the difference between the chlorine added to a sample and the chlorine residual after a specified time.

In the chlorination of sewage and treatment plant effluents before discharge to a watercourse, it is the usual practice to add chlorine in an amount equivalent to only a fraction of the chlorine demand. For this reason, free available chlorine is seldom found in such effluents. In sewage and sewage effluents the differentiation of free available chlorine from combined available chlorine is not made.

When chlorine is used for odor control, slime and insect control on trickling filters, and control of activated-sludge bulking, the amount of chlorine used in milligrams per liter is known as the *chlorine requirement* rather than as the *chlorine demand*. These practices fall in the realm of the "state of the art" rather than in the province of analytical chemistry.

If the analyst has need to determine chlorine residuals, the methods are adequately covered in *Standard Methods* (3). The amperometric titration method is the most accurate and subject to the least interference from color and turbidity, which are always present in wastewater.

### 5. Dissolved Oxygen (DO)

The amount of oxygen held in solution, as a gas, is termed *dissolved oxygen* and is usually referred to as DO. The dissolved oxygen test forms an integral part of the determination of the biochemical oxygen demand.

Normally sewage does not contain dissolved oxygen unless it is very fresh; consequently, raw and settled sewages are not tested for dissolved oxygen. The presence of oxygen in a treatment plant effluent is an indication that a high degree of treatment has been accomplished. If dissolved oxygen is found in sufficient concentration in the watercourse below the effluent outfall, there is little danger that putrefactive odors will develop. Thus, we see DO is a most significant measure of pollution.

A sample of sewage or sewage effluent for the dissolved oxygen determination should be taken in such a manner that the dissolved oxygen content is not changed in sampling. Sampling is best accomplished in a manner which ensures a severalfold displacement of the liquid through the sampling bottle without entrainment of air bubbles. The analyst is referred to *Standard Methods* (4) for special procedures in collecting samples for the dissolved oxygen test. The temperature of the water should always be recorded in degrees centigrade at the time the sample is taken so that the result can be expressed in terms of percentage of saturation if it is so desired. It is important at times to know if the percentage of saturation of dissolved oxygen will meet the requirements for odor and aquatic life in streams which receive discharges from sewage treatment plants.

The most common method used for determination of atmospheric oxygen dissolved in a liquid is based on the method developed in 1888 by Winkler (43). The method depends on the oxidation of manganous hydroxide by oxygen in solution and the subsequent titration of an equivalent amount of iodine set free from potassium iodide. The method requires only simple apparatus and can be carried out in a very short time.

The original Winkler method is applicable only to relatively pure samples that do not contain interfering substances, such as nitrites, ferrous salts, and easily oxidized organic matter. To correct for these interferences various modifications have been made on the basic Winkler method. The method of choice for sewage and effluents is the Alsterberg modification as outlined in *Standard Methods* (5). This method is intended for use where more than 0.1 mg/liter of nitrite nitrogen and less than 1.0 mg/liter of ferrous iron are present. Nitrites are commonly found in well oxidized sewage effluents and may form during the incubation period in the biochemical oxygen demand determination. The nitrites become nitrous acid in the standard Winkler procedure, which by liberating iodine in the final titration gives an apparent high DO. In the Alsterberg modification, sodium azide is added in combination with the alkaline iodide solution. If the sample contains no nitrite ion, the addition of the sodium azide is of no disadvantage. When nitrites are present, they are removed after the acidification step according to the following reaction:

$$NaN_3 + H_2SO_4 \rightarrow NaHSO_4 + HN_3$$

$$HNO_2 + HN_3 \rightarrow N_2 + N_2O + H_2O$$

It is essential that the solution be acidic or the following reaction will occur:

$$2NaN_3 + I_2 \rightarrow 2NaI + 3N_2$$

Sewage and sewage effluents are constantly changing due to biological action; therfore, the DO should be run immediately upon collection of the sample. Once the test is started, it should be carried out as expeditiously as possible, so that the error due to easily hydrolyzable organic matter is reduced. Numerous forms of organic matter are capable of being oxidized by dissolved oxygen at pH 12. This corresponds to the pH of the sample when the alkaline iodide solution is added.

The amount of oxygen is very important in the activated sludge process. An adequate amount of air should be supplied to maintain aerobic conditions. Levels higher than are necessary increase the cost of treatment and can result in loss of sludge clarification. The amount of air is generally controlled by determinations of dissolved oxygen at the inlet, midpoint, and outlet of the aeration tanks. The DO is usually lowest near the influent end of the aeration tank and increases toward the effluent end. Normally a dissolved oxygen content of 2 mg/liter is required at the outlet end of the aeration tank in order to maintain aerobic conditions throughout the tank. The Winkler method for measuring the dissolved oxygen in the aeration tank is of questionable value because the sludge rapidly removes oxygen from solution. Modification (E) of the Winkler method (6) employs an inhibiting agent in the sample bottle to stop the deoxygenation at the time of sampling. The membrane electrodes (20,31) are more suitable for establishing the amount of aeration. The voltametric probes are simple, rugged, and capable of continuous analysis of oxygen. Their main feature is the use of a plastic membrane to separate the sensing element from the test solution to minimize electrode poisoning. The membrane is impermeable to organic contaminants, but permeable to gaseous oxygen. The probes have a high temperature coefficient; however, the temperature of sewage changes so slowly that this is not a serious disadvantage. A certain minimum flow must be maintained near the tip of the probes. This again does not offer any drawback to their use in an aeration tank, unless air bubbles impinge upon the sensing surface.

## 6. Oxygen Demand

The ultimate purification of sewage by either sewage treatment processes or self-purification in a running stream is by oxidation of the organic matter. There are two analytical parameters for determining the amount of oxidizable matter present in wastes. The first is universally known as the *biochemical oxygen demand* (BOD). The second method is known in the United States as the *chemical oxygen demand* (COD). This test has not been internationally standardized, but is used by a few other countries under a different name. The two tests are not directly comparable, for the chemical method does not differentiate between matter that is biologically stable and unstable. The two methods are empirical and do not indicate the total quantity of any particular constituent; therefore, it is essential that they be conducted according to a standard method. The exact procedures for both of these methods are fully outlined in *Standard Methods* (7).

### a. BIOCHEMICAL OXYGEN DEMAND (BOD)

The BOD test is perhaps the most widely used determination in sewage analyses. It is a measure of the amount of oxygen required to maintain aerobic conditions during the decomposition of the organic matter by microorganisms. The test consists of determining the dissolved oxygen of a sample, or a diluted sample, before and after incubation for 5 days at 20°C in the absence of light. This measurement should not be construed as being the ultimate oxygen demand of a sample, for the time required for complete satisfaction of the BOD is infinitely long. Although there are limitations on the interpretation of data from a single time interval, it is not usually practical to determine daily intervals. Details on the development of the BOD test and the determination of BOD constants can be found in the works of Streeter and Phelps (39) and Theriault (41).

The oxidation in the BOD test proceeds in two stages. First the carbonaceous matter is oxidized, and then nitrification begins. In raw or settled sewage, the first stage lasts 7 to 10 days. In highly purified effluents, the nitrification stage can proceed simultaneously with the carbonaceous oxidation. Attempts have been made to prevent nitrification in various ways; however, none has been so completely successful as to be included as a standard method. There has been some controversy as to whether the oxygen used during nitrification should be included in the value for the 5-day BOD of effluents. Since nitrification represents a demand on the oxygen of a receiving stream, it should be included in the BOD value.

The BOD test can be used as a measure of the putrescibility of sewage, but it is more appropriate for samples at low oxygen demand. If the BOD is measured at various stages in the sewage treatment process, it will indicate the efficiency of each step. As a control measure, the test is of little value for 5 days have passed before results are available. The real value lies in using the results in design, in filter loading, and in calculating operational efficiencies. In addition, BOD determinations are required by many states on effluents discharged into waterways of the United States.

### b. CHEMICAL OXYGEN DEMAND (COD)

Since the middle of the 19th century, numerous attempts have been made to devise a chemical method for determining the organic content of wastewater as a replacement for the inaccurate method based on the loss of weight on a residue upon ignition. With so many investigators who were not in close contact with each other, it is only natural that several variations are to be found in the literature. These variations include differences in oxidant, differences in digestive temperature, and differences in the way the excess oxidant is determined. Each of these variables is capable of exerting an effect upon the results, thereby making the early data extremely difficult to compare. Today only three methods are in general use. The English chemists tend to use sulfuric acid and potassium permanganate at a temperature of 27°C for 4 hr. This method has been referred to in the English journals as "oxygen consumed," "oxygen absorbed," "permanganate value, 4 hr," and if run for 3 min as "permanganate value, 3 min." Their test should not be confused with the previous method that was used in the United States and known as "oxygen consumed." This method is different in that the sample was digested for 30 min at 100°C. The analyst is cautioned to be careful in comparing his results with other workers unless he knows the details of the procedure that was used. In the United States it is usual to assume that the method given in the current edition of *Standard Methods* is used unless the contrary is stated.

The present method known in this country as "chemical oxygen demand" (7) and in England as the "dichromate value" uses potassium dichromate and sulfuric acid as the oxidizing agent. The method has the advantage of requiring a shorter time and giving results that are fairly close to theoretical for a large number of organic compounds. In the absence of oxidizable inorganic matter, such as nitrites, ferrous salts, and chlorides, the test is a partial measure of the carbonaceous matter in a sample. The method determines the carbonaceous portion of nitrogenous compounds, but not the ammonia. Not all organic compounds are completely oxidized by this wet combustion method, but by using silver sulfate as a catalyst in the refluxing solution the efficiency is increased. In most sewages and sewage effluents, the COD gives a reasonable estimate of the carbonaceous content of the sample.

In domestic waste, chlorides can be a source of error. In the absence of silver sulfate, the oxidation of the chloride ion is quantitative. Thus, in determining the chloride content it is possible to apply a correction, since 1.0 mg/liter chloride is equivalent to 0.23 mg/liter of oxygen. When silver sulfate is added at the start of the test, the oxidation of the chloride is not fully suppressed, and no suitable correction can be applied. If the addition of the silver sulfate is delayed until 30 min after refluxing is started, then, theoretically, all chloride has been oxidized and the correction can be applied. In practice, this has not been found satisfactory due to the cyclic reaction between chloride and nitrogenous substances. The reaction is thought to proceed by dichromate oxidation of chloride to free chlorine with the formation of chloramines from the ammonia present, followed by then the liberation of gaseous nitrogen and chloride. This cycle can then be repeated as long as there is present nitrogenous matter capable of being oxidized.

These difficulties can be avoided by using the procedure of Dobbs and Williams (26). They found that mercuric sulfate added to the sample complexed the chlorides effectively up to 500 mg/liter and to a high degree at 1000 mg/liter. This procedure has been included in the latest edition of *Standard Methods,* and the analyst should adopt it, for it retains the catalytic action of silver sulfate, suppresses chloride interference, and prevents the cyclic amine reaction.

The chemical oxygen demand test provides a valuable means for rapidly estimating the total organic content of sewage or effluent. From a comparison of COD on the raw sewage and any other stage in the treatment process, one can determine whether the plant is functioning properly. The COD test should be supplemented by the 5-day BOD test when facilities are available. There is no fixed relationship between the BOD and COD, but it must be established for each specific waste at a given stage of treatment. For example, the ratio may be 2:1 on a given raw sewage and 5:1 on a secondary effluent during winter operation and higher during summer operation. When this ratio is well established for a particular plant, it is possible to estimate the 5-day BOD in 3 hr by multiplying the COD value by the determined factor.

The difference between the COD and BOD values will give an indication of the type of waste. If the sewage contains a high concentration of cellulose, lignins, or other substances that are difficult for microorganisms to oxidize, the COD value will be much greater than the BOD value. Distillery and refinery wastes usually give higher BOD than COD values. Good judgment must be exercised in comparing data from these tests. One should always suspect inhibitory substances in the sewage that interfere with the biological test if the BOD value is much lower than the COD value.

### 7. Solids

The solids in sewage or effluents that pass through a mat of asbestos fiber in a Gooch crucible are defined as *dissolved solids,* and those that are retained on the mat are classified as *suspended* solids. Both dissolved and suspended solids are differentiated further as *fixed* and *volatile,* the fixed being the portion not volatilized by ignition at 600°C. If the ignition is properly performed, the loss in weight will give a crude idea of the amount of organic matter in the sample. The suspended and dissolved solids are reported as milligrams per liter, and the volatile content is normally reported as percentage of the solid matter in the sample.

The conventional Gooch method is time consuming, and the amount of suspended matter removed during filtration depends on the thickness of the mat. For this reason, various alternative filtering materials have been suggested. Of these, the most promising are the glass-fiber filter papers that fit into a perforated Gooch crucible (25,30,33,37). The filters are said to retain particles of about 0.5 $\mu$ size. As a routine procedure for the determination of suspended solids, the glass-fiber filter method requires less skill, and close agreement between replicates can be readily obtained. The filters must be washed and ignited before being used for determining volatile solids, or considerable error can result. Small losses of filter mat can be quite significant when it is realized that often suspended solids are more than 80% volatile; thus, the remaining fixed solids, from a 50-ml sample, will frequently weigh less than 2 mg. The analyst should familiarize himself with the accepted gravimetric procedure of conditioning and bringing crucibles to constant weight.

Another test conducted on wastewater is the determination of settleable solids by means of an Imhoff cone. The cone is filled to the liter mark and after 1 hr, the volume of the settleable matter is read directly as milliliters per liter from the graduated tip of the cone. Settleable matter may be determined on a weight basis (mg/liter) by considering the settleable solids as the difference between the suspended matter and the nonsettleable matter.

The primary clarifiers have for their main purpose the removal of settleable solids. The efficacy of sedimentation can be determined by measuring the settleable solids before and after tank treatment. It is desirable that after the influent sample is collected, time equal to the detention period of the tank be permitted to elapse before the effluent sample is taken. From the amount of solids removed, the gas yield to be expected from the digestion can be estimated.

The terms settleable solids and suspended solids are often confused in the literature, although the methods of determination are clearly described in *Standard Methods* (8,9). Until they have settled to the bottom of a tank or a waterway, all settleable solids are suspended solids. While only a fraction would be considered settleable by the above test, all suspended solids will eventually settle because of biological and chemical flocculation. Where stream standards have been promulgated or where effluent standards are used, the test for suspended solids is the one required by state agencies. The quantity of suspended solids is important because their removal is one of the more difficult problems in sewage treatment.

The control of the amount of suspended solids in the aeration tank is one of the more important factors in the operation of an activated sludge plant. The sludge content of the mixed liquor is checked frequently so as to control the proportion of return and waste sludge. There is no single optimum for all plants, but values between 1500 and 2500 mg/liter of suspended solids are the most common.

## 8. Nitrogen

The relationship that exists between the various forms of nitrogen compounds and the changes that can occur in sewage treatment processes are of great interest to sanitary chemists and engineers. The valence changes brought about by living microorganisms can be either positive or negative, depending on whether oxygen is present or not.

The nitrogen in fresh sewage is in the form of organic nitrogen or ammonia. During aerobic treatment, the organic nitrogen is converted into ammonia nitrogen, which in turn is oxidized to nitrites and nitrates. A completely treated sewage shows a relatively high proportion of nitrates and is said to be well nitrified. Nitrites and nitrates are reduced by bacteria under anaerobic conditions to ammonia.

As the forms of nitrogen change rapidly in sewage and effluent samples, they should be analyzed as soon as possible after collection. If a lapse of time is unavoidable, the nitrogen balance can be maintained by adding 1 ml of concentrated $H_2SO_4$ per liter of sample.

In determining the nitrogen in the various forms in which it occurs in sewage and sewage effluents, it is desirable that the results be expressed in comparable terms. It has become standard practice to express the results as nitrogen rather than ammonia, nitrate ion, etc.

### a. Organic Nitrogen

Not much is known about the specific nitrogenous compounds in sewage and sewage effluents. For years it was the custom to determine the "albuminoid" nitrogen. This term was applied to the part of organically combined nitrogen that was set free as ammonia when the sample was heated with an alkaline solution of potassium permanganate. It was considered as easily decomposable organic nitrogen that should be reduced by sewage treatment. This determination is seldom used today and has been replaced by a test for organic nitrogen. Organic nitrogen is considered to be the total nitrogenous matter in the sample, except that present as ammonia, nitrites, and nitrates. The organic nitrogen can be calculated by subtracting the ammonia nitrogen from the total Kjeldahl or by determining it directly by the Kjeldahl method after first distilling off the ammonia from a buffered sample. The lack of agreement among analysts on the optimum conditions for the determination has resulted in several hundred papers in the literature on the Kjeldahl determination of nitrogen. The procedure given in *Standard Methods* (10) is effective for general use on domestic sewage and sewage effluents. This procedure is basically that of McKenzie and Wallace (32). Without modification, it would not give quantitative results on wastes containing nitro, nitroso, or azo compounds.

The extent of decomposition of carbonaceous matter by microorganisms depends not only on the nature, but also on the amount of available nitrogen. For every unit of carbon decomposed as a source of energy, a certain amount of nitrogen is assimilated, whether the latter is present in the form of proteins, simple degradation products, or inorganic salts. Thus, for efficient and successful biological oxidation of organic waste, a minimal quantity of nitrogen is required for synthesis of new cells. This is not a problem with domestic waste, but can become a problem if a treatment plant receives industrial waste with a high BOD and a small amount of nitrogen. At plants where the digested and undigested sludge is sold for fertilizer, the total nitrogen content of the sludge is determined.

## b. Ammonia Nitrogen

Ammonia nitrogen determination is a measure of the nitrogen present in a sample in the form of ammonia, ammonium hydroxide, and ammonia salts. Ammonia nitrogen results from bacterial decomposition of organic matter or by the reduction of nitrates. Under aerobic conditions, the amount of ammonia nitrogen will decrease as the sewage undergoes treatment and becomes more stable.

Direct Nesslerization may be used for rapid routine determination of ammonia nitrogen if the turbidity and natural color can be eliminated with flocculation (12). When more precise results are desired, the ammonia should be distilled from a buffered sample. The ammonia in the distillate can then be determined by either Nessler solution or titration. Absorption of the ammonia by boric acid and back-titration with standard strong acid is more suitable for samples containing more than 1 mg/liter of ammonia nitrogen.

The analyst should not use or keep solutions of ammonia in the same room where ammonia determinations are being performed.

No further discussion is deemed necessary on this determination, because it is fully covered by Taras (40) and *Standard Methods* (13).

## c. Nitrite Nitrogen

Nitrites in sewage or effluents are not stable, but are reduced to ammonia or are oxidized to nitrates. For this reason, they are of interest only in the overall nitrogen balance of a dynamic biochemical system.

The preferred method of analysis is a modification of the Griess-Ilosvay method (11,29), based on the diazotization of sulfanilic acid by nitrite and the coupling of this compound with 1-naphthylamine. This method is exceedingly sensitive and free from most interferences. It is suitable for samples containing less than 2 mg/liter of nitrite nitrogen. Concentrations greater than this cause the complex dye to precipitate. This will rarely happen in the analysis of sewage and sewage effluents, as the concentration is usually less than 1 mg/ml.

## d. Nitrate Nitrogen

Nitrates are the highest stage of oxidation of the nitrogenous matter in sewage and sewage effluents. The nitrification process that occurs in the final stages of activated sludge and trickling filter treatment involves a biological oxidation which changes ammonia nitrogen into nitrites and nitrates.

A great variety of methods for the estimation of nitrate nitrogen have been proposed. The majority of these fall into three types: (1) reduction of the nitrate radical, (2) nitration by the nitrate radical, and (3) oxidation by the nitrate radical. All three types are given in Standard Methods (14). It is not surprising that the nitrate determination is one of the more difficult tests when one realizes that all the methods were known at the turn of the 20th century and yet they are still listed as tentative methods.

The most widely used method is the one based on the reaction of nitrate with phenoldisulfonic acid to produce a nitro derivative that rearranges in alkali to form a yellow color. Nitrate nitrogen concentrations as low as 1 $\mu$g yield a faint color. The development of this determination after its conception by Sprengel in 1888 is one of the more interesting investigations in the history of the chemistry of water examination (38). This is especially true of the series of articles written by Chamot and his co-workers (21–24).

The main interferences of this method are chlorides, nitrites, and organic matter. The greatest source of error is due to the chlorides. The procedure in Standard Methods recommends adding an equivalent amount of standard silver sulfate for chloride removal. Many analysts prefer to add just slightly less than the equivalent amount to prevent any possibility of having an excess of silver ions. Excess silver ions will produce an off-color when the final color is developed with potassium hydroxide. Ammonium hydroxide could be used for this, but ammonia fumes are not desirable in the laboratory when traces of ammonia are being determined concurrently. In spite of its limitations, the phenoldisulfonic acid method has reached a stage of maturity where acceptable values are possible.

In recent years there has been renewed interest in the brucine method for nitrate determination. Nitrate reacts with brucine in sulfuric acid, forming a red-colored oxidation product which changes quickly to yellow. The use of brucine and strychnine as colorimetric reagents for nitrates has been known for many years. Although these procedures do not suffer from chloride interferences, they have given extremely erratic results. ASTM in 1958, adopted a brucine procedure based mainly on the work of Hasse (28) and Noll (36).

The disadvantages of the brucine methods are that the color does not obey Beer's law and the variability of the color from one test to another necessitates the simultaneous development of color in samples and standards. With the phenoldisulfonic acid method, standards can be kept for about 3–4 weeks. There is a real need for a simple, rapid, accurate method for determining nitrates that would have universal application.

Nitrate determinations are of interest in sewage works examination as showing the degree of nitrification. The presence of nitrates furthermore is important as indicating the conditions of an effluent or stream, because the nitrate is usually reduced at about the same time that the dissolved oxygen is entirely exhausted. Trickling filters are probably the most neglected part of a sewage plant, yet upon them depends to a large degree the quality of the effluent turned out by a plant. As previously stated, a trickling filter is an oxidation device, and its effluent should be well oxidized. By comparing the organic nitrogen of the primary effluent with the forms of nitrogen in the final effluent, the efficiency of the filter can be measured.

## 9. Sludge Index

The settling characteristics of activated sludge have been expressed in several ways. In 1920, while investigating 12 sewage works, Theriault and co-workers (42) used the term "sludge ratio." He computed the value by dividing the milligrams per liter of suspended solids in the aeration tank by the volume in milliliters occupied by the sludge after settling a liter of mixed liquid for a period of 15–30 min. Donaldson (27) in 1931 reviewed Theriault's work and proposed as a routine test "sludge index." Donaldson's sludge index was 10 times the sludge ratio used by Theriault. He obtained his value by dividing the percentage of suspended solids by weight times 100 by the sludge volume in the aeration tank, settled 30 min. Today this method is known as the "sludge density index" (SDI) (15). With this method, values above 1.0 are considered satisfactory for normal operation. In 1934, Mohlman (35) summarized the various procedures for calculating the sludge index. He recommended that the sludge index be defined as the volume in cubic centimeters occupied by 1 g of activated sludge after settling the aerated liquor for 30 min. This method seemed the most logical to him, for the index increased with increased "bulking" of the sludge. With this method, index values less than 100 are considered satisfactory. In the present *Standard Methods* (16) this method is listed as the "sludge volume index" (SVI).

It is immaterial whether the sludge volume index or sludge density index is used since both are based on the relation between the volume of the settled sludge and the weight of suspended solids. The sludge index is helpful in the control of the activated sludge aeration process. It can give a warning that the sludge is starting to bulk, which will result in a poor effluent. No single value is considered as critical, but what is important is that the index consistently shows a well settling sludge. When sludge has a high water content and will not settle to a small volume, it is referred to as "sludge bulking."

## III. LABORATORY CONTROL OF SLUDGE DIGESTION

Digestion of primary and excess activated sludges normally causes most of the difficulty in the operation of a wastewater treatment plant. Just not enough attention is given to their control. One of the reasons for this is that some of the control analyses require a moderate amount of equipment and some technical skill. The second reason is that many operators have assumed that once proper equilibrium is established, the digester will function with very little care. This is far from being true.

Volatile solids in the sludge, gas production, pH of the supernatant, total alkalinity (17) of the sludge, and volatile acid (18) are all useful in charting the changes occurring in a digestion tank. Of these, the total alkalinity is perhaps the most important, as it is more reliable in indicating the trend than is the pH. A drop in total alkalinity shows that the digestion balance is not being maintained, while rising values indicate an approach to equilibrium. Acids are formed as the primary fermentation products of carbohydrates, fats, and proteins. In a properly functioning digestion tank, these organic acids are further broken down to carbon dioxide and methane. If the rate of acid production in the primary stage of fermentation is greater than the rate of methane production, there will be a tendency for the development of acidity if the buffer value of the liquid is low. It has been determined that when the total alkalinity of the supernatant is twice that of the volatile acids, one can expect good digestion.

The digestion process proceeds most rapidly within the general pH range of 6.8–7.4. A pH drop to approximately 6.4 generally is associated with cessation of significant methane production. An excess accumulation of organic acids usually precedes by several days an unfavorable drop in the pH of a digester. This is why many plants prefer to determine the volatile acids twice a week. If at any time the amount of volatile acids starts to rise, they should be determined each day. The total volatile acid concentration in a digester is not as important as sudden fluctuations.

The quantity and quality of gas produced indicate the condition of a digester. The amount produced is usually about 12 ft$^3$ per pound of volatile matter destroyed. Its constituents will vary in different plants, but the gas will consist of 65–75% methane and 25–35% carbon dioxide in normal digestion. If gas production decreases and/or the carbon dioxide content of the gas increases, the equilibrium of the digester is upset. Many of the smaller treatment plants are not equipped to run gas analyses. At these plants, much can be learned about the methane content by observing the color of the flame when it is burned. When the digester gas is used for a gas engine, regular gas analyses must be made in the laboratory. Hydrogen sulfide can create corrosion problems if it exceeds 0.1% by volume.

The efficiency of digestion tanks is measured by the reduction of volatile solids. Analyses of the total and volatile solids in the raw and digested sludges will indicate the organic loading on the unit and the accomplishment. Well digested sludge will usually show a reduction in volatile matter of 50% or more.

The exact procedures for the analyses discussed in digester control are adequately covered in *Standard Methods* or have been reviewed in Section II-B of this chapter.

### REFERENCES

1. Association of British Chemical Manufacturers and Society for Analytical Chemistry, *Recommended Methods for the Analysis of Trade Effluents,* W. Heffer and Sons, Cambridge, 1958.
2. American Public Health Association, American Water Works Association, and Water Pollution Control Federation, *Standard Methods for the Examination of Water and Wastewater,* 12th ed., American Public Health Association, New York, 1965.
3. American Public Health Association, American Water Works Association, and Water Pollution Control Federation, *Standard Methods for the Examination of Water and Wastewater,* 12th ed., American Public Health Association, New York, 1965, pp. 375–380.
4. American Public Health Association, American Water Works Association, and Water Pollution Control Federation, *Standard Methods for the Examination of Water and Wastewater,* 12th ed., American Public Health Association, New York, 1965, pp. 405–406.
5. American Public Health Association, American Water Works Association, and Water Pollution Control Federation, *Standard Methods for the Examination of Water and Wastewater,* 12th ed., American Public Health Association, New York, 1965, pp. 406–410.

6. American Public Health Association, American Water Works Association, and Water Pollution Control Federation, *Standard Methods for the Examination of Water and Wastewater,* 12th ed., American Public Health Association, New York, 1965, p. 413.

7. American Public Health Association, American Water Works Association, and Water Pollution Control Federation, *Standard Methods for the Examination of Water and Wastewater,* 12th ed., American Public Health Association, New York, 1965, pp. 415–421, 510–514.

8. American Public Health Association, American Water Works Association, and Water Pollution Control Federation, *Standard Methods for the Examination of Water and Wastewater,* 12th ed., American Public Health Association, New York, 1965, pp. 424–426.

9. American Public Health Association, American Water Works Association, and Water Pollution Control Federation, *Standard Methods for the Examination of Water and Wastewater,* 12th ed., American Public Health Association, New York, 1965, pp. 540–541.

10. American Public Health Association, American Water Works Association, and Water Pollution Control Federation, *Standard Methods for the Examination of Water and Wastewater,* 12th ed., American Public Health Association, New York, 1965, pp. 402–404.

11. American Public Health Association, American Water Works Association, and Water Pollution Control Federation, *Standard Methods for the Examination of Water and Wastewater,* 12th ed., American Public Health Association, New York, 1965, pp. 400–402.

12. American Public Health Association, American Water Works Association, and Water Pollution Control Federation, *Standard Methods for the Examination of Water and Wastewater,* 12th ed., American Public Health Association, New York, 1965, pp. 389–390.

13. American Public Health Association, American Water Works Association, and Water Pollution Control Federation, *Standard Methods for the Examination of Water and Wastewater,* 12th ed., American Public Health Association, New York, 1965, pp. 389–392.

14. American Public Health Association, American Water Works Association, and Water Pollution Control Federation, *Standard Methods for the Examination of Water and Wastewater,* 12th ed., American Public Health Association, New York, 1965, pp. 392–400.

15. American Public Health Association, American Water Works Association, and Water Pollution Control Federation, *Standard Methods for the Examination of Water and Wastewater,* 12th ed., American Public Health Association, New York, 1965, p. 542.

16. American Public Health Association, American Water Works Association, and Water Pollution Control Federation, *Standard Methods for the Examination of Water and Wastewater,* 12th ed., American Public Health Association, New York, 1965, pp. 541–542.

17. American Public Health Association, American Water Works Association, and Water Pollution Control Federation, *Standard Methods for the Examination of Water and Wastewater,* 12th ed., American Public Health Association, New York, 1965, pp. 369–530.

18. American Public Health Association, American Water Works Association, and

Water Pollution Control Federation, *Standard Methods for the Examination of Water and Wastewater,* 12th ed., American Public Health Association, new York, 1965, pp. 538–539.

19. American Society for Testing Materials, *Manual on Industrial Water and Industrial Waste Water,* 2nd ed., Philadelphia, 1959.
20. Carritt, D. E., and J. W. Kanwisher, *Anal. Chem.,* **31,** 5 (1959).
21. Chamot, E. M., and D. S. Pratt, *J. Amer. Chem. Soc.,* **31,** 922 (1909).
22. Chamot, E. M., and D. S. Pratt, *J. Amer. Chem. Soc.,* **32,** 630 (1910).
23. Chamot, E. M., D. S. Pratt, and H. W. Redfield, *J. Amer. Chem. Soc.,* **33,** 366 (1911).
24. Chamot, E. M., D. S. Pratt, and H. W. Redfield, *J. Amer. Chem. Soc.,* **33,** 381 (1911).
25. Chanin, G., E. H. Chow, R. B. Alexander, and J. Powers, *Sewage Ind. Wastes,* **30,** 1062 (1958).
26. Dobbs, R. A., and R. T. Williams, *Anal. Chem.,* **35,** 1064 (1963).
27. Donaldson, W., *Sewage Works J.,* **4,** 48 (1932).
28. Haase, L. W., *Chem. Z.,* **50,** 372 (1926).
29. Ilosvay, L., *Bull. Soc. Chim. France* 2[3], 388 (1889).
30. Jenkins, D., *Water Waste Treat. J.,* **9,** 66 (1962).
31. Mancy, K. H., W. C. Westgarth, and D. A. Okun, *Purdue Univ. Eng. Bull. Ext.,* **112,** 508 (1963).
32. McKenzie, H. A., and H. S. Wallace, *Australian J. Chem.,* **7,** 55 (1954).
33. Melbourne, K. V., *J. Inst. Sewage Purif.,* **1964,** 392.
34. Ministry of Housing and Local Government, *Methods of Chemical Analysis as Applied to Sewage and Sewage Effluents,* 2nd ed., Her Majesty's Stationery Office, London, 1956.
35. Mohlman, F. W., *Sewage Works J.,* **6,** 119 (1934).
36. Noll, C. A., *Anal. Chem.,* **17,** 426 (1945).
37. Nusbaum, I., *Sewage Ind. Wastes,* **30,** 1066 (1958).
38. Sprengel, H., *Ann. Phys. Chem.,* **121,** 188 (1864).
39. Streeter, H. W., and Phelps, E. B., *U.S. Public Health Serv. Bull.,* **146** (1925).
40. Taras, M. J., "Nitrogen" in *Colorimetric Determination of Nonmetals,* D. F. Boltz, Ed., Interscience, New York, 1958, pp. 75–160.
41. Theriault, E. J., *U.S. Public Health Serv. Bull.,* **173** (1927).
42. Wagenhals, H. H., E. J. Theriault, and H. B. Hommon, *U.S. Public Health Serv. Bull.,* **132** (1923).
43. Winkler, L. W., *Ber. Deut. Chem. Ges.,* **21,** 2843 (1888).

# Subject Index

## A

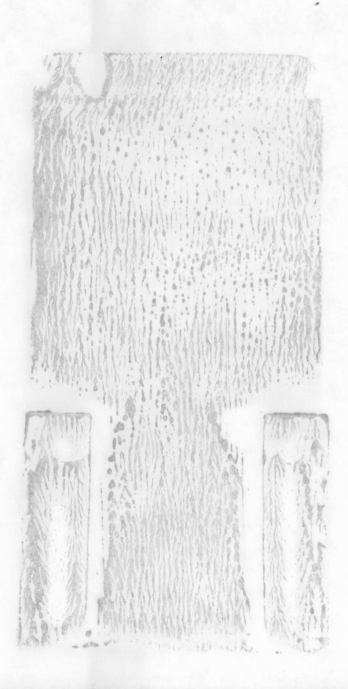